COMPILER
TECHNIQUES

AUERBACH Computer Science Series

Ned Chapin, Ph.D., General Editor

COMPILER
TECHNIQUES

Edited by BARY W. POLLACK

AUERBACH®
publishers

princeton
philadelphia
new york
london

To my wife,

Kimberly,

and

to my parents,

Seymour and Evelyn Pollack

CONTENTS

CONTRIBUTORS

BAUER, F. L., Gutenberg University, Mainz, Germany.

BURKHARDT, WALTER H., Computer Control Company, Inc., Framingham, Mass.

DARDEN, STEPHEN C., Computer Learning and Systems Corp., Chevy Chase, Md.

ELSON, M., IBM Systems Development Division, Boulder, Colo.

EVANS, ARTHUR, Jr., Computation Center, Carnegie-Mellon University, Pittsburgh, Pa.

FELDMAN, JEROME A., Lincoln Laboratory, Massachusetts Institute of Technology, Lexington, Mass.

FEURZEIG, W., University of Chicago, Chicago, Ill.

FLOYD, ROBERT W., Computer Associates, Inc., Wakefield, Mass.

FREEMAN, DAVID N., IBM General Products Division Development Laboratory, Endicott, N.Y.

GEAR, C. W., Department of Computer Science, University of Illinois, Urbana, Ill.

GRIES, D., Rechenzentrum der Technischen Hochschule, Münich, Germany, and University of Illinois, Urbana, Ill.

GRIES, DAVID, Computer Science Dept. and Stanford Linear Accelerator Center, Stanford University, Stanford, Calif.

HELLER, STEVEN, Computer Learning and Systems Corp., Chevy Chase, Md.

HOLT, ANATOL W., Applied Data Research, Inc., Princeton, N.J.

INGERMAN, P. Z., University of Pennsylvania, Philadelphia, Pa.

IRONS, EDGAR T., Communications Research Division, Institute for Defense Analyses, Princeton, N.J.

KATZAN, HARRY, Jr., Pratt Institute, Brooklyn, N.Y.

KNUTH, DONALD E., California Institute of Technology, Pasadena, Calif.

KORENJAK, A. J., *Formerly*: RCA Laboratories, Princeton, N.J. *Presently*: Applied Research Institute, Princeton, N.J.

xi

McILROY, M. DOUGLAS, Bell Telephone Laboratories, Inc., Murray Hill, N.J.

McKEEMAN, W. M., Stanford University, Stanford, Calif.

MOULTON, P. G., University of Wisconsin, Madison, Wis.

MULLER, M. E., University of Wisconsin, Madison, Wis.

PAUL, M., Rechenzentrum der Technischen Hochschule, München, Germany, and University of Illinois, Urbana, Ill.

PERLIS, ALAN J., Carnegie Institute of Technology, Pittsburgh, Pa.

RAKE, S. T., IBM United Kingdom Laboratories, Hursley, England.

RAPHAEL, BERTRAM, Stanford Research Institute, Menlo Park, Calif.

ROSEN, SAUL, *Formerly*: Consultant, System Development Corp., Santa Monica, Calif. *Presently*: Purdue University, Computer Sciences Department, Lafayette, Ind.

SAMELSON, K., Johannes Gutenberg University, Mainz, Germany.

SETHI, RAVI, *Formerly*: Bell Telephone Laboratories, Murray Hill, N.J. *Presently*: Department of Electrical Engineering, Princeton University, Princeton, N.J.

ULLMAN, J. D., *Formerly*: Bell Telephone Laboratories, Murray Hill, N.J. *Presently*: Department of Electrical Engineering, Princeton University, Princeton, N.J.

WIEHLE, H. R., Rechenzentrum der Technischen Hochschule, München, Germany, and University of Illinois, Urbana, Ill.

PREFACE

The purpose of this book is to present the most important techniques currently used in the construction of compilers. These techniques include the use of formal language theory in syntax-directed compilation, specific procedures for the calculation of addresses for variables and data, methods for optimization and for storage allocation, and the techniques for the detection and correction of errors.

We intend this volume both for students in courses in compiler implementation and for professionals who must implement and maintain compiler systems within both the academic and nonacademic communities.

It is not within the scope of this book to discuss topics such as language design, the relationship between languages and operating systems, or the mechanics of maintaining compilers. Rather, we assume that we are presented with a specific language description in some formal or relatively unambiguous manner and a description of the operating environment for both the compiler and object code. We then ask what techniques are available for the implementation of a compiler for this language and machine. This book attempts to answer that question by presenting a collection of the most important state-of-the-art papers and articles in the field of compiler construction.

Prior to describing the contents of this book we wish to define some of the terms that will be used. A translator is a software system that transforms the statements of one computer language into statements in some other computer language. The first language is usually called the source language; the second language may be called the object language, target language, machine language, or some other descriptive name.

A compiler is a translator that transforms a high-level (or problem-oriented) language such as ALGOL or PL/I into a low-level language such as assembly language or machine language. An incremental compiler translates statements of a language, one statement at a time: This is in contrast to the usual case where the whole program is input to the compiler, which then makes several passes before emitting code. Incremental compilers are generally used in interactive or terminal-oriented environments wherein the user interacts with the computer directly via a keyboard, console, display unit, or other such device.

An interpreter is a program that instead of translating source code executes it directly by determining the meaning of each statement or part of a statement as it is encountered and by computing its value or generating its effect (e.g., input/output).

The syntax of a language is the set of formal rules which describes its form: how statements may be formed, which constructs are legal, the order in which statements must occur, and so forth.

The semantics of a statement is its meaning, including what values are to be computed, the code necessary to compute them, and any side effects that are to occur, such as input, output, and setting internal switches.

A single formal rule of a syntax is called a production.

A grammar is the set of productions describing some language plus the set of symbols used in the productions.

Parsing is the process of determining which productions are used in the construction of a sentence of a language; a program that performs this process is called a parser. More formal definitions of these concepts may be found in Ginsburg, *The Mathematical Theory of Context-Free Languages* (McGraw-Hill, New York, 1966).

A compiler-compiler is a translator to which input is a source language describing a compiler for some language and which as output gives a program that is a compiler for that language. A meta compiler is a translator that translates a high-level language to some other language (also possibly high-level). The difference between compiler-compilers and meta compilers is not very distinct, nor is this terminology adhered to strictly.

An enhansible language is one that provides built-in facilities for the addition and modification of its operators, operands, and data types. LISP and APL are examples of enhansible languages. An extendible language is one that is flexible enough to allow the addition of new statement forms as well.

We have divided the book into eight chapters. Chapter 1 provides an overview and introduction to the history, concepts, terminology, and algorithms described in the rest of the book. A much more lengthy and detailed introduction to compiler writing may be found in Davis' "Programming Language Processors" in Advances in Computers, Vol. 7 (Academic Press, New York, 1966).

Chapter 2 introduces the topics of syntax-directed and table-directed compilation. It includes a description of grammar, language, syntax, and semantics, and the relationships among them.

Chapter 3 discusses parsing and the construction of parsers. Here we look in depth at grammars and formal grammar theory and its usage in syntax-directed compilers.

Chapter 4 presents a discussion of the allocation of resources, stressing two in particular: time and memory. Several articles deal with time optimization; the chapter concludes with a presentation of techniques for memory allocation.

Chapter 5 treats the most poorly documented topics in compiler writing—those of error detection and error correction. Few general techniques are currently known for these subjects, perhaps accounting for the dearth of available literature.

Chapter 6 discusses specific compilers and compiler philosophies. A series of descriptions of compilers is presented, giving insight into the structure and organization of compilers in general and how specific implementation problems may be approached.

Chapter 7 presents specific techniques to be used in the implementation of compilers including techniques for code generation, procedure calls, address calculation, and the translation of computational expressions.

We conclude the book in Chapter 8 with several topics related to compiler implementation: meta compilers, compiler-compilers, and macro capabilities, both for construction and extension of compilers.

I am very deeply indebeted to Dr. Ned Chapin for his initial suggestion that this book be written and for his continuing encouragement and guidance throughout the course of its preparation.

I offer thanks to the authors as a group and to the ACM, AFIPS Press, Inc., Berkeley Enterprises, Inc., Hayden Publishing Co., Inc., the IBM Corporation, the IEEE, and Pergamon Press, Ltd., for their kind permission to reproduce the articles included.

My special thanks go to my advisor, Dr. William F. Miller, for providing the environment and the time necessary for this book's preparation.

My thanks also go to the Stanford Linear Accelerator Center for providing the research facilities, library, and computer time without whose aid this book would have been much more difficult to write.

The cooperation of the Association for Computing Machinery in permitting the use of 18 papers from the *Communications of the ACM* and the *Journal of the Association for Computing Machinery* is gratefully acknowledged.

1.

INTRODUCTION

1.0. OVERVIEW

The purpose of this chapter is to introduce several of the concepts and terms discussed in this book and to give the reader some amount of perspective with which to view the articles in the chapters which follow.

Burkhardt's article opens with a discussion of the relationship of problems to computer languages in which to state them and the translation of languages to languages. The primary thrust of his paper is in the direction of possible universal programming languages.

In Article 1.2, Knuth discusses the construction of language translators from a historical point of view. He introduces operator precedence, Polish notation, stacks, syntax direction, and many other subjects which are dealt with more fully in the remainder of this book.

1.1. Universal Programming Languages and Processors—A Brief Survey and New Concepts

by Walter H. Burkhardt

1.1.1. INTRODUCTION

Progress in any field depends on the materialization of new ideas. But before this is possible, these ideas have to be found, investigated, developed, and adapted to the changing world.

In computing, i.e., the use of computers for the solution of problems, new ideas are available everywhere, although the implications behind them and the influence on the state-of-the-art are generally not very well understood. Therefore it is often difficult to separate the wheat from the chaff.

But even valuable ideas are not always useful and welcome. That is especially the case when the basis for them is not adequately prepared. To know which ideas are useful at present, it is necessary to evaluate the state-of-the-art to determine how developments in the field will proceed. There are other reasons. One might be to give the nonspecialist a fast orientation; another is to readjust the basis in a fast growing and changing field.

The last decade brought a tremendous gain in overall computer power and for a unit outlay as well. Therefore, it is not too surprising if many old values have to be changed and new ones appear.

EDITOR'S NOTE: This article reproduced by permission of the author and the publisher: *Proc. AFIPS* vol. 27 (1965), FJCC, pp. 1–21.

The advent of computers gave a very useful tool for the solution of many tasks for which the statement of the problem was given in a fixed mathematical form. This is due to the special nature of computers, with the memories, the circuit logic, and electronic switching elements having easy adaptation to mathematical problems and to a tremendous bulk of knowledge in the form of mathematical formalism.

There are now on the one side machines with more or less special features for the solution of particular problems, and on the other the problems, given sometimes in a self-contained formulation, sometimes in only a vague and inexact form, and ranging over the whole spectrum of life, science, and society. The medium to combine both is known as programming. This function consists of mapping a solution given to the problems on the machine, but now better defined as dividing the problems into elementary task components and translating them into terms of the machine.

In this paper, the interface between the problems and the machines will be discussed with emphasis on the tools for the solutions—the programming languages and processors.

1.1.1.1. *Statement of Problem*

The application of computers for solving problems in technical, scientific, and commercial fields has been very successful. But progress is hampered by the fact that the machines accept primarily only their own special language, on digital computers composed of number sequences. These sequences are mostly long chains of zeros and ones—which is rather unintelligible to humans and quite different from the languages in which the tasks are and can be easily described.

1.1.1.2. *Possible Solutions*

There are two possibilities for solving the difficulties made by the gap between the languages of machines and the languages of problems. One solution would be to adapt the languages of the machines by developing machine languages more general and closer to the problems encountered, the high-level language computers; the other one would be to adapt the problems to the machines. This is done presently with intermediate languages, between machines and problems, which are easier for people to use than contemporary absolute machine languages.

HIGH-LEVEL LANGUAGE COMPUTERS. This would mean to develop a machine which could communicate in a higher language. Suggested rather early, and attempted to implement to some extent (for example, in the SEAC machine[1]) this idea could give an elegant solution to the problem. Therefore perhaps it is revived in newer designs,[2,3] and it is even suggested to use a language of the ALGOL-type[4] as machine language.[†] In addition to the drawbacks due to the insufficiencies of contemporary programming languages (and these are the only candidates at present for high-level machine languages) there are several factors opposed to such a development.

The arguments of high cost for circuitry and restrictions to the applications area are mainly based on the economic feasibility of such designs. But with an advent of very cheap components and assembly methods, these restrictions could change in the future.

The arguments of altering bases must be taken more seriously. The development is neither fixed on the problem side nor on the machine side.

Development on the Problem Side.   To illustrate this point a simple example might be taken. In applications to commercial problems a basic function is certainly sorting, which is used over and over again. So it would seem natural to include a machine operation for sorting in the repertoire of such high-level commercial machines. But what technique of sorting[5] should be implemented? The best technique to be selected depends on the data formats and on the machine configurations so that selecting only one technique is not very feasible. But inclusion of several different techniques is highly unlikely. This example will show the difficulties for only one task function. The overall requirements complicate the situation so much that no reasonable solution is in sight.

Development on Machine Side.   Many opinions state the view that the development on the machine side is now fixed.[6] But this belief seems prejudiced and premature. For example, in the near future memory hierarchies (let's say a memory of 128-word diode storage with 50 nanoseconds and 2048 words thin film or thin wire with 200 nanoseconds and backup storage of 32,768 words at 600 nanosecond cycle time. Behind these might be bulk core storage, drums, disks, and tapes) could give a user more computer power (according to the principle of limited resources) than the more conventional recent design; or mastery of parallel execution features, etc. Although this argument affects mainly the internal design of a possible high-level language machine, it complicates the picture and eliminates

---

† A similar step in this direction is sometimes attempted in microprogrammed machines with some higher-level language implemented in memory in a semifixed manner.

many suggestions for solutions. The potentialities for a standard machine (or assembly) language are impeded too by this aspect.

SOLUTIONS BY INTERMEDIATE LANGUAGES. The solution by intermediate steps between problem and machine languages via programming was at least in the past the most successful one. It can easily be seen that the closer to the problem the steps are taken, the more powerful and quickened the solution will be. So the region between problems and machines contains software levels of differing machine and problem independence.

Efficiency of Machine Use. Whenever a programming language is different from actual low-level machine language, questions concerning the efficient use of the hardware are apt to arise. These seem to be of greatest importance on slow and expensive machines. Linearly extrapolated, the emphasis on these questions is decreased to 2 percent when relating a machine with 0.5-microsecond cycle time in 1965 to one with 25-microsecond cycle time in 1951 at the same price. Interestingly, the highest requirements for run-time optimization with compilers are imposed on hardware which is inadequate for the intended problem solutions (e.g., optimization in FORTRAN II on the 704 and in ALPHA on the M20[8] for the solution of difficult partial differential equations). With the need for faster computers[9] and a decline in prices for hardware, as in the past decade, these efficiency questions are bound to diminish and perhaps to disappear altogether.

Hierarchy of Programming Languages. Different hierarchies of programming languages are already proposed,[10] where the criterion is the machine configuration concerned. Of course many other characteristics could be chosen for classification of programming languages, but the one here presented in respect to machine independence seems to be most interesting. A good measure for the level is the degree of declarative freedom for the user. Therefore on the lowest level would be the absolute machine languages and with more declarative possibilities gradually increasing up to the problem level of declarative languages as follows:

Absolute machine languages (machine level)	No declarative freedom
Assembly languages	No specification of names and locations necessary
Procedural languages	No detailed machine commands necessary

Problem-oriented languages	Language elements from problem but command structure procedural
Specification languages, augmented by semantics	Description of relations in the problem, freedom of procedure
Declarative languages (problem level)	Description of the problem, freedom of procedure and solution

The levels from absolute machine language to procedural languages are very well known from the literature of recent years. (Sometimes in the past, procedural languages like FORTRAN, ALGOL, and JOVIAL were incorrectly denoted as problem-oriented languages.) Examples for problem-oriented languages are found in APT, COGO, SIMSCRIPT, etc.[11] The block-notation languages[12] for analog-hybrid simulation on digital computers are examples of augmented specification languages. Semantic content is there defined by the fixed meaning of the block names (in MIDAS[13] they are the operations and the operands by means of the successor specification). Recently an example for another use of a specification language in an applications program was published[14] where Backus-Naur-Form specification was adopted. As can be expected, the experience reported stresses the improved facilities (compared with conventional programming languages) in programming, check-out, and incorporating changes into the program over conventional programming languages. Perhaps the first example in declarative languages, although not on the level designed by the term today, was the dynamic analysis language DYANA.[15] Some other approaches are described in a recent paper.[16]

Translation among Programming Languages. All programming languages above the actual machine language impose the necessity for translation to that language. This task is done by a translator, compiler, or assembler, hereafter called a processor.

Two different aspects have to be distinguished concerning the translation of programs:

1. Translations horizontally on one level

2. Translations vertically to other levels

Obviously, all translations can be regarded as composed of these two possibilities to various degrees. The requirements for the practicability of translation are:

- The rules for the connections of elements in the languages (the grammars or syntaxes)
- The elements of the languages (the dictionaries)
- Their respective relations in both languages as well

1. Translations Horizontally. Horizontal translations of programs among different programming languages of the same level are in general not possible. The reasons are that the results of one operation (in extended sense) in a program in source language (the language of the input) may determine the kind of operation to be used next in the program, and that often the target equivalent of a source language item is not available. The criterion for translatability is that all operations in the source language can be translated separately into the target language (the language of the output) in respect to power and extend. Translatability from one source language A to a target language B gives, however, no indications for translatability from B to A. Whenever some operations are not translatable, they may be simulated, e.g., interpreted at run time. Because of the huge number of redundant operation parts involved, interpreted programs run normally orders of magnitudes slower than comparable translated ones on the same machine.

2. Translation Vertically. Vertical translation of programs is divided into (a) upward and (b) downward translation.

(a) Upward translations impose generally the same requirements as those detailed for horizontal translations. A special case governs the upward translation of previously downward translated programs. Contrary to some opinion,[17] no relevant information for the execution of a program is lost in the translation process, only the redundant. Therefore, if the translation algorithm is given, all necessary information can be retrieved from the programs that had been translated before, to build a fully equivalent program on the former level.

(b) Downward translations are normally not difficult, because the languages on the higher levels are so designed as to give a specific and determined target equivalent on the lower level for each source language element.

Now, by the mechanical transformation of the program (a description of a problem or its solution) into representations of other levels with or without intermediate levels (e.g., DYANA → FORTRAN II, FORTRAN II → SAP704, SAP704 → 704) not more solutions of a problem are obtained, but only different representations of the program. Therefore, with regard to problem considerations, all different representations of one program (e.g., diagrams augmented by text, DYANA, FORTRAN II, SAP, and 704), and all programs giving the same results for the same sets of data, are said to be equivalent. A similar relation is given among specification languages or notations.[18] Continuing this thought, most efficiency questions, grammar, and syntax peculiarities and details, though interesting and necessary for the development of the transformation processors, are definitely unimportant and sometimes even undesirable for the solution of a task in applications programming.

Experience with High-Level Programming Languages. The aspects of the historical development of high-level programming languages (with regard to machine independence) are described in detail elsewhere.[11] It might be stressed that FORTRAN was not the first high-level language of algebraic type but had forerunners in Rutishauser's algebraic language on the ERMETH in Zurich and in Laning and Zirler's language on WHIRLWIND in MIT. Even MATH-MATIC for the UNIVAC I, a commercially available machine, was earlier. But the small UI (a decimal and alphanumeric machine with only 45 instructions) did not really necessitate and justify a high-level algebraic language; this was later required with the more complex machines of von Neumann-type, like the 704.

The advantages of high-level programming languages are more apparent the more the considered languages are independent from the machines. These advantages are:

1. Easier learning and use than lower-level languages, because they are less complicated

2. Time savings in programming of solutions for problems

3. Time savings in debugging and correcting the problems

4. Easier modification possibilities for slightly different problems

5. Higher machine independence for transition to other computers, and otherwise for compatibility with hardware

6. Better documentation (compatibility among programs and different programmers)

7. More powerful structuring in terms of problem

Points (1), (2), and (3) were stressed in the past and found most important.[19] Nowadays (4) and (5) receive more attention and in the future (5), (6), and (7) may become the dominant ones.

It is interesting to note that points (1) through (4) have been similarly known to engineers for decades for the solution of problems in formal instead of numerical notation.

Most astonishing is the large number of programs still written in a low-level language.[20] This can only be explained by a steep information gradient between the knowledge in the field and the application programmers, or better, their managers.

1.1.1.3. *Development of New High-Level Programming Languages*

INTRODUCTION. The development of new high-level programming languages, at least in the past, has been more evolutionary than revolutionary. So the step from FORTRAN to ALGOL brought with it these advantages in order of their estimated importance:

- Chained logical decision sequences
- Block structure of program parts
- Free notation format
- Lifting of various machine restrictions (i.e., number of subscripts in variables, modes of expressions, etc.)

Unfortunately, due perhaps to the ambiguities embedded in ALGOL and its definition, the gain from switching over to ALGOL programming from FORTRAN is considered marginal. Despite all the efforts in the past, less than 10 percent of all programs for scientific and engineering applications are coded in ALGOL[20]—which is not a striking triumph for a successor to FORTRAN.[21] Similarly, less than 5 percent of the programs in the same area are coded in FORTRAN IV—what can be cautiously described as failure of the new facilities incorporated in FORTRAN IV over FORTRAN II. The use of a programming language by applications programmers has to be the measure for its success. If one is not sufficiently used, a programming language is certainly as dead and obsolete as Mayan or Babylonian and perhaps of just academic interest.

REQUIREMENTS FOR A NEW HIGH-LEVEL PROGRAMMING LANGUAGE. Several important design criteria—often violated even in recent designs—have to be stressed.

Close Relationship to the Problems in the Desired Area. This allows the user a concise and powerful description of the processes and concepts.

Uniqueness. Each item in a correct program has to have one unique and defined meaning. This is required by all compatibility reasons.

Simplicity and Clearness of Notation. The language has to be developed and designed with a programming notation for ease of learning, use, and handling of the language in the intended problem area. (Of course, that does not exclude a formal and rigid definition of the language. But such a definition should hardly ever be imposed upon a user.) Requirements for readability and intelligibility are included here. This point of convenience has to be the main criterion for the standardization of programming languages. Admittedly, generally one proposed standard is better than another, if it is more convenient for the user.

Completeness. A good programming language should be able to handle all occurring tasks within its designed scope, without need for using means from outside. Good counterexamples are the missing string-handling facilities in FORTRAN and the input/output part in ALGOL 60.

Segmentation. For the practical application of programming languages to large problems, efficient segmentation features are desirable so that parts of problems can be handled independently.

Compatibility with Existing Programming Languages. In addition to compatibility in other respects, one is important with regard to the already accumulated knowledge of problem solutions (the program libraries). These libraries consist of two parts — one created by the present user working with the language and the other developed elsewhere or earlier with other languages. The first part requires elements in the language to build up and use older programs and program parts in new connotations; the second demands some means for translation or interpretation of old libraries.

DEVELOPMENT POSSIBILITIES. There are three ways of developing a new programming language:

- Cleaning up and refining existing languages
- Elaboration and combination of known useful features
- Development from the basic requirements of a problem area

All three methods were used in the past, either separately or combined.

PROLIFERATION AND SOLUTIONS: The application of computers with high-level languages to different problem areas causes a proliferation of programming languages according to the vernaculars in the application fields. There are two different possibilities:

1. If single programming languages are to be developed close to the vernaculars, then some incompatibility will exist between these.

2. On the other hand, if an intermediate language somewhere in the middle between problems and machines will be accepted as the programming standard, then much more effort has to be spent on defining the problems to the computers.

The historical development of progress in the computer field favors the first alternative, while computer manufacturers and operations managers of computer installations try to hold to the second one. Possible solutions to the dilemma might be found in:

(a) Inclusion of language elements of neighboring problem areas into programming languages presently in use or being developed, or opening the borders to that area; for an intermediate language with the scope of an UNCOL[22] but on a higher level or as a subset of a universal programming language

(b) Development of universal programming languages

(c) Development of universal processors

Universality in this respect is meant to comprise at least the elements of two really different problem areas (not vertical combinations or notations[23]).

Several proposals for the first of these solutions (inclusion of language elements) are already reported. Of these, BEEF[24] and ALGOL-Genius[25] are both designed to combine a programming language for algorithmic with one for commercial procedures. More ambitious in this respect is the NPL-SHARE[26,27] language to combine in addition the elements of real-time and command languages.

It is most noticeable that software systems (languages and processors) developed upwards from the machines by combination of existing elements do not tend to please many users. Despite the desirability of larger extended systems, there are always users who do not need the new scope and are unwilling to pay for the clumsiness and complication due to inadequate design.

Other development possibilities going from a fixed base are found in the features of open-ended systems. To some extent at present, the combining of languages of two areas results in at least a partial universal programming language.

1.1.2. UNIVERSAL PROGRAMMING LANGUAGES

1.1.2.1. *Definition*

A universal programming language can be defined as a complete set of elements to describe the problems and solutions in all problem areas. If such a language can be developed, the design requirements will be the same as for a single high-level programming language (see the requirements listed above), but much more valid.

1.1.2.2. *Mathematical Definition and Development*

It is easy to define mathematically the design and development of a universal programming language in general.

The complete set S_i of all equivalent programs[†] p_{ikl} for the solution of problem k in one area is given by

$$S_i = U_i p_{ikl}$$

Then the operation δ selects from this set a program, maximal in respect to power of problem description

$$D_k = \delta U_i p_{ikl}$$

Now all maximal programs of one problem area form a new complete set S_k:

$$S_k = U_k\, \delta U_i p_{ikl}$$

From this new set, operation γ extracts the language elements and operations for the given area to form the language for the problem area G_j:

$$G_j = \gamma U_k\, \delta U_i p_{ikl}$$

For the generalized and universal programming language Λ_u, the complete set S_l, generated by U_l, of all languages G_l has to be considered, combined, and integrated by the operation λ to give

$$\Lambda_u = \lambda U_l \gamma U_k\, \delta U_i p_{ikl}$$

As may be recognized, the operations, δ, γ, and λ are very complex and difficult, but the most serious drawback seems to be the large extent of the various sets required. But this is the only way for development, be it by methods of evolution via open-ended languages or by revolution via problem analysis and then language determination as given by an example in Ref. 28.

1.1.2.3. Old Proposals

The problem of proliferation of programming languages was recognized rather early especially in respect to the effects on processor production.[22,29] So UNCOL, a universal computer-oriented language was proposed as an

---

[†] See "Translation among Programming Languages" in Section 1.1.1.2.

interface between high-level programming languages and computers. Due to the open-endedness on both sides of problems and machines, such a scheme cannot easily be designed on the basis of a fixed language. On the other hand, examples for this scheme are known as notations, e.g., the prefix notation.[30] But this design level seems to be inadequate for a satisfactory solution to the problem.

A similar restriction is imposed on the well-known flow-chart notation to be used as a universal programming language, or even as a programming language. (Recent rumors suggest flow charts to be used on oscilloscope terminals for on-line programming.)

1.1.2.4. *Design Possibilities*

As mentioned in Section 1.1.1.2, there are two possibilities for the design of universal languages. One is a conventional approach with open-ended languages and processors so that the users will develop gradually the required high-level programming languages in the interesting problem areas. Then from time to time the now achieved status of a system should be re-evaluated and reshaped to avoid and eliminate inefficiencies and obsolescence. So gradually the best language for a problem area will mature. As soon as there are enough languages developed for different problem areas, then the design of a universal one can be envisaged.

The more direct method suggested by the mathematical definition is to investigate the nature of the problems, depict the elements for description and solution, and combine these into a high-level programming language. This method was used to develop the new programming language BEST for commercial applications.[28] The reported five years of labor seem relatively high, but the rewards justify the effort to eliminate all the inadequacies and inconsistencies which arrive at the fire-line with programming languages, designed by mutual consent at conference tables.

1.1.3. UNIVERSAL PROCESSORS

1.1.3.1. *General Requirements and Notation*

DEFINITION AND FEASIBILITY. A universal processor can be defined as a program for transformation of all programs from all required problem areas into all required target languages. The extent of such a processor is dependent on the definition of the requirements of the problems and of the machines.

Processors which accept programs in a number of different programming languages are well known.[31] But no successful experience (aside from the projects outlined below) could be found for easy combining of different target languages. This is certainly no accident, as will be stressed later. The target language area poses heavier and more stringent requirements on processors than the source language area where it is possible to easily combine several compilers for different languages (but for the same machine) into one system and to invoke the one momentarily required by control cards (e.g., in IBSYS[31]). The difficulties for the target language arise mainly because of a third language parameter in a processor, its own language, i.e., the one in which the processor is written or the language of the machine on which the processor has to run.

DESIGN AND IMPLEMENTATION.   At the source language side of a processor, besides the simple IBSYS concept, a higher degree of integration could be obtained by (1) accepting mixtures of statements of different languages, perhaps with indicators as to which languages they belong; and (2) accepting the elements of different languages intermixed. This requires that incompatibilities among the languages are removed. (For example, the definitions of identifiers in FORTRAN and COBOL are incompatible, with blanks having no meaning in FORTRAN, but used as separators in COBOL.) So it is proved that a fairly universal programming language cannot be developed by simply combining useful features from different other languages.

If only a restricted universal processor can be developed, then by feeding a copy of it to itself a desired less-restricted one could be produced automatically.

GENERAL NOTATION.   A processor can be defined as a function (f) for transformation of a program given in one language into that of another. The parameters of this function f are then:

α) Source language of programs to the processor
β) Target language of programs from the processor
γ) Own language of the processor
δ) Variables for measuring the efficiencies
ε) A variable for the method used in the processor, etc.

So the processor can be designated by $f(\alpha, \beta, \gamma, \delta, \varepsilon, \ldots)$.

TRANSFORMATION OF PROGRAMS BY PROCESSORS.   A source program is, for example, a given set V_{li} of (i) statements (s_i) in source language A for the solution of problem 1 and similarly a target program can be defined:

$$P_l = V_{li}s_i(A) \qquad \text{as source program}$$
$$P'_l = V_{lk}s_k(B) \qquad \text{as target program in language B}$$

The application of the transformation function gives the relations:

$$V_{lk}s_k(B) = fV_{li}s_i(A) \qquad \text{for languages separate translatable only on the program level}$$

$$= V_{li}gs_i(A) \qquad \text{requires a different transformation algorithm}$$

$$= V_{li}fV_{jm}s_m(A) \qquad \text{for languages separate translatable on block level; a block is defined as the set } V_m s_m(A)$$

$$= V_{li}fs_i(A) \qquad \text{for languages separate translatable on the statement level}$$

$$= V_{li}s_i(fA) \qquad \text{for languages separate translatable on the language level}$$

SIMPLIFIED NOTATION. The most interesting and important questions with processors are concerned with the function of changing the language representation of programs (especially by translating them to actual machine language). Therefore, if no regard is given to other than the language parameters, the function is reduced to

$$f = f(A, B, C)$$

Of course the other parameters cannot be completely ignored, but they depend on other variables. (Measured efficiency of a processor depends on the methods used, while efficiency requirements are functions of hardware speeds and costs again, etc.; so other parameters are omitted here.)

Now a new symbol for a processor is introduced in Fig. 1.1.1. It designates a processor translating from source language A into target language B and is itself written in (its own) language C. Sometimes a label as a name

FIGURE 1.1.1

for a processor will be used and inserted into the empty space at the left side of the symbol. Where one language parameter in the following is not specified or pertinent, the space for it is left empty.

1.1.3.2. *Examples of the New Symbol*

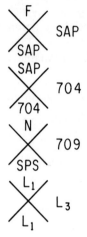

is a FORTRAN compiler written in SAP, translating from FORTRAN to SAP.

is a SAP assembler given in 704 machine language and translating from SAP to 704 machine language.

is a NELIAC compiler translating from NELIAC to 1401 SPS and running on the 709.

is a precompiler translating into the source language (e.g., for error checking in programs) and running on machine with language $L3$.

1.1.3.3. *Mode of Processor Use*

Basically two different modes of processor use can be distinguished: translative and interpretive.

1. Interpretive Mode. The interpretive mode of processor use is characterized by the handling of data and source statements at the same time, according to Fig. 1.1.2.

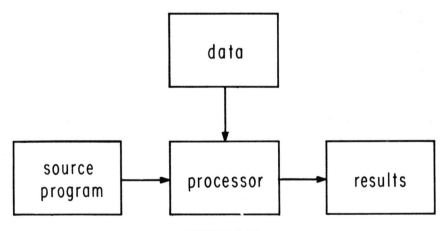

FIGURE 1.1.2

2. Translative Mode. The translative mode is characterized by the processing of source program and data at different times, at compile time and at run time, respectively, as in Fig. 1.1.3. It must be understood that the execution of the target program at run time is itself considered again as interpretation.

3. For Real-Time Interpretive. In real-time concurrent processing, the schemes would look like Fig. 1.1.4a.

4. For Real-Time Translative see Fig. 1.1.4b.

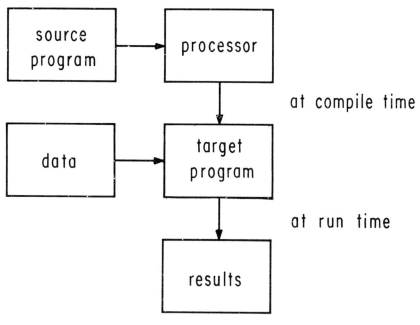

FIGURE 1.1.3

GENERAL USE OF PROCESSORS. The general use of processors is given by feeding (designated by the simple arrow →) a program into the processor to receive (designated by the double arrow ⇒) the program in another representation. Figure 1.1.5 is the translation process of a program from source language L_1 to target language L_2 by a processor running on a machine with language L_3.

A more interesting case is that the program fed to the processor can itself be a processor. When it is written in its own-source language it is represented as in Fig. 1.1.6. Here it is explained that a processor written in its source language can be translated to any other language for which a processor exists. From this prospect was derived the old requirement that

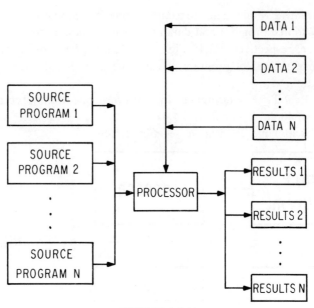

FIGURE 1.1.4A

each processor should be written in its source language. On the same
process is based nowadays the production of assemblers for new machines.
Details on that method will be explained later.

When the processor is written in its own-target language, this gives

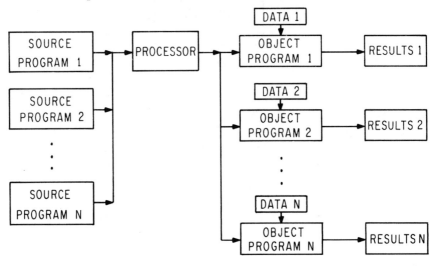

FIGURE 1.1.4B

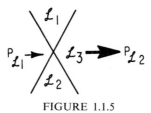

FIGURE 1.1.5

Fig. 1.1.7. This is the ancient method of processor construction by writing it in its target language. So it is possible to build up on already available processors. An example of this is the old FORTRAN compiler written in SAP and translating to SAP, which is then translated by the SAP assembler into 704 machine language, but it needed the SAP assembler in the translating process from FORTRAN to 704 code.

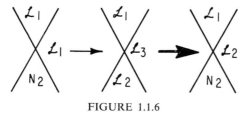

FIGURE 1.1.6

RESTRICTIONS ON THE PARAMETERS   The variables in the transformation function $f(A, B, C)$ of a processor are certainly not independent even among themselves. The following functional relations among the language parameters are interesting. Previous mention has been made of the relation between the target and the own language of a processor. Another, but not a very stringent one, governs the relation between source language elements and their target language equivalents.

It will now be assumed that the relations can be defined and the variables separated. Several cases are then distinguished:

1. The source-language parameter A is independent of the other ones, so that no functional relation is given there:

$$A \neq h_1(B); \qquad A \neq h_2(C)$$

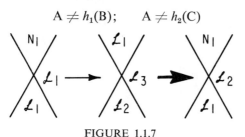

FIGURE 1.1.7

2. The target language variable B depends not on the source or on the own language:

$$B \neq h_3(A); \qquad B \neq h_4(C)$$

3. Both source and target language are not related to the own language (but might depend on each other):

$$A \neq h_2(C); \qquad B \neq h_4(C)$$

4. All language parameters are independent among themselves.

The design of universal processors will now be investigated according to these restrictions.

Universal Processors. Universal processors can be designed under the restrictions of the previous paragraph and will be treated in the same order.

1. A scheme for a universal processor limited by restriction (1) could be derived as follows: If the processor is not dependent with the source language either on target or on the own language, then the source language part could be made exchangeable. As soon as one processor with this characteristic would be available, processors for all different source languages could be constructed running and translating for the same machines. By transforming another processor with the same characteristic according to Fig. 1.1.8, processors could be written in all languages for which exchangeable definitions exist, and then translated to the designated machines. The task of writing $2m \times n$ processors for n languages and m machines (there are only $m \times n$ processors if the possibility of translation of programs on one machine for running on another machine is excluded) is now reduced to the writing of $2m$ processors or m, respectively for the m machines and of n language descriptions for the n source languages.

2. The case where the target language is considered independent of source and own language is even more interesting. Then target language descriptions for the machine could be developed and inserted into the processor to give a scheme for processors to translate for all machines.

Applying the same principle to the translation of processors could give a universal processor with any desired target and own language require-

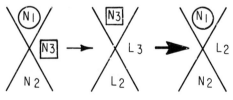

FIGURE 1.1.8

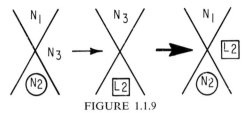

FIGURE 1.1.9

ments, such as Fig. 1.1.9. The requirements for a universal processor system would now be to write *n* processors for *n* source languages and *m* target language definitions for *m* machines. These *n* processors would be written preferably in a high-level language (N_3) for which a processor with the same characteristics for exchangeable target equivalents has been given already.

3. The case that source and target language are independent from the own processor language (although they may depend on each other, case 1) would give a very powerful and general system. By the application of the scheme to itself, any desired own language and so a rather general universal processor scheme could be obtained, as in Fig. 1.1.10.

The implementation requirements would now be to develop one processor with removable source and target language equivalent parts in two copies, and the definitions for each pair of source-target languages, giving $m \times n$ definitions if they are dependent on each other (case 31) or $m+n$ definitions if they are independent (case 32).

4. When all language parameters are independent, then we have the most general universal processor scheme. Of course this brings not more solutions than could already be obtained in case 32. The requirements here would be to have one processor with the desired characteristics and $m + n$ descriptions of source, target, and own languages.

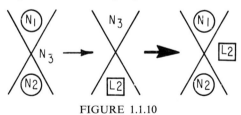

FIGURE 1.1.10

1.1.3.4. *Discussion*

The schemes for universal processors described in the preceding section are outlined on the assumption that the language parameters of processors are independent of other variables and among themselves, at least to a certain degree. Some relationships among source, target, and own language are known. But up to now it was never proved or disproved that perhaps they could be separated, and if so, under what conditions. It can be seen, for example, that between source and target language only a simple connective relationship exists, but the requirements then imposed on the own language were not yet evaluated.

The area of source languages is now fairly well understood, although the techniques are still not in the best conceivable state; much work is left to be done; some is going on and progressing satisfactorily. But knowledge of the others is very insufficient and incomplete.

Many investigations in the past were dedicated to the theory of automata. However, most results from these investigations are too general or of too low a level to be of great value to present-day computers with their variety of special hardware features. Only in the recent past some work was performed on models of more contemporary machines.[29]

As long as actual computers are not well understood there will not be much hope for very successful development of useful universal processors.

The following section describes the various reported projects for automated processor production and compares these to the described scheme of universal processors.

1.1.3.5. *Projects for Universal Processors*

GENERAL SCHEME AND SURVEY. All literature uncovered in recent years regarding projects for proposals on universal processors fit into the same general scheme. There is always input I, consisting of a processor or its description, or the description of the source language. Input II is sometimes missing (in some cases of a processor description for I), or consists of specifications of the target language, and of a source program in interpretive cases in addition to that. See Fig. 1.1.11.

The different elements for input and the obtained output are summarized in Table 1.1.1.

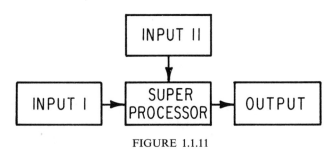

FIGURE 1.1.11

Table 1.1.1

Project	Input I	Input II	Resulting Processor	Special Features
High-level and special language use	Processor written in high-level or special processor writing language	—	Processor in low-level language	High-level languages applied to processor construction
UNCOL	Processor in UNCOL to translate to UNCOL	—	Processor for UNCOL on designed machine	Reduction in number of processors required
CLIP-JOVIAL	Processor in high-level language	—	Processor in low-level for original language	"Bootstrapping"
NELIAC	Processor in high-level language	—	Same as above	Same as above
XTRAN	Processor in high-level language (with connectors?)	Target machine macros	Processor in low-level for designated language	Exchangeability of target language equivalent
SLANG	Processor in SLANG—POLMI	Target language description to generate the equivalents	Same as above	Generation of target equivalents from a description
TOOL	Processor in TOOL	Library of macros	Same as above	Translation for new machines
Syntax method	Language specification in terms of M	Source program in L	Target program in M	Interpretive processor accepting language L specification
TGS	1. Language specification L	1. Macros for M	Same as above	Interpretive processor with extensive descriptions and specifications
	2. Generation statement tables for selection	2. Source program	Processor in M	
Meta A	Description of language L in terms of M	—	Processor in M	System written in specification languages
Meta B	Description of language L with connectors	List of target equivalents (macros)	Same as above	System in specification language separable for given source and target languages
Applicative Expressions	Description of L in Applicative Expressions	Machine definition in Applicative Expressions	Same as above	Same as above with Applicative Expressions as specification language

Two different approaches can be distinguished, one starting with a processor or the description of a translation process and the other starting with definitions for the source language. The processor-based projects are generally the older ones, thus reflecting the progress in the field.

1.1.3.6. *Processor-Based Projects*

1. High-Level or Special High-Level Language Use. To gain the advantages of programming using high-level languages (see Section 1.1.1) in the construction of processors, projects based on this were tried rather early and often abandoned immediately. The main reasons were the inadequacies of high-level languages of those days (mainly FORTRAN and ALGOL) for processor descriptions, and unfamiliarity with the new technique. To alleviate the difficulties, special high-level languages were developed.[33],[34] The scheme here is working like Fig. 1.1.12.

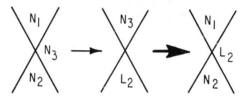

FIGURE 1.1.12

However, the gains by these projects for the construction of universal processors can be considered marginal because the original number of processors required is not reduced and, in addition to that, one processor for the high-level description language is required for each machine. This scheme is reported only for the sake of completeness and because it is used heavily in other projects.

2. UNCOL. In this project the first suggestion for a system of some sort of a universal processor was given.[22],[29] It calls for an intermediate language (see Section 1.1.2.3) together with the appropriate processors. The requirements are here reduced to $m + n$ processors for n languages and m machines, instead of $m \times n$ (without translation of programs to run on other machines). For each source language a processor has to be written in UNCOL translating into UNCOL and then for each machine one translating into machine language.

In the production process the processor (written in UNCOL) for the source language is translated by a processor from UNCOL to machine language as in Fig. 1.1.13. All programs then written in source language N_1 are

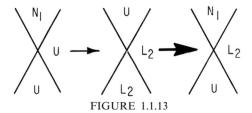

FIGURE 1.1.13

translated by this new processor, running on machine with language L_2, into programs in UNCOL. These programs are then finally translated to machine language L_2 by the translator from UNCOL to machine language L_2 (already required above), as in Fig. 1.1.14.

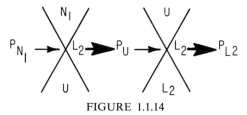

FIGURE 1.1.14

3. CLIP-JOVIAL. Very similar to both the UNCOL and high-level language project is basically the CLIP-JOVIAL approach. Several different versions are reported, one without intermediate language and another, more advanced, with it.[35] The diagram for the simpler version looks like Fig. 1.1.15. Prac-

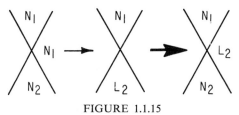

FIGURE 1.1.15

tically, the high-level language scheme where the source language is used for description with:

N_1 the CLIP language (a dialect of ALGOL 58 with additional features for table packing, string handling, storage overlapping, and local and global declarations)

N_2 assembly language

L_2 709 machine language

The more advanced version uses an interesting "bootstrapping" method for adapting the processors to different machines. See Fig. 1.1.16.

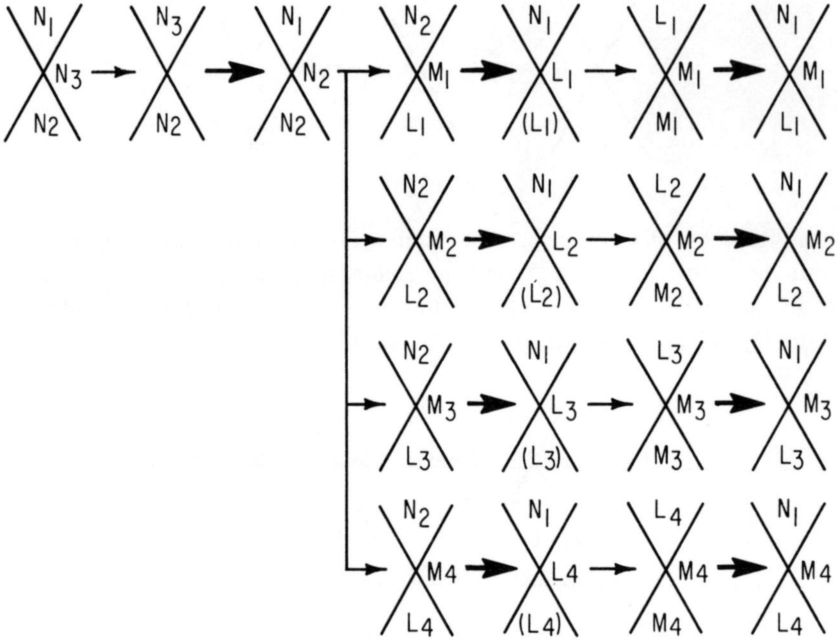

FIGURE 1.1.16

The parameters are given as in Fig. 1.1.17 with the indication of $-A$ after a computer name standing for assembly language for that machine, and the computer name alone standing for its machine language. The parameters (L_i) indicate the insertion of the appropriate target language equivalents for the intermediate language N_2 and the patching up for it.

A processor is written in CLIP to translate from source to intermediate language and is itself translated by the CLIP processor into intermediate language. For each machine, a processor is now written for translation from intermediate to assembly language of that machine. With these processors, the former processor is translated into assembly language, and the target equivalent in intermediate language is exchanged for the one in

N_1	N_2	N_3	L_1	L_2	L_3	L_4	M_1	M_2
JOVIAL	INTERMEDIATE	CLIP	709-A	2000-A	ANFSQ-A	MILITARY-A	709	2000

M_3	M_4
ANFSQ	MILITARY

FIGURE 1.1.17

assembly language. At last, the resulting processors are translated by the assemblers to the appropriate machines.

A universal processor scheme requires:

- One processor for each source language written in CLIP and translating to the intermediate language
- One processor for each machine to translate from intermediate language to assembly language, the target equivalents for the intermediate language for patching up in the insertion
- One CLIP processor for the intermediate language (and the assemblers for the different machines)

The main difficulty here is to design an intermediate language in a fixed form for many source languages (e.g., the UNCOL concept[†]).

4. NELIAC. In NELIAC likewise the high-level language is used for the programming of the processors.[36] The most interesting feature here is the bootstrapping scheme to obtain the processors for different machines.[37] In the original version on the U460 (COUNTESS), about 20 percent of the processor was handwritten and in machine language inserted into the processor (indicated by $N_{C/460}$), after completion of writing the processor in its source language.

In the notation symbols for the original names are retained as follows:

$$N_C \qquad\qquad N_{709}$$
NELIAC for the Countess   NELIAC for the 709

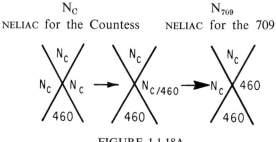

FIGURE 1.1.18A

The NELIAC-Countess processor was produced with the patched-up processor, in Fig. 1.1.18A. This version was used in the production of the processors for the B200, the CDC 1604, IBM 704 and the 709 machines according to Fig. 1.1.18B for the 709.

For each machine, two different versions of the processors have to be written, one in the NELIAC language for the Countess and the other in the NELIAC language for the desired machine.

[†] See *AFIPS Conference Proceedings*, Vol. 27 (1965), Section IIC.

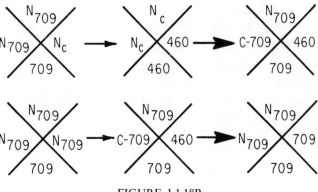

FIGURE 1.1.18B

The procedure is to write a processor for a source language to a target language in a high-level language for which there is a compiler running on a machine. This processor is first translated to run on that machine. Then the processor is written in its source language and translated to its proper machine by the one already obtained. This process is the direct equivalent of the old assembler production method, which has been writing the assembler for a new machine first in an assembly language of a running machine and then translating it to run on this machine. The assembler was then again written, but in its source language and translated by the already obtained assembler to run on and translate for its proper machine.

5. XTRAN. To adapt the processors for different source languages, the XTRAN system[21] accepts those written in a simplified version of ALGOL '58 with string-handling facilities (XTRAN language) and the set of the macros for the particular machine. Two different sets of macros are used; one is machine-independent of the three-address type (as an intermediate language) and the other consists of the macros of an actual machine in assembly or machine language. The XTRAN system translates the processor for a source language into the machine-independent macros, accepts the definition of these macros in terms of the machine-dependent ones, and then replaces the former with the latter. See Fig. 1.1.19.

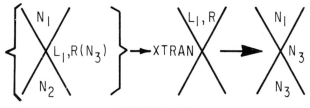

FIGURE 1.1.19

The requirements for a scheme of universal processors are:

- One processor for each source language written in XTRAN (L_1)
- One set of machine-dependent macros for each machine
- The XTRAN system

Unfortunately no experience is published yet for this system. This might be due to unsatisfactory performance for the macro setup.[38]

6. SLANG. The SLANG system[39] is very similar to XTRAN, but is more ambitious to generate by itself the macros from a definition of the target machine. The SLANG compiler accepts in addition to that a description of the processor in SLANG-POLMI, designated by S in Fig. 1.1.20. Of course

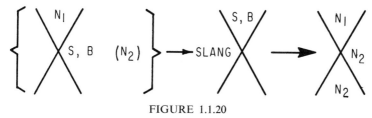

FIGURE 1.1.20

the building up of the target equivalents from a machine description is usually a very difficult task, if in general possible at all. And the POLMI language might not be definable in a fixed set. Therefore it is not surprising that no further experience with this system is yet reported in the literature.

The requirements for a universal processor scheme using this system are:

- One processor written in SLANG-POLMI for each source language
- One description for each target machine

7. TOOL. A peculiar system was reported in TOOL.[40] It translates processors written in the TOOL language for other machines. The target equivalents for a new machine are extracted from a library file. So the automated translation of processors given in TOOL, designated by T, to different machines is handled. Generally, processor notation gives the system in Fig. 1.1.21. In this case, the universal processor scheme would require:

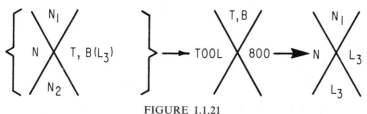

FIGURE 1.1.21

- One processor written in TOOL for each source language
- One library of target equivalents for each machine (presumably with appropriate connectors)

As can be seen, this scheme is very similar to the method from SLANG. Without further details this scheme was reported to be working satisfactorily and to be running on the H800 and H400.

1.1.3.7. *Description Based Projects*

THE SYNTAX-DIRECTED METHOD. The reported projects use a syntactic description of the source language[41,42] and are compiling interpretively, as in Fig. 1.1.22. The reason for the requirement of interpretive mode here lies in the fact that the different language parameters of a processor are interwoven, but already to a much lower degree than in straightforward processors.

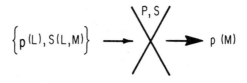

FIGURE 1.1.22

The requirements for a universal processor scheme here are that the syntax description be separable from the superprocessor and that one description be developed for each source-target language pair.

TGS—THE TRANSLATOR-GENERATOR-SYSTEM. An ensuing development to the syntax-directed method is given by the translator-generator-system TGS,[43,44] using macroconcepts like the XTRAN project (see paragraph 5 on XTRAN in Section 1.1.3.4).

This scheme accepts as input besides the program to be translated:

1. A sort of Backus-Naur-Form definition of the source language
2. A table for macrodescription and code selection for the target language
3. The generation strategy tables for the description of the linkage between source and target definitions

The supercompiler consists of five parts (see Fig. 1.1.23) working subsequently on the source program. Most interesting among them are:

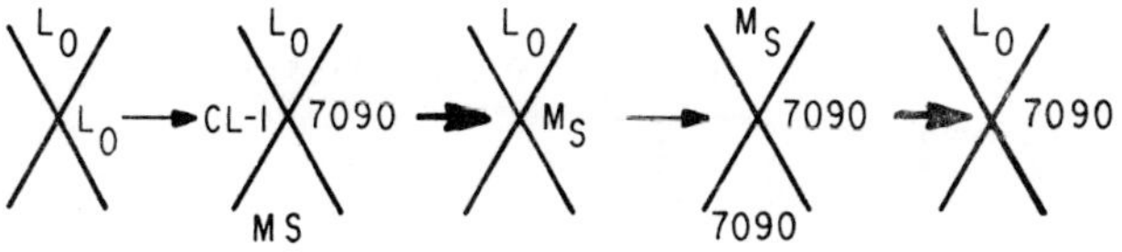

FIGURE 1.1.23

1. A syntactic analyzer for the source program to convert some piece of input string into an internal representation (a tree form is used)

2. A generator phase translating the internal representation into an n-address instruction form, depending on syntactic context

3. An optimizer phase for source and target program optimization, eliminating invariant computations out of loops and common sub-expressions (thus being source-language-dependent to a certain degree) and assigning special registers (thus being machine-dependent to a certain degree)

4. A code-selector phase driven by the code-selector table to produce symbolic machine code.

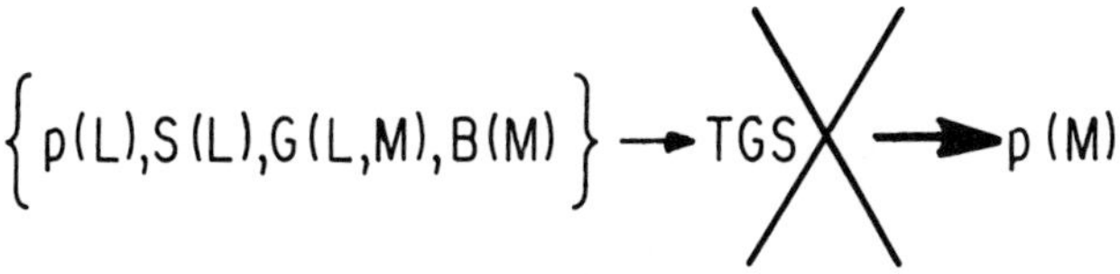

FIGURE 1.1.24

The translation process looks like Fig. 1.1.24.

Most important is the endeavor to achieve an object code optimized to a rather high degree at the cost of great difficulty in the description of the code selection. In addition to that, the algorithms seem to be source- and target-language-dependent (with respect to algorithmic languages containing expressions and loops, and to machines possessing special registers, both in a given form).

For the production of the system, a bootstrap technique is used, starting from the algebraic language L_0 (the language of the CL-I system[45] in which the system was originally written) as shown in Fig. 1.1.25.

A universal processor scheme based on this project would require:

• One BNF definition for each source language
• One table for macro description and code selection for each target language
• One generation strategy table for each source-target language pair

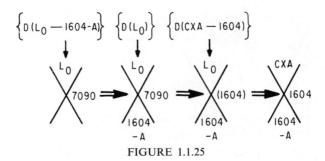

FIGURE 1.1.25

META-LANGUAGE COMPILER DIRECT.   Likewise derived from the
syntax-directed method,[46] this project uses a meta-language description of
a source language in terms of the semantic target equivalents as basic
elements of the language on the problem side.[47] This description is then
compiled by the meta-language compiler into a processor written in the
target equivalents of the meta-language compiler, as in Fig. 1.1.26.

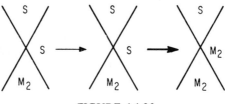

FIGURE 1.1.26

The meta-language compiler was originally written in its augmented
specification language and compiled by itself; see Fig. 1.1.27. Since no
machine was available to accept the meta-language specification, this
translation was done initially by hand. The target equivalent for M_1 and

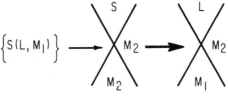

FIGURE 1.1.27

M_2 are normally rather far different from operations and elements found
on actual computers. Therefore they have to be interpreted in terms of
those for execution.

Requirements for a universal processor scheme are here:

- One meta-linguistic description for each source language
- One set of target equivalents for each machine and set of basic semantic elements of each source language
- The meta-language compiler

META-LANGUAGE COMPILER INDIRECT.   Based on the previous project a method more machine-independent can be proposed, using the macro principle. Here the basic semantic elements of the source language would be separated from the source language description and referred to by connectors. These are then inserted or executed to obtain translative or interpretive mode. The production of a processor would be accomplished according to Fig. 1.1.28.

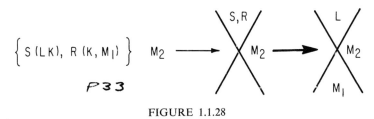

FIGURE 1.1.28

A universal processor scheme requires here:

- One description for each source language
- One set of target equivalents for each machine plus the target equivalents of new basic semantic elements in a new source language
- The meta-language compiler

One special aspect of this method has to be stressed. By the design process of a source language in terms of the basic semantic elements, these elements can be separated in a form in which they are required for the development of a universal programming language (see Sections 1.1.2.2 and 1.1.2.4).

APPLICATIVE EXPRESSIONS.   Another proposal for a universal processor project could use Applicative Expressions[48] and would be very similar to the method described above. Both source and target language would be described in Applicative Expressions with connectors used for the correct interplay. Although this scheme might be more general, it seems to introduce many redundancies and to complicate the description, as the examples in Ref. 48 prove. The process would be as in Fig. 1.1.29. The requirements for universal processors in this instance are similar to those in the preceding paragraph.

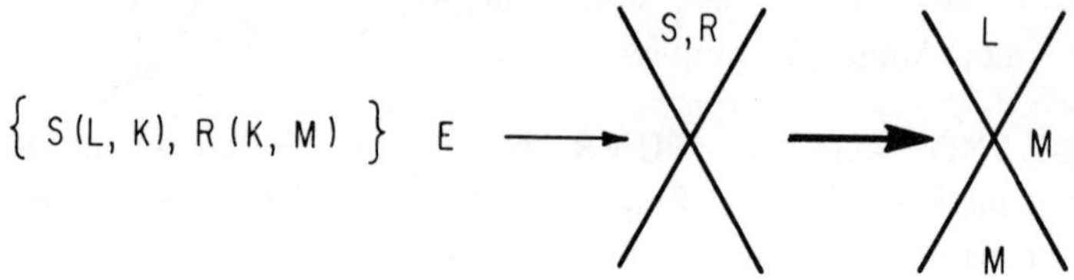

$$\left\{\; S\,(L,\,K),\; R\,(K,\,M)\;\right\}\;\; E \;\longrightarrow\; \overset{S,R}{\times} \;\longrightarrow\; \overset{L}{\underset{M}{\times}}\,M$$

FIGURE 1.1.29

1.1.3.8. *Discussion*

All reported projects try to gain some power for the construction of processors in the direction of universal processors. There are basically three different starting points:

1. The own language for the processor
2. The source language of the processor
3. The target language of the processor

The first point is stressed by all methods to alleviate the specifications of the processor to various degrees from the use of a high-level language for explicitly writing the processor to the syntax table specification in TGS.

The complete definition of a source language can specify at the same time a recognizer for programs written in that language. This characteristic is used in the description-based projects.

Techniques for the target language specification to use a processor on different computers were attempted rather early as they were important to the development of software in the variety of different computer designs. But, as far as can be seen, the obtained results are still very far from a satisfactory solution to the problem—if it is possible to find even a fairly general solution. Unfortunately no detailed experience with the XTRAN and TOOL projects is reported.

Several interesting methods are used for bootstrapping, i.e., the adaption of a processor to a special computer mechanically. They range from the old assembler construction method used in NELIAC to rather elaborate and sophisticated ones, as in TGS. Of course, the whole subject needs much more effort to develop the techniques for a fairly general universal processor scheme or to prove that the plan is not possible, and to state the conditions as to which way it would then be possible. But new ideas for solutions and new insights into the problems will certainly bring much more progress than was achieved in the past. This paper is intended to serve as a basis for such a development.

SYMBOLISM

A	For designation of the source language of a processor
B	For designation of the target language of a processor
C	For designation of the own language of a processor
$B(M)$	Description of a target machine
$D(L)$	Description of the language L
E	Designates Applicative Expressions
$f(\alpha, \beta, \gamma, \delta, \varepsilon, \ldots)$	Processor function
$f(A, B, C)$	Processor function with regard to the language parameters
$G(L, M)$	Connective relation
K	Connectors
L_i	With i as a number designating a language parameter
M	Macros
N_i	Similar to L_i
P(L)	Program in L
R	A list
$S(L, M)$	Language specification of syntax type for source language L and target language M
U	As language designator for UNCOL
U_k, V_k	As a set operator in respect to k
X	A processor
$D \underset{B}{\overset{A}{\times}} C$	A processor with source language A, target language B, own language C, and name D
{ }	The braces are used to combine some input other than a single processor or program
$\rightarrow$	Simple arrow for designating the feed-in to a processor
$\Rightarrow$	Double arrow for designating the output from a processor

REFERENCES

1. Slutz, R. J., "Engineering Experience with the SEAC," *Proc. EJCC* (1951), pp. 90–93.

2. Haley, A. C. D., "The KDF9 Computer System," *Proc. FJCC* (1962), pp. 108–120.

3. "Burroughs B5000," in *Data Processing Encyclopedia*, Detroit, 1961, pp. 50–55.

4. Samelson, K., "Programming Languages and their Processors," *Proc. IFIP Congr.* (1962), Munich, pp. 487–492.

5. See, for example, M. H. Hall, "A Method of Comparing the Time Requirements of Sorting Methods," *Comm. ACM*, vol. 5 (May 1963), pp. 259–263.

6. See, for example, F. P. Brooks, Jr., "The Future of Computer Architecture," *Proc. IFIP Congr.* (1965), New York, pp. 87–91.

7. Barton, R. S., "A Critical Review of the State of the Programming Art," *Proc. SJCC* (1963), pp. 169–177.

8. Yershov, A. P., "ALPHA—An Automatic Programming System of High Efficiency," *IFIP Congr.* (1965), New York.

9. Ward, J. A., "The Need for Faster Computers," *Proc. Pacif. Comp. Conf.* (1963), pp. 1–4.

10. Clippinger, R. F., "Programming Implications of Hardware Trends," *Proc. IFIP Congr.* (1965), New York, pp. 207–212.

11. Rosen, S., "Programming Systems and Languages," *Proc. SJCC* (1964), Washington, D.C., pp. 1–15.

12. Brennan, R. D., and Linebarger, R. V., "A Survey of Digital-Analog Simulator Programs," *Simul.* vol. 3 (December 1964), pp. 22–36.

13. Peterson, H. E., *et al.*, "MIDAS—How It Works and How It's Worked," *Proc. FJCC* (1964), pp. 313–324.

14. Schorr, H., "Analytic Differentiation Using a Syntax Directed Compiler," *Comp. J.*, vol. 7 (January 1965), pp. 290–298.

15. Theodoroff, T. J., and Olsztyn, J. T., "DYANA, Dynamic Analyzer-Programmer I & II," *Proc. EJCC* (1958), pp. 144–151.

16. Young, J. W., Jr., "Non-Procedural Languages," *7th Ann. Tech. Symp., Southern Calif. Chapter, ACM* (March 1965).

17. Opler, A., *et al.*, "Automatic Translation of Programs from One Computer to Another," *Proc. IFIP Congr. Munich* (1962), pp. 245–247.

18. Gorn, S., "Specification Languages for Mechanical Languages and Their Processors, a Baker's Dozen," *Comm. ACM*, vol. 4 (December 1961), pp. 532–542.

19. Backus, J. W., *et al.*, "The FORTRAN Automatic Coding System," *Proc. WJCC* (1957), pp. 188–198.

20. Bromberg, H., "Surveys of Computer Language Use," *Data Proc. Mag.* (April 1965), p. 37.

21. Bemer, R. W., "Survey of Modern Programming Techniques," *Comp. Bull.* (March 1961), pp. 127–135.

22. Steel, T. B., "A First Version of UNCOL," *Proc. WJCC* (1961), p. 371.

23. See, for example, K. Iverson, "Recent Applications of a Universal Programming Language," *IFIP Congr.* (1965), New York, and *IBM Syst. Journ.*, vol. 2 (June 1963), pp. 117–128.

24. Moraff, N., "Business and Engineering Enriched FORTRAN (BEEF)," *Proc. 19th ACM Conf.* (1964), Phila. DI. 4.

25. Langefors, B., "ALGOL-Genius, A Programming Language for General Data Processing," *BIT*, vol. 4, no. 3 (1964), pp. 162–176.

26. *NPL Technical Report*, IBM Publications No. 320-0908, Poughkeepsie, New York, December 1964.

27. *Computer Review*, vol. 6, no. 2, ref. 7275 (March-April 1965), pp. 108–112.

28. Ziegler, J. R., "Computer-Generated Coding (BEST)," *Datamat.* (October 1964), pp. 59–61.

29. Bratman, H., "An Alternate Form of the UNCOL Diagram," *Comm. ACM*, vol. 4 (March 1961), p. 142.

30. See, for example, C. L. Hamblin, "Translation to and from Polish Notation," *Comp. J.*, vol. 5 (October 1962), pp. 210–213.

31. Noble, A. S., and Talmadge, R. B., "Design of an Integrated Programming and Operating System, I & II," *IBM Syst. J.*, vol. 2 (June 1963), pp. 152–181.

32. See, for example, C. C. Elgot and A. Robinson, "Random Access Stored Program Machines," *Comp. J.*, vol. 11 (October 1964), pp. 365–399.

33. Garwick, J. V., "Gargoyle, a Language for Compiler Writing," *Comm. ACM*, vol. 7 (January 1964), pp. 16–20.

34. Hoare, C. A. R., "A Programming Language for Processor Construction," *IFIP Congr.* (1965), New York.

35. Englund, D., and Clark, E., "The CLIP-translator," *Comm. ACM*, vol. 4 (January 1961), pp. 19–22.

36. Watt, J. B., and Wattenburg, W. H., "A NELIAC-generated 7090-1401 Compiler," *Comm. ACM*, vol. 5 (February 1962), pp. 101–102.

37. Halstead, M. H., *Machine Independent Computer Programming*, Spartan Books, Washington, D.C., 1962, pp. 37 ff.

38. See, for example, G. Letellier, "A Dynamic Macro Generator for Optimum Use of Machine Facilities by a Translated Program," *IFIP Congr.* (1965), New York.

39. Sibley, R. A., "The SLANG-system," *Comm. ACM*, vol. 4 (January 1961), pp. 75–84.

40. Opler, A., "TOOL, A Processor Construction Language," *Proc. IFIP Congr.* (1961), Munich, p. 513.

41. Irons, E. T., "A Syntax-Directed Compiler for ALGOL 60," *Comm. ACM*, vol. 4 (January 1961), pp. 51–55.

42. Cheatham, T. E., and Sattley, K., "Syntax Directed Compiling," *Proc. SJCC* (1964), Washington, D.C., pp. 31–57.

43. Warshall, S., and Shapiro, R. M., "A General Table-Driven Compiler," *Proc. SJCC* (1964), Washington, D.C., pp. 59–65.

44. Cheatham, T. E., "The TGS-II Translator-Generator System," *IFIP Congr.* (1965), New York.

45. Cheatham, T. E., *et al.*, "CL-I, an Environment for a Compiler," *Comm. ACM*, vol. 4 (January 1961), pp. 23–27.

46. Glennie, A., "On the Syntax Machine and the Construction of a Universal Compiler," Carnegie Tech. Rep. No. 2 (AD-240512), July 1960.

47. Schorre, D. V., "A Syntax Oriented Compiler Writing Language," *Proc. 19th ACM Conf.* (1964), Phila., D1.3.

48. Burge, W. H., "The Evaluation, Classification and Interpretation of Expressions," *Proc. 19th ACM Conf.* (1964), Phila., A1.4.

1.2. A History of Writing Compilers

by Donald E. Knuth

1.2.1. INTRODUCTION

In the field of programming for computers, the time seems to be ripe for a look back at the evolution of techniques used in writing algebraic compilers. People with experience writing translators should profit by some reflection on the historical trends; and people who are more accustomed to using compilers than to creating them will perhaps feel more familiar with compilers if they see how such programs evolved. This article therefore attempts to review briefly the history of techniques for writing a compiler.

A great development of compiler languages, of course, has taken place, as well as of techniques for translating them, but we will concern ourselves primarily with the techniques.

The first compilers came into being about the same time that I was becoming exposed to computers. You might say that I learned computing from reading a listing in the assembly language SOAP I (Symbolic Optimum Assembly Program I) of the first compiler IT (Internal Translator).[1] An enormous number of compilers have been written since then; I cannot, of course, claim to be familiar with even most of them. I am only vaguely

EDITOR'S NOTE: This article reproduced by permission of the author and the publisher: *Computers and Automation* (December 1962), pp. 8–14.

aware of the developments in the Soviet Union and in Europe. But I have examined closely the internal workings and machine language of a large number of American compilers produced by various groups all over the country, and I hope the ones I have examined represent a good cross section. Also I have written three compilers (in the summers of 1958, 1960, and 1962) and each of these three looks quite different from the other two, reflecting the changing times. This is the background from which this article is written.

A true history gives dates of events and names of people, but I will not do that. In this field there has been an unusual amount of parallel discovery of the same technique by people working independently. Perhaps you remember the time when three different people, in the same month, sent in the same idea for counting binary ones in a computer word to the *Communications of the ACM*. The literature of compiling has many, many accounts of what is essentially the same thing, by people who were obviously unaware that others had made the same discovery. I read somewhere recently that the GAT compiler, written at the University of Michigan, was written using an algorithm due to the Soviet Academician A. P. Yershov, and I'll wager this comes as quite a surprise to the people at Michigan who weren't consciously borrowing a Russian compiler algorithm. Other references give credit to H. Kanner's algorithm, or that of A. Oettinger, or B. Arden and R. Graham, or K. Samelson and F. I. Bauer, or H. Huskey and W. H. Wattenburg, etc., etc. I know of several other people who invented the same thing and never published it. The question as to who was really the first to discover a certain technique will probably never be answered, but it is not really important. In fact this latter question has very little meaning, since those named above and others discovered to a greater or less degree various aspects of a technique, and it has been polished up through the years into a very pretty algorithm which none of the originators fully realized. So I cannot give credit to one without giving it to all; let it suffice to say merely that the compiling art has been advanced by many people with many ingenious ideas. Of course Dr. Alan Perlis and his co-workers at Purdue and Carnegie deserve credit for showing that compiling is possible in the first place.

1.2.2. DECOMPOSITION OF FORMULAS

So much for introductory remarks. Try now for a moment to imagine that nobody has ever written a compiler before, but that somebody has asked you to write one. Chances are that one difficulty will overshadow all the others in your mind, namely how to translate arithmetic expressions. We all recognize algebraic formulas simply by looking at them and reading them off; but how can this be done by a machine, without asking it to be able to "think" first? Take for example $[(Y * Z) + (W * V)] - X$, where "$*$" stands for multiplication; we must systematically begin with the formula and find a way to evaluate it, taking one step at a time.

The first solution to this problem, used in the IT compiler, was based on the concept of parenthesis levels. When I learned algebra, we were taught to use parentheses first, then brackets around the parentheses, then braces, and if we had to go farther, we used extra large parentheses or something. I think the first time I was taught that only parentheses were really necessary was when I learned a compiler language. (This concept was well known to logicians but I doubt if it was generally known until compiler languages became popular.)

We can draw a kind of "contour map" of an expression, going up one unit for each left parenthesis, and going down one unit for each right parenthesis, and the "altitude" thus achieved is the so-called parenthesis level. (See Fig. 1.2.1.) In the IT compiler a maximum parenthesis level of

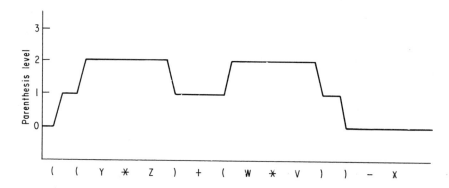

FIGURE 1.2.1   Contour map of the expression $((Y + Z) + (W * V)) - X$.

ten was allowed, and the formulas were processed by breaking them into levels. Precedence or rank of operators was not recognized; for example, $A + B/C$ was $A + (B/C)$ and $A/B + C$ was $A/(B + C)$.

In order to see how a translation algorithm might be organized around the concept of parenthesis level, we can investigate the method shown in Fig. 1.2.2, which shows a grossly simplified version of the IT algorithm. It goes something like this: A binary operator has a corresponding so-called

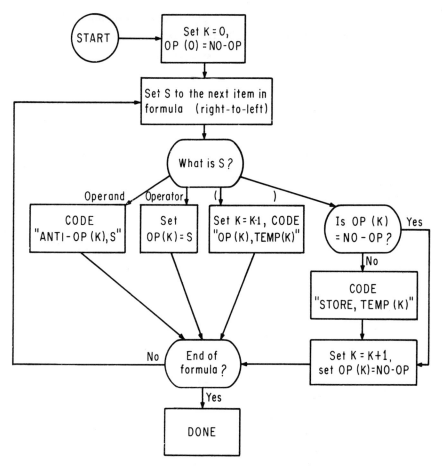

FIGURE 1.2.2   Translation based on parentheses levels, without considering precedence operators.

anti-operator such that

$$A \text{ op } B = B \text{ anti-op } A$$

Since $A + B = B + A$, plus is its own anti-op, and the anti-op of "/" is "inverse divide." Remington Rand computers tend to have only the "inverse divide" command, and IBM computers tend to have only the "divide" command in the machine language, but for simplicity we will assume that both commands are on our machine, and that there is even an "inverse subtract" command. We will also think of NO-OP ("no-operation") and

LOAD as anti-operators of each other, and if you want some justification for this you should ponder over the formulas

$$\text{LOAD (b)} = 0 + b \qquad \text{NO-OP (b)} = b + 0$$

The algorithm is roughly: Take the next item, from right to left in the formula. Then branch four ways, depending on the type of item:

1. For an operand (a variable or constant), output machine language code "anti-op (K), operand"; the counter K represents the parenthesis level and it starts out at zero; and there is a ten-place OP table, OP (0) through OP (9). The meaning of "anti-op (K)" is, "The anti-operator of OP (K)."

2. For an operator, save this operator in position OP (K) of the OP table.

3. For a left parenthesis, decrease K by 1, and then output the machine language code "OP (K), TEMP (K)." TEMP (K) is the Kth temporary storage cell.

Item	OP Table			Code Produced
	NO-OP			
X	NO-OP			LOAD X
−	−			
)	−	NO-OP		STORE TEMP (0)
)	−	NO-OP	NO-OP	
V	−	NO-OP	NO-OP	LOAD V
*	−	NO-OP	*	
W	−	NO-OP	*	MULTIPLY W
(	−	NO-OP		NO-OP TEMP (I)
+	−	+		(note: a NO-OP may be deleted from the code)
)	−	+	NO-OP	STORE TEMP (I)
Z	−	+	NO-OP	LOAD Z
*	−	+	*	
Y	−	+	*	MULTIPLY Y
(	−	+		ADD TEMP (I)
(	−			SUBTRACT TEMP (0)

FIGURE 1.2.3 Item-by-item action produced by the parenthesis-level method of Fig. 1.2.2 when it is applied to the formula $((Y * Z) + (W * V)) - X$. Notice how the OP-table, if tipped on its side and reflected, corresponds to the contour map in Fig. 1.2.1.

4. For a right parenthesis, check first if OP (K) = "NO-OP," and if not, output the code "STORE, TEMP (K)." Then increase K by 1, and set OP (K) equal to "NO-OP" for the new value of K.

Repeat the above process until the end of the formula is reached. This whole process will be clear if we look at a play-by-play account of the method as it acts on the formula "((Y * Z) + (W * V)) − X." This is given in Fig. 1.2.3. The interested reader will learn a lot if the tries to revise the method to work from left to right rather than right to left. Right to left was used here because it was done that way in IT; an equally simple algorithm which goes from left to right can be given, and it is instructive to discover what changes are necessary.

Note: IT also treated "A + B + C − D/E" as "A + (−B) + C + (−D)/E"; this simplified algorithm doesn't. To the basic concept represented by the method of Figure 1.2.2, a large amount of material has to be added to handle negation, subscripting, function calls, constants, mixed fixed, and floating-point arithmetic, and so on.

1.2.3. OPERATOR PRECEDENCE

The lack of operator priority (often called precedence or hierarchy) in the IT language was the most frequent single cause of errors by the users of that compiler. So people hunted for ways to supply the hierarchy automatically. The IT parenthesis-level scheme didn't lend itself to this very readily. An ingenious idea used in the first FORTRAN compiler was to surround binary operators with peculiar-looking parentheses:

+ and − were replaced by))) + (((and))) − (((

* and / were replaced by)) * ((and)) / ((

** was replaced by) ** (

and then an extra "(((" at the left end ")))" at the right were tacked on. The resulting formula is properly parenthesized, believe it or not. For example, if we consider "(X + Y) + W/Z," we obtain

$$((((X))) + (((Y)))) + (((W))/((Z)))$$

This is admittedly highly redundant, but extra parentheses need not affect the resulting machine language code. After the above replacements are made, a parenthesis-level method can be applied to the resulting formulas.

A close examination of this process later showed that it isn't really necessary to insert the parentheses at all; the same effect can be achieved by merely comparing *adjacent* operators, and doing first the operation with higher priority. This led to another approach to the translation problem; namely, to start moving along the statement until finding something which can be done, then going back and doing it, going forward to get more, and so on. This is the idea of essentially looking for an inner pair of parentheses, then working outward, rather than the "outside-in" approach of parenthesis levels mentioned earlier. The new idea had the advantage that it could be easily adapted to handle operator hierarchies, and this led directly to the efficient scheme which is used (in so many equivalent guises) nowadays. The modern technique was discovered in several ways; another way to run across it is to write a program to translate from arithmetic statements to expressions in "Polish notation"—a parenthesis-free way to represent formulas—and then to write a second program to translate from Polish notation to machine language. Each program is rather trivial in itself, and the combination of the two programs gives the same algorithm as discovered in other ways.

Shortly I will discuss the details of the new algorithm, but first I will list the main "bright ideas" which went into its discovery:

(1) The first bright idea was the realization that information which is saved for further use when translating can be conveniently kept in a *stack* (which is also known as a *nest* or *pushdown* or *cellar* or *yo-yo list* or *last-in-first-out* or *first-in-last-out*, etc.; the number of different names indicates the number of different discoverers of the algorithm). A stack is distinguished from other types of tables by the fact that only the item at the "top" of the stack (i.e., the youngest item, the one placed on most recently) is actually important at any given time. An example of this occurred in the parenthesis-level method, where the OP table was really a stack. With the new method, the height of the stack takes the place of the former parenthesis level.

(2) The second bright idea was that comparison of adjacent operator priorities provides a valuable criterion, and no more than this is needed to properly interpret a formula.

(3) The third bright idea was that parentheses can be treated as operators with priorities, giving a more elegant algorithm.

Now we will study the new algorithm, which is given in Fig. 1.2.4. We start by assigning priority numbers to symbols, according to Table 1.2.1.

Here ":=" stands for the replacement operation, "↑" for exponentiation, and "÷" for integer division as in ALGOL. Functions of a single variable are unary operators which have priority 4 in the chart.

A rough description of Fig. 1.2.4 can be given as follows: We "scan"

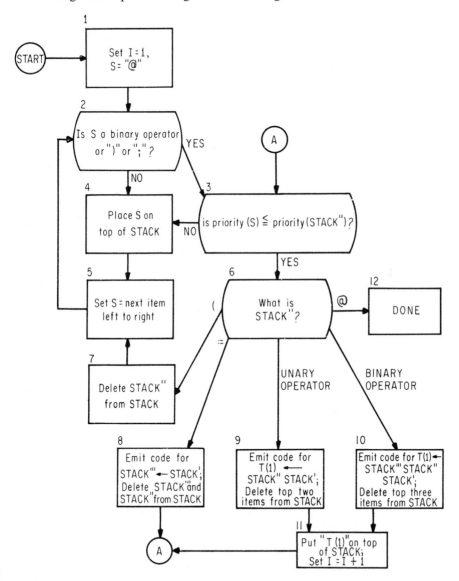

FIGURE 1.2.4 A version of the "modern" translation algorithm. The notation STACK' denotes the top item in STACK and STACK" signifies the next from the top, and so on.

Table 1.2.1

Priority	Symbols				
0	@	:	:=	(	)
1	+	−			
2	*	/	÷		
3	↑				
4	ABS	SQRT	etc.		

along the expression (left to right this time) until we find some operation which can be performed *regardless* of what will occur in the remainder of the expression. The actual precise conditions for this appear in boxes 2 and 3 of the flow chart. As soon as we see something we can definitely do regardless of future input, we do it; meanwhile we save the unused portion of the formula in STACK. The formula is followed on the right by a semicolon.

Box 1 starts out by setting the counter I to one, and artificially inserts the character "@" at the left end of the statement to mark the left boundary.

Box 2 tests the item S; if S is a binary arithmetic operator (add, subtract, multiply, divide, integer divide, or raise to a power) or a right parenthesis or a semicolon, this may initiate some action. Otherwise S is a variable, a constant, a left parenthesis, the replacement operator, the symbol @, or a unary operator such as ABS or negation, and then we merely go to box 4 to save S on the stack for future action.

Box 3 is the all-important hierarchy test. The second item from the top of STACK is an operator (if all is working properly), and if it has higher priority in the table than S has, or if they have equal priority, the time has come to initiate compiler action. However, if S has higher priority, we must wait for future developments, so we merely go to box 4.

Box 4 puts S on top of the STACK to save it for later action.

Box 5 steps along to the next item in the formula.

Box 6 is the entry to various generators; we now branch to the generator for the operator which is second from the top of STACK.

Box 7, the left parenthesis generator, merely removes the left parenthesis from the middle of STACK.

Box 8 is the replacement generator; the top three items of STACK are of the form X := Z. The code for this is now generated, and only Z is left on the STACK.

Box 9 is the generator for a unary operator; the top two items of STACK are of the form OP X, and we compile the code for "T(I) := OP X." T(I) represents the *I*-th computed result.

Box 10 is the generator for a binary operator; the top three items of STACK are of the form X OP Y, and we compile the code for "T(I) := X OP Y."

Box 11 puts the result of the previous computation, T(I), as an operand on STACK, and advances I by 1, then returns to the priority test.

Box 12 is the generator for the symbol @ which is entered when the entire statement has been translated.

```
              STACK  S  INPUT
                    @  U := V := X + COS ( Y * Z ) / W ;
                  @ U  :=  V := X + COS ( Y * Z ) / W ;
                @ U := V :=  X + COS ( Y * Z ) / W ;
              @ U := V  :=  X + COS ( Y * Z ) / W ;
            @ U := V := X  + COS ( Y * Z ) / W ;
          @ U := V := X + COS ( Y * Z ) / W ;
        @ U := V := X + COS ( Y * Z ) / W ;
      @ U := V := X + COS ( Y * Z ) / W ;
    @ U := V := X + COS ( Y * Z ) / W ;
  @ U := V := X + COS ( Y * Z ) / W ;
@ U := V := X + COS ( Y * Z ) / W ;
                                                    CODE
@ U := V := X + COS ( Y * Z ) / W ;
  @ U := V := X + COS ( T₁ ) / W ;            T (1) := Y * Z
    @ U := V := X + COS T₁ / W ;
      @ U := V := X + T₂ / W ;                T (2) := COS(T(1))
        @ U := V := X + T₂ / W ;
          @ U := V := X + T₂ / W ;
            @ U := V := X + T₃ ;              T (3) := T(2)/W
              @ U := V := T₄ ;                T (4) := X + T(3)
                @ U := T₄ ;                   V    := T (4)
                  @ T₄ ;                       U    := T (4)
```

FIGURE 1.2.5 Snapshots of the algorithm of Fig. 1.2.4 applied to the replacement statement "U := V := X + COS(Y * Z)/W;".

Notice that the algorithm given in Fig. 1.2.4 handles more complex input than that in Fig. 1.2.2. While the earlier flow chart applied only to formulas with binary operations and parentheses, the new one can also be used for unary operators and multiple assignment statements, and it treats operator priorities properly. As an example of the operation of Fig. 1.2.4, a snapshot description of the method applied to the statement "U := V := X + COS(Y * Z)/W;" is given in Fig. 1.2.5. Here COS stands for "cosine of."

With this statement, all of the input gets put onto the STACK until the right parenthesis is sensed. The right parenthesis forces out the multiplication operator, and then it also forces out the matching left parenthesis. Then the "/" symbol causes COS to be computed, and finally the ending semicolon triggers all of the remaining operators.

Once again, it would be a worthwhile exercise for the reader to try to modify the algorithm; this time to make it go from right to left, rather than from left to right. (Hint: The test in box 3 should not branch to box 6 on equality, lest $X - Y - Z$ be translated incorrectly. It will also be convenient to assign the priority "-1" to a left parenthesis!)

1.2.4. THE OBJECT PROGRAM PRODUCED

Let us turn back now to our original problem; you are supposed to write a compiler, remember? Your first worry, that of how to systematically decompose formulas, has been pretty well settled by now; the next problem is to generate efficient machine language code. The vast majority of the literature on compilers deals with the analysis of algebraic expressions, and comparatively little has ever been written about generation of the object program (which is the really important part). Due to all the research which has gone into recognition of formulas, this syntactical analysis is today the most trivial part of writing a compiler. A person cannot really begin to write a good compiler until he sits down and takes a good look at the object computer, and figures out exactly what code should come out of it, given each statement. So far we have just discussed the input to the compiler; but as everyone knows, output is the important thing.

The earliest compilers sometimes turned out shockingly poor machine code. For example, one compiler (which I will not name) would compute

$$A = B + C$$

with the sequence of instructions

```
LOAD       B
STORE      working-storage-1
LOAD       C
STORE      working-storage-2
LOAD       working-storage-1
ADD        working-storage-2
STORE      working-storage-1
LOAD       working-storage-1
STORE      A
```

plus several NO-OP instructions thrown in. This sequence computes the correct answer all right; but another compiler for the same computer later achieved a 7 : 1 reduction ratio in the number of instructions compiled in a typical program. This is, of course, an extreme example, but notice that the IT compiler algorithm turned out the instructions LOAD X, STORE TEMP (0) in Fig. 1.2.3 and these two instructions are quite unnecessary. Most of the early compilers would do this. (The first FORTRAN compiler, on the other hand, took fairly great care to produce efficient code, although the methods used were quite painful.) One of the first attempts to eliminate extraneous instructions was to go ahead and compile them as usual, but later to recognize that they were unnecessary and at that point to "un-compile" them, removing them from the code. In this case, the object code was being used as a stack. A fairly elaborate algorithm was used, so that from:

```
LOAD NEGATIVE ABSOLUTE   A
STORE                    TEMP
LOAD                     B
MULTIPLY                 C
ADD                      TEMP
```

the code

```
LOAD               B
MULTIPLY           C
SUBTRACT ABSOLUTE  A
```

would be produced.

With the "modern" algorithm, however, this saving of temporary storage is accomplished so easily it is virtually a free by-product of the method.

It is interesting to pursue this matter further, however, and to consider the expression

$$A * B + (C * D + E * F)$$

Suppose we have a fancy machine with two accumulators; the modern algorithm, adapted in a straightforward way, would produce

LOAD	1	A
MULT	1	B
LOAD	2	C
MULT	2	D
STORE	2	TEMP
LOAD	2	E
MULT	2	F
ADD	2	TEMP
ADD	1	ACCUMULATOR-2

The STORE in TEMP could have been saved if A * B had been computed last; in other words, we should prefer to write

$$(C * D + E * F) + A * B$$

Our modern algorithm was effectively able to rewrite "A + B * C" as "B * C + A" but could not make the switch on higher-order expressions. This leads to a "generalized modern algorithm" for an n-register machine, which scans formulas until it gets to an expression which cannot be computed with less than n registers before it starts to produce object code. For $n = 1$ this gives the former algorithm, and for $n > 1$ it gives some small improvement in minimizing temporary storage. The latter method requires more structure to its list than a simple pushdown stack, however. There is even a generalization to a "zero-register" machine, in which it is immaterial what order is used for calculation. (This would be a machine similar to the Burroughs B 5000 except having only one fast register at the top of its stack; a Polish-notation machine with $n + 1$ fast registers would use a temporary storage minimization algorithm equivalent to that for a conventional machine with n accumulators for optimum efficiency.)

Many refinements can easily be added to the modern algorithm to help produce better code. For example, a sign can be attached to each operand, so that computed results can be negated and algebraic identities can be employed. COS(A − B ∗ C) can be calculated by

LOAD	B
MULT	C
SUBTRACT	A
RETURN JUMP	COS

That is, the machine can easily rewrite the expression as COS(B ∗ C − A). A similar technique which I haven't seen published yet, although it is fairly old, is to attach an absolute value tag also, so that the ADD AB-SOLUTE and similar instructions can be utilized on various object machines. Attaching a type indicator (fixed or floating point) to operands and computed partial results is another obvious extension.

A refinement which is only slightly more difficult to add is to treat groups of statements together so that if no labels intervene between statements it is possible to remember what the preceding statement left in the accumulator.

A whole series of interesting techniques has been designed to optimize the use of index registers in loops. Most of these require several passes. I must mention briefly the question of many passes vs. one pass. It is well nigh impossible nowadays to define exactly what a "pass" is. Back in the old days the number of passes was the number of times we took the cards out of the punch hopper, put them in the reader, and perhaps changed plugboards. But now there are so-called one-pass compilers for sequential machines. How many passes is a load-and-go compiler?[†] Probably zero passes, since it takes one less than one pass.

Ignoring the difficulty of defining a pass, however, we can find many arguments pro and con about relative merits. The one-pass compiler is considerably faster because multipass schemes spend a good deal of time physically generating an intermediate language and later translating it back again. But there are on the other hand many things which cannot be done well in one pass, such as checking for common subexpressions and optimizing loops. Many programmers, however, are not concerned with

---

[†] A *load-and-go compiler* is one in which a person enters as input some algebraic statements, and the compiler translates these into machine language and immediately transfers control to this new program. Thus with a "load-and-go compiler" the first output consists of the answers.

such refinements; if they wanted a really good object program they would have it written in machine language by an expert programmer. I can't settle the argument, but I do think it is a valid point that there should not be *n* passes if the object programs produced are not noticeably better than could be done in *n* − 1 passes.

1.2.5. ORGANIZATION OF THE COMPILER

I have tried to point out that most compilers use essentially the same techniques in different guises for formula translation. The real place where they differ is in their organization and timing of the basic components; in the structure of their programs. I will discuss briefly the principal types of organization.

1.2.5.1. *Symbol Pairs*

IT and RUNCIBLE and many other compilers were organized around a symbol-pair concept. At the close of each operation, the two symbols L and R are moved; L → R, next character → L (right-to-left scanning). Then the pair LR is looked up in a table, thus giving the entry to a generator program for this case. Any information that was needed for future use was stored in tables. There were several pushdown lists (stacks), but nobody realized it at the time. Beyond this the organization was pretty much of a hodgepodge which couldn't be broken into logical parts. These compilers grew like Topsy and were the result of several years of patching. The program was so interwoven that every time something was changed in RUNCIBLE, six other seemingly unrelated things would fail. And we had the entire compilation process in just as disorganized a fashion in our minds. We knew it was correct and why, but to explain it to anyone required at least 100 boxes on a horrible flow chart, which actually couldn't be untangled. That was the algorithm, and it worked, and it fitted onto the IBM 650 drum, but it was a mess. For all anybody knew at that time, however, that was the only way it could be done.

1.2.5.2. *Operator Pairs*

A next step is to use operator pairs rather than symbol pairs to control the operation. The operands distribute themselves nicely between operators, so an essentially identical plan as the above can be used, except adjacent operators are used to reference a table of generators. This gives some economy over the previous method, since operands are put into a single class. This type of organization is used in the NELIAC compilers and the generator tables are called CO-NO or NO-CO tables by the authors. I understand CO-NO tables are especially good for translating input programs written in Hawaiian.

1.2.5.3. *Simple Scan*

Further improvement can be gained by lumping *operators* into classes, as well as operands. Only a few classes of operators are actually necessary; e.g., for FORTRAN, we would have perhaps four classes of operators:

(1) Those which require immediate action when first sensed; e.g., READ, DO

(2) Those which are placed immediately on the stack when first sensed, e.g., SIN (for "sine of"), ABS (for "absolute value of"), left parenthesis

(3) Those which are not placed on the stack until their priority is more than the preceding operator, e.g., binary operators

(4) Those which are never placed on the stack but their priority is used as in (3) to force out previous operators, e.g., comma, semicolon

The main control is along the lines of the modern algorithm given in Fig. 1.2.4, with an input routine to condense identifiers and constants into single items. Usually, however, many stacks are used instead of one, for convenience, typically including some of the following:

(1) Operand stack

(2) Operator stack (it is quite helpful to separate 1 and 2, although not necessary)

(3) Mode stack (this gives the meaning of commas)

(4) Subscript stack (where computed subscripts wait their turn)

(5) Temp storage stack (a list of locations available for temporary storage cells in the object program)

(6) DO stack (for controlling DO loops)

and so on.

1.2.5.4. *Recursive Organization*

Some recent compilers are written with generators that work recursively. Typically when a construct (part of a formula) is recognized as being of a certain syntactical type, its generator is brought out. Somehow the end of the construct is detected, and this causes the generator to go into action. For example, there might be a generator for variables. If it happens to encounter an array variable, the "expression" generator will be entered for the subscript, and it may call on the variable generator, which may call on the expression generator, etc. Delimiters are used to take generators out of control at the appropriate time. Examples of such compilers are the threaded-list compiler at Carnegie Tech and the B5000 ALGOL compiler at Burroughs.

1.2.5.5. Syntax-Directed Compilers

Another form of recursive compiler is called "syntax-directed," and is very closely related to the former type. Such a compiler is, theoretically, completely general, since it is built to operate from an arbitrary syntax list (description of the language) and an arbitrary semantics list (description of the meaning of the language in terms of the object computer). These are still in the experimental stages and, with apologies to Ned Irons and the other researchers, I must say they appear to be primarily of theoretical interest at the present time. The syntax of a language has to be carefully rewritten in order to produce efficient object code, and the creation of semantical tables is as cumbersome a job as writing generators for ordinary compilers. Compilers organized along the lines of Section 1.2.5.3 or 1.2.5.4 can be easily modified for all but major language revisions; so no great advantage to syntax-directed compilers has been proved as yet. I certainly do not want to discourage anyone from working on a syntax-directed compiler, for there is good reason to believe that significant strides forward in this direction are possible and that syntax-directed compilers will be very important in the future. On the contrary, I hope to stimulate more people toward working in this potentially fruitful area which has as yet been unable to compete with handmade compilers. As we have seen, the recognition of syntax is one of the simpler facets of compiling; a good deal of research needs yet to be done to simplify the real problem of how to produce efficient code once the syntax has been recognized.

1.2.5.6. Multipass Compilers

A fairly large number of compilers operate in two passes; the first pass is organized something like the class in Section 1.2.5.3, and it produces a pseudocode analogous to the "T(I) := Y * Z" output of Fig. 1.2.4. The second pass uses this pseudocode to generate the object program. I would classify such compilers under the category of Section 1.2.5.3.

This last category of compiler organization is rather for those expensive compilers which consist of *many* separate passes. Such compilers defy simple explanation, and the only way to learn to know them is to spend a good deal of time studying what each pass does and how it fits into the whole scheme. There is usually very little in common between two such compilers, and all I can say is that the well-written ones of this type usually are built around some major modification of a one-pass compiler, designed to produce more efficient object programs from a more thorough analysis of the source program.

REFERENCES

A complete bibliography of the compiler literature is hard to give; actually it would be quite distressing to try to read many of the articles. This will happen because so many of them are about how that particular author discovered the same thing as other authors (although it may take several hours to realize what he has discovered and what he hasn't). Therefore, I will give only a short bibliography, for use by those interested in pursuing the subject further.

The complexity in the first translators is indicated in two articles:

Knuth, D., "RUNCIBLE—Algebraic Translation on a Limited Computer," *Communications of the ACM*, November 1959. In this article I include a flow chart of a portion of the RUNCIBLE compiler, and also make the untrue statement that such an algorithm may well be the only possible one to use on a small computer such as the IBM 650.

Peter Sheridan, "The Arithmetic Translator-Compiler of the IBM Fortran Automatic Coding System," *Communications of the ACM*, February 1959. This article is rather heavy reading, but it will at least impress the reader with the complexity of the algorithm.

NELIAC compilers are discussed as the principal subject of the book *Machine Independent Computer Programming* by Maurice Halstead, Spartan Books, Washington, D.C., 1962. "No-co" is a term used by the authors of NELIAC meaning "Next-Operator—Current-Operator."

Excellent expositions for the beginner of the modern scanning algorithm have been written by Robert Floyd: "An Algorithm for Coding Efficient Arithmetic Operations," *Communications of the ACM*, January 1961, and "A Descriptive Language for Symbol Manipulation," *ACM Journal*, October 1961.

Finally, to study the organization of various compilers, the entire January 1961 issue of the *ACM Communications* is recommended. Of special interest is "The Internal Organization of the MAD Translator," by B. Arden, B. Galler, and R. Graham. This is one of the few articles in the literature which discusses some general methods for generation of the object program without a separate generator for each special case.

1. "Internal Translator (IT); A Compiler for the IBM 650," by H. A. Perlis, J. W. Smith, and H. R. Van Zoeren, Carnegie Institute of Technology Computer Center, Pittsburgh, Pa., 1956.

Note: When I wrote this article in 1962, I believed that working algebraic compilers had not appeared until about 1957. After further research, however, I found that about a dozen compilers or near-compilers were actually developed before 1954! A complete history of compilers should mention the work of Züse in Germany, Rutishauser in Switzerland and Böhm in Italy, Glennie in England, and Mauchly, Laning, Zierler, Hopper, and others in the United States. Their work was done at a time when few programmers were worried about programming time versus machine time and before there were appropriate journals to publish the results, so the earliest compilers were all but forgotten by the time I wrote this article. I plan to include a complete history of the subject in my *The Art of Computer Programming*, volumes 5 and 7, D.E.K., June 1971.

2.

SYNTAX- AND TABLE-DIRECTED COMPILATION

2.0. OVERVIEW

Various techniques have been devised for translating programming languages. Among these are statement categorization, keyword recognition or template matching, syntax direction, and table direction. The most important techniques developed during the past few years are certainly the last two, and they comprise the subject matter for the present chapter. Broadly, syntax-directed compilation is the use of a formal syntax to control the translation process. Table-directed compilation is the specific case where the control mechanism may be expressed in the form of a table. The description of programming languages by formal syntax is a relatively recent development; the use of syntax to control translation is the natural outgrowth of research done in this area of computer science.

The grammars used to describe programming languages are almost universally of the context-free or phrase-structure form. Not all languages are describable within this class of grammars (e.g., ALGOL, nor is it particularly desirable to describe some programming languages formally. FORTRAN, for example, is much more easily described in English than by a formal syntax because it has so few statement types and they are of such a specialized form.

The determination of the formal structure of a statement (program), given a grammar, is termed "parsing." Either during the parsing procedure or once a parse has been obtained, the semantics or meaning of the statement (program) may be determined. This includes the emission of code representing the function of the statement (program), setting of flags and switches, modification of variables internal to the translator, and similar modifications. Parsing and formal syntax are described in greater detail in Chapter 3.

Construction of syntaxes adequate for the description of a language is a moderately difficult process. The problem becomes more complex when additional demands are made on the form of the grammar; for example, unambiguity, bounded context, and precedence. The reader is again referred to Chapter 3 for more details. The process of syntax writing is today more of an art than a formal technique. Consequently, almost no literature is available on the subject.

The formalization of semantics is one of the current areas of research in computer science. It is an extremely difficult subject and few general results have been thus far obtained. Feldman's work on FSL is perhaps the best available to date. (See Ref. 4 in Section 2.3.) Currently, formal semantics are expressed as instructions to some meta machine, which are then either interpreted or compiled into physical machine code.

One of the most significant results of the research done in this subject is the linking of syntax with semantics in a manner that not only completely and formally describes the syntax of all statements of a language, but also simultaneously defines their meaning. This has led to work in formally proving that a compiler is correct; that is, proving that it compiles syntactical statements into the correct semantics. The reader is referred to the work of McCarthy and Painter ("Correctness of a Compiler for Arithmetic Expressions," *AMS Symposium in Appl. Math.*, vol. 19 (1967)).

An important feature of syntax- and table-direction is that in a carefully designed compiler, the addition or modification of the language may be done modularly without the necessity for major revision of the translator. It is for this reason that these techniques are widely used for the implementation of extendible and enhansible compilers (see Chapter 8).

The construction of syntax- or table-directed compilers is rather poorly documented except for examples of specific languages. The techniques involved are identical to those used for the construction of finite-state machines and deterministic automata, and a table-directed compiler is actually just such a large machine (automaton). A formal syntax for a language is not necessary for the construction of the syntax table, but it is usually constructed because it facilitates implementation in most cases.

The semantics of a language that is compiled by a table is contained implicitly within the entries of the table; as such, the relationship between syntax and semantics may not be so apparent as in the syntax-directed case. However, table-directed compilers usually execute extremely quickly, which is perhaps a compensating advantage.

The detection of syntax errors in both cases is relatively straightforward. The parser or table-directed procedure finds itself in an impossible situation and cannot continue to translate. However, the correction of errors, or attempted correction of errors, is a most difficult subject, and it forms the subject matter of Chapter 5.

This chapter opens with an article by Floyd which surveys the relationship of syntax and programming languages. He describes context-free (phrase-structure) grammars, distinguishes between syntax-directed and syntax-controlled analyses, and introduces formal language theory. (We follow current usage in using the term "syntax-directed analysis" for phrase-structure and non-phrase-structure grammars, and do not use the term "syntax controlled" at all.)

Article 2.2 by Irons presents an example of a syntax-directed compiler that will translate arbitrary source languages into arbitrary target languages. The author describes a meta language for the expression of the source language, gives examples of its use, and concludes with a description of the translator itself.

In Article 2.3, Feldman then discusses a scheme for the formalization of semantics and its application in a syntax-directed compiler.

2.1. The Syntax of Programming Languages—A Survey

by Robert W. Floyd

2.1.1. SUMMARY

The syntactic rules for many programming languages have been expressed by formal grammars, generally variants of phrase-structure grammars. The syntactic analysis essential to translation of programming languages can be done entirely mechanically for such languages. Major problems remain in rendering analyzers efficient in use of space and time and in finding fully satisfactory formal grammars for present and future programming languages.

2.1.2. INTRODUCTION

In recent years, few programming languages designed for widespread use have escaped having the more orderly part of their formation rules and restrictions presented in one of several simple tabular forms, somewhat like the axioms of a formal mathematical system. ALGOL, JOVIAL, FORTRAN, NELIAC, COBOL, BALGOL, MAC, APT, and their offshoots have all been defined

---

EDITOR'S NOTE: This article reproduced by permission of the author and the publisher: *IEEE Trans.* EC 13, no. 4 (August 1964), pp. 346–353.

in such a fashion (see Sections A and B of the References). For some of these languages, the formalism is easy and natural. For others, it is not; FORTRAN[A9] suffers needlessly, bound in the unaccustomed corsetry of her younger rival's design. Whatever the merits of formal grammars in general, some languages are best defined in words. Where formal grammars are appropriate, however, mathematical and linguistic analysis provides compilers of lower cost and high reliability, and theoretical knowledge about the structure and value of the language itself.

2.1.3. PHRASE-STRUCTURE GRAMMARS

The most representative and fruitful example of the use of a formal grammar in defining a programming language is the use of a phrase-structure grammar to specify most of the syntactic rules of ALGOL 60.[A7,A8,B1,B5] The form for grammatical rules used in the report which officially defines ALGOL 60 is typified[A1] by

$$\langle \text{for statement} \rangle \; :: = \langle \text{for clause} \rangle \, \langle \text{statement} \rangle \mid \langle \text{label} \rangle : \langle \text{for statement} \rangle$$

This assertion can be read "A FOR statement is defined to be a FOR clause followed by a statement, or a label followed by a colon ':' followed by a FOR statement." The symbol ': :=' stands for 'is defined to be'; '|' stands for 'or' and is used to separate alternative forms of the definiendum. The angular brackets '⟨ ⟩' are used to enclose each name of a phrase type, distinguishing it as a name, rather than the thing named. This is the reverse of the way quotation marks are used in English, for the same purpose, to distinguish

> The baby can say "one word"

from

> The baby can say one word.

Names of phrase types appearing in the text are hyphenated to show explicitly that the separate words of a name need have no individual meaning and that the name as a whole is used as a technical term, without such connotations as its individual words may suggest. The angular brackets enclosing a name in a grammatical rule share this function. A complete set of grammatical rules for a language written in a format equivalent to that of the example is a *phrase-structure grammar* (PSG); a language definable by a PSG is a *phrase-structure language* (PSL).[†]

In general, a phrase-structure grammar, taken as a set of definitions, provides a list of alternative constructions in a definition for each syntactic type, where each construction is a list of characters and syntactic type names. A construction represents the set of phrases which can be formed by replacing each syntactic type name with a phrase of that type; the phrases of a certain type are all those represented by some construction in the definition of that type. There is usually a single syntactic type, called "program" (or "sentence"), which is used in the definition of no other type; the set of phrases of this type is the language defined by the grammar. On the one hand, PSG's can define some languages of considerable complexity; on the other, such simple sets of strings as that consisting of '*abc*,' '*aabbcc*,' '*aaabbbccc*,' etc., are demonstrably not definable by any phrase-structure grammar.[C4]

It is evident that a complete definition of a programming language may be expressed far more concisely by a PSG than by the corresponding English sentences and that it is humanly impossible to read or write those sentences, with their hundreds of occurrences of 'is defined to be,' 'followed by,' and 'or.' If a phrase-structure grammar is nearly adequate to define a language, then most of the rules defining the language can be neatly and compactly listed without explanation, conserving space, time, and clarity; attention may be concentrated on the few syntactic rules which do not fit the pattern of phrase definitions.

As mentioned above, the rules of a PSG are analogous to axioms. One who has somehow obtained a program and an understanding of its structure can use a PSG to prove the program is well formed and to demonstrate the structure to others. The usefulness of a PSG to a programmer writing in the language, or to the compiler which translates it into machine language coding, is less apparent. A grammar does not tell us how to synthesize a specific program; it does not tell us how to analyze a particular given program.[‡]

[†] The type of grammar described here is sometimes called a *context-free* phrase-structure grammar, as distinguished from a more general type of grammar, the *context-dependent* phrase-structure grammar. The latter has no known applications to programming languages, the term "phrase-structure" is not necessarily appropriate for a context-dependent grammar, and the term "context-free" has certain misleading implications; we will therefore use the short term "phrase-structure grammar" for what is sometimes also called a context-free phrase-structure grammar,[C6] simple phrase-structure grammar,[C1] or Type 2 grammar.[C4]

[‡] See Chomsky,[C3] p. 48.

In order to construct programs in a phrase-structure language, one may interpret every rule of its grammar as a permit to perform certain acts of substitution. Assigning a symbol to each syntactic type of a grammar, let us interpret each rule as allowing the substitution, for the definiendum, of any one of the alternative definientes. Applying these substitution rules repeatedly to the symbol designating the syntactic type 'program' for 'sentence," we arrive eventually at a sequence of symbols in which no further substitutions can take place; this string is a program or sentence in the language, the process by which it was produced being an abbreviated proof of its sentencehood. The symbols designating syntactic types, for which substitutions may be made, are called *nonterminal characters*; those undefined symbols which form sentences are the *terminal characters*.

Take, for instance, the grammar:

    a) ⟨sentence⟩ → ⟨noun⟩ ⟨predicate⟩
    b) ⟨predicate⟩ → ⟨verb⟩ ⟨noun⟩
    c) ⟨noun⟩ → John | Mary
    d) ⟨verb⟩ → loves.

Successive substitution, starting with ⟨sentence⟩, gives the sequence

    1) ⟨sentence⟩
    2) ⟨noun⟩ ⟨predicate⟩
    3) John ⟨predicate⟩
    4) John ⟨verb⟩ ⟨noun⟩
    5) John ⟨verb⟩ Mary
    6) John loves Mary.

This sequence, a derivation of the sentence "John loves Mary," is an abbreviation of the following proof:

    1) Any sentence is a sentence.
       a) A noun followed by a predicate is a sentence.
    2) Any noun followed by any predicate is a sentence.
       c) 'John' is a noun.
    3) 'John' followed by any predicate is a sentence.
       b) A verb followed by a noun is a predicate.
    4) 'John' followed by any verb followed by any noun is a sentence.
       c) 'Mary' is a noun.
    5) 'John' followed by any verb followed by 'Mary' is a sentence.
       d) 'Loves' is a verb.
    6) 'John loves Mary' is a sentence.

From this point of view, a sentence in a phrase-structure language is the
last line of a derivation from the symbol '⟨sentence⟩,' provided that no
further substitutions are possible.[†] The grammar is regarded not as an
axiom scheme for validating sentences but as a device for generating them.
When a PSG is considered as a generative grammar, its rules are commonly
called *productions*. The two viewpoints are substantially equivalent, but
the generative viewpoint, by making explicit the process by which sentences
are constructed, makes the grammar a more tractable object of study. A
writer of programs in a PSL can now be thought of as a device to generate
sentences, with choices between alternatives governed, for example, by
the structure of a flow chart of the program. Not enough is known about
linguistic behavior to specify the mechanism of choice in detail.

A compact representation of a derivation is the syntax tree;[C3,G1] the
syntax tree for the derivation above is shown in Fig. 2.1.1. In general, a

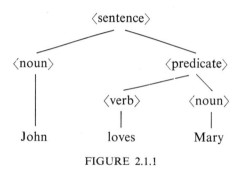

FIGURE 2.1.1

syntax tree is like a genealogical tree for a family whose common ancestor
is ⟨sentence⟩, where the immediate descendants (sons) of a symbol form
one of the alternatives of the definition of that symbol, and where only
the terminal characters fail to have descendants. Such a tree represents a
derivation of the sentence formed by its terminal characters. It also illustrates the structure of the sentence; the terminal descendants of any
node on the tree form a phrase in the sentence, of the type designated by
that node. In a language satisfactorily described by its grammar, the phrases
of a sentence are its meaningful units. Some compilers take advantage of
this, creating a syntax tree as a structured representation of the information
contained in the source program. Suitable processes then translate the tree
into a computer program, or a derivation tree for an equivalent sentence
in another language, or a related sentence in the same language.

[†] See Chomsky,[C3] ch. 4.

2.1.4. SYNTAX-DIRECTED ANALYSIS

A syntax-directed analyzer might be defined as any procedure capable of constructing a syntax tree for an arbitrary sentence in an arbitrary PSL. This ideal, however, is rarely achieved; most syntax-directed analyzers are restricted to languages whose grammars satisfy certain special conditions. Let us consider a typical procedure for syntax-directed analysis.

Because the analyzer makes use of a complicated hierarchy of subordinate goals in seeking its principal goal, we will introduce it with a metaphor. Suppose a man is assigned the goal of analyzing a sentence in a PSL of known grammar. He has the power to hire subordinates, assign them tasks, and fire them if they fail; they in turn have the same power. The convention will be adhered to that each man will be told only once "try to find a G" where G is a symbol of the language, and may thereafter be repeatedly told "try again" if the particular instance of a G which he finds proves unsatisfactory to his superiors. Depending on the form of the definition of G, each subordinate (e.g., S) should adopt an appropriate strategy:

1) If G is a terminal character, and if it is the next character of the sentence, S must cover the character, and report success to his superior. If it is not the next character of the sentence, S must report failure. After success, if told by his superior to try again, S must report failure and uncover the character.

2) If $G \rightarrow G_1$, S must appoint a subordinate S_1 with the command, "Try to find a G_1." S repeats S_1's report to his superior, firing S_1 on a report of failure. If told to try again, S must tell S_1 to try again, again transmitting the report to his superior and firing S_1 on failure.

3) If $G \rightarrow G_1 G_2 \cdots G_n$, S must appoint successively one subordinate S_i for each G_i, with the command, "Try to find a G_i." If S_i succeeds, i is increased by one, a new subordinate hired, and the process repeated until $i > n$, when S reports success. If S_i fails S_i is fired, i is decreased by one and if $i > 0$, the new S_i (predecessor of he who failed) told to try again. If $i = 0$, S reports failure, having exhausted all ways of finding a G. If after success, S is told to try again, he sets $i = n$, tells S_i to try again, and proceeds as before on S_i's report.

4) If $G \rightarrow G_1 \mid G_2 \mid \cdots \mid G_n$, S must appoint successively one subordinate S_i for each G_i, with the command, "Try to find a G_i." If S_i fails he is fired, i is increased by one, a new subordinate hired, and the process repeated until $i > n$, when S reports failure. If S_i succeeds, S reports success. If

after success S is told to try again, he tells S_i (who succeeded) to try again, and proceeds as before on S_i's report.

5) All more complicated definitions can be regarded as built up from the first four types.

As an example, take the sentence '*abc*' and the grammar

$$X \rightarrow Yc$$
$$Y \rightarrow a \mid Z$$
$$Z \rightarrow ab$$

in which X represents $\langle$sentence$\rangle$. S_1 is appointed to find an X. S_1 appoints S_2 to find a Y. S_2 appoints S_3 to find '*a*.' S_3 covers '*a*,' reports success. S_2 reports success. S_1 appoints S_4 to find '*c*.' S_4 sees '*b*' in the sentence, reports failure. S_1 fires S_4 and tells S_2 to try again. S_2 tells S_3 to try again. S_3 uncovers '*a*,' reports failure. S_2 fires S_3, then appoints S_3 to find a Z. S_3 appoints S_4 to find '*a*.' S_4 covers '*a*,' reports success. S_3 appoints S_5 to find '*b*.' S_5 covers '*b*,' reports success. S_3 reports success. S_2 reports success. S_1 appoints S_6 to find '*c*.' S_6 covers '*c*,' reports success. S_1 reports success. The organization chart of S_1 and his subordinates,

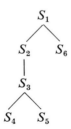

when labeled with goals rather than names, gives the syntax tree

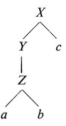

of the sentence '*abc*.'

This metaphor conceals certain difficulties by relegating bookkeeping tasks to imaginary men who are assumed to automatically appear when hired, disappear when fired, remember the names of their subordinates and superiors, and so on. It is not difficult, however, by the use of a stack (pushdown list) to simulate the process on a computer, making the entire process explicit. As a convenience for the analyzer, let each definiens of the grammar be followed by the additional symbols "$|$ $\dashv$," so that "$A \to B \mid CD$" would be rewritten "$A \to B \mid CD \mid \dashv$." Each subordinate in the metaphor is represented by an element S_λ of a stack, and contains five fields: $goal_\lambda$, the fixed goal given to S_λ by this superior; i_λ, the place in the definition of *goal* at which S_λ is reading in the grammar; sup_λ, the name of S_λ's superior (i.e., his location in the stack); sub_λ, the name of S_λ's most recently appointed subordinate; and $pred_\lambda$, the predecessor of S_λ among the subordinates of his superior. For each field, a zero specifies the absence of a value. The chief executive of the process, S_1, is set initially to have a goal of '⟨sentence⟩' with all other fields set to zero. The index λ signifies the subordinate S_λ who is currently active; the index ν signifies the first element of the stack to which no goal is currently assigned. The index j signifies the first uncovered character of the input string. The grammar is represented by the vector *gram*, of which each character either belongs to the language defined or is one of $(\to, |, \dashv)$. All occurrences of S, *goal*, i, *sup*, *sub*, and *pred*, unless otherwise indexed, are implicitey indexed with λ.

When the algorithm terminates successfully, the contents of the stack represent a syntax tree for the sentence taken from the input string. Each word in the stack represents a node in the tree, where *goal* represents the label of the node, i is the index in *gram* of the '$|$' following the rule of the grammar applied at that node, *sup* designates the parent node, *sub* designates the rightmost son of the node, and *pred* designates the sibling immediately to the left of the node. Only *goal*, *sub*, and *pred* are needed in order to construct the tree. Thus the tree

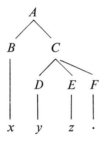

would be represented by the stack:

	Goal	i	sup	sub	pred
1	A	?	0	4	0
2	B	?	1	3	0
3	x	0	2	0	0
4	C	?	1	9	2
5	D	?	4	6	0
6	y	0	5	0	0
7	E	?	4	8	5
8	z	0	7	0	0
9	F	?	4	10	7
10	.	0	9	0	0

Figure 2.1.2 is a flow chart for this process. There follows an item-by-item explanation of the flow chart.

A = Chief executive S_1 is appointed to find a sentence. S_2 awaits employment.

B = You are a newly appointed subordinate (S_λ); determine whether your goal is a nonterminal (defined) character, or terminal.

C, D = If the first character of the input sentence is your goal, cover it and report success to your superior; otherwise report failure and await temporary unemployment.

E = Find the beginning of the definition of your goal, by means not described here. Prepare to read that definition.

F, G, H = If you have reached a '|' in the definition of your goal, report success unless you are the chief executive, in which case you have analyzed the sentence.

I, J, K = If you have exhausted all alternatives in the definition of your goal, report failure unless you are the chief executive, in which case the input is not a sentence.

L = Otherwise, appoint a subordinate whose goal is the next character in the definition of your goal. His superior is you, his predecessor your previously junior subordinate. Remember only your most recent subordinate, protect him from other assignments, and await his report.

M = Report success to your superior, who proceeds through the definition of his goal.

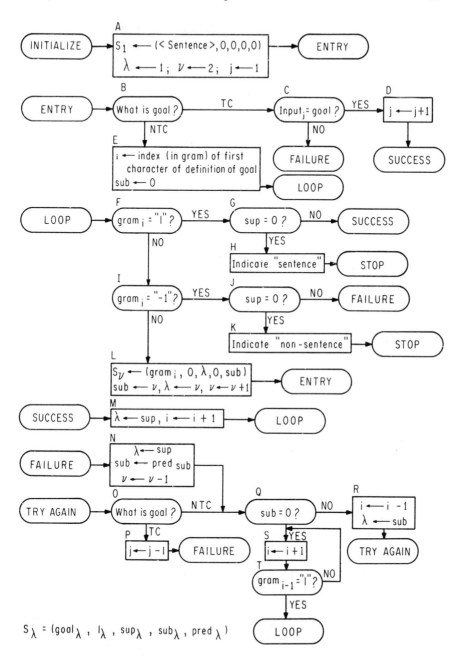

FIGURE 2.1.2 Flow chart for syntax-directed analysis.

$N =$ Report failure to your superior, who will take your pre-decessor as his junior subordinate and fire you.

$O =$ When told to try again, determine again whether your local is terminal or not.

$P =$ If terminal, uncover the input character you previously cov-ered, and report failure.

$Q, R =$ If goal is nonterminal, tell your junior subordinate to try again.

$S, T =$ If your have no junior subordinate, you have exhausted an alternative; try the next one.

The serious and intrinsic flaw of the algorithm is that it fails for grammars whose rules contain certain types of cyclic formations. If the definition of A contains an alternative beginning with A, or if one of the alternatives for A begins with B, one of those for B begins with C, and one of these for C begins with A; e.g., then certain choices of input string lead the procedure into an infinite loop. A grammar containing such formations is called *left-recursive*.[G3] It is possible, at some cost to the explanatory power of a grammar, to reformulate it excluding left-recursive definition.[C11] This has been successfully done for several programming languages in the COMPASS compiler.[D5,D15] A second type of syntax-directed analyzer, which is free of the left-recursion problem, constructs the syntax tree, not from the top down, but from the bottom up;[C11,D2,D5,D8,G4] it is, however, as presently formulated, subject to other restrictions. All syntax-directed analyzers currently known are further restricted in practice to nonpathological lan-guages; if a sentence is chosen at random from the grammar

$$S \rightarrow A \mid B$$
$$A \rightarrow (A) \mid (B) \mid x$$
$$B \rightarrow (A] \mid (B] \mid y,$$

analysis will require a time which increases exponentially with the length of the sentence, if read from left to right. At each character of the first half of the sentence, choice must be made between two alternatives. Not until the second half of the sentence is read is any information gained about the correctness of these choices. Typical processes will back up and try again many times before hitting on the right pattern. A related grammar may be designed to exhaust the patience of all known syntax-directed analyzers, whether their prejudices be left, right, or center.

It is not known whether a method of syntactic analysis is possible for which the time required for analysis does not increase exponentially with the length of the sentence, even for pathological languages. Known methods of full generality, such as the systematic generation of all sentences until a match is found, would be unacceptably slow even for short sentences. The properties of programming languages which make them legible to human readers, however, allow them to be analyzed by simple and efficient methods. A case in point is COBOL, for which a syntax-directed analyzer is greatly simplified because each choice among alternative constructions can be decided by examining the first character or word of that construction.[D6]

2.1.5. SYNTAX-CONTROLLED ANALYSIS

An alternative approach to syntactic analysis of phrase structure languages, sometimes called *syntax-controlled* analysis, entails a preliminary processing of a grammar during which matrices, tables, and lists are constructed, describing in some sense the possible constructions of the grammar. Analysis of sentences then makes use of these tabulations, and may even dispense entirely with the original grammar.

As an example, let us consider precedence analysis,[E2] which is a formalization and extension of methods of analysis which were used in compilers even before formal grammars were employed in defining programming languages. From the grammar of ALGOL it is possible to deduce that in any ALGOL program if a left parenthesis '(' is followed by a multiplication sign '×,' separated by at most one phrase, then there is some phrase to which the multiplication sign and any phrase adjacent to it belong, but not containing the left parenthesis. The relation is symbolized, '($\lessdot \times$,' where the sign '$\lessdot$' is read 'yields precedence to.' Similarly, if '×' is followed by '+' with at most one phrase between, some phrase contains the multiplication sign and any phrases adjacent to it, but not the plus sign. This relation is symbolized '$\times \gtrdot +$,' where '$\gtrdot$' is read 'takes precedence over.' We may deduce that whenever

$$\text{`} \cdots (a \times b + \cdots \text{'}$$

occurs in an ALGOL program, and a and b are arbitrary phrases, then '$a \times b$' is a phrase. A third relation, '($\doteq$),' applies to characters of equal precedence. While analysis based on precedence relations does not yield a complete derivation of a sentence, it determines the phrases of the sentence and the operators connecting them, which is normally sufficient information for use by a compiler.

Not every grammar is amenable to precedence analysis. Yet, like phrase-structure grammars, matrices representing precedence relations are generally adequate for the description of the structure of programs in standard programming languages. Because a precedence matrix can be derived from a grammar and applied to syntactic analysis by a completely mechanical process, precedence analysis offers much the same flexibility and universality as does syntax-directed analysis.

Neither syntax-directed nor syntax-controlled analyzers are capable, by themselves, of dealing with nonsentences. Syntax-directed analyzers are usually incapacitated by syntactic errors in their input sentences.[D5,D9] Precedence methods are more flexible, but still require explicit specification of error recovery policies. Chomsky has proposed that an adequate grammar for a natural language must account for our ability to interpret ungrammatical sentences.[G3] Such grammars are doubly necessary for programming languages, at least to the extent of localizing the effects of programming errors.

2.1.6. ADEQUACY

The phrase-structure grammar, though developed as a model for natural language, is generally considered inadequate to represent either the structure or the constraints imposed on sentences in most natural languages.[C3,C5] Nor is the PSG sufficient to fully describe the formation rules of most programming languages. Most require, for example, that the arithmetic type of each variable be declared before using it in a formula or that dimensions of an array be specified before referring to one of its elements. Rules of this type cannot be incorporated in a PSG;[C7] nor can the rules for writing DO loops in FORTRAN.[A9] Any rule requiring that two or more constituent phrases of a construction be identical (or different) is almost certainly beyond the scope of phrase-structure definition, as is the indication of scope of nested loops by indentation.

The PSG is nonetheless a valuable tool for describing languages, both natural and artificial. Chomsky has described it as the only theory of grammar with any linguistic motivation that is sufficiently simple to permit serious abstract study. Most published PSG's for programming languages, while not serving as complete definitions, define languages which include the programming languages as subsets satisfying simple restrictions, and correctly account for the structure of programs.

2.1.7. EXTENSIONS

The use of curly brackets around a part of a rule in a PSG is sometimes used to signify an arbitrary number, possibly zero, of occurrences of the form described within the brackets. As a refinement, super- and subscripts on the closing bracket, if present, signify upper and lower limits on the number. A variant uses square brackets to signify an optional single occurrence of the form described within the brackets. The COBOL syntax uses a two-dimensional display of alternatives and options. While none of these operators extends the generative power of PSG's, they all increase the convenience and explanatory power. For example, a phrase-structure description of the function $f(a, b, c, d)$, if general enough to deal with functions of arbitrarily many variables, leads to such absurdities as assertions that 'a, b' is a phrase but 'c, d' is not. A definition using curly brackets,

$$\langle \text{function} \rangle \rightarrow \langle \text{function name} \rangle (\langle \text{expression} \rangle \{, \langle \text{expression} \rangle \})$$

avoids designating as phrases any parts of the function except those which serve as names or have values.

An extension to permit specification that two component phrases of a construction must be identical increases the generative power of PSG's. Such a mechanism is used in Input Language (Siberian ALGOL)[A5] to permit programs to contain relations like "$Alpha_1 \leq \cdots \leq Alpha_n$," but not "$Alpha_1 \leq \cdots \leq Beta_n$." It seems unlikely, however, that extensions will be found which, while retaining the explanatory power of PSG's, permit the complete description of even the present generation of computer languages.

2.1.8. THEORY OF FORMAL LANGUAGES

There exists a rapidly growing body of theory of PSG's and other formal models of language. Some of the results are of interest to the designer of compilers and the writer of programming manuals, such as the possibility of listing the allowed character pairs which may occur in programs, or the possible initial characters of each phrase type.[C1,E2] Others pertain to the design of programming languages, such as the absence of a general procedure to determine whether a PSG generates ambiguous sentences,[C2,C6,C8,C10] the existence of recognizable classes of grammars which are free from ambiguity,[E1,E2,E3] and the existence of languages for which all PSG's are ambiguous.[C5,C14] Chomsky[C4] and Bar-Hillel, Perles, and Shamir[C1] are important original papers on the general theory of PSG's; Chomsky[C5] is a thorough survey of known results about PSG's and related language-generating devices.

2.1.9. UNSOLVED PROBLEMS

Many questions of practical importance in the design of programming languages and their compilers are unanswered; some have not, to the writer's knowledge, been stated in print. It is not known, for example, how to synthesize a phrase-structure grammar for a programming language, given the precedence relations of its operators. Such a synthesis method would have prevented the costly ambiguities originally present in ALGOL 60. For a given language, it is not known how to synthesize a grammar which best displays the structure of its sentences, best accommodates a particular method of syntactic analysis, or best accounts for the structure of sentences containing slight syntactic errors. It is not known whether an analyzer is possible which would not consume excessive space and time, even for pathological languages. Some of these questions are capable of precise formulation, but even rule-of-thumb solutions for any of them would be valuable.

REFERENCES

References include subjects related to the syntax of programming languages insofar as they illuminate the problems of analysis and synthesis of formally defined programming languages. Entries are arranged by subjects, alphabetically by author within each subject. Particularly recommended as introductions to their subjects are A7, A12, B1, C1, C3, C4, C5, D5, D12, E2, E4, F10, G1, G3 (subjects are designated by letter, individual papers by number).

A. Formal Grammars for Programming Languages

1. Backus, J. W., "The syntax and semantics of the proposed international algebraic language of the Zürich ACM-GAMM conference, *Proc. Internat'l. Conf.*, Information Processing, UNESCO, Paris (June 1959), pp. 125–132.

2. Berman, R., Sharp, J., and Sturges, L., "Syntactical charts of COBOL 61," *Comm. ACM*, vol. 5 (May 1962), p. 260.

3. Brooker, R. A., and Morris, D., "A description of the Mercury Autocode in terms of a phrase structure language," in *Annual Review in Automatic Programming*, Pergamon Press, The Macmillan Co., New York, N.Y., vol. 2 (1961), pp. 29–66.

4. Brown, S. A., Drayton, C. E., and Mittman, B., "A description of the APT language," *Comm. ACM*, vol. 6 (November 1963), pp. 649–658.

5. Ershov, A. P., Kohuzhin, G. I., and Voloshin, Yu. M., "Input language for a system of automatic programming," Academy of Science U.S.S.R. Computing Center, Moscow; 1961 (Russian). Academic Press, London; 1963 (English).

6. Huskey, H. D., Love, R., and Wirth, N., "A syntactic description of BC NELIAC," *Comm. ACM*, vol. 6 (July 1963), pp. 367–375.

7. Naur, P. *et al.*, "Report on the algorithmic language ALGOL 60," *Comm. ACM*, vol. 3 (May 1960), pp. 299–314. "Annual Review of Automatic Programming," Pergamon Press, The Macmillan Co., New York, N.Y., vol. 2 (1961), pp. 351–390. *Numerische Mathematik*, vol. 2 (March 1960), pp. 106–136.

8. Naur, P. *et al.*, "Revised report on the algorithmic language ALGOL 60," *Comm. ACM*, vol. 6 (January 1963), pp. 1–7. *Numerische Mathematik*, vol. 4 (March 1963), pp. 420–452. *Computer Journal*, vol. 5 (January 1963), pp. 349–367.

9. Rabinowitz, I. N., "Report on the algorithmic language FORTRAN II," *Comm. ACM*, vol. 5 (June 1962), pp. 327–337.

10. Shaw, C. J., "A specification of JOVIAL," *Comm. ACM*, vol. 6 (December 1963), pp. 721–736.

11. Shaw, C. J., "JOVIAL—a programming language for real-time command systems," in *Annual Review in Automatic Programming*, Pergamon Press, The Macmillan Co., New York, N.Y., vol. 3 (1963), pp. 53–119.

12. Taylor, W., Turner, L., and Waychoff, R., "A syntactical chart of ALGOL 60," *Comm. ACM*, vol. 4 (September 1961), p. 393. (See A7.)

13. Wirth, N., "A generalization of ALGOL," *Comm. ACM*, vol. 6 (September 1963), pp. 547–554.

14. Youden, W. W., "An analysis of ALGOL 60 syntax," Data Proc. Systems Div., Nat. Bureau of Standards, Washington, D.C.; August 15, 1961. (See A7.)

15. "Index to ALGOL 60 syntactical chart," Training and Education Dept., E.D.P., RCA, Camden, N.J.; October 20, 1961. (See A12.)

16. "COBOL 61, revised specifications for a common business-oriented language," U.S. Govt. Printing Office, Washington, D.C., O-598941; 1961.

B. *Expositions of Languages Defined by Formal Grammars*

1. Bottenbruch, H., "Structure and use of ALGOL 60," *J. ACM*, vol. 9 (April 1962), pp. 161–221.

2. Dijkstra, E. W., "A primer of ALGOL 60 programming," Academic Press, New York, N.Y.; 1962.

3. Huskey, H. D., Halstead, M. H., and McArthur, R., "NELIAC—a dialect of ALGOL," *Comm. ACM*, vol. 3 (August 1960), pp. 463–468.

4. Knuth, D. E., and Merner, J. N., "ALGOL 60 confidential," *Comm. ACM*, vol. 4, pp. 268–272 (June 1961).

5. McCracken, D. D., "A Guide to ALGOL Programming," John Wiley & Sons, Inc., New York, N.Y.; 1962.

6. McCracken, D. D., "A Guide to COBOL Programming," John Wiley & Sons, Inc., New York, N.Y.; 1963.

7. Naur, P., "A Course of ALGOL 60 Programming," Regnecentralen, Copenhagen, Denmark; 1961.

8. Ross, D. T., "The design and use of the APT language for automatic programming of numerically controlled machine tools," *Proc. Computer Applications Symposium*, ITT Res. Inst., Chicago, Ill. (1959), pp. 80–99.

9. Sammet, J. E., "Basic elements of COBOL 61," *Comm. ACM*, vol. 5 (May 1962), pp. 237–253.

10. Sammet, J. E., "Detailed description of COBOL," in *Annual Review in Automatic Programming*, Pergamon Press, The Macmillan Co., New York, N.Y., vol. 2 (1961), pp. 197–230.

11. Schwarz, H., "An Introduction to ALGOL," *Comm. ACM*, vol. 5 (February 1962), pp. 82–95.

12. Reference Manual, 709/7090 FORTRAN Programming System, IBM Form No. C28-6054-2.

13. Bolliet, L., Gastinel, N., and Laurent, P. J., "Un Nouveau Langage Scientifique— ALGOL—Manual Pratique," Hermann, Paris, France; 1964.

C. General Theory of Phrase-Structure Grammars

1. Bar-Hillel, Y., Perles, M., and Shamir, E., "On formal properties of simple phrase structure grammars," Applied Logic Branch, Hebrew Univ. of Jerusalem, Tech. Rept. No. 4; 1960. *Zeitschrift für Phonetik, Sprachwissenschaft und Kommunikationsforschung*, vol. 14 (1961), pp. 143–172. Summarized in *Comp. Rev.*, vol. 4, (September-October 1963), pp. 213–214.

2. Cantor, D. G., "On the ambiguity problem of Backus systems," *J. ACM*, vol. 9 (October 1962), pp. 477–479.

3. Chomsky, N., "Syntactic Structures," Mouton and Co., The Hague, Netherlands; 1957.

4. Chomsky, N., "On certain formal properties of grammars," *Inf. and Control*, vol. 2, (June 1959), pp. 137–167. (Addendum) "A note on phrase structure grammars," *Inf. and Control*, vol. 2 (December 1959), pp. 393–395.

5. Chomsky, N., "Formal Properties of Grammars," in *Handbook of Mathematical Psychology*, John Wiley & Sons, Inc., New York, N.Y., vol. 2 (1963), pp. 323–418.

6. Chomsky, N., and Schützenberger, M. P., "The Algebraic Theory of Context-Free Languages," in *Computer Programming and Formal Systems*, North-Holland, Amsterdam (1963), pp. 118–161.

7. Floyd, R. W., "On the non-existence of a phrase structure grammar for ALGOL 60," *Comm. ACM*, vol. 5 (September 1962), pp. 483–484.

8. Floyd, R. W., "On ambiguity in phrase structure languages," *Comm. ACM*, vol. 5 (October 1962), pp. 526, 534.

9. Gorn, S., "Detection of generative ambiguities in context-free mechanical languages," *J. ACM*, vol. 10 (April 1963), pp. 196–208.

10. Greibach, S. A., "The undecidability of the ambiguity problem for minimal linear grammars," *Inf. and Control*, vol. 6 (June 1963), pp. 119–125.

11. Greibach, S. A., "Inverses of phrase structure generators," Ph.D. dissertation, Harvard University, Cambridge, Mass.; June 1963.

12. Landweber, P. S., "Three theorems on phrase structure grammars of type 1," *Inf. and Control*, vol. 6 (June 1963), pp. 131–136.

13. Matthews, G. H., "Discontinuity and asymmetry in phrase structure grammars," *Inf. and Control*, vol. 6 (June 1963), pp. 137–146.

14. Parikh, R. J., "Language-generating devices," Res. Lab. of Electronics, MIT, Cambridge, Mass., Quarterly Progress Rept., No. 60 (January 15, 1961), pp. 199–212.

15. Schützenberger, M. P., "On context-free languages and pushdown automata," *Inf. and Control*, vol. 6 (September 1963), pp. 246–264.

16. See also E2, G3, G4.

D. Syntax-Directed Analysis

1. Barnett, M. P., and Futrelle, R. P., "Syntactic analysis by digital computer," *Comm. ACM*, vol. 5 (October, 1962), pp. 515–526.

2. Bastian, A. L., Jr., "A phrase-structure language translator," Air Force Cambridge Res. Labs., Hanscom Field, Mass., Rept. No. AFCRL-69-549 (August 1962).

3. Brooker, R. A., and Morris, D., "A general translation program for phrase-structure languages," *J. ACM*, vol. 9 (January 1962), pp. 1–10.

4. Brooker, R. A., and Morris, D., "A compiler for a self-defining phrase structure language," Univ. of Manchester, England (undated).

5. Cheatham, T. E., Jr., and Sattley, K., "Syntax-directed compiling," *Proc. Spring Joint Computer Conf.*, Spartan Books, Baltimore, Md., vol. 25 (1964), pp. 31–57.

6. Conway, M. E., "Design of a separable transition-diagram compiler," *Comm. ACM*, vol. 6 (July 1963), pp. 396–408.

7. Ingerman, P. Z., "A syntax oriented compiler...," Moore School of Elec. Engineering, Univ. of Penn., Philadelphia; April 1963.

8. Irons, E. T., "A syntax directed compiler for ALGOL 60," *Comm. ACM*, vol. 4 (January 1961), pp. 51–55. (See also reference D13.)

9. Irons, E. T., "An error-correcting parse algorithm," *Comm. ACM*, vol. 6 (November 1963), pp. 669–673.

10. Irons, E. T., "The structure and use of the syntax-directed compiler," in *Annual Review in Automatic Programming*, Pergamon Press, The Macmillan Company, New York, N.Y., vol. 3 (1963), pp. 207–227.

11. Lediey, R. S., and Wilson, J. B., "Automatic-programming-language translation through syntactical analysis," *Comm. ACM*, vol. 5 (March 1962), pp. 145–155.

12. Lucas, P., "The structure of formula-translators," Mailüfterl, Vienna, Austria, ALGOL Bulletin Suppl. No. 16; September 1961. *Elektronische Rechenanlagen*, vol. 3 (August 1961), pp. 159–166.

13. Mayoh, B. H., "Irons' procedure DIAGRAM," *Comm. ACM* (letter of correction), vol. 4 (June 1961), p. 284.

14. Reynolds, J. C., "A compiler and generalized translator," Applied Math. Div., Argonne Natl. Lab., Argonne, Ill. (undated).

15. Warshall, S., "A syntax-directed generator," *Proc. Eastern Joint Computer Conf.*, Spartan Books, Baltimore, Md., vol. 20 (1961), pp. 295–305.

16. See also C11, G4.

E. Syntax-Controlled Analysis

1. Eickel, J., Paul, M., Bauer, F. L., and Samelson, K., "A syntax-controlled generator of formal language processors," *Comm. ACM*, vol. 6 (August 1963), pp. 451–455.

2. Floyd, R. W., "Syntactic analysis and operator precedence," *J. ACM*, vol. 10 (July, 1963), pp. 316–333.

3. Floyd, R. W., Bounded context syntactic analysis," *Comm. ACM*, vol. 7 (February 1964), pp. 62–67.

4. Graham, R., "Bounded context translation," *Proc. Spring Joint Computer Conf.*, Spartan Books, Baltimore, Md., vol. 25 (1964), pp. 17–29.

5. Paul, M., "ALGOL 60 processors and a processor generator," *Proc. IFIP Congress*, North Holland, Amsterdam (1962), pp. 493–497.

F. Non-Syntactic Methods of Analysis

1. Dijkstra, E. W., "Making a translator for ALGOL 60," Annual Review in Automatic Programming, Pergamon Press, The Macmillan Company, New York, N.Y., vol. 3 (1963), pp. 347–356.
2. Dijkstra, E. W., "ALGOL 60 translation," Stichting Mathematisch Centrum, Amsterdam, The Netherlands, ALGOL Bulletin Suppl. No. 10; November 1961.
3. Evans, A., Jr., "An ALGOL 60 compiler," Computation Center, Carnegie Inst. of Technology, Pittsburgh, Pa., Rept. No. C.R.O-4; August 27, 1963.
4. Floyd, R. W., "A descriptive language for symbol manipulation," J. ACM, vol. 8 (October 1961), pp. 579–584.
5. Grau, A. A., "Recursive processes and ALGOL translation," Comm. ACM, vol. 4 (January 1961), pp. 10–15.
6. Grau, A. A., "The structure of an ALGOL translator," Oak Ridge Natl. Lab., Oak Ridge, Tenn., Rept. No. ORNL-3054; February 9, 1961.
7. Grau, A. A., "A translator-oriented symbolic language programming language," J. ACM, vol. 9 (October 1962), pp. 480–487.
8. Naur, P., "The design of the GEIR ALGOL compiler," Nordisk Tidskrift for Informations, Behandling, pt. I, vol. 3, p. 124; 1963.
9. Ross, D. T., "An algorithmic theory of language," Electronic Systems Lab., MIT, Cambridge, Mass., Rept. No. ESL-TM-156; November 1962.
10. Samelson, K., "Programming languages and their processing," Proc. IFIP Congress (1962), pp. 487–492.
11. Samelson, K., and Bauer, F. L., "Sequential formula translation," Comm. ACM, vol. 3 (February 1960), pp. 76–83.

G. Related Work on Analysis of Natural Languages

1. Bobrow, D. G., "Syntactic analysis of English by computer—a survey," Proc. Fall Joint Computer Conf., Spartan Books, Baltimore, Md., vol. 24 (1963), pp. 365–387.
2. Cheatham, T. E., Jr., and Warshall, S., "Translation of retrieval requests couched in 'semi-formal' English-like language," Comm. ACM, vol. 5 (January 1962), pp. 34–39.
3. Chomsky, N., and Miller, G. A., "Introduction to the formal analysis of natural languages," in "Handbook of Mathematical Psychology," John Wiley & Sons, Inc., New York, N.Y.; vol. 2 (1963), pp. 269–322.
4. Kuno, S., and Oettinger, A. G., "Multiple-path syntactic analyzer," Proc. IFIP Congress, North Holland, Amsterdam (1962), pp. 306–312.
5. See also C3.

H. Miscellaneous Devices Useful in Performing Syntactic Analysis

1. Floyd, R. W., "Ancestor" (Algorithm 96), Comm. ACM, vol. 5 (June 1962), pp. 344–345.
2. Holt, A. W., "A mathematical and applied investigation of tree structures for computer syntactic analysis," Ph.D. dissertation, Univ. of Penna., Philadelphia; 1963.
3. Warshall, S., "A theorem on Boolean matrices," J. ACM, vol. 9 (January 1962), pp. 11–12.

I. Supplementary Bibliographies

1. Kirsch, R. A., "The application of automata theory to problems in information retrieval (with selected bibliography)," National Bureau of Standards, Washington, D.C., Rept. No. 7882; March 1, 1963.

2. Kesner, O., "Bibliography: ALGOL references," *Comp. Revs.*, vol. 3 (January-February 1962), pp. 37–38.

3. Voloshin, U. M., "Bibliography on automatic programming," Institut Matematiki Sibirskogo Otdeleniia Akademii Nauk S.S.S.R., Novosibirsk; 1961.

4. Yngve, V. H. *et al.*, "Towards better documentation of programming languages," (ALGOL 60, COBOL, COMIT, FORTRAN, IPL-V, JOVIAL, NELIAC), *Comm. ACM*, vol. 6 (March 1963), pp. 76–92.

5. Youden, W. W., "Index to the Communications of the ACM volumes 1–5, 1958–1962," *Comm. ACM*, vol. 6 (March 1963), pp. I 1–32.

6. "ALGOL references in the Communications of the ACM, 1960-1961," *Comm. ACM*, vol. 4 (September 1961), p. 404.

7. "Automatic programming—a short bibliography," in *Annual Review in Automatic Programming*, Pergamon Press, The Macmillan Co., New York, N.Y., vol. 1 (1960), pp. 291–294.

8. See also B13, C5, C6, E1, E5, F9, F10, G1, G3, which contain extensive bibliographies relevant to their subjects.

2.2 The Structure and Use of the Syntax-Directed Compiler

by Edgar T. Irons

2.2.1. INTRODUCTION

A compiler is generally understood to be a program operating on a digital computer which translates one (object) language into another (target) language. To serve in this capacity, the compiler must contain a set of rules for recognizing the structure of strings in the object language and for performing the translation. In many compilers this set of rules is inextricably intertwined with the program which performs the recognition and transiation.

This article describes the structure and use of a compiling system in which the *translator* is independent of the *translation rules* and hence is independent of either the object or target language. Section 2.2.2 gives the meta language in which the translation rules are expressed. Section 2.2.3 contains a set of examples illustrating the use of the meta language to specify translations of an algorithmic language into the language of a hypothetical machine. Section 2.2.4 describes the recognition procedure which is the heart of the language independent translator.

EDITOR'S NOTE: This article reproduced by permission of the author and the publisher: *Annual Review of Automatic Programming*, vol. 3, Pergamon Press Ltd., Oxford, England, 1963; distributed by The Macmillan Company, New York.

2.2.2. THE META LANGUAGE

The translation rules consist of a series of sentences, each one consisting of a syntax formula followed by a string of symbols designating the semantics of that syntax formula. The sentences have the following form:

Let S be a syntax unit: either a meta-linguistic variable or a symbol of the input language.

Let P denote a semantic unit: either a symbol of the output language or a designator of a string of such symbols.

Each sentence of the specifications then has the form:

$$\underbrace{SSSS \ldots SS}_{\text{Components}} \rightarrow \underbrace{S}_{\text{Subject}} \quad \underbrace{\{PPPPPPPP \ldots P\}}_{\text{Definition}}$$

The syntax unit S following the meta symbol $\rightarrow$ in any sentence is the 'subject' of the sentence, and the syntax units to the left of $\rightarrow$ are the 'components' of the sentence. The string $PPPP \ldots PP$ between the meta symbols {and} is the 'definition' of the sentence. Specifically, P may have one of the following three forms:

1. Any symbol (p) of an output language. The output language alphabet may contain any symbols, but when that alphabet does contain the symbols

$$\{ \varrho \, ' \phi \, [\,] \, ; \, \}$$

special conventions will hold in the cases described below.

2. Any output string designator of the form

$$\underbrace{\varrho \, '' \ldots \, ' n}_{\text{may be empty}} \, \underbrace{[p \leftarrow PP \ldots P \, ; p \leftarrow PP \ldots P \, ; \ldots \, ; p \leftarrow PP \ldots P]}_{\text{may be empty}}$$

where P and p are defined as above, and n is an integer designating a particular string.

If a string designator (2) is of the simple form ϱ_n it denotes the string which is the *definition* of the sentence whose subject is the nth component to the left of $\rightarrow$ in the sentence containing the designator ϱ_n. If the string designator is of the form

$$\varrho_n[p \leftarrow PP \ldots P \, ; \ldots \,]$$

it denotes the same string but with substitutions made as indicated; namely, with the symbol p replaced at every occurrence by the symbols $PPPPP \ldots PP$, these substitutions being made one after the other from left to right. Examples are given below.

3. An output string function designator of the form

$$\underbrace{\phi'' \ldots 'n}_{\text{may be empty}} \underbrace{[PPP \ldots P; PP \ldots P; \ldots; PP \ldots P]}_{\text{may be empty}}$$

where P is defined as above, and n is an integer designating a particular string function.

Then output function designator ϕ, of (3), is used to specify a function of the strings $PPPPP \ldots PP$ enclosed between the brackets following the function designator. The integer n serves to identify a particular function which is relevant to some particular set of syntactic sentences. They serve to enhance the descriptive ability of the output language, and constitute part of the description of an input language.

Consider as an example of the use of string designators the following five sentences specifying a translation of an input string consisting of some series containing the letters a and b to an output string composed of the letters A, B, c and y, t, m.

$$a \rightarrow \text{letter } \{Ax\}$$
$$b \rightarrow \text{letter } \{Bt\}$$
$$\text{letter} \rightarrow \text{iden} \{\varrho_1\}$$
$$\text{iden letter} \rightarrow \text{iden } \{\varrho_2\varrho_1[t \leftarrow m]\}$$
$$\text{iden} \rightarrow \text{simvar } \{\varrho_1[x \leftarrow y]\}$$

The diagram of the input string

babaa

is shown in Fig. 2.2.1.

The meaning of the final syntactic unit 'simvar' is

BtAyBmAyAy

Note that Fig. 2.2.1 is unique under the following two conventions (which we will assume throughout the report):

1. That the diagram encompass the entire string.
2. That as many brackets be drawn as possible (e.g., we cannot leave off the bracket for 'simvar' above).

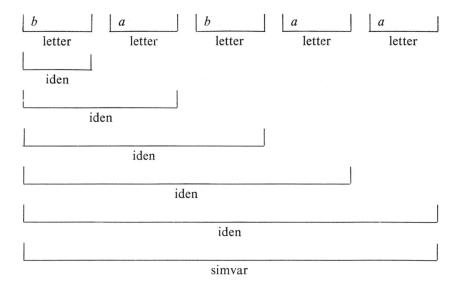

FIGURE 2.2.1

An example of a function ϕ is one whose value is a string of the characters *0 1 2 3 4 5 6 7 8 9*, concatenated to represent the *number* of symbols in the parameter string of the function on any use. If we identify this function by the integer 1 and change syntactic statement (39) in Section 2.2.3.1 to

$$\text{iden} \to \text{simvar } \{\phi_1[\varrho_1]\}$$

the meaning of the string of our example would now be merely the characters

1 0

The meta symbol ' serves as a left meta parenthesis counter to allow the output language to contain the meta symbols of the description, so that an input language may be described in terms of—and hence translated into—the meta language. This convention enables a translator to modify the set of translation specifications it is currently using according to the particular input string it is examining. This enabling convention depends on the use of the symbols {and} as meta parentheses. If in any definition of a syntactic sentence the number of ' following any occurrence of ϱ or ϕ is *not* equal to

(the number of {s to the left) − 1

then the symbol ϱ or ϕ and its associated symbols

$$[\,;\leftarrow\,]$$

will be treated as symbols of type 1 rather than in the way described above. The meta symbols {and} are always treated as symbols of type 1, when they occur in the string of a definition. If the last sentence of the descriptions of the example were changed to

$$\text{iden} \rightarrow \text{simvar } \{\varrho_1 \rightarrow \text{realtype } \{\varrho_1'[x \leftarrow y]\phi_1\}\}$$

the translation of the string *babaa* would be

$$BtAxBmAxAx \rightarrow \text{realtype } \{BtAyBmAyAy\phi_1\}$$

2.2.3. SOME TYPICAL META-LINGUISTIC CONSTRUCTIONS FOR AN ALGEBRAIC COMPILER

In the following examples, the object languages are taken from sections of ALGOL 60 and similar algebraic languages. The target language is the symbolic language of a simple, single address machine. The format for a machine instruction is

$$III \ldots I : 000 - III \ldots I;$$

The strings of I's represent identifiers to indefinite length, each composed of strings of letters or digits, with the first character a letter. The 0's represent three-letter mnemonic machine instructions from the following list:

LDA m	Bring contents of m to accumulator
ADD m	Add contents of m to accumulator (floating point)
SUB m	Subtract contents of m from accumulator (floating point)
MPY m	Multiply contents of m by contents of accumulator (floating point)
DIV m	Divide contents of accumulator by content of m (floating point)
STA m	Store the contents of accumulator in m
GEJ m	Transfer to m if accumulator ≥ 0
LEJ m	Transfer to m if accumulator ≤ 0
UEJ m	Transfer to m if accumulator $\neq 0$
JMP m	Transfer unconditionally to m
RND	Round the contents of the accumulator

A possible sequence of instructions is

LDA-APG; SUB-APX; GEJ-G0101; LDA-APX; G0101 :STA-APQ;

2.2.3.1. *Example 1: Simple Arithmetic Expressions*

The following set of statements serves to specify a translation of simple arithmetic expressions into machine language. The expressions allowed are a subset of the ALGOL arithmetic expressions, and the syntax describing them is a direct subset of that used in the ALGOL report.

$$A \rightarrow \text{letter } \{A\} \tag{1}$$

$$B \rightarrow \text{letter } \{B\} \tag{2}$$

$$\cdot \qquad\qquad\qquad\qquad \cdot$$
$$\cdot \qquad\qquad\qquad\qquad \cdot$$
$$\cdot \qquad\qquad\qquad\qquad \cdot$$

$$z \rightarrow \text{letter } \{z\} \tag{26}$$

$$\text{letter} \rightarrow \text{iden } \{\varrho_1\} \tag{27}$$

$$\text{iden} \quad \text{letter} \rightarrow \text{iden } \{\varrho_2\varrho_1\} \tag{28}$$

$$\times \rightarrow \text{multop } \{\text{MPY}\} \tag{29}$$

$$/ \rightarrow \text{multop } \{\text{DIV}\} \tag{30}$$

$$+ \rightarrow \text{addop } \{\text{ADD}\} \tag{31}$$

$$- \rightarrow \text{addop } \{\text{SUB}\} \tag{32}$$

$$\text{iden} \rightarrow \text{primary } \{\text{LDA} - \varrho_1\} \tag{33}$$

$$(\text{arithex}) \rightarrow \text{primary } \{\varrho_2\} \tag{34}$$

$$\text{primary} \rightarrow \text{term } \{\varrho_1\} \tag{35}$$

$$\text{term multop primary} \rightarrow \text{term} \tag{36}$$

$$\left. \begin{array}{l} \{\varrho_1; \text{STA} - t; \varrho_3[t \leftarrow ti]; \varrho_2 - t\} \\ \text{term} \rightarrow \text{termsum } \{\varrho_1\} \end{array} \right\} \tag{37}$$

$$\left. \begin{array}{l} \text{termsum addop term} \rightarrow \text{termsum} \\ \{\varrho_1; \text{STA} - t; \varrho_3[t \leftarrow ti]; \varrho_2 - t\} \end{array} \right\} \tag{38}$$

$$\text{termsum} \rightarrow \text{arithex } \{\varrho_1\} \tag{39}$$

Using this set of specifications, the expression

$$AB + (C - D) * B$$

would be diagrammed as in Fig. 2.2.2.

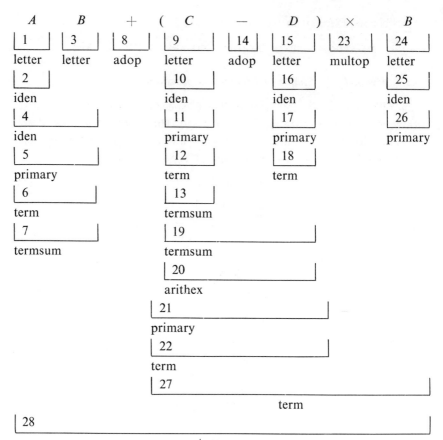

FIGURE 2.2.2

The output code associated with each of the brackets above is

1, 2	A
3	B
4	AB
5, 6, 7	LDA——AB
8	ADD
9, 10	C
11, 12, 13	LDA——C
14	SUB

15, 16, 17, 18	LDA——D
19, 20, 21, 22	LDA——D; STA——t; LDA——C; SUB——t
23	MPY
24, 25	B
26	LDA——B
27	LDA——B; STA——t; LDA——D; STA——ti; LDA——C; SUB——ti; MPY——t
28	LDA——B; STA——;t LDA——D; STA——ti; LDA——C; SUB——ti; MPY——t; STA——t; LDA——AB; ADD——t

The final translation of the arithmetic expression is attached to the outer-most bracket (28). It is assumed that temporary storage cells are labeled 't,' 'ti,' etc.

Although this translation does indeed produce machine code which calculates the value of the arithmetic expression, it is clear that this code is unnecessarily long. The quality of the translation is poor because we have specified the syntax of the object language in such a way as to minimize the number of specification statements. For purposes of defining the language (in terms of our machine language) this indeed is desirable. On the other hand, in keeping the number of statements to a minimum we have restricted the number of output code groups (definitions) which can appear in a translation. Thus we have not been able to specify better translations in some frequently occurring special configurations of the object string.

For example, if the termsum and term in Statement (38) were respectively

$$A * B \quad \text{and} \quad C * D$$

then our way of putting together their translations in the definition of (38) would produce a 'good' translation, but if they were simply identifiers, say

$$A \quad \text{and} \quad B$$

we would rather produce

$$\text{LDA } A; \text{ ADD } B$$

The above syntax does not permit this output, since in Statement (38) we do not know the detailed composition of the term or termsum.

2.2.3.2. *Example 2: More Efficient Output Code*

To avoid the difficulty of Example 1, we can arrange the syntax so that a simple identifier cannot compose a term or termsum all by itself, and then specify the syntactic structure for 'addition' and 'multiplication' of identifiers separately; in so doing, we recognize separately the special cases with which we wish to deal. We change the specifications by deleting Statement (33) from the specifications of Example 1 (so that an identifier may not be a primary, term, or termsum) and add the following specifications (to specify the syntax and semantics of 'adding' and 'multiplying' identifiers):

$$\text{iden multop iden} \quad \rightarrow \text{term } \{\text{LDA} - \varrho_3; \varrho_2 \text{---} \varrho_1\} \tag{36.1}$$

$$\text{term multop iden} \quad \rightarrow \text{term } \{\varrho_3; \varrho_2 \text{---} \varrho_1\} \tag{36.2}$$

$$\text{iden} \quad \times \quad \text{primary} \rightarrow \text{term } \{\varrho_1; \text{MPY} \text{---} \varrho_3\} \tag{36.3}$$

$$\text{iden} \quad / \quad \text{primary} \rightarrow \text{term } \{\varrho_1; \text{STA} - t; \text{LDA} \text{---} \varrho_3; \text{DIV} - t\} \tag{36.4}$$

$$\text{iden} \quad \text{addop iden} \rightarrow \text{termsum } \{\text{LDA} - \varrho_3; \varrho_2 \text{---} \varrho_1\} \tag{38.1}$$

$$\text{termsum addop iden} \rightarrow \text{termsum } \{\varrho_3; \varrho_2 \text{---} \varrho_1\} \tag{38.2}$$

$$\text{iden} \quad + \quad \text{term} \rightarrow \text{termsum } \{\varrho_1; \varrho_2 \text{---} \varrho_3\} \tag{38.3}$$

$$\text{iden} \quad - \quad \text{term} \rightarrow \text{termsum } \{\varrho_1; \text{STA} - t; \text{LDA} - \varrho_3; \text{SUB} \text{---} t\} \tag{38.4}$$

$$\text{iden} \rightarrow \text{arithex } \{\text{LDA} \text{---} \varrho_1\} \tag{39.1}$$

With the expanded set of specifications, we can produce a considerably better translation of the string

$$AB + (C - D) * B$$

The string is diagrammed in Fig. 2.2.3. The output code for each bracket is

1, 2	A
3	B
4	AB
5, 6	C
7	SUB
8, 9	D
10, 11, 12, 13	LDA——C; SUB——D
14	MPY
15, 16	B
17	LDA——C; SUB——D; MPY——B
18	LDA——C; SUB——D; MPY——B; ADD——AB

In constructing the specifications for this example, we have taken advantage of the commutativity of addition and multiplication.

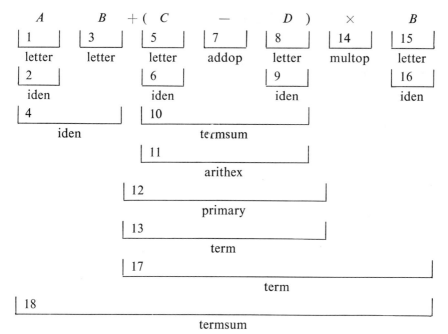

FIGURE 2.2.3

2.2.3.3. Example 3: A Pair of Useful Definition Functions

The specification statements of this example show the use of 'tag' generation functions in specifying a translation of control statements of an object language to machine language. Two functions are used.

1. The generation function ϕ_1 has as its value a string consisting of the letter L followed by two digits. The digits are generated in such a manner that each generated string is unique in any translation (unless there are more than 99 occurrences of ϕ_1 in a translation).

2. The retrieving function $\phi_2[n]$ has as its value the string identical to that generated by ϕ_1 in its nth occurrence before the occurrence of $\phi_2[n]$ *within one definition*.

For example, the definition

$$\{\phi_1\phi_1\varrho_1\phi_2[1]\phi_2[2]\}$$

would yield the string

L01 L02 XXX ... X L02 L01

where the X's represent the string produced by the ϱ_1 string designator.

Note that whether or not the string

$$XXX \ldots X$$

contains any strings generated by ϕ_1, the string given above is the same.

The following specifications give the translation rules for a subset of ALGOL conditional expressions (arithmetic expressions are specified as in Example 1 or 2):

$< \rightarrow$ relop {GEJ}

$> \rightarrow$ relop {LEJ}

$\neq \rightarrow$ relop {UEJ}

iden relop iden $\rightarrow$ bprimary {LDA——ϱ_3; SUB——ϱ_1; ϱ_2——j}

bprimary $\rightarrow$ bterm {ϱ_1}

bterm $\wedge$ bprimary $\rightarrow$ bterm {ϱ_3; ϱ_1}

bterm $\rightarrow$ bsum {ϱ_1}

bsum $\vee$ bterm $\rightarrow$ bsum {$\varrho_3[j \leftarrow \phi_1]$; JMP $- \phi_1$; $\phi_2[2] : \varrho_1$; $\phi_2[1]$:}

bsum $\rightarrow$ boolex {ϱ_1}

if boolex **then** arithex **else** arithex $\rightarrow$ arithex
{$\varrho_5[j \leftarrow \phi_1]$; ϱ_3; JMP $- \phi_1$; $\phi_2[2] : \varrho_1$; $\phi_2[1]$:}

Using these specifications, the expression

if $X < Y \vee W > Z$ **then** A **else** B

is diagrammed and translated as in Fig. 2.2.4. The output code is then

1, 2	X
3	GEJ
4, 5	Y
6, 7, 8	LDA $- X$; SUB $- Y$; GEJ $- j$
10, 11	W
12	LEJ
13, 14	Z
15, 16	LDA $- W$; SUB $- Z$; LEJ $- j$
17, 18	LDA $- X$; SUB $- Y$; GEJ $- $ L21; JMP $- $ L22; L21 : LDA $- W$; SUB $- Z$; LEJ $- j$; L22:
19, 20	A
21	LDA $- A$
22, 23	B

24   LDA — *B*

25   LDA — *X*; SUB — *Y*; GEJ — L21; JMP — L22;
            L21 : LDA — *W*; SUB — *Z*; LEJ — L11;
            L22 : LDA — *A*; JMP — L12;
            L11 : LDA — *B*;
            L12:

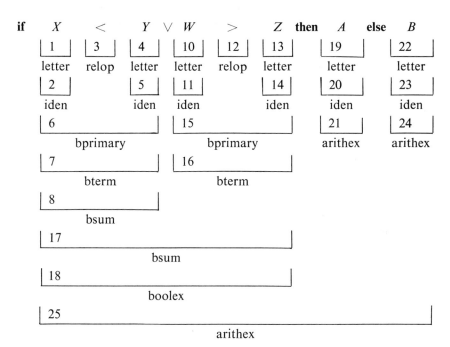

FIGURE 2.2.4

2.2.3.4. *Example 4: Dealing with Declarative Information*

In some of the object languages with which we are concerned, information is given in the form of declarative statements which affect the interpretation of sections of the object language strings. For example, we might wish the expression

$$A + B$$

to specify ordinary addition of *A* to *B* or complex addition of *A* to *B*, depending on whether or not there occurred elsewhere in the same object string the declarative statements

real *A, B*   or   **complex** *A, B*

To cope with such languages, we adopt a multipass translating system where the earlier passes translate the declarative statements into syntactic specifications which are appended to partially completed specifications for later passes.

As an example of this system consider an object language in which a complete string in the language consists of a list of declarative statements followed by a list of nondeclarative statements. For simplicity we will restrict the declarations to those declaring variables to be of type **real** or of type **integer**. The effect of an **integer** declaration is to cause rounding of the value of an arithmetic expression in a statement of the form

$$\text{identifier} = \text{arithex}$$

If the variable has been declared **real**, the value of the arithmetic expression is *not* rounded.

The following specifications (for the first pass) give translation rules for producing syntax statements from the declarations, while ignoring the rest of the string.

$$A \rightarrow \text{letter } \{A\}$$
$$B \rightarrow \text{letter } \{B\}$$
$$\vdots$$
$$Z \rightarrow \text{letter } \{Z\}$$

$$\times \rightarrow \text{glot } \{\ \}$$
$$- \rightarrow \text{glot } \{\ \}$$
$$\vdots$$

everything but characters **integer, real** and **end**

$$\text{letter} \rightarrow \text{glot } \{\ \}$$
$$\text{letter} \rightarrow \text{iden } \{\varrho_1\}$$
$$\text{iden letter} \rightarrow \text{iden } \{\varrho_2\varrho_1\}$$
$$\textbf{integer } \text{iden} \rightarrow \text{glot } \{\varrho_1 \rightarrow \textbf{intvar } \{\varrho_1'\}\}$$
$$\textbf{real } \text{iden} \rightarrow \text{glot } \{\varrho_1 \rightarrow \textbf{realvar } \{\varrho_1'\}\}$$
$$\text{glot} \rightarrow \text{mglot } \{\varrho_1\}$$
$$\text{mglot glot} \rightarrow \text{mglot } \{\varrho_2\varrho_1\}$$
$$\text{mglot } \textbf{end} \rightarrow \text{program 1 } \{\varrho_2\}$$

The translation produced from the string

$$\textbf{real } X; \ \textbf{integer } Y; \ Y = X \textbf{ end}$$

is shown in Fig. 2.2.5.

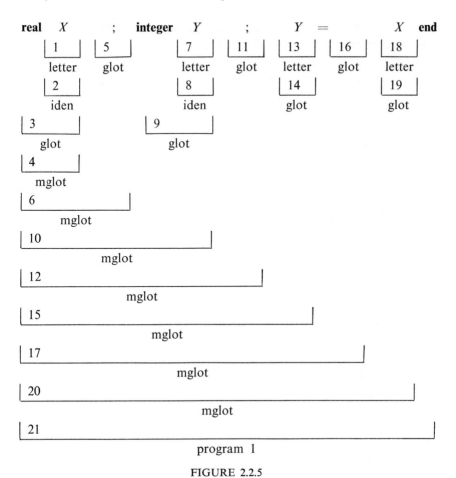

program 1

FIGURE 2.2.5

The output code is then

1, 2	X
3, 4, 6	$X \rightarrow$ **realvar** $\{X\}$
7, 8	Y
9	$Y \rightarrow$ **intvar** $\{Y\}$
10, 12, 15, 17, 20, 21	$X \rightarrow$ **realvar** $\{X\}$
	$Y \rightarrow$ **intvar** $\{Y\}$
13	Y
18	X
5, 11, 14, 16, 19	

To illustrate the effect of the first pass on the second, we add the following specifications to those used in Example 2:

$$realvar = arithex \rightarrow statement\ \{\varrho_1; \text{STA} - \varrho_3\}$$

$$intvar = arithex \rightarrow statement\ \{\varrho_1; \text{RND} - ; \text{STA} - \varrho_3\}$$

$$\textbf{real}\ realvar \rightarrow declaration\ \{\ \}$$

$$\textbf{integer}\ intvar \rightarrow declaration\ \{\ \}$$

$$declaration \rightarrow declist\ \{\ \}$$

$$declist; declaration \rightarrow declist\ \{\ \}$$

$$statement \rightarrow statlist\ \{\varrho_1\}$$

$$statlist; statement \rightarrow statlist\ \{\varrho_3; \varrho_1\}$$

$$declist; statlist\ \textbf{end} \rightarrow program\ 2\ \{\varrho_2\}$$

$$realvar \rightarrow iden\ \{\varrho_1\}$$

These specifications together with those produced by the first-pass translation above, namely,

$$X \rightarrow \textbf{realvar}\ \{X\}$$

$$Y \rightarrow \textbf{intvar}\ \ \{Y\}$$

comprise the complete specifications for the second translating pass for the string

$$\textbf{real}\ X;\ \textbf{integer}\ Y;\ Y = X\ \textbf{end}$$

The translating diagram and the resulting translation are shown in Fig. 2.2.6. The output code is then

1	X
4	Y
2, 3, 5, 6	
7	Y
8, 9	X
10	LDA $- X$
11, 12, 13	LDA $- X$; RND $-$; STA $- Y$

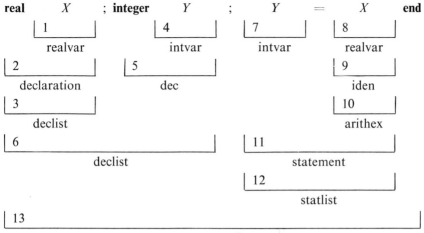

program 2

FIGURE 2.2.6

2.2.3.5. *Example 5: Specifications which Admit Nonunique Diagramming*

In all of the examples given thus far, the specifications have been written in such a way that it is possible to diagram any legal object string in only one way. It is useful in some cases to construct specifications which allow more than one diagram to be drawn on the same string if a convention is adopted to dictate which of the possible diagrams is to be drawn during a translation. A natural convention is that in drawing the diagram, the first specifications in a list are used first.

One application of this type of specifications is in producing error indications during a translation when an illegal object string is given. We construct specifications for a larger language which includes, as a subset, the language in which we are interested—the larger language consisting of all possible strings in the alphabet of the sublanguage. Hence every possible symbol string will be translated into *something*. In particular, strings not in the sublanguage will be translated into text, thereby indicating that parts of the object string are outside the sublanguage. In this way, one achieves a translation of strings in the sublanguage as before but, in addition, one obtains diagnostic information about illegal strings where they occur rather than just an indication that the whole string is illegal (i.e., cannot be diagrammed).

The following set of specifications, when appended to the end of the specifications for Example 2, illustrates the discussion above:

$$\text{letter} \rightarrow \text{set } 1 \; \{\varrho_1\}$$
$$\text{digit} \rightarrow \text{set } 1 \; \{\varrho_1\}$$
$$\text{set } 1 \rightarrow \text{set } 2 \; \{\varrho_1\}$$
$$+ \quad \rightarrow \text{set } 2 \; \{+\}$$
$$- \quad \rightarrow \text{set } 2 \; \{-\}$$
$$\times \quad \rightarrow \text{set } 2 \; \{\times\}$$
$$/ \quad \rightarrow \text{set} \quad \{/\}$$
$$\text{set } 2 \rightarrow \text{set } 3 \; \{\varrho_1\}$$
$$(\quad \rightarrow \text{set } 3 \; \{(\}$$
$$) \quad \rightarrow \text{set } 3 \; \{)\}$$
$$\text{set } 1 \rightarrow \text{mset } 1 \; \{\varrho_1\}$$
$$\text{mset } 1 \text{ set } 1 \rightarrow \text{mset } 1 \; \{\varrho_2\varrho_1\}$$
$$\text{set } 2 \rightarrow \text{mset } 2 \; \{\varrho_1\}$$
$$\text{mset } 2 \text{ set } 2 \rightarrow \text{mset } 2 \; \{\varrho_2\varrho_1\}$$
$$\text{set } 3 \rightarrow \text{mset } 3$$
$$\text{mset } 3 \text{ set } 3 \rightarrow \text{mset } 3 \; \{\varrho_2\varrho_1\}$$
$$\text{mset } 1 \rightarrow \text{primary} \; \{\text{ERROR}\text{---}\varrho_1\}$$
$$(\text{mset } 2) \rightarrow \text{primary} \; \{\text{ERROR}\text{---}(\varrho_2)\}$$
$$\text{mset } 3 \rightarrow \text{arithex} \; \{\text{ERROR}\text{---}\varrho_1\}$$

The alphabet here consists of the symbols which may occur in arithmetic expressions, namely, the letters and

$$+ - * / (\;)$$

Using this set of specifications, the string

$$A + B(B *)$$

which is *not* an arithmetic expression would be diagrammed and translated as in Fig. 2.2.7.

The output code is then

1, 2	A
4, 5, 6, 7	B
8	$\times$
9	$B \times$
10, 11	ERROR——$(B \times)$
12	ERROR——$(B \times)$; ADD $- A$

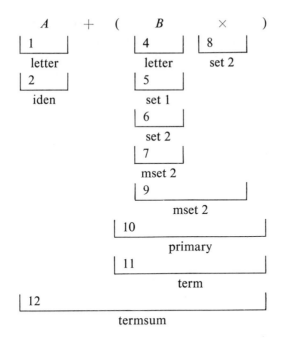

FIGURE 2.2.7

2.2.4. THE TRANSLATOR

The translator is a program which operates on a set of specifications already described and on a string of symbols in the object language for those specifications. It produces a string of symbols in the output language. The translator itself is completely independent of either language and may operate on *any* object language which can be described by the specifications of Section 2.2.2.

The heart of the translator is a program which 'diagrams' a string of input symbols by referencing the specifications. The output of this program is a linked list connecting selected definitions together.

In the operation of the translator, this output list serves as input to a second program which forms the output string from the indicated sequences of definitions.

The diagramming program, given below in ALGOL, is programmed as a recursive procedure. Essentially, given the name of a syntactic unit and the index of a symbol in the input string, the program will try to form the syntactic unit from the longest possible string of symbols following the one indicated. If it is possible to form the requested syntactic unit, the program will place in its output string a linked list indicating the definitions of the syntactic units which compose the requested syntactic unit, and supply as an output parameter its location in the output string of this list. If it is not possible to form the requested syntactic unit from the indicated string, the failure is reported.

In the machine implementation of this ALGOL program the translation specifications are stored in a semilinked list, represented in the ALGOL program by the three vectors STAB, STC, and TRAN. This list is constructed in the memory of the machine from the string of symbols which are the specifications. In the ALGOL program, as in the machine representation, the syntactic units and symbols of both languages are represented by integers.

In the tabling of the translation specifications, the numerical representation of the left most syntactic unit of any sentence is taken as the index of the integer vector TRAN. The value of any element of TRAN is the index of the element of STAB, which is the syntactic unit following the first in some sentence. If the first syntactic unit is the leftmost one of more than one sentence, the value of STC [TRAN [syntactic unit]] is the index of the syntactic unit following the first in its second occurrence. The linkages are continued from the second element in the same way. The *definition* follows the syntactic unit which is the subject of the sentence. In the tabling, the subject is treated in the same manner as the components, the fact that it *is* the subject being indicated by the brace which follows it. The symbol → is ignored. The following example illustrates the composition of the three vectors. The five sentences

$$\text{SVAR} + \text{SVAR} \to \text{TSUM} \ \{\text{LDA} \ \varrho_1\}$$
$$\text{SVAR} + \text{TERM} \to \text{TSUM} \ \{\text{ADD} \ \varrho_2\}$$
$$\text{SVAR} - \text{SVAR} \to \text{TSUM} \ \{\ldots\}$$
$$\text{SVAR} - \text{TERM} \to \text{TSUM} \ \{\ldots\}$$
$$\text{SVAR} - \text{TRIM} \to \text{TSUM} \ \{\ldots\}$$

would be linked as follows:

```
SVAR + SVAR  TSUM {LDA ...}
     |    ↓
     |  TERM TSUM {        }
     ↓  − SVAR  TSUM {        }
           ↓
        TERM TSUM {        }
           ↓
        TRIM TSUM {        }
```

Thus, SVAR may be followed by $+$ or $-$, while $+$ may be followed by TERM or SVAR, etc. This same information is stored in the machine representation by the three vectors STC, STAB, and TRAN. The vector STAB consists of elements of the tree ordered by exhausting one horizontal line, then adding the next branch from the last junction passed, etc. In the position corresponding to one element of the tree, STC lists the location of the next alternate *element* which could have been reached from the junction which led to this element. The vector TRAN has one entry for each syntactic name. The value of the entry is the index of STC and STAB where the tree for that name begins. The composition of the vectors for the above example would be

	TRAN	STC-idx	STC-val	STAB-idx	STAB
SVAR	I 1	I 1	I 4	I 1	$+$
TERM		I 2	I 3	I 2	SVAR
			0		TSUM
$+$			0		$\{$
			0		$\}$
$-$		I 3	0	I 3	TERM
			0		TSUM
			0		$\{$
			0		$\}$
		I 4	0	I 4	$-$
		I 5	I 6	I 5	SVAR
			0		TSUM
			0		$\{$
			0		$\}$
		I 6	I 7	I 6	TERM
			0		TSUM
			0		$\{$
			0		$\}$
		I 7	0	I 7	TRIM
			0		TSUM
			0		$\{$
			0		$:$
			0		$\}$

where I*n* is the integer which is the index of the adjacent component.

In order to determine when indeed the longest string of input symbols meeting the requirements of the requested syntactic unit have been found, the diagramming routine makes use of a 'precedence matrix'. This matrix,

SUCCR, is constructed in its elementary form while the syntax tables are constructed, and is then extended to form the complete matrix. If SUCCR $[p, q]$ is true, then syntactic unit p is the first element of a sentence whose subject is either q or whose subject is the first element of a sentence whose subject is either q or $\cdots$ and so on.

Vectors STAB, STC, TRAN, and SUCCR are considered to be global to the procedure DIAGRAM shown in Fig. 2.2.8. Other global parameters of DIAGRAM are the vectors INPUT and OUTPUT and their indices, j and k, respectively, these vectors being the input string of symbols and the output string.

The output string consists of positive and negative integers. If an element is positive, it is the index of an element of STAB which begins a definition in some sentence. Each such positive element will be followed by $n - 1$ negative integers, these being the negative of indices of other *positive* elements of the output string which are in turn links to other definitions; n is the number of components of the sentence in question, and the jth element of OUTPUT after any positive element is the link to the definition of the jth component to the left of the subject of the sentence, whose definition begins in STAB at the spot marked by the positive element. This string of integers is then very much like an assembler macro notation, and in fact is translated to the final output string in a quite similar manner. Of course the symbol substitution and invocation of compiling functions of the definitions must be done as the integer string is unraveled.

In the operation of DIAGRAM, the parameter i marks the spot in STAB which is currently of interest; DIAGRAM first examines all the components of sentences following the component discovered one level up in the recursion to determine whether the elements at the current location in the input string will form any of these components. If the input string meets the requirements of one of the components, the successors of this component are specified as the ones to be examined in the next call of DIAGRAM. If it does not, DIAGRAM then specifies—in order—the successors of the subjects following the component discovered on the last level of recursion as the next components to be considered, until either one of the subjects leads to a correct path, or until the list of subjects is exhausted. If the list is exhausted before a correct path is found, exit is made through ERROR to pass back the information that the path in question did not lead to success.

Since each step forward through the syntax table causes another recursion of DIAGRAM, it is not possible to eliminate a path through the table until all possible (according to the input string) paths have been examined, or until the requested syntactic unit has been formed. Hence, if the paths from value i, GOAL; integer PARAM; label ERROR; comment i is the starting position in the syntax table STAB. GOAL is the requested syntax unit. If this unit is discovered, the index of the appropriate definition string is placed in the output string, and the negative index of the output string is assigned to PARAM. If not the procedure exits via ERROR;

```
begin integer J, K, I, OTCEL;
Boolean sw;
J := j; K := k; I := i;
START: if STAB [i + 1] ≠ LEFTBRACE then
    begin j := j + 1;
        sw := if INPUT [j] = STAB [i] then true else false;
        if SUCCR [INPUT [j], STAB [i]] then begin DIAGRAM (TRAN [INPUT[j]], STAB [i], OTCEL, NOGO);
            go to CONTINUE end
        else begin NOGO: if sw then go to CONTINUE
            else begin RETRACE: j = J
                k := K end end end START;

i := STC [i];
if i ≠ 0 then go to START;
i := I;
NEWSTART: if STAB [i + 1] = LEFTBRACE then begin OTCEL := i + 2;
    if STAB [i] = GOAL then begin PARAM := -k;
        sw := true end
    else sw := false;
    if SUCCR [STAB [i], GOAL] then begin DIAGRAM (TRAN [STAB [i]], GOAL, PARAM, NOPATH);
        go to FOUND end
    else NOPATH: if sw then go to FOUND end NEWSTART;

i := STC [i];
if i ≠ 0 then go to NEWSTART;
j := J;
k := K;
go to ERROR;
CONTINUE: DIAGRAM (i + 1, GOAL, PARAM, RETRACE);
FOUND: OUTPUT [k] := OTCEL;
k := k + 1 end.
```

FIGURE 2.2.8

one structure to another in the table are unique (that is, if the syntax allows a unique diagramming of any input string), the sentence may be tabled in any order. If the paths are not unique, DIAGRAM gives preference to the first sentences in the table. Note, however, that the order of the sentences may have some effect on the efficiency of the diagramming process.

Other local parameters of DIAGRAM are sw, a Boolean variable which indicates that a syntactic unit has been discovered (though not necessarily that it encompasses the longest possible set of elements in the input string), and the constant LEFTBRACE ({), which indicates that the syntactic unit preceding it is a subject. (The meta symbol → is ignored in the tabulation.)

2.3. A Formal Semantics for Computer Languages and Its Application in a Compiler-Compiler

by Jerome A. Feldman

2.3.1. SUMMARY

A semantic meta language has been developed for representing the meanings of statements in a large class of computer languages. This meta language has been the basis for construction of an efficient, functioning compiler-compiler. An informal discussion of the meta language based on the example of a complete translator for a small language is presented.

2.3.2. INTRODUCTION

One of the most significant developments in the study of computer languages has been the formalization of syntax. Besides greatly improving communications between people, formalized syntax has led to new results in the theory and practice of programming. As early as 1960, Irons[7] was able to construct a compiler whose syntax phase was independent of the source language being translated. This work and that of other early contributors such as Brooker and Morris[1] led to speculation that the entire compilation process could be automated. The problem was to develop a

---

EDITOR'S NOTE: This article reproduced by permission of the author and the publisher: *Comm. ACM*, vol. 9, no. 1 (January 1966), pp. 3–9.

single program which could act as a translator for a large class of languages
differing from each other in substantial ways. To solve this so-called compiler-compiler problem, one must find appropriate formalizations of the
syntax and semantics of computer languages.

The formalization of semantics for some language L will involve representing the meanings of statements in L in terms of an appropriate meta
language. The meanings of statements in the meta language are assumed
to be known (primitive). If L is a computer language, the semantics of
L must involve a description of its translator. One example of a semantic
meta language is the order code of a computer. An order code or assembly
language can certainly describe any translation possible on its machine,
and in fact these have been the only kinds of semantic meta languages in
general use. Unfortunately, these lack several properties which one would
like to see in a semantic meta language.

An adequate semantic meta language should permit the description of
the source language to be as natural as possible. It should be readable so
that other people can understand the meaning of the source language being
defined. It should allow a description which is sufficiently precise and
complete to enable efficient automatic compilation. Finally, the meta
language should not depend on the characteristics of a particular computer.

Since there are satisfactory ways of representing syntax, the formalization of semantics should make possible a complete formal description of
computer languages. With a complete formal description available, one
could organize a compiler as shown in Fig. 2.3.1.

When a compiler for some language L is required, the following steps
are taken. First the formal syntax of L, expressed in a syntactic meta
language, is fed into the syntax loader. This program builds tables which
will control the recognition and parsing of programs in the language L.
Then the semantics of L, written in a semantic meta language, is fed into
the Semantic Loader. This program builds another table, this one containing a description of the meaning of statements in L. Finally, everything
to the left of the double line in Fig. 2.3.1 is discarded, leaving a compiler
for L.

The resulting compiler is a table-driven translator based on a recognizer
using a single pushdown stack. Each element in this stack consists of two
machine words—one for a syntactic construct and the other holding the
semantics of that construct. When a particular construct is recognized, its
semantic word and the semantic table determine what actions the translator
will take.

This entire system is based on the formalization of syntax and semantics,

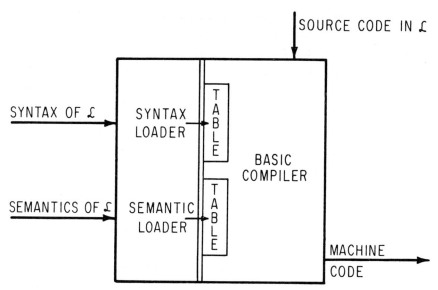

FIGURE 2.3.1   A compiler-compiler.

but not on the particular representations chosen. The remainder of this article is devoted to a discussion of two meta languages used in the compiler-compiler at the Carnegie Institute of Technology. The reasons for choosing these particular formalizations are discussed in detail in Ref. 4 and are not mentioned here. The system has been running since early in 1964 and translators for a number of languages have been completed.

In the following discussion examples from the appendices are frequently used. These describe a subset of ALGOL called the *small language*. Appendix A consists of the formal syntax of the small language in Backus Normal Form. Its syntax in recognizer-oriented form is Appendix B, while Appendix C contains its formal semantics. Appendices B and C form a complete description and were used just as they appear, to build a compiler for the small language.

2.3.3. SYNTAX

The syntax phase of the system is based on the model of a sequential recognizer with a single pushdown stack. The syntactic meta language, Production Language, is a vehicle for describing the behavior of this recognizer and is thus a recognizer-oriented syntactic meta language. The formal properties of this type of meta language have been discussed else-where[3-5] and are not treated here.

The syntax of a source language, when written in Production Language (PL), will specify the operation of the recognizer as it scans a piece of text in that source language. When a character is scanned, it is brought into the stack of the recognizer. The symbol configuration at the top of this stack is compared with the PL specification of the language being translated. When the characters in the stack match one of the specified configurations, certain changes are made in the stack. If a match is not attained, the stack is compared with the next PL statement. This process is repeated until a match is found or until the stack is discovered to be in an error state.

The format of a statement (production) in PL is given below:

Label   L5 L4 L3 L2 L1 | → R3 R2 R1 | Action Next

In this scheme the first vertical bar from the left represents the top of the stack of the recognizer. The symbols L5 $\cdots$ L1 in a given production will be characters which could be encountered in translating the source language. The symbol in position L1 is at the top of the stack. Only the top N characters ($1 \leq N \leq 5$) need be present, the others being blanks which are always matched. In addition, any of L5 $\cdots$ L1 may be the symbol $\langle SG \rangle$ which represents any character and is always matched. The symbols L5 $\cdots$ L1 constitute the "specified configuration" mentioned above.

A match occurs when the characters actually in the stack during trans-lation are the same as L5 $\cdots$ L1 in the production being compared. If a match occurs, the remainder of the information in the matched production is used. The "→" specifies that the stack is to be changed. The symbols in positions R3 $\cdots$ R1 name the characters which must occupy the top of the stack after the change. If no "→" occurs, then the stack will not be changed and R3 $\cdots$ R1 should be blank.

As an example, consider the statement labeled T1 in Appendix B. This production is matched when the characters at the top of the stack are

$$T * P \quad \langle SG \rangle$$

The execution of the production T1 will leave the stack in the configuration

$$T \quad \langle SG \rangle$$

Such a production would be used in a language like ALGOL to recognize a multiplication.

The statement "EXEC 10" in the "action" field of the production T1 is a call for the semantic routine associated with multiplication. The semantic routines are written in the semantic meta language FSL, which is described in the next section. The other possible actions are "ERROR n" which prints an error message, "HALT" which ends compilation, and "SCAN" which causes a new character to be read into the top of the stack.

The "next" field of the production T1 contains the symbol "T2". This specifies that the next production to be compared with the stack is the one labeled "T2". If the label in the "next" field is preceded by an asterisk, a SCAN is executed before the transfer is made.

The productions in Appendix B were designed to be used with a preprocessor which replaced all ALGOL identifiers with the symbol I in the stack. The meaning of the other symbols in Appendix B is presented in Table 2.3.1.

Table 2.3.1. Table of mnemonics

Symbol	Meaning	Symbol	Meaning
BE	Boolean expression	SBE	simple Boolean expression
E	arithmetic expression	T	term
F	factor	UN	unconditional
I	identifier	⟨OP⟩	$+ - * / \uparrow$
ICL	if clause	⟨PM⟩	$+ -$
P	primary	⟨RL⟩	$= \neq < >$
S	statement	⟨TD⟩	$* /$
		⟨TP⟩	REAL BOOL LABL

The symbols in Table 2.3.1 containing angle brackets (the last five) represent class names and are used as a shorthand device. For example, the production on line D1 is equivalent to three productions using REAL, BOOL, and LABL, respectively.

Production Language constitutes an excellent tool for the writing of syntax processors. For a detailed discussion, including error-recovery techniques, see Ref. 2. Of interest here is the usage of PL as a syntactic vehicle for the semantic meta language.

2.3.4. SEMANTICS

The Formal Semantic Language (FSL) discussed in this section was originally developed as a theoretical system. The various constructs in FSL were chosen to formalize the operations needed to describe translators. They were selected with no thought of implementation and no particular computer in mind. After some time users began to attempt the description of some common programming languages and implementation of FSL was begun. The interaction of these three forces, preconceived formalism, hardware implementation, and human users, forged the system into its final form.

In its present form, FSL itself can be considered a problem-oriented computer language. The problem involved is the representation of meaning in computer languages. A complete description of the FSL programming system is given in Ref. 4. The discussion here will attempt to present the basic features and general nature of FSL. The presentation will include frequent references to Appendix C which contains a semantic description of the small language.

The basic unit in an FSL program is the labeled statement or sentence. As mentioned in Section 2.3.3, a production may include a statement of the form "EXEC n" in its "action" field. The semantic routine labeled "n" will be executed each time that production is matched. A semantic routine may generate code, change the state of the translator, or both.

The distinction between run time and compile time operations is a crucial one in FSL and is always represented explicitly. The means of doing this is the use of paired code brackets "CODE(" and ")". Any statement enclosed in code brackets specifies an action to be taken at run time, while any statement not so enclosed describes action occurring at translate time. An example may help clarify this point.

The normal operand in a translator is a machine address. Suppose two such operands are separated by a plus sign. If the expression so formed is not enclosed in code brackets the two *addresses* will be added. This operation could be used in a translator to compute another address for use in compiling code.

If the sum of the two operands occurred within code brackets an entirely different meaning would result. In this case the FSL system would generate code to perform an addition at run time. The addends at run time would be the run time *contents* of the addresses used as operands in the original expression. Many FSL constructs will have two different meanings, depending on whether or not they are within code brackets.

Since any FSL program is the description of a translator, we would expect to find constructs in FSL which formalize devices used in compiler writing. One of the principal tasks of a compiler is the recording and use of information about the state of the program being translated. This is usually done with various operations involving cells, tables, pushdown stacks, and tag bits.

In FSL one declares the storage needed for a particular translator at the beginning of the description of that translator. For the small language of Appendix C only a symbol table, SYMB, is required. As declared, it will hold four words of information for each of 200 symbols. These will be the internal name, address, data type, and level for each symbol.

Tables are constructed by means of the FSL operation ENTER, which forms its parameters into a row of the specified table. An example of the use of ENTER may be found in routine 4 of Appendix C. Semantic routine 4 is called by the production on line D1 of Appendix B whenever a real variable is declared in a small-language program. At that point the information on the declared variable is placed into the symbol table for further use.

The cells declared for the small-language translator are used as temporaries and counters. The two stacks STR and SYM are used in connection with the block structure. When a new block is entered (routine 2) the storage pointer and symbol table pointer are saved in STR and SYM, respectively. At the end of a block (routine 29) the pointers are restored, affecting the reallocation of storage and table space.

It is also possible to define alphanumeric constants, called TITLEs, for use in a translator. In Appendix C, the title words REAL, BOOL and LABE are used in the symbol table to specify the data types of declared variables.

The final type of translator storage, the DATA tag, does not occupy a full word and is used in rather special ways. The language designer using FSL can declare data types and tag each operand with the bits corresponding to its type. The FSL system itself can, at present, recognize and compile code for the data types LOGIC, INTEGER, SINGLE and DOUBLE. Thus, the addition of two variables tagged DOUBLE would automatically be compiled by the system as a double precision operation.

The translator writer could also choose to use other data types such as COMPLEX, ARRAY, or TREE. In a language which dealt with complex arithmetic, variables could be tagged COMPLEX and tests could be made on the type of variables occurring in an arithmetic statement. However, the actual semantics of each complex operation would have to be written in terms of the operations on SINGLE or DOUBLE variables which are part of the system.

In addition to the declared translator storage, there are a number of system cells which are part of the FSL system. Among the most important are the pointers CODELOC, STORLOC, and TEMPLOC. The pointer CODELOC contains the address where the next word of compiled code will be placed and is incremented by the system as code is generated. It is also available to the language designer and might be used in dealing with labels, conditionals, or subroutines.

STORLOC is the pointer to the next available storage location for the data of the source program. More is said about its use below. The cell TEMPLOC points to the next available temporary to be used by the system in compiling code. In Appendix C, TEMPLOC is reset to its initial value at the end of each assignment statement (routines 16, 20, 24). The cell T3 was assigned the initial value of TEMPLOC in routine 0 which is executed at the beginning of each source program.

As mentioned in Section 2.3.3, the semantics of each source language construct is kept in the main stack along with its syntactic type. The FSL operands LEFT1 ⋯ LEFT5 and RIGHT1 ⋯ RIGHT3 allow one to access the semantic words of the stack before and after a production has been matched. Consider the example of the production labeled B3 in Appendix B. This is matched when an "IF CLAUSE" of the small language has been scanned. The semantics of "IF CLAUSE" is the same as that of the Boolean expression currently in LEFT2. In the action field of B3 there is a call for semantic routine 21:

$$21 \downarrow \quad \text{RIGHT1} \leftarrow \text{LEFT2} \quad \downarrow$$

This routine causes the semantics of the construct, which was second from the top of the stack when the production was matched, to be assigned to the top element of the stack after the production has been executed.

There is also a set of compile time temporaries (COMT s) available to the language designer using FSL. The COMT s may appear with symbolic subscripts and are the only compile time cells with this feature.

We are now able to consider, in some detail, the processing of arithmetic statements in the small language. As we have seen, semantic routine 4 is called when a real variable is declared in a source program.

$$4 \downarrow \quad \text{TO} \leftarrow \text{STORLOC; SET[TO, DOUBLE]};$$
$$\text{ENTER [SYMB; LEFT2, TO, REAL, LEV]};$$
$$\text{STORLOC} \leftarrow \text{STORLOC} + 2 \downarrow$$

The current value of STORLOC is placed in a temporary and tagged with bits marking it a double-precision operand. Then a description of the variable is placed in the symbol table, SYMB. The entries for the variable arc its name, the tagged address, the word REAL, and the current level. Finally the storage pointer, STORLOC, is increased by two.

When an identifier is scanned in an arithmetic statement (P1 of Appendix B) semantic routine 9 is called.

$$9\downarrow \quad \text{CONST[LEFT]} \rightarrow \text{RIGHT1} \leftarrow \text{LEFT1}:$$
$$\text{SYMB[LEFT1, , \$,]} = \text{REAL} \rightarrow \text{RIGHT1} \leftarrow$$
$$\text{SYMB[LEFT1 , \$, ,]: FAULT 1 \$\$} \downarrow$$

Routine 9 is an example of a nested conditional statement in FSL. The FSL conditional statement is of the form

$$\langle \text{Boolean expression} \rangle \rightarrow \langle \text{statement} \rangle : \langle \text{statement} \rangle \ \$$$

so that ":" corresponds to the ALGOL separator ELSE.

In semantic routine 9, the predicate CONST is applied to the identifier (in LEFT1) to test if it is a constant. If so, the stack is adjusted and the routine terminates. If not, the identifier is a variable and must be looked up in the symbol table. The table lookup is accomplished in FSL through a special table operand of the form

$$\text{SYMB[LEFT1, , \$,].}$$

This operand initiates a search of the table SYMB for an entry in the first row which equals the contents of LEFT1. Then the position of the $ is used to select the desired entry of the matched row.

In routine 9 the third entry (data type) of the matched row is selected and compared with the title word REAL. If they are the same, the variable is declared to be real and all is well. In this case the second entry (tagged address) of the matched row in SYMB is assigned as the semantics of the real variable. If the variable is not of type REAL or is not in the table at all, the statement FAULT 1 will be executed. This causes the printing of an error message on the listing of the source language program being compiled.

A real variable used correctly in an arithmetic statement will carry in its semantic word much of the information needed to generate efficient code. Besides the address and data type computed in routine 9, the semantic word has several bits set by the system. Some of these state whether the operand is a constant, is fixed or floating, is in the accumulator, is of the wrong sign, or is to be indirectly accessed. It is not within the scope of this paper to discuss how all of this information is used by generators to produce machine code. The important point is that the translator designer using FSL need not deal directly with the complex problem of code generation. The system is currently able to generate quite respectable code from simple descriptions like those in routines 10–14 of Appendix C.

The one complication in these routines arises from the use of the operands VALUE1 ··· VALUE3. As described above, the system records information about the interim state of computations. The VALUE operands specify which stack position should hold this information. The special VALUE operands are used (rather than RIGHT1 ··· RIGHT3) to tell the system not to compile a store command despite the fact that "←" appears within code brackets.

One of the more complicated problems in compiler design is the proper translation of undefined forward references. For example, in the small-language conditional statement, a transfer of control to the end of a statement of unknown length must be compiled. There is an FSL construct called the floating address, or FLAD, which greatly simplifies the treatment of this case. When a FLAD is used as the operand of a transfer command, the system notes that an address will have to be added to that statement. In the proper place the designer will use an ASSIGN [FLAD*n*] statement. The system will then put the current value of CODELOC into the transfer command. Each FLAD is actually a pushdown stack so that nested statements may be handled easily.

The recognition of an IF CLAUSE as part of a conditional statement in the small language would lead to a call of routine 3:

3↓   PUSH[FLAD1, 0]; CODE (¬ LEFT1 → JUMP[FLAD1]) ↓

First FLAD1 is preserved, allowing for nested conditionals. If the value at run time of the Boolean expression is FALSE a transfer of control must be made. When the end of "TRUE" part of the conditional is found (routine 7) the transfer address is filled in by the statement ASSIGN[FLAD1].

If the small-language conditional statement had included an ELSE, the flow would have been through routines 6 and 27 and would require two FLADS. The ASSIGN command automatically does a POP of the FLAD after assigning it. Notice that routine 3 uses a FSL conditional statement inside code brackets. This has the same form as a conditional outside-code bracket and is natural to use. However, the system recognizes that the statement is inside-code brackets and compiles all the tests and transfers into the running program.

This is an indication of the design philosophy of FSL. Like any good problem-oriented computer language, FSL attempts to shelter the user from irrelevant machine details. Each particular construct incorporated in the language was chosen as the most economical way to provide the information needed for translator construction. Perhaps the best way to decide the merits of the result is to study the operation of the compiler described in Appendices B and C. There is not enough information above to allow one to follow the treatment of labels (routine 25, 26) which is more involved, but the remainder of the translator should be readable.

2.3.5. CONCLUSIONS

The programming system described above has been running since early in 1964 on the G-20 at Carnegie Tech. The implementation required only about six man-months to complete, largely because the production loader and code generators were adapted from existing programs. Since FSL is itself a programming language, we were able to write the production syntax of FSL and use it in the semantic loader. The semantics of FSL was written in assembly language. A more detailed discussion of the implementation, along with more documentation, may be found in Ref. 4.

The author has taught the FSL system to undergraduates for two terms. Although they had only an average of one year of programming experience, the better students were able to complete various translators as term projects. Equally encouraging was the ability of each student to describe his translator to the others in one or two class hours. Among the languages for which translators were completed are FORTRAN, ALGOL, LISP, and Markov Algorithms.

More recently a production compiler for an extremely complex language, Formula ALGOL,[10] has been written in FSL. The FSL system is currently being implemented on a number of different computers. There are major development efforts at Carnegie Tech and Lincoln Laboratory which should yield improved systems in the near future.

At this point it will (one hopes) occur to the reader that it would be extremely difficult to construct a LISP translator with the language described above. The difficulty is that we have described techniques for a pure compiler, while LISP requires many decisions to be made at run time. Such a language demands a highly interpretive translator using storage and decision-making features at run time.

There is in FSL the ability to declare tables, stacks, and temporaries which will exist for the translator's use at run time. The description of these operands and the associated operations were omitted from this paper for the sake of brevity. There are, however, no FSL primitives which deal directly with list structure, and this is a weakness of the system. It is also unfortunate that input-output is the same (similar to Ref. 9) for all languages defined in the FSL system.

A more serious weakness is the inability of the system to adequately treat assembly languages. The trouble arises because the FSL description must be machine independent while an efficient assembler is extremely machine dependent. The resolution of this difficulty involves a formalization of the properties of computers. This is one of the most interesting unsolved problems in computing and has significance in many areas of computer science.

There were also some intriguing formal questions raised in the development of FSL. We decided here to bypass these formal questions as well as those concerned with implementation. A somewhat more comprehensive treatment may be found in Ref. 4.

The formal systems described here are the result of a consideration of the basic properties of computer languages. The results already seem to be of considerable practical and pedagogical value. One would hope that they will also help provide some insight into the nature of computer-oriented languages.

REFERENCES

1. Brooker, R., and Morris, D., "An Assembly Program for a Phrase Structure Language," *Comput. J.*, vol. 3 (1960), p. 168.

2. Evans, A., "An ALGOL 60 Compiler," ACM Nat. Conf., Denver, Colo. (1962).

3. Evey, R., "The Theory and Applications of Pushdown Store Machines," Doctoral Thesis, Harvard U., May 1963.

4. Feldman, J. A., "A Formal Semantics for Computer Oriented Languages," Comput. Ctr., Carnegie Institute of Technology, 1964.

5. Floyd, R., "Bounded Context Syntactic Analysis," *Comm. ACM*, vol. 7 (February 1964), pp. 62–67.

6. ———. "A Descriptive Language for Symbol Manipulation," *J. ACM*, vol. 8 (October 1961), pp. 579–584.

7. Irons, E., "A Syntax Directed Compiler for ALGOL 60," *Comm. ACM*, vol. 4 (January 1961), pp. 51–55.

8. Markov, A. A., "Theory of Algorithms," OTS 60-51085.

9. Perlis, A. J., "A Format Language," *Comm. ACM*, vol. 7 (February 1964), pp. 89–97.

10. Perlis, A. J., Iturriaga, R., and Standish, T., "A Preliminary Sketch of Formula ALGOL," Comput. Ctr., Carnegie Institute of Technology, April 1965.

APPENDIX A. Syntax of a Small Language

⟨arithmetic expression⟩ ::= ⟨term⟩ | ± ⟨term⟩ | ⟨arithmetic expression⟩ ± ⟨term⟩

⟨term⟩ ::= ⟨factor⟩ | ⟨term⟩ */ ⟨factor⟩

⟨factor⟩ ::= ⟨primary⟩ | ⟨factor⟩ ↑ ⟨primary⟩

⟨primary⟩ ::= ⟨identifier⟩ | (⟨arithmetic expression⟩)

⟨simple Boolean⟩ ::= ⟨identifier⟩ | ⟨arithmetic expression⟩ ⟨relation⟩ ⟨arithmetic expression⟩

⟨Boolean⟩ ::= ⟨simple Boolean⟩ | ⟨if clause⟩ ⟨simple Boolean⟩ ELSE ⟨Boolean⟩

⟨if clause⟩ ::= IF ⟨Boolean⟩ THEN

⟨if statement⟩ ::= ⟨if clause⟩ ⟨unconditional⟩

⟨assignment⟩ ::= ⟨identifier⟩ ← ⟨arithmetic expression⟩ | ⟨identifier⟩ ← ⟨Boolean⟩

⟨go to statement⟩ ::= GO TO ⟨identifier⟩

⟨conditional⟩ ::= ⟨if statement⟩ | ⟨if statement⟩ ELSE ⟨statement⟩

⟨unconditional⟩ ::= ⟨assignment⟩ | ⟨go to statement⟩ | ⟨block⟩

⟨declaration⟩ ::= ⟨type⟩ ⟨type list⟩ | ⟨declaration⟩; ⟨type⟩ ⟨type list⟩

⟨type⟩ ::= REAL | BOOLEAN | LABEL

⟨type list⟩ ::= ⟨identifier⟩ | ⟨type list⟩, ⟨identifier⟩

⟨head⟩ ::= BEGIN | BEGIN ⟨declaration⟩ | ⟨head⟩; ⟨statement⟩
  ⟨block⟩ ::= ⟨head⟩ END

⟨statement⟩ ::= ⟨conditional⟩ | ⟨unconditional⟩ | ⟨empty⟩ | ⟨identifier⟩ : ⟨statement⟩

APPENDIX B. Production Syntax of the Small Language

```
S0                          BEGN                EXEC 1    *D1
                            <SG>                ERROR 0   Q1
D1                          <TP>                          *D2
                  BEGN END  →        S          *S1
                  BEGN ;    →        BEGN        *D1
            BEGN |→  <SG>  →HEAD ;   <SG>        S1
                  BEGN <SG>  →HEAD ;  <SG>        S1
D2          REAL I  <SG>                EXEC 4    D3
            BOOL I  <SG>                EXEC 5    D3
            LABL I  <SG>                EXEC 30   D3
D3          <TP> I   ,    →        <TP>  SCAN     *D2
    |→      <TP> I   ;    →        |→             *D1
            <TP> I   ;    →        |→             *D1
                     <SG>                ERROR 1   Q1
```

S1				BEGN				EXEC 2	*D1
				IF					*B1
				GO					*G1
				;	→	S	;		S9
				END					S9
				I					*S2
S2			I	:	→			EXEC 26	*S1
			I	←					*EX1
				⟨SG⟩				ERROR 2	Q1
I1			←	ICL					*B1
			IF	ICL					*B1
		SBE	ELSE	ICL					*B1
				ICL				EXEC 3	*S1
				⟨SG⟩				ERROR 4	Q1
UN1		ICL	UN	⟨SG⟩					C1
			UN	⟨SG⟩	→	S	⟨SG⟩		S9
				⟨SG⟩				ERROR 5	Q1
C1		ICL	UN	ELSE				EXEC 6	*S1
		ICL	UN	⟨SG⟩	→	S	⟨SG⟩	EXEC 7	S9
				⟨SG⟩				ERROR 6	Q1
P1				I	→	P		EXEC 9	*F1
				(					*P1
				+	→				*P1
				−					*P1
				⟨SG⟩				ERROR 7	Q1
F1	F	↑	P	⟨SG⟩	→	F	⟨SG⟩	EXEC 28	F2
			P	⟨SG⟩	→	F	⟨SG⟩		F2
F2			F	↑					*P1
T1	T	*	F	⟨SG⟩	→	T	⟨SG⟩	EXEC 10	T2
	T	/	F	⟨SG⟩	→	T	⟨SG⟩	EXEC 11	T2
			F	⟨SG⟩	→	T	⟨SG⟩		T2
T2			T	⟨TD⟩					*P1
E1	E	+	T	⟨SG⟩	→	E	⟨SG⟩	EXEC 12	E2
	E	−	T	⟨SG⟩	→	E	⟨SG⟩	EXEC 13	E2
		−	T	⟨SG⟩	→	E	⟨SG⟩	EXEC 14	E2
			T	⟨SG⟩	→	E	⟨SG⟩		E2
E2			E	⟨PM⟩					*P1
		(	E	)	→	P		EXEC 15	*F1
			E	⟨RL⟩					*P1
	I	←	E	⟨SG⟩	→	UN	⟨SG⟩	EXEC 16	UN1
	E	=	E	⟨SG⟩	→	SBE	⟨SG⟩	EXEC 17	B2
	E	<	E	⟨SG⟩	→	SBE	⟨SG⟩	EXEC 18	B2
	E	>	E	⟨SG⟩	→	SBE	⟨SG⟩	EXEC 19	B2
	E	⟨RL⟩	E	⟨SG⟩	→	SBE	⟨SG⟩	EXEC 17	B2
				⟨SG⟩				ERROR 8	Q1

Label					match	→	out1	out2	action	goto
B1					IF					*B1
					+	→				*P1
					−					*P1
					(					*P1
B4				I	⟨OP⟩	→	P	⟨OP⟩	EXEC 8	F1
				I	⟨RL⟩	→	E	⟨RL⟩	EXEC 8	*P1
				I	⟨SG⟩	→	SBE	⟨SG⟩	EXEC 20	B2
				I						*B4
B2				SBE	ELSE					*B1
				SBE	⟨SG⟩	→	BE	⟨SG⟩		B3
B3			IF	BE	THEN	→		ICL	EXEC 21	I1
	ICL	SBE	ELSE	BE	⟨SG⟩	→	BE	⟨SG⟩	EXEC 22	B3
		I	←	BE	⟨SG⟩	→	UN	⟨SG⟩	EXEC 23	UN1
EX1					I					*EX2
					IF					*B1
					+	→				*P1
					−					*P1
					(					*P1
EX2				I	⟨OP⟩	→	P	⟨OP⟩	EXEC 8	F1
				I	⟨RL⟩	→	E	⟨RL⟩	EXEC 8	*P1
		I	←	I	⟨SG⟩	→	UN	⟨SG⟩	EXEC 24	UN1
					⟨SG⟩				ERROR 8	Q1
G1				GO	I	→		UN	EXEC 25	*UN1
					⟨SG⟩				ERROR 9	Q1
S9	ICL	UN	ELSE	S	⟨SG⟩	→	S	⟨SG⟩	EXEC 27	S9
	ICL	UN	ELSE	UN	⟨SG⟩	→	S	⟨SG⟩	EXEC 27	S9
		HEAD	;	S	;	→	HEAD	;		*S1
		HEAD	;	S	END	→		UN	EXEC 29	ND1
ND1						→	UN	→			→	EXEC 31	Q1
					⟨SG⟩					*UN1
Q1					⟨SG⟩				HALT	Q1
*	END									

APPENDIX C. Formal Semantics of the Small Language

BEGIN TABLE SYMB[200,4]; CELL LEV, T0, T1, T2, T3, T4, T5; STACK STR, SYM;
TITLE REAL, BOOL, LABE; DATA LOGIC, INTEGER, SINGLE, DOUBLE;

0↓ T3 ← TEMPLOC ↓

1↓ LEV ← 0; STR ← STORLOC; SYM ← LOC[SYMB] ↓

2↓ LEV ≠ 0 → PUSH[STR, STORLOC]; PUSH[SYM, LOC[SYMB]]$; TALLY [LEV] ↓

3↓ PUSH[FLAD1, 0]; CODE(¬ LEFT1 → JUMP[FLAD1]$) ↓

4↓ T0 ← STORLOC; SET[T0, DOUBLE]; ENTER[SYMB; LEFT2, TO, REAL, LEV]; STORLOC ← STORLOC + 2 ↓

5↓   ENTER[SYMB; LEFT2, STORLOC, BOOL, LEV]; TALLY[STORLOC]↓

6↓   PUSH[FLAD2, 0]; CODE(JUMP[FLAD2]); ASSIGN[FLAD1]↓

7↓   ASSIGN[FLAD1]↓

8↓   CONST[LEFT2] → RIGHT2 ← LEFT2: SYMB[LEFT2, ,$,] = REAL →
       RIGHT2 ← SYMB[LEFT2,$, ,]: FAULT 1$$↓

9↓   CONST[LEFT1] → RIGHT1 ← LEFT1: SYMB[LEFT1, ,$,] = REAL →
       RIGHT1 ← SYMB[LEFT1,$, ,]: FAULT 1$$↓

10↓   CODE(VALUE2 ← LEFT4 * LEFT2)↓

11↓   CODE(VALUE2 ← LEFT4/LEFT2)↓

12↓   CODE(VALUE2 ← LEFT4 + LEFT2)↓

13↓   CODE(VALUE2 ← LEFT4 − LEFT2)↓

14↓   CODE(VALUE2 ←— LEFT2)↓

15↓   RIGHT1 ← LEFT2↓

16↓   SYMB[LEFT4, ,$,] = REAL → COMT2 ← SYMB[LEFT4,$, ,];
       CODE(COMT2 ← LEFT2); TEMPLOC ← T3: FAULT 3$↓

17↓   CODE(VALUE2 ← LEFT4 = LEFT2)↓

18↓   CODE(VALUE2 ← LEFT4 < LEFT2)↓

19↓   CODE(VALUE2 ← LEFT4 > LEFT2)↓

20↓   CONST[LEFT2] → RIGHT2 ← LEFT2: SYMB[LEFT2, ,$,] = BOOL →
       RIGHT2 ← SYMB[LEFT2,$, ,]; SET[RIGHT2, LOGIC]; TEMPLOC ←
       T3: FAULT 3$$↓

21↓   RIGHT1 ← LEFT2↓

22↓   CODE(LEFT5 → TEMPLOC ← LEFT4: TEMPLOC ← LEFT2$); RIGHT2
       ← TEMPLOC; SET[RIGHT2, LOGIC]; TALLY[TEMPLOC]↓

23↓   SYMB[LEFT4, ,$,] = BOOL → COMT2 ← SYMB[LEFT4,$, ,]; CODE
       (COMT2 ← LEFT2): FAULT 4$↓

24↓   COMT4 ← SYMB[LEFT4,$, ,]; CONST[LEFT2] → COMT2 ← LEFT2:
       SYMB[LEFT2, ,$,] = SYMB[LEFT4, ,$,] → COMT2 ← SYMB[LEFT2,
       $, ,]: FAULT5 $$; TEMPLOC ← T3; CODE(COMT4 ← COMT2)↓

25↓   SYMB[LEFT1, ,$,] ≠ LABE → FAULT6: COMT2 ← LOC[SYMB[LEFT1,
       $, ,]]; COMT3 ← ⟨COMT2⟩; SYMB[LEFT1, , ,$] ≠ 0 → CODE(JUMP
       [COMT3]): CODE(JUMP[CHAIN[COMT2]]) $$↓

26↓   SYMB[LEFT2, ,$,] ≠ LABE → FAULT6: SYMB[0, , ,$] ← 1; ASSIGN[LOC
       [SYMB[LEFT2,$, ,]]] $↓

27↓   ASSIGN[FLAD2]↓

28↓   CODE(VALUE2 ← LEFT4 ↑ LEFT2)↓

29↓   MINUS[LEV]; POP[STR, STORLOC]; POP[SYM, LOC[SYMB]]↓

30↓   ENTER[SYMB; LEFT2, 0, LABE, 0]↓

31↓   CODE(STOP)↓

3.

PARSING

3.0. OVERVIEW

In this chapter we deal with both formalities and pragmatics of the process of parsing computer languages. Parsing may be defined as the process of determining the syntax tree of a sentence of some language, given the grammar that describes that language. The notions of syntax, syntax tree, language, grammar, and similar language structures are formal concepts developed during the past ten years, and are defined and described in the articles by Gries, Floyd, and Korenjak.

Prior to 1959, linguistic theory was not well enough developed for compiler writers to utilize most formal results. Before this time, all compilers were of the "brute force" variety: They operated primarily a line at a time, first categorizing each new statement by type; then, by a rather complicated process, emitting code that represented the semantics or meaning of the source statement.

In 1959, Backus proposed a formal notation for representing the syntax of programming languages which was simple, straightforward, and relatively concise. His notation was expanded by Naur in 1960, and was utilized for the formal description of the ALGOL 60 programming language. This notation has come to be known as BNF, for Backus-Naur Form.

During this period, Chomsky and other linguists were investigating formal syntax; in 1963 these investigations culminated in the classification of four language types: Type 0, unrestricted rewriting systems; Type 1, context-sensitive systems; Type 2, context-free systems; and Type 3, finite-state systems. Most programming languages fall almost entirely within the Type 2 classification. Thus, the context-free (or phrase-structure) languages and their associated grammars have had the widest investigation. Most of the terminology describing parsing and formal syntax stems from this work, and an understanding of the basic concepts is valuable in reading the articles of this chapter.

In addition, a large number of theorems have closely linked the fields of automata theory and finite-state machine theory to the theory of languages, and a corresponding set of theorems have linked both fields to that of recursive function theory.

More recently, several important subsets of context-free languages (grammars) have been defined. Among these are operator precedence languages, precedence languages, bounded-context languages, and LR(k) languages.

Perhaps one of the most interesting topics within the subject of parsing is that of parsing strategies. There are two basic methods for parsing a sentence, "top-down" and "bottom-up." Bottom-up parsing concentrates on finding a series of productions that may be applied to reduce the sentence to simpler and simpler forms until finally the sentence symbol is all that remains. Top-down parsing, on the contrary, begins with the sentence symbol and attempts to find productions that eventually yield the source sentence. Both methods have their advantages and disadvantages in terms of speed, ease of recognition, problems relating to backup, recursion, and ambiguity. Each of the subsets mentioned above attempts to eliminate one or more of these problems; in particular, all attempt to parse more efficiently than, for instance, a general context-free parser.

Formal semantics is one of the least understood subjects in the area of compiler writing and relatively little has been published on the subject. Most semantics systems wind up being somewhat *ad hoc* and are usually based on a specific interpreter or compiler. One notable exception is the lambda-calculus system of Church (*Annals of Math. Studies*, no. 6(1951), Princeton Univ. Press). The interested reader is referred to his work and the later work of McCarthy and his associates on the development of the LISP programming language (Computation Lab. Report, MIT, 1962). An excellent summary of the work in this area may be found in Section IV-B of Feldman and Gries' paper, "Translator Writing Systems" (*Comm. ACM*, vol. II, no. 2 (February 1968)), which contains an excellent summary of the state-of-the-art of constructing compilers and a review of all major parsing techniques.

Transition matrices are introduced by Gries in Article 3.1. His techniques yield an efficient left-to-right parser, given a Backus-Naur Form grammar and a pushdown stack.

Article 3.2 by Floyd defines phrase-structure, operator, and precedence grammars, illustrates their use, and concludes with a formal presentation of the theory of these grammars.

The concluding article by Korenjak summarizes pragmatic portions of Knuth's paper "On the Translation of Languages from Left to Right" (Inform. Contr. 8, December 1965, p. 122) and extends his algorithms so that they are more efficient in both time and space. An example of an LR(1) parser for ALGOL is presented at the conclusion of the article.

The reader is especially urged to read Wirth and Weber's paper, "EULER— a generalization of ALGOL and its formal definition" (*Comm. ACM*, vol. 9, nos. 1 and 2 (Jan.-Feb. 1966)) for an expanded description of simple precedence grammars. The papers in Chapter 2 bear directly on parsing and the construction of recognizers as well.

3.1. Use of Transition Matrices in Compiling

by David Gries

3.1.1. SUMMARY

An algorithm is described which constructs from a suitable BNF grammar an efficient left-right recognizer for sentences of the corresponding language. The type of recognizer, used in a number of compilers, operates with a pushdown stack and with a transition matrix. Two examples illustrate how such recognizers may be used effectively for other purposes besides the usual syntax checking. Key words and phrases: transition matrices, compilation, translation, grammar, context-free language, formal language, parsing. CR categories: 4.12, 5.23.

3.1.2. INTRODUCTION

A central problem in writing a compiler for a nontrivial programming language is the syntactic analysis by mechanical means of formulas in the language. This has led to the design of algorithms capable of constructing efficient mechanical analyzers (or recognizers) for a significant and useful class of formal languages.[3,6,7,15] Our purpose is to present another such

EDITOR'S NOTE: This article reproduced by permission of author and the publisher: *Comm. ACM*, vol. 11, no. 1 (January 1968), pp. 26–34.

construction algorithm for constructing left-right recognizers which use a *transition matrix* and stack. This type of recognizer, first introduced by Samelson and Bauer,[13] is very fast but uses a fair amount of space. A transition matrix is just a switching table which lets one determine from the top symbol of the stack (denoting a row of the table) and the next symbol of the program to be processed (represented by a column of the table) whether a reduction should be made, or whether the incoming symbol should be pushed onto the stack. This technique is also closely related to Conway's separable transition diagrams.[2]

Our aim is not just to design another theoretical construction algorithm, but to produce a *practical* algorithm—one which can be used to help build compilers. It must be flexible, and fairly easy to insert the necessary semantic interpretations, once the recognizer has been constructed. We have tried to design is so that the constructed recognizer would be fairly similar to those produced intuitively for a number of compilers.[13,9] To this end, our first restriction is that the set of productions form an *operator grammar*.[6] This restriction also is a rather natural way to reduce the size of storage necessary to implement a recognizer. The syntax of the usual ALGOL-like languages can easily be represented by such a grammar. One may also describe suitable restrictions on the general phrase structure grammar which allow the use of a transition matrix; however, it was felt that this would not lead to practical recognizers.

The notation and terminology is introduced in Section 3.1.3. In Section 3.1.4 operator grammars and augmented operator grammars are presented and the relations between them are discussed. In Section 3.1.5 the sufficient conditions are given for an operator grammar to be unambiguous and the recognizer and its construction are discussed. The implementation of the recognizer is discussed in Section 3.1.6. In Section 3.1.7 a sentence is analyzed. Sections 3.1.8 and 3.1.9, while not essential parts of the transition matrix discussion, are added to illustrate the inclusion of semantics and to illustrate other uses of analyzers besides usual syntax checking.

3.1.3. NOTATION, TERMINOLOGY, BASIC DEFINITIONS

Let $\mathscr{V}$ be a given set: the *vocabulary*. Elements of $\mathscr{V}$ are called *symbols* and are denoted here by capital italic letters, S, T, U, etc. Finite sequences of symbols—including the empty sequence $(\wedge)$—are called *strings* and are denoted by small italic letters u, v, y, z, etc. The set of all strings over $\mathscr{V}$ is denoted by $\mathscr{V}^*$.

If $z = xy$ is a string, x is a *head* and y a *tail* of z.

A *production* or *syntactic* rule $\Phi: U \to x$ (sometimes written $U ::= x$) is an ordered pair consisting of a symbol U and a nonempty string x. U is called the *left part* and x the *right part* of Φ. We assume that $U \neq x$.

Let $\mathscr{G}$ be a finite set of productions $\Phi_1, \ldots, \Phi_n$. y *directly produces* z ($y \Rightarrow z$) by application of the production $U \to x$ and conversely z *directly reduces* into y, if and only if there exist strings u, v such that $y = uUv$, $z = uxv$, and the production $U \to x$ is an element of $\mathscr{G}$.

y *produces* z ($y \overset{*}{\Rightarrow} z$) and conversely z *reduces* into y if and only if there exist strings $x_0, \ldots, x_n$ such that $y = x_0$, $x_n = z$ and $x_{i-1} \Rightarrow x_i$ ($i = 1, \ldots, n; n \geq 1$). z is also said to be a *derivation* of y of length n.

Let $\mathscr{G}$ be a set of productions $\Phi_1, \ldots, \Phi_n$. If $\mathscr{V}$, the vocabulary, contains exactly one "distinguished" symbol Z which occurs in no right part of a production, and a nonempty set $\mathscr{B}$ of symbols which appears only in the right part of productions, then $\mathscr{G}$ is a *phrase structure grammar*. The symbols of $\mathscr{B}$ are called *terminal* or *basic symbols* and are denoted by capital letters T, T_1, T_2, etc. The letters U, V always denote symbols in $\mathscr{V} - \mathscr{B}$ and are called *nonterminal* symbols. (When discussing grammars for programming languages, we will, of course, allow words like **if** and **then** as terminal symbols. Nonterminals will always be enclosed in angle brackets "$\langle$" and "$\rangle$".)

$x \in \mathscr{V}^*$ is called a *sentential form* of $\mathscr{G}$ if either $Z = x$ or $Z \overset{*}{\Rightarrow} x$. The set of *sentences* x—i.e., the set of sentential forms consisting only of *terminal symbols*—constitutes the *phrase-structure language* $L_{\mathscr{G}}$; that is,

$$L_{\mathscr{G}} := \{x \mid Z \overset{*}{\Rightarrow} x \land x \in \mathscr{B}^*\} \tag{2.1}$$

Without restricting the set of phrase-structure languages we assume that

$$U \not\Rightarrow U, \qquad U \in \mathscr{V} - \mathscr{B}; \tag{2.2}$$

if $U_1 \overset{*}{\Rightarrow} U_k$, then the sequence

$$U_1 \to U_2, \; U_2 \to U_3, \; \ldots, \; U_n \to U_k \tag{2.3}$$

is unique; and

every symbol may be used in deriving some sentence: for each symbol $S \in \mathscr{V}$ there exists strings x, z, t such that $Z \overset{*}{\Rightarrow} xSz$ and either $S \in \mathscr{B}$ or $S \overset{*}{\Rightarrow} t$ where $t \in \mathscr{B}^*$. $\qquad$ (2.4)

$\langle\text{prog}\rangle \rightarrow \langle\text{state}\rangle$

$\langle\text{prog}\rangle \rightarrow \langle\text{if cl}\rangle\langle\text{state}\rangle$

$\langle\text{if cl}\rangle \rightarrow \textbf{if } \langle\text{expr}\rangle \textbf{ then}$

$\langle\text{state}\rangle \rightarrow \langle\text{if cl}\rangle\langle\text{state}\rangle \textbf{ else } \langle\text{state}\rangle$

$\langle\text{state}\rangle \rightarrow \textbf{var} := \langle\text{expr}\rangle$

$\langle\text{expr}\rangle \rightarrow \langle\text{expr}\rangle \textbf{ or var}$

$\langle\text{expr}\rangle \rightarrow \textbf{var}$

FIGURE 3.1.1 A grammar.

A *syntax tree* corresponding to a derivation $Z \overset{*}{\Rightarrow} S_1 \ldots S_n$ is a labeled tree where the root is labeled with the distinguished nonterminal Z and where every application of a production is indicated by *branching*; thus the application of the production $U \rightarrow S_j \ldots S_{j+k}$ is indicated by a *branch*: $k + 1$ lines emanating downward from the node labeled U to nodes labeled $S_j, S_{j+1}, \ldots, S_{j+k}$, in order. The *end nodes*—those nodes with no lines emanating downward from them—concatenated form the string $S_1 \ldots S_n$. For example, a syntax tree for the derivation

$$\langle\text{prog}\rangle \overset{*}{\Rightarrow} \textbf{if } \langle\text{expr}\rangle \textbf{ then var} := \langle\text{expr}\rangle \qquad (2.5)$$

in the grammar of Fig. 3.1.1 is given in Fig. 3.1.2.

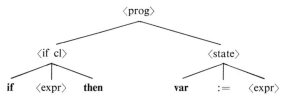

FIGURE 3.1.2

Although there is no other syntax tree for the sentential form above there are several derivations that result from the tree, since the order of replacing nonterminals currently appearing in the string is arbitrary. The syntax tree is more theoretically important in many respects than the derivation. Thus an *unambiguous* grammar is defined as one in which every sentence (and therefore every sentential form) has exactly one syntax tree.

It has been shown that there exists no algorithm which decides whether an arbitrary grammar is unambiguous. However, a sufficient condition for a grammar to be unambiguous is subsequently derived, and a method is explained which determines whether a given grammar satisfies this condition.

3.1.4. OPERATOR AND AUGMENTED OPERATOR GRAMMARS AND LANGUAGES

If no production Φ_i of the phrase-structure grammar $\mathscr{G}$ takes the form $U \rightarrow x V_1 V_2 y$ for some (possibly empty) strings x, y and nonterminal symbols V_1 and V_2, then $\mathscr{G}$ is called an *operator grammar* (OG).[6] The phrase-structure language $L_\mathscr{G}$ generated by an OG is then called an *operator language*.

Floyd[6] proved that in an operator grammar no sentential form contains two adjacent nonterminal symbols—i.e., if $z \xrightarrow{*} x$ then there exist no strings x_1 and x_2 and no nonterminals V_1 and V_2 such that $x = x_1 V_1 V_2 x_2$. The grammar in Fig. 3.1.1 is not an operator grammar, since $\langle$if cl$\rangle$ and $\langle$state$\rangle$ are both nonterminal. The grammar in Fig. 3.1.3, which is equivalent to (generates the same language as) the grammar in Fig. 3.1.1, *is* an operator grammar.

$\langle$prog$\rangle \rightarrow \langle$state$\rangle$

$\langle$prog$\rangle \rightarrow$ **if** $\langle$expr$\rangle$ **then** $\langle$state$\rangle$

$\langle$state$\rangle \rightarrow$ **if** $\langle$expr$\rangle$ **then** $\langle$state$\rangle$ **else** $\langle$state$\rangle$

$\langle$state$\rangle \rightarrow$ **var** $:= \langle$expr$\rangle$

$\langle$expr$\rangle \rightarrow \langle$expr$\rangle$ **or var**

$\langle$expr$\rangle \rightarrow$ **var**

Nonterminal symbols: $\langle$prog$\rangle$ $\langle$state$\rangle$ $\langle$expr$\rangle$

Terminal symbols: **if   then   else   var   :=   or**

FIGURE 3.1.3   An operator grammar.

Let us assume we have an operator grammar $\mathscr{G}$. We now reduce the maximum number of symbols in the right side of a production to three by altering the productions. This simplifies the recognizer and allows a direct correspondence to be set up between states of the transition matrix and certain nonterminals of the grammar. The change does not essentially alter the structure of the grammar, but consists of inserting intermediate productions. For instance, the string "**if** $\langle$expr$\rangle$ **then** $\langle$state$\rangle$" can be directly produced from the nonterminal "$\langle$state$\rangle$" of the OG in Fig. 3.1.3, as illustrated by the subtree in Fig. 3.1.4(a). However, we will change the production

$\langle$state$\rangle \rightarrow$ **if** $\langle$expr$\rangle$ **then** $\langle$state$\rangle$

to

$\langle$if*$\rangle \rightarrow$ **if**

$\langle$if-then*$\rangle \rightarrow \langle$if*$\rangle$ $\langle$expr$\rangle$ **then**

$\langle$state$\rangle \rightarrow \langle$if-then*$\rangle$ $\langle$state$\rangle$

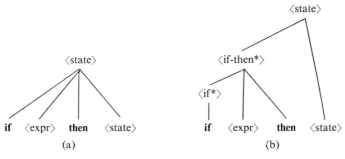

FIGURE 3.1.4   Subtrees.

yielding the syntax tree of Fig. 3.1.4(b). The newly introduced nonterminals are called *Starred Non Terminal Symbols* (SNTS) and are distinguished from the old nonterminals of the original OG, called *Unstarred Non Terminal Symbols* (UNTS), by the presence of an asterisk "*". The new grammar we call an *Augmented Operator Grammar* (AOG), $\mathscr{G}_A$ corresponding to the operator grammar $\mathscr{G}$.

To construct an AOG $\mathscr{G}_A$ from an OG $\mathscr{G}$, the following step 1 is repeated until no longer applicable, then step 2 until no longer applicable, and finally steps 3a and 3b alternately until no longer applicable.

Step 1. If there is a production $U_1 \to T_2 y_1$ (y_1 may be empty), and if k new symbols $U_1^*, \ldots, U_k^*$ have been created so far, create a new symbol U_{k+1}^*, replace each production $U_i \to T_2 y_i$ (each production whose right part begins with T_2) by the production $U_i \to U_{k+1}^* y_i$, and insert the production $U_{k+1}^* \to T_2$ into the grammar.

After step 1 all productions have one of the forms

$$U_1 \to U_2, \qquad U_1 \to U_2 T y, \qquad U_1 \to U^* y, \qquad U^* \to T,$$

where y contains no introduced symbol U^*.

Step 2. If there is a production $U_1 \to U_2 T_2 y_1$ (where U_1 and U_2 are original nonterminals of the OG), and if k new symbols have been created so far, create a new symbol U_{k+1}^*, replace each production $U_i \to U_2 T_2 y_i$ (each production whose right part begins with $U_2 T_2$) by $U_i \to U_{k+1}^* y_i$, and insert the production $U_{k+1}^* \to U_2 T_2$.

After step 2 all productions have one of the forms

$$U_1 \to U_2, \qquad U_1 \to U^* y, \qquad U^* \to UT, \qquad U^* \to T$$

where y contains no introduced symbol U^*.

Step 3a. If there is a production $U_1 \to U_2^* T_2 y_1$, and if k new symbols have been created so far, create a new symbol U_{k+1}^*, replace each production $U_i \to U_2^* T_2 y_i$ by $U_i \to U_{k+1}^* y_i$, and insert the new production $U_{k+1}^* \to U_2 T_2^*$.

Step 3*b*. If there is a production $U_1 \rightarrow U_2^* U_2 T_2 y_1$, and if k new symbols have been created so far, create a new symbol U_{k+1}^*, replace each production $U_i \rightarrow U_2^* U_2 T_2 y_i$ by $U_i \rightarrow U_{k+1}^* y_i$, and insert the new production $U_{k+1}^* \rightarrow U_2^* U_2 T_2$.

An AOG has only productions of one of the forms given in Fig. 3.1.5.

$$U_1 \rightarrow U_2, \quad U_1 \rightarrow U^*, \quad U_1 \rightarrow U^* U_2$$

$$U^* \rightarrow T, \quad U^* \rightarrow UT, \quad U_2^* \rightarrow U_1^* T, \quad U_2^* \rightarrow U_1^* UT$$

FIGURE 3.1.5   Production forms in an AOG

As an example, consider the OG in Fig. 3.1.3. Step 1 changes it to the grammar in Fig. 3.1.6A; step 2 to the grammar in Fig. 3.1.6B; and step 3 to the grammar in Fig. 3.1.6C.

It is obvious that one can easily reconstruct the original OG from the AOG if the new SNTS (Starred Non Terminal Symbols) are distinguished from the old UNTS. Note that an AOG is not necessarily an operator grammar.

We now give a series of lemmas which result in the fact that if the AOG is unambiguous, then the corresponding OG is also unambiguous. Sufficient

$\langle$prog$\rangle \rightarrow \langle$state$\rangle$

$\langle$if*$\rangle \quad \rightarrow$ **if**

$\langle$var*$\rangle \rightarrow$ **var**

$\langle$prog$\rangle \rightarrow \langle$if*$\rangle \langle$expr$\rangle$ **then** $\langle$state$\rangle$

$\langle$state$\rangle \rightarrow \langle$if*$\rangle \langle$expr$\rangle$ **then** $\langle$state$\rangle$ **else** $\langle$state$\rangle$

$\langle$state$\rangle \rightarrow \langle$var*$\rangle :=\langle$expr$\rangle$

$\langle$expr$\rangle \rightarrow \langle$expr$\rangle$ **or var**

$\langle$expr$\rangle \rightarrow \langle$var*$\rangle$

FIGURE 3.1.6A   AOG construction—step 1.

$\langle$prog$\rangle \quad \rightarrow \langle$state$\rangle$

$\langle$if*$\rangle \quad \rightarrow$ **if**

$\langle$var*$\rangle \quad \rightarrow$ **var**

$\langle$expr-or*$\rangle \rightarrow \langle$expr$\rangle$ **or**

$\langle$prog$\rangle \quad \rightarrow \langle$if*$\rangle \langle$expr$\rangle$ **then** $\langle$state$\rangle$

$\langle$state$\rangle \quad \rightarrow \langle$if*$\rangle \langle$expr$\rangle$ **then** $\langle$state$\rangle$ **else** $\langle$state$\rangle$

$\langle$state$\rangle \quad \rightarrow \langle$var*$\rangle :=\langle$expr$\rangle$

$\langle$expr$\rangle \quad \rightarrow \langle$expr-or*$\rangle$ **var**

$\langle$expr$\rangle \quad \rightarrow \langle$var*$\rangle$

FIGURE 3.1.6B   AOG construction—step 2.

⟨prog⟩	→ ⟨state⟩
⟨if*⟩	→ **if**
⟨var*⟩	→ **var**
⟨expr-or*⟩	→ ⟨expr⟩ **or**
⟨if-tehn*⟩	→ ⟨if*⟩⟨expr⟩ **then**
⟨if-else*⟩	→ ⟨if-then*⟩⟨state⟩ **else**
⟨var-:=*⟩	→ ⟨var*⟩ :=
⟨expr-var*⟩	→ ⟨expr-or*⟩ **var**
⟨prog⟩	→ ⟨if-then*⟩⟨state⟩
⟨state⟩	→ ⟨if-else*⟩⟨state⟩
⟨state⟩	→ ⟨var-:=*⟩⟨expr⟩
⟨expr⟩	→ ⟨expr-var*⟩
⟨expr⟩	→ ⟨var*⟩

FIGURE 3.1.6C   AOG construction—step 3.

conditions for the unambiguousness of the AOG then also suffice for the unambiguousness of the OG. The lemmas are quite obvious, once the construction algorithm is understood; we do not give detailed proofs.

LEMMA 1. *Each* SNTS *U^* of the* AOG *appears as the left part of only one production $U^* \to x$; the corresponding right part x appears as the right part of no other production (by construction).*

LEMMA 2. *If the* SNTS's *U^* are numbered in the order in which they were introduced, $U_1^*, U_2^*, \ldots, U_i^*$, and if a production $U_i^* \to U_j^* y$ exists in the* AOG, *then $i > j$ (by construction).*

LEMMA 3. *For each production $U \to y$ with $y \notin \mathscr{V} - \mathscr{B}$ of the* OG *there exists a unique set of productions $U_1^* \to y_1$, $U_2^* \to U_1^* y_2$, $\ldots$, $U_n^* \to U_{n-1}^* y_n$, $U \to U_n^* y_{n+1}$ of the* AOG *such that $y = y_1 y_2 \cdots y_{n+1}$.*

Lemma 3 follows directly from the construction and Lemma 1 and 2.

LEMMA 4. *For each different syntax tree of a sentential form s of the* OG *we can construct a different syntax tree of s relative to the* AOG *by substituting for each branch*

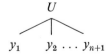

the unique branches corresponding to the productions described in Lemma 3, to wit:

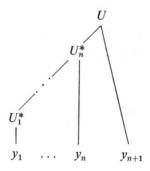

In other words, we arrive at a derivation of s relative to the AOG by substitution for each application of a production $U = y_1 \ldots y_{n+1}$ (where $y_1 \ldots y_{n+1} \neq U_1$, for some U_1) the applications $U = U_n^* y_{n+1}, \ldots, U_1^* = y_1$.

This results directly from Lemma 3. Since in an unambiguous grammar each sentence s has only one syntax tree, we have finally

LEMMA 5. *If an AOG is unambiguous, the corresponding OG must also be unambiguous.*

If $s = xyz$ is a sentential form, then y is a *phrase* of s provided there is a UNTS or SNTS V and a sentential form xVz such that $V \overset{*}{\Rightarrow} y$. A phrase is thus the concatenated end nodes of some subtree of the syntax tree for s. A *prime phrase* of s (in an AOG) is a phrase which contains at least one terminal character of SNTS, but no phrase other than itself (compare with Ref. 6, p. 318). Thus, if y is a prime phrase of $s = xyz$ there exists a sentential form xV_1z (where V_1 is a UNTS or SNTS) such that $V_1 \rightarrow y$; or $V_1 \rightarrow y_1$, $y_1 \overset{*}{\Rightarrow} y$, and all the direct productions in $y_1 \overset{*}{\Rightarrow} y$ are applications of productions $U_i \rightarrow U_j$ for UNTS U_i and U_j. For example, in the grammar of Fig. 3.1.6C the sentential form

$$\textbf{if } \langle \text{expr} \rangle \textbf{ then } \langle \text{var-}\!:=\!* \rangle \langle \text{expr} \rangle$$

has the two prime phrases **if** and $\langle \text{var-}\!:=\!* \rangle \langle \text{expr} \rangle$. Other phrases contain at least one of these two. From Fig. 3.1.5, any prime phrase of an AOG must have one of the forms:

$$U^* \qquad U^*T \qquad T \qquad U^*U \qquad UT \qquad U^*UT \qquad (3.1)$$

3.1.5. UNIQUE PARSING OF AN AOG

In this section sufficient conditions are given for an AOG to be unambiguous. The proof that the conditions suffice also illustrates the method of *parsing* or *recognizing* sentences of an AOG. The *recognizer* is of the *left-right bottom-up* variety;[5] it consists of *reducing a* sentence *to* the distinguished symbol Z as follows.

Let $s = s_0$ be the sentence to be analyzed. If s_0 contains a prime phrase, replace a *leftmost* prime phrase x by an appropriate SNTS or UNTS V_1 (see the definition of a prime phrase in Section 3.1.4) yielding the sentential form s_1. Iterate the procedure; at each step replace a leftmost prime phrase of s_i by some SNTS or UNTS V_{i+1} to obtain s_{i+1}. Since each step diminishes either the number of terminals or the number of SNTS's in s_i, the process must in a finite number of steps result in $s_m = U_m$ where $Z = U_m$ or $Z \overset{*}{\Rightarrow} U_m$. The sequence $U_m = s_m \overset{*}{\Rightarrow} s_{m+1} \overset{*}{\Rightarrow} \cdots \overset{*}{\Rightarrow} s_0$ is a skeleton representation of the derivation; only a finite number of steps corresponding to applications of productions of the form $U_i \rightarrow U_j$ must be introduced, but this determination is essentially trivial because of the restriction in an OG (and thus in an AOG) that derivations of the form $U_i \rightarrow U_j$ be unique. An example of a parse is given in Section 3.1.7.

Since the *ordering* of applications of productions in a derivation has no bearing on the syntax tree corresponding to the derivation, we have an unambiguous grammar if we can show that at each step of a parse the following two statements are true:

1. There exists a *unique leftmost* prime phrase in s_i (no overlapping of prime phrases); and
2. The UNTS or SNTS V which replaces this leftmost prime phrase is also unique.

For if these statements are true we have constructed the only possible derivation, aside from reorderings of the applications of productions. In order to give the sufficient conditions we need the following set $\mathscr{L}(S)$:

$$\mathscr{L}(S) = \{S_1 \mid xS_1Sy \text{ is a sentential form for some } x, y\}.$$

is a sentential form for some x, y. $\mathscr{L}(S)$ is just the set of symbols which are adjacent and to the left of S in some sentential form. The construction of $\mathscr{L}$ or related sets has been discussed elsewhere (see for instance Wirth and Weber[15]). We therefore do not wish to discuss it at length and just state that

$$S_1 \in \mathscr{L}(S) \qquad \text{if and only if} \qquad \{S_1 \doteq S \lor S_1 \lessdot S \lor S_1 \gtrdot S\},$$

where $\doteq$, $\lessdot$ and $\gtrdot$ are the *precedence relations* defined by Wirth and Weber.[15]

We now list sufficient conditions for an AOG to be unambiguous.

Condition 1.   For each pair U_i^*, T_j where U_i^* is an SNTS and T_j a terminal, at most one of the following three statements is true:

$$\exists \text{ a production } U \to U_i^* \text{ such that } U \in \mathscr{L}(T_j) \qquad (4.1)$$

$$\exists \text{ a production } U^* \to U_i^* T_j \qquad (4.2)$$

$$\exists \text{ a production } U^* \to T_j \text{ such that } U_i^* \in \mathscr{L}(U^*) \qquad (4.3)$$

Furthermore, if (4.1) holds, there is only one such UNTS U (the SNTS U^* in (4.2) or (4.3) is already unique, by construction of the AOG).

Condition 2.   For each triple U_i^*, U_1, T_j where U_i^* is an SNTS, U_1 a UNTS, and T_j a terminal, at most one of the following statements is true:

$$\exists \text{ a production } U \to U_i^* U_2 \text{ where } U \in \mathscr{L}(T_j), \text{ and either}$$
$$U_2 = U_1 \text{ or } U_2 \overset{*}{\Rightarrow} U_1; \qquad (4.4)$$

$$\exists \text{ a production } U^* \to U_i^* U_2 T_j \text{ where } U_2 = U_1 \text{ or } U_2 \overset{*}{\Rightarrow} U; \qquad (4.5)$$

$$\exists \text{ a production } U^* \to U_2 T_j \text{ where } U_i^* \in \mathscr{L}(U^*), \text{ and either}$$
$$U_2 = U_1 \text{ or } U_2 \overset{*}{\Rightarrow} U_1. \qquad (4.6)$$

Furthermore, if (4.4) holds, both U and U_2 are unique, while if (4.5) or (4.6) holds, U_2 is unique.

Remembering the possible forms of prime phrases in an AOG, it is clear that if U_i^*, $U_i^* T_j$, or T_j is a prime phrase of a sentential form in the context $U_i^* T_j$, then (4.1), (4.2), resp. (4.3) must be true. Similarly for $U_i^* U_1$, $U_i^* U_1 T_j$, or $U_1^* T_j$ to be a prime phrase in the context $U_i^* U_1 T_j$, (4.4), (4.5), resp. (4.6) must be true. We can now prove the main

THEOREM.   *If Conditions* 1 *and* 2 *hold in an* AOG, *the* AOG *is unambiguous.*

The theorem is proved if we show that the following proposition P is true for each sentential form s_i of a parse. $P(x)$ is defined for a string x by:

(a) x has either the form (4.7) or (4.8);
(b) a leftmost prime phrase of x does not contain U_i, $i < l$ (see (4.7), (4.8));

(c) a *leftmost* prime phrase does not contain T_i, $i > 1$;

(d) the leftmost prime phrase is unique;

(e) the SNTS or UNTS which replaces the leftmost prime phrase is unique.

$$U_1^* U_2^* \ldots U_{l-1}^* U_l^* T_1 \ldots T_m \tag{4.7}$$

$$U_1^* U_2^* \ldots U_{l-1}^* U_l^* U_1^* T_1 \ldots T_m \tag{4.8}$$

For any sentential form x of the form (4.7) or (4.8), (c) is obvious, since some prime phrase must contain T_1 (see (3.1) for the possible forms of prime phrases in an AOG). Also, if (a), (b), (c) are true for a string x, then the leftmost prime phrase is either

(1) U_l^*, $U_l^* T_1$, or T_1, in case (4.7); or

(2) $U_l^* U_1$, $U_l^* U_1 T_1$ or $U_1 T_1$, in case (4.8).[†]

Conditions 1 and 2 imply that both the leftmost prime phrase and the symbol to which it should be reduced are unique. Thus (a), (b) imply (c), (d), and (e).

For the sentence $s = s_0 = T_1 \ldots T_m$ to be parsed, (a) and (b) are obvious (s_0 has the form (4.7) where $l = 0$). Thus $P(s_0)$ is true. Suppose $P(s_i)$ is true for $i = 0, 1, \ldots, k$. We show that $P(s_{k+1})$ is also true, by listing the possible forms of s_{k+1}, derived by replacing the leftmost prime phrase of s_k as described in (4.1) to (4.6).

s_k	$\Leftarrow$	s_{k+1}	
$U_1^* U_2^* \ldots U_{l-1}^* U_l^* T_1 \ldots T_m \Leftarrow U_1^* U_2^* \ldots U_{l-1}^* U T_1 \ldots T_m$			(4.9)
$U_1^* U_2^* \ldots U_{l-1}^* U_l^* T_1 \ldots T_m \Leftarrow U_1^* U_2^* \ldots U_{l-1}^* U^* T_2 \ldots T_m$			(4.10)
$U_1^* U_2^* \ldots U_{l-1}^* U_l^* T_1 \ldots T_m \Leftarrow U_1^* U_2^* \ldots U_{l-1}^* U_l^* U^* T_2 \ldots T_m$			(4.11)
$U_1^* U_2^* \ldots U_{l-1}^* U_l^* U_1 T_1 \ldots T_m \Leftarrow U_1^* U_2^* \ldots U_{l-1}^* U T_1 \ldots T_m$			(4.12)
$U_1^* U_2^* \ldots U_{l-1}^* U_l^* U_1 T_1 \ldots T_m \Leftarrow U_1^* U_2^* \ldots U_{l-1}^* U^* T_2 \ldots T_m$			(4.13)
$U_1^* U_2^* \ldots U_{l-1}^* U_l^* U_1 T_1 \ldots T_m \Leftarrow U_1^* U_2^* \ldots U_{l-1}^* U_l^* U^* T_2 \ldots T_m$			(4.14)

In each case, by renumbering the subscripts we arrive at either form (4.7) or (4.8) for s_{k+1}; thus (a) is true for s_{k+1}. (b) is obvious in all cases except

---

[†] Note that a reduction $U \to U_l$ or $U^* \to T_1$ at this time would result in a string which is not a sentential form, since the grammar is an AOG (two original nonterminals of the OG would eventually appear adjacent).

(4.11) and (4.14), since by hypothesis $U_1^*, \ldots, U_{l-1}^*$ are not prime phrases. In these two cases, if U_l were a prime phrase, it would have also been a prime phrase in s_k, in violation of condition 1 or 2. Thus (b) is also true for s_{k+1} and the theorem is proved.

The algorithm which constructs a recognizer from a suitable operator grammar is then straightforward. First check that, if $U_1 \overset{*}{\Rightarrow} U_j$, the sequence of productions $U_1 \rightarrow U_2 \rightarrow U_3 \rightarrow U_j$ is unique. Next construct the AOG. Then determine $\mathscr{L}(S)$ for all terminal symbol and SNTS S. Now for each U_i^* and T_j search the productions to see whether (4.1), (4.2), or (4.3) hold, and if so, record the production number (or just the left part) together with the reducible phrase. If for some U_i^* and T_j two different reductions are found to be possible, then some sentence may not be parsed unambiguously using this recognizer. Note that this does not mean that the grammar is ambiguous; it just has not satisfied our sufficiency conditions. Triples U_i^*, U_1, and T_j are handled similarly.

At each step of a parse only the symbols U_i^*, T_j, and perhaps U_1 are needed to determine the leftmost prime phrase and the symbol to which it should be reduced. U_1 is always included in the leftmost prime phrase if it appears, while U_i^* or T_1 may or may not be. The class of grammars whose sentences can be parsed by such a recognizer is therefore a subset of the class of [1, 1] bounded context grammars;[7] at most, one symbol to the left and one to the right of the possible leftmost prime phrase is necessary to determine it and the symbol to which it should be reduced.

3.1.6. TRANSITION MATRIX AND STACK

We discuss here the implementation of the recognizer described in Section 3.1.5 and, in connection with this, how the constructor should record the reductions to be made. We will use the usual pushdown stack $ST_1, ST_2, \ldots, ST_l$ to store the symbols $U_1^*, U_2^*, \ldots, U_l^*$ respectively (see (4.7) and (4.8)), while the location $U1$ will be **empty** or will contain the nonterminal U_1. Thus the stack and $U1$ always contain that part of the sentence which has undergone transformation (see (4.7) and (4.8)).

The leftmost prime phrase—and the symbol to which it is to be reduced— is therefore completely determined by ST_l (containing U_i^*), $U1$ (empty or containing U_1), and the "incoming symbol" T_1. Thus it is not necessary to search into the stack for the prime phrase (see, for instance, Ref. 15); this is one of the reasons for the construction of the AOG.

Now for each valid pair U_i^*, T_j and for each valid triple U_i^*, U_1, T_j, the constructor builds several statements, in some appropriate language, to make the reduction. There are only six possible forms for these reductions, as illustrated by the reductions of s_k to s_{k+1} in (4.9) through (4.14). For instance, in (4.9) the leftmost prime phrase is U_i^* and it is to be reduced by U. The constructor could produce the following ALGOL-like statements:

> **comment** delete top stack element; $l := l - 1$;
>
> **comment** store U into $U1$; $U1 := $ "U";

The statements for the reduction in (4.11) would be

> **comment** add new stack element; $l := l + 1$;
>
> **comment** store U^* in it; $ST_l := $ "U^*"; $U1 := $ **empty**;
>
> **comment** get new terminal symbol from source program; *scan*;

As can be seen, the statements are simple and would be easy to produce automatically. We must now devise a way to pick out the correct set of statements to execute the reduction, depending on ST_l, $U1$, and T_1. For this we build a *transition matrix* M of subroutine numbers. To each possible SNTS U^* we assign a row of the matrix; to each possible terminal T we assign a column. The element $M_{U^*,T}$ of the matrix will be the number of a subroutine S_{U^*T} to execute. At S_{U^*T} the contents of $U1$ can be examined—perhaps by a series of **if** statements—to determine the statements to execute the appropriate reduction. Both M and the subroutines S_{U^*T} can, of course, be constructed automatically.

The recognizer then consists of repeatedly executing the subroutine determined by ST_l and T_1, the incoming terminal symbol. As an example,

1   $\langle$progr$\rangle ::=$ **phi** $\langle$prog$\rangle$ **phi**

2   $\langle$prog$\rangle ::= \langle$state$\rangle$

3   $\langle$prog$\rangle ::=$ **if** $\langle$expr$\rangle$ **then** $\langle$state$\rangle$

4   $\langle$state$\rangle ::=$ **if** $\langle$expr$\rangle$ **then** $\langle$state$\rangle$ **else** $\langle$state$\rangle$

5   $\langle$state$\rangle ::=$ **var** $:= \langle$expr$\rangle$

6   $\langle$expr$\rangle ::= \langle$expr$\rangle$ **or var**

7   $\langle$expr$\rangle ::=$ **var**

Nonterminal symbols: $\langle$progr$\rangle$ $\langle$prog$\rangle$ $\langle$state$\rangle$ $\langle$expr$\rangle$

Terminal symbols: **phi if then else var** $:=$ **or**

FIGURE 3.1.7 The grammar.

consider the grammar of Fig. 3.1.7, which is the same as that in Fig. 3.1.3 except for the addition of the production

$$\langle progr \rangle \rightarrow \textbf{phi} \ \langle prog \rangle \ \textbf{phi}$$

The terminal phi has been added to delimit the sentence. The matrix is given in Fig. 3.1.8; the subroutines, in Fig. 3.1.9. The names of the SNTs U^* as produced by the constructor are just the names of the symbols which they replaced when the AOG was constructed, separated by hyphens and followed by an "*".

		phi	if	then	else	var	:=	or
1	$\langle phi^* \rangle$	2	1	0	0	1	0	0
2	$\langle if^* \rangle$	0	0	3	0	1	0	4
3	$\langle if\text{-}expr\text{-}then^* \rangle$	5	1	0	6	1	0	0
4	$\langle if\text{-}expr\text{-}then\text{-}state\text{-}else^* \rangle$	7	1	0	7	1	0	0
5	$\langle var^* \rangle$	9	0	9	9	0	8	9
6	$\langle var\text{-}:=^* \rangle$	10	0	0	10	1	0	4
7	$\langle expr\text{-}or^* \rangle$	0	0	0	0	11	0	0
8	$\langle expr\text{-}or\text{-}var^* \rangle$	9	0	9	9	0	0	9

FIGURE 3.1.8   The matrix.

0   *error*

1   **if** $U1 \neq \textbf{empty}$ **then** *error*; $L \leftarrow L + 1$; $ST(L) \leftarrow T1$ **concatenated with** "*"; *scan*;

2   **if** $U1 = \langle prog \rangle$ **or** $U1 = \langle state \rangle$ **then** *success exit* **else** *error*

3   **if** $U1 \neq \langle expr \rangle$ **then** *error*; $ST(L) \leftarrow \langle if\text{-}expr\text{-}then^* \rangle$; $U1 \leftarrow \textbf{empty}$; *scan*

4   **if** $U1 \neq \langle expr \rangle$ **then** *error*; $L \leftarrow L + 1$; $ST(L) \leftarrow \langle expr\text{-}or^* \rangle$; $U1 \leftarrow \textbf{empty}$; *scan*

5   **if** $U1 \neq \langle state \rangle$ **then** *error*; $L \leftarrow L - 1$; $U1 \leftarrow \langle prog \rangle$

6   **if** $U1 \neq \langle state \rangle$ **then** *error*;
    $ST(L) \leftarrow \langle if\text{-}expr\text{-}then\text{-}state\text{-}else^* \rangle$; $U1 \leftarrow \textbf{empty}$; *scan*

7   **if** $U1 \neq \langle state \rangle$ **then** *error*; $L \leftarrow L - 1$; $U1 \leftarrow \langle state \rangle$

8   **if** $U1 \neq \textbf{empty}$ **then** *error*; $ST(L) \leftarrow \langle var\text{-}:=^* \rangle$; *scan*

9   **if** $U1 \neq \textbf{empty}$ **then** *error*; $L \leftarrow L - 1$; $U1 \leftarrow \langle expr \rangle$

10 **if** $U1 \neq \langle expr \rangle$ **then** *error*; $L \leftarrow L - 1$; $U1 \leftarrow \langle state \rangle$

11 **if** $U1 \neq \textbf{empty}$ **then** *error*; $ST(L) \leftarrow \langle expr\text{-}or\text{-}var^* \rangle$; *scan*

FIGURE 3.1.9   Matrix subroutines.

3.1.7. EXAMPLE OF A PARSE

To parse the sentence

phi if var then var := var phi

of the OG in Fig. 3.1.7, we start with the configuration as shown in step 1 in Table 3.1.1. The row of the matrix labeled ⟨phi*⟩ (Fig. 3.1.8) and the column labeled **if** determine subroutine 1 of Fig. 3.1.9. The first statement checks to make sure $U1$ is **empty**. The stack pointer L is then increased and

Table 3.1.1

Step	L	Stack	$U1$	$T1$	Rest of String	Subroutine
1	1	⟨phi*⟩	empty	if	var then var := var phi	1
2	2	⟨if*⟩ ⟨phi*⟩	empty	var	then var := var phi	1
3	3	⟨var*⟩ ⟨if*⟩ ⟨phi*⟩	empty	then	var := var phi	9
4	2	⟨if*⟩ ⟨phi*⟩	⟨expr⟩	then	var := var phi	3
5	2	⟨if-expr-then*⟩ ⟨phi*⟩	empty	var	:= var phi	1
6	3	⟨var*⟩ ⟨if-expr-then*⟩ ⟨phi*⟩	empty	:=	var phi	8
7	3	⟨var-:=*⟩ ⟨if-expr-then*⟩ ⟨phi*⟩	empty	var	phi	1
8	4	⟨var*⟩ ⟨var-:=*⟩ ⟨if-expr-then*⟩ ⟨phi*⟩	empty	phi		9
9	3	⟨var-:=*⟩ ⟨if-expr-then*⟩ ⟨phi*⟩	⟨expr⟩	phi		10
10	2	⟨if-expr-then*⟩ ⟨phi*⟩	⟨state⟩	phi		5
11	1	⟨phi*⟩	⟨prog⟩	phi		2(stop)

the SNTS $\langle$if*$\rangle$ (since $T1 =$ "if") is put in ST_2. "var" is then scanned, yielding step 2. The row labeled $\langle$if*$\rangle$ and column labeled **var** now determine subroutine 1. Here we check $U1$ for **empty**, increase the stack pointer, put $\langle$var*$\rangle$ on the stack, and scan the next symbol, yielding step 3. Continuing in this manner gives the configurations shown at the beginning of each of the following steps.

3.1.8. REPRESENTATION OF NONTERMINALS IN THE STACK

Strictly speaking, one should insert the nonterminal symbol U itself into $U1$. This is, however, neither practical nor necessary. In practice, nonterminals fall into classes whose elements are the same semantically. For instance, in ALGOL the nonterminals $\langle$primary$\rangle$, $\langle$factor$\rangle$, $\langle$term$\rangle$, $\langle$simple arith expr$\rangle$ are introduced only to help define the precedence of operations. In a compiler, they would all be represented by an address specifying a location which gives the type, location of the value during execution time (accumulator, register, storage location), etc. The determination of which U is actually in $U1$ turns out to be almost always a *semantic evaluation*, which would have to be done anyway. There is therefore very rarely any list searching to determine which U is $U1$, but just a semantic evaluation of $U1$. Accordingly, a reduction $U \rightarrow x$ is accomplished by inserting into $U1$ a description of the object designated by U and not U itself. Notice that we assume in the discussion of the method that productions $U_i \rightarrow U_j$ have no "interpretation rule" associated with them, which is usually the case.

One should also have a second stack $ST2_1, \ldots, ST2_l$ which runs parallel to the first stack and which can be used systematically to store semantic information. If we formally parse the ALGOL statement

$$\textbf{begin } A := (B + E) + C * D \textbf{ end}$$

there will be in the stack at some time the elements:

ST_i	$U1$
$\langle$term$-$**$\rangle$	$\langle$identifier$\rangle$
$\langle$expr$-+$*$\rangle$	
$\langle$var$-:=$*$\rangle$	
$\langle$begin*$\rangle$	
$\langle$phi*$\rangle$	

However, we can use the second stack to contain semantic information; $U1$ is therefore no longer necessary.

ST_i	$ST2_{i-}$
$\langle$term$-$**$\rangle$	(semantics of D)
$\langle$expr$-+$*$\rangle$	(semantics of C)
$\langle$var$-:=$*$\rangle$	(semantics of $B + E$)
$\langle$begin*$\rangle$	(semantics of A)
$\langle$phi*$\rangle$	(any necessary information)

This conforms very well to the way in which semantics were implemented in Ref. 9.

3.1.9. OTHER USES OF TRANSITION MATRICES

Two other uses will be introduced here, both concerned with optimizing the calculation of addresses of subscripted variables within for-loops.[10,9,13] Our goal is just to illustrate how transition matrices in particular and recognizers in general may be used to perform varied tasks. The only prerequisite is to be able to describe the task to be done as a grammar.

Provided that a **for** loop meets certain conditions, calculation of the address of a subscripted variable $A[E_1, \ldots, E_n]$ occurring in the statement of the **for** loop may be optimized if the E_i satisfy certain restrictions, some of which we list here:

1. E_i is *linear* in the loop variable of the **for** loop, $i = 1, \ldots, n$. That is, E_i may be put in the form "$C_1 * I + C_2$", where C_1 and C_2 are expressions not containing the loop variable I.
2. E_i contains only simple integer variables, integer constants, parentheses (and), and the operators $+$, $-$, and $*$.
3. The variables appearing in the E_i do not change within the **for** loop statement.

Restrictions 1 and 2 may be checked systematically using the (operator) grammar in Fig. 3.1.10. If $A[E_1, \ldots, E_n]$ is the subscripted variable and $\rangle$const el$\rangle \overset{*}{\Rightarrow} [E_1, \ldots, E_n]$, then $A[E_1, \ldots, E_n]$ satisfies restrictions 1 and 2 and moreover no E_i contains the loop variable. If $\langle$lin el$\rangle \overset{*}{\Rightarrow} [E_1, \ldots, E_n]$, then similarly $A[E_1, \ldots, E_n]$ satisfies restrictions 1 and 2 but at least one E_i contains the loop variable.

1	⟨const elem⟩ ∷= [	⟨const subs⟩	]
2	⟨lin elem⟩ ∷= [	⟨lin subs⟩	]
3	⟨const subs⟩ ∷= ⟨const expr⟩		
4	∷= ⟨const subs⟩ ,		⟨const expr⟩
5	⟨lin subs⟩ ∷= ⟨lin expr⟩		
6	∷= ⟨lin subs⟩ ,		⟨lin expr⟩
7	∷= ⟨lin subs⟩ ,		⟨const expr⟩
8	∷= ⟨const subs⟩ ,		⟨lin expr⟩
9	⟨const expr⟩ ∷= ⟨const expr⟩ ⟨+ or −⟩		⟨const term⟩
10	∷= ⟨+ or −⟩ ⟨const term⟩		
11	∷= ⟨const term⟩		
12	⟨const term⟩ ∷= ⟨const term⟩ *		⟨const fact⟩
13	∷= ⟨const fact⟩		
14	⟨const fact⟩ ∷= (⟨const expr⟩		)
15	∷= **integer**		
16	∷= **integer var**		
17	⟨lin expr⟩ ∷= ⟨lin expr⟩ ⟨+ or −⟩		⟨lin term⟩
18	∷= ⟨const expr⟩ ⟨+ or −⟩		⟨lin term⟩
19	∷= ⟨lin expr⟩ ⟨+ or −⟩		⟨const term⟩
20	∷= ⟨+ or −⟩ ⟨lin term⟩		
21	∷= ⟨lin term⟩		
22	⟨lin term⟩ ∷= ⟨const term⟩ *		⟨lin fact⟩
23	∷= ⟨lin term⟩ *		⟨const fact⟩
24	∷= ⟨lin fact⟩		
25	⟨lin fact⟩ ∷= (⟨lin expr⟩		)
26	∷= **loop var**		

Nonterminal symbols:

⟨const elem⟩   ⟨lin elem⟩   ⟨const subs⟩   ⟨lin subs⟩

⟨const expr⟩   ⟨const term⟩   ⟨const fact⟩   ⟨lin expr⟩

⟨lin term⟩   ⟨lin fact⟩

Terminal symbols:

[ ] , ⟨+ or −⟩ * ( ) **integer** **integer var** **loop var**

FIGURE 3.1.10 Linear subscript check grammar.

The grammar in Fig. 3.1.10 yields a 9×10 transition matrix with subroutines.[8]

As a second example we look at the **for** loop itself. We want it to have the form

$$\text{for } I \leftarrow E_1 \text{ step } E_2 \text{ until } E_3 \text{ do } S;$$

where the variables in E_2 do not change within the statement S, E_2 does not contain the loop variable I, and the E_i are integer expressions. The further restriction is again made, that the E_i consist only of integer simple variables, integer constants, (,), $+$, $-$, and $*$. Note that E_1 and E_3 may contain the loop variable I, but E_2 may not. The variables in E_2 should be listed for further checking.

The grammar of Fig. 3.1.11 is then constructed. The terminal **int cons, var** represents the class of integer constants and simple integer variables (except the loop variable of this loop). Note also the terminal symbol $\langle +, -, * \rangle$, meaning $+$, $-$, or $*$. Since we are not interested in the precedence of the operators $+$, $-$, $*$, we have simplified the productions for arithmetic expressions. Thus $*$ is used as a unary operator. Since we assume that the

1	⟨for loop⟩	::= **for**	**loop var**	←		⟨exp2⟩
		step	⟨exp1⟩	**until**		⟨exp2⟩
		do				
2	⟨exp1⟩	::= ⟨exp1⟩	⟨+, −, *⟩	⟨exp1 fact⟩		
3		::= ⟨+, −, *⟩	⟨exp1 fact⟩			
4		::= ⟨exp1 fact⟩				
5	⟨exp1 fact⟩	::= (	⟨exp1⟩	)		
6		::= **int cons, var**				
7	⟨exp2⟩	::= ⟨exp1⟩	⟨+, −, *⟩	⟨exp2 fact⟩		
8		::= ⟨exp2⟩	⟨+, −, *⟩	⟨exp1 fact⟩		
9		::= ⟨exp2⟩	⟨+, −, *⟩	⟨exp2 fact⟩		
10		::= ⟨+, −, *⟩	⟨exp2 fact⟩			
11		::= ⟨exp2 fact⟩				
12	⟨exp2 fact⟩	::= (	⟨exp2⟩	)		
13		::= **loop var**				

Nonterminal symbols:

⟨for loop⟩   ⟨exp1⟩   ⟨exp1 fact⟩   ⟨exp2⟩   ⟨exp2 fact⟩

Terminal symbols:

for   loop var   ←   step   until   do   ⟨+, −, *⟩   (   )   **int cons, var**

FIGURE 3.1.11   Loop checker.

subscripts have been or are being checked for syntactical errors by another part of the compiler, this will never happen. Grammars should always be constructed according to what they will be used for, and should be as simple as possible.

One can incorporate the "loop checker" and optimizable subscript checker into an existing syntax checker as follows: All three are put in memory together. The main syntax checker executes as it normally does, performing the usual "steps" described already. See Fig. 3.1.12.

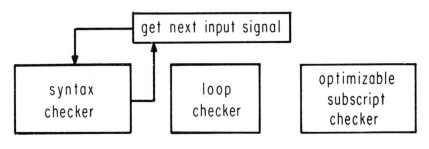

FIGURE 3.1.12

When a **for** is scanned, the syntax checker activates the loop checker. Thereafter both process in parallel. The syntax checker processes one symbol and then passes it on to the loop checker, which when finished returns to the syntax checker to process the next symbol. See Fig. 3.1.13.

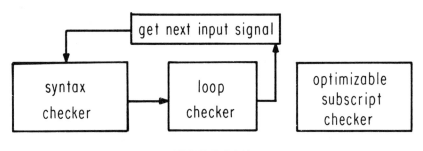

FIGURE 3.1.13

The loop checker disconnects itself as soon as it determines that the loop is not of the right form, or when it is finished. Similarly, the optimizable subscript checker is connected when the "[" of the subscript variable $A[E_1, \ldots, E_n]$ is first scanned. The optimizable variable checker disconnects itself when finished or when it is determined that this subscripted variable does not satisfy one of the restrictions. See Fig. 3.1.14.

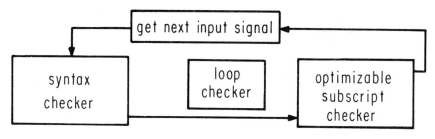

FIGURE 3.1.14

The loop checker and optimizable subscript checker are not concerned with errors and error recovery. If any error occurs, they simply disconnect themselves, or will be disconnected by the syntax checker itself.

3.1.10. DISCUSSION AND SUMMARY

The transition matrix technique is closely related to Conway's separable transition diagram technique.[2] In Ref. 2 every syntactic type is represented by a labeled diagram such as that in Fig. 3.1.15.

To analyze using transition diagrams, we start at the first node of the first diagram, and go from node to node, as follows:

(a) If the label on a line leaving the current node matches the input symbol, read the next input symbol and traverse the line to the next node. This corresponds to an intermediate reduction to a SNTS within a production of the OG, reductions (4.10) and (4.13); we are still analyzing the same syntactic type.

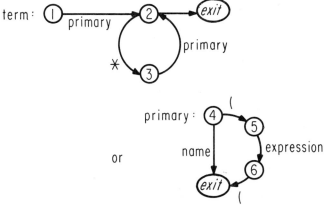

FIGURE 3.1.15

(b) If there is no node as described in (a), there may be a line labeled with a nonterminal (syntactic entity). If so, we want to try to reduce part of the sentence to this entity and traverse this line. To do this, the current diagram name and code number are pushed into a stack, and the diagram for the new syntactic entity is entered, corresponding roughly to reductions (4.11) and (4.14).

(c) If (a) and (b) do not produce anything, an unlabeled node is traversed.

(d) When a syntactic entity is recognized (analysis completed) we find ouselves at an *exit* node. Here, we pop the top stack element and return to the diagram and node specified by it. This corresponds exactly to reductions (4.9) and (4.12).

These two methods are the same except for the treatment of nonterminals. In the transition diagram technique, nonterminals (syntactic types) U are recognized by calling the appropriate diagram and traversing the line labeled U upon successful completion; in the transition matrix technique U is actually stored in the stack when it has been recognized. The two methods exhibit the usual trade-off between space and time; the transition matrix technique is fast but uses much space, since the matrix is usually sparse, while the diagram technique takes no more space than is necessary, but may take more time, since there may be many lines leaving a single node.

Tixier's thesis[14] describes a constructor which generates a recognizer which consists essentially of Conway's separable transition diagrams (finite state automata).

The ideas in this paper been used intuitively in the ALCOR-ILLINOIS 7090 compiler.[9,1] The second pass actually contains the three matrices illustrated in Section 3.1.9. The matrix technique has its most important use, in my opinion, in a student system, where a very fast compiler resides in core and must also produce excellent error messages. Because the syntax checker matrix for ALGOL is so large (on the 7090 (100×45)) and because over 60 percent of the array elements represent illegal symbol pairs, a much wider variety of error messages is efficiently possible. An algorithm is being developed for producing, from the grammar, an error-recovery subroutine for each "error" element of the matrix. Another advantage of the matrix technique is the simplicity of the overall design.

The only disadvantage is the space used. A partial solution to this problem might be to parse those constructions of the grammar which are most used (for instance, expressions), using the matrix technique and to use some other slower but less space-consuming technique for the rest of the grammar.

The contruction algorithm has been programmed in Extended ALGOL[16] and tested on the Burroughs 5500 at Stanford. A 58×42 matrix was produced for Floyd's[6] ALGOL-like language (116×42 when two rows for each SNTS were used to avoid some checking of $U1$ each time).

ACKNOWLEDGMENT

The author is indebted to Jerome Feldman, Niklaus Wirth, and the referees for their critical comments.

REFERENCES

1. Bayer, R., Murphree, E., Jr., and Gries, D., *User's Manual for the* ALCOR-ILLINOIS 7090 ALGOL-60 *Translator*, 2d ed. U. of Illinois, Urbana, Ill., 1964.

2. Conway, M. E., "Design of a Separable Transition-Diagram Compiler," *Comm. ACM*, vol. 6 (July 1963), pp. 396–408.

3. Eickel, J., Paul, M., Bauer, F. L., and Samelson, K., "A Syntax Controlled Generator of Formal Language Processors," *Comm. ACM*, vol. 6 (August 1963), pp. 451–455.

4. Feldman, J. A., "A Formal Semantics for Computer Languages and Its Application in a Compiler-Compiler," *Comm. ACM*, vol. 9 (January 1966), pp. 3–9.

5. Feldman, J. A., and Gries, D., "Translator Writing Systems," *Comm. ACM*, vol. 11 (February 1968).

6. Floyd, R. W., "Syntactic Analysis and Operator Precedence," *J. ACM*, vol. 10 (July 1963), pp. 316–333.

7. ———. Bounded context syntactic analysis, *Comm. ACM*, vol. 7 (February 1964), pp. 62–67.

8. Gries, D., "The Use of Transition Matrices in Compiling," Tech. Rep. No. CS 57, Computer Science Dept., Stanford U., Stanford, Calif., March 17, 1967.

9. Gries, D., Paul, M., and Wiehle, H. R., "Some Techniques Used in the ALCOR-ILLINOIS 7090," *Comm. ACM*, vol. 8 (August 1965), pp. 496–500.

10. Hill, V., Langmaack, H., Schwarz, H. R., and Seegmüller, G., "Efficient Handling of Subscripted Variables in ALGOL 60 Compilers," *Proc. 1962 Rome Symposium on Symbolic Languages in Data Processing*. Gordon and Breach, New York, 1962, pp. 311–340.

11. Naur, P. (ed.), "Report on the Algorithmic Language ALGOL 60," *Numer. Math.*, vol. 2 (1960), pp. 106–136; also *Comm. ACM*, vol. 3 (May 1960), pp. 299–314.

12. ———. "Revised Report on the Algorithmic Language ALGOL 60," *Comm. ACM*, vol. 6 (January 1963), pp. 1–17.

13. Samelson, K., and Bauer, F. L., "Sequential Formula Translation," *Comm. ACM*, vol. 3 (February 1960), pp. 76–83.

14. Tixier, V., "Recursive Functions of Regular Expressions in Language Analysis," Tech. Rep. CS 58, Computer Science Dept., Stanford U., Stanford, Calif., March 1967.

15. Wirth, N., and Weber, H., "EULER: A Generalization of ALGOL, and Its Formal Definition, Part I," *Comm. ACM*, vol. 9 (January 1966), pp. 13–25.

16. *Burroughs B5500 Information Processing Systems Extended* ALGOL *Language Manual.*

3.2. Syntactic Analysis and Operator Precedence

by Robert W. Floyd

3.2.1. ABSTRACT

Three increasingly restricted types of formal grammar are phrase-structure grammars, operator grammars, and precedence grammars. Precedence grammars form models of mathematical and algorithmic languages which may be analyzed mechanically by a simple procedure based on a matrix representation of a precedence relation between character pairs.

3.2.2. INTRODUCTION

The central problem in constructing a compiler for a nontrivial programming language is the syntactic analysis by mechanical means of formulas in the language. Such mechanical analyzers are conventionally constructed "by hand"; freedom from syntactic errors is achieved with difficulty, and subsequent additions or modifications to the source language, even though readily incorporated in the formal grammar, may necessitate extensive alterations to the analyzer.

EDITOR'S NOTE: This article reproduced by permission of the author and the publisher: *J. ACM*, vol. 10, no. 3 (July 1963), pp. 316–333.

146

Efforts have been made[1] to construct analyzers capable of analyzing any of a wide class of phrase-structure languages, operating interpretively under control of a tabular representation of the grammar for the current language. Such "syntax directed" analyzers presently seem to be inefficient, although detailed information is lacking.

There is a significant and useful class of formal languages, however, for which the design of an efficient mechanical analyzer may be determined in a simple way from the grammar of the language itself. It will be our purpose to characterize this class of languages, to describe the construction of an analyzer, and to verify the correctness and uniqueness of the resulting analysis.

3.2.3. DEFINITIONS AND CONVENTIONS

Numerous results used in the paper,[†] but not essential to an intuitive understanding of the new techniques presented, are proved in Appendix A. References to Appendix A appear as [T1] or [C1], designating Theorem 1 and Corollary 1, respectively. [Other source references are cited as superscript numbers.]

The properties of *characters* and *strings* of characters are well known and will be used informally. Characters will be represented by italic capitals, strings by lower-case italic letters, and the null string by Λ. If x and y are strings, xy is the *concatenation* of x and y, formed by writing x followed by y. If $z = xy$ is a string, x is a *head* and y a *tail* of z. A head of z consisting of a single character is the *initial character* of z; a tail of z consisting of a single character is the *final character* of z.

A *language* is a set of strings, and a *grammar* a means of defining a language and ascribing structure to its strings. The set of characters under consideration is the vocabulary V, and the set of strings over a vocabulary is W_V.

A *production* $U \to u$ is an ordered pair consisting of a character U and a nonempty string u. The relation $w \to v$ holds (with respect to a set P of productions) if there are strings x and y and a character U such that $w = xUy$, $v = xuy$ and $U \to u$ is a production of P. The relation $w \Rightarrow v$ holds (with respect to P) if there is a finite sequence $w = w_0, w_1, \ldots, w_n = v$ ($n \geq 0$) such that $w_{i-1} \to w_i$ ($1 \leq i \leq n$). The sequence $w_0, w_1, \ldots, w_n$

[†] The research reported in this paper was sponsored in part by the Air Force Cambridge Research Laboratories, Office of Aerospace Research, under Contract AF19(628)-419.

is said to be a *derivation*[†] of v from w, and v is a *w-derivative*. The relation "$\Rightarrow$" is reflexive and transitive; $x \Rightarrow x$; and if $x \Rightarrow y$ and $y \Rightarrow z$, then $x \Rightarrow z$. If $x_i \Rightarrow y_i$ ($1 \le i \le n$) then $x_1 x_2 \ldots x_n \Rightarrow y_1 y_2 \ldots y_n$. Conversely, if $x \Rightarrow y$ and $x = x_1 x_2 \ldots x_n$, then there are strings $y_1, y_2, \ldots, y_n$ such that $y = y_1 y_2 \ldots y_n$ and $x_i \Rightarrow y_i$ ($1 \le i \le n$). See Ref. 4 and [T1, C1]. If $x \Rightarrow y$, then y is nonempty if and only if x is nonempty.

If P is a set of productions containing exactly one character S which appears only on the left of "$\rightarrow$", and a nonempty set T of (terminal) characters which appear only on the right of "$\rightarrow$", then P is a *phrase-structure grammar*.[3,4] The derivatives of S (with respect to P) are *sentential forms* and the sentential forms in W_T are the *sentences* of the *phrase-structure language L_P*. Without restricting the set of phrase-structure languages, we shall assume that for each character Y of P there are strings x, z, and t such that $S \Rightarrow xYz$, $Y \Rightarrow t$, and $t \in W_T$; that is, every character may be used in deriving some sentence.

If no production of the phrase-structure grammar P takes the form $U \rightarrow xU_1 U_2 y$, where U_1 and U_2 are nonterminal characters (NTC), then P is an *operator grammar* and L_P is an *operator language*. It is readily shown by induction [T3, C3] that if P is an operator grammar, then no derivative of any character, and in particular no sentential form, contains two adjacent NTC.

In an operator grammar, there are three relations, some or all of which may hold between two terminal characters T_1 and T_2:

(1) $T_1 \doteq T_2$ if there is a production $U \rightarrow xT_1 T_2 y$ or $U \rightarrow xT_1 U_1 T_2 y$, where $U_1 \in V - T$.

(2) $T_1 \gtrdot T_2$ if there is a production $U \rightarrow xU_1 T_2 y$ and a derivation $U_1 \Rightarrow z$ where $U_1 \in V - T$ and T_1 is the rightmost terminal character of z.

(3) $T_1 \lessdot T_2$ if there is a production $U \rightarrow xT_1 U_1 y$ and a derivation $U_1 \Rightarrow z$ where $U_1 \in V - T$ and T_2 is the leftmost terminal character of z.

A *precedence grammar* is an operator grammar for which no more than one of the three relations holds between any ordered pair T_1, T_2 of terminal symbols. The relations are called *precedence relations*. The goal of the paper as a whole is to provide techniques to recognize precedence grammars, to construct matrix representations of their precedence relations, and to analyze sentences by means of such precedence matrices.

[†] Strictly speaking, a derivation of v from w must specify, for each step $w_{i-1} \rightarrow w_i$, which character of w_{i-1} is operated on and by which production. We shall make implicit use of this requirement.

3.2.4. GENERAL DISCUSSION

An example of a precedence grammar P_1 is the following:

$$S \rightarrow A$$
$$A \rightarrow A + B$$
$$A \rightarrow B$$
$$B \rightarrow B * C$$
$$B \rightarrow C$$
$$C \rightarrow (A)$$
$$C \rightarrow \lambda$$

In P_1, $T = \{+, *, (,), \lambda\}$ and $V - T = \{S, A, B, C\}$. If $C \Rightarrow z$, then the leftmost terminal character (LTC) of z must be (or λ. If $B \Rightarrow z$, the LTC of z must be (, λ, or *. Continuing in the same manner, we arrive at a table (Fig. 3.2.1) showing the possible left- and rightmost terminal characters (LTCD and RTCD) of the derivatives of each NTC.

NTC	LTCD	RTCD
C	$(\lambda$	$)\lambda$
B	$(\lambda *$	$)\lambda *$
A	$(\lambda * +$	$)\lambda * +$
S	$(\lambda * +$	$)\lambda * +$

FIGURE 3.2.1

Because of the production $C \rightarrow (A)$, the relation $(\doteq)$ holds in P_1. Because $A \rightarrow A + B$ and * is a RTCD of A, $* \gtrdot +$. Because $C \rightarrow (A)$ and (is a LTCD of A, $(\lessdot)$. The complete matrix of precedence relations is shown in Fig. 3.2.2.

	(	λ	*	+	)
)			$\gtrdot$	$\gtrdot$	$\gtrdot$
λ			$\gtrdot$	$\gtrdot$	$\gtrdot$
*	$\lessdot$	$\lessdot$	$\gtrdot$	$\gtrdot$	$\gtrdot$
+	$\lessdot$	$\lessdot$	$\lessdot$	$\gtrdot$	$\gtrdot$
(	$\lessdot$	$\lessdot$	$\lessdot$	$\lessdot$	$\doteq$

FIGURE 3.2.2

If $s = xyz$ is a sentential form, then y is a *phrase* of s, provided there is a sentential form $x'Yz'$ for which $x' \Rightarrow x$, $Y \Rightarrow y$, and $z' \Rightarrow z$, where $Y \in V - T$. Equivalently, y is a phrase of $s = xyz$ if there is a sentential form xYz for which $Y \Rightarrow y$, $Y \in V - T$. A *prime phrase* is a phrase which contains at least one terminal character, but no prime phrase other than itself. Thus in L_{P_1} the sentential form $C * C * (\lambda + B)$ contains only the prime phrases $C * C$ and λ; each other phrase either consists of a NTC or contains one of the prime phrases. Every sentential form containing more than one character contains at least one prime phrase [T13].

In a precedence language, there is a simple technique for recognizing prime phrases [T12]. If a string x appears in the context BxC within a sentential form s, where B and C are terminal characters, x contains the terminal characters $A_1, A_2, \ldots, A_n$ ($n \geq 1$), and $B \lessdot A_1$, $A_n \gtrdot C$, $A_i \doteq A_{i+1}$ ($1 \leq i \leq n - 1$), then x is a prime phrase. (Note that the non-terminal characters of x are ignored in this decision.) If x is not preceded by any character in s, we consider $B \lessdot A_1$ to be true; similarly, if no character of s follows x, we consider $A_n \gtrdot C$ to be true. This convention is implemented automatically if each sentential form s is written in the augmented form $\vdash s \dashv$, with $\vdash \lessdot A$ and $A \gtrdot \dashv$ for all A in T.

The process of syntactic analysis of a sentential form s may now be described. The string is written in the augmented form $s_0 = \vdash s \dashv$. If s_0 contains a prime phrase, the prime phrase is replaced by the NTC N_1, yielding the string s_1. The procedure is iterated, some prime phrase of s_i being replaced by N_{i+1} to obtain s_{i+1}. Since each step diminishes the number of terminal characters in s_i, the process must in a finite number of steps result in $s_m = \vdash N_m \dashv$. Denoting s_i' as the string such that $\vdash s_i' \dashv = s_i$, the sequence $S \Rightarrow s_m' \Rightarrow s_{m-1}' \Rightarrow \cdots \Rightarrow s_1' \Rightarrow s_0' = s$ is a skeletal representation of a derivation of s. The details of the derivation may usually be filled in

i	s_i	Prime phrases
0	$\vdash(\lambda + \lambda) * \lambda\dashv$	$\lambda, \lambda, \lambda$
1	$\vdash(N_1 + \lambda) * \lambda\dashv$	λ, λ
2	$\vdash(N_1 + N_2) * \lambda\dashv$	$N_1 + N_2, \lambda$
3	$\vdash(N_3) * \lambda\dashv$	$(N_3), \lambda$
4	$\vdash N_4 * \lambda\dashv$	λ
5	$\vdash N_4 * N_5\dashv$	$N_4 * N_5$
6	$\vdash N_6\dashv$	

FIGURE 3.2.3

without difficulty, substituting the appropriate nonterminal symbol of P for each N_i, and determining the derivation of $s_i' \Rightarrow s_{i-1}'$ for each value of i. Since each of these derivations takes the form $xN_iz \Rightarrow xyz$, where y is a prime phrase, and since the number of possible prime phrases is finite, this determination is essentially trivial.

Consider by way of example the sentence $(\lambda + \lambda) * \lambda$ of P_1. Since $(\lessdot \lambda \gtrdot +$, the first occurrence of λ in $s_0 = \vdash (\lambda + \lambda) * \lambda \dashv$ is a prime phrase, and s_1 is $\vdash (N_1 + \lambda) * \lambda \dashv$. Continuing in this manner, we have the skeletal derivation of Fig. 3.2.3, where the leftmost prime phrase of s_i is chosen for analysis at each step.

To complete the derivation, we must establish derivations of

$$S \Rightarrow N_6 \qquad N_4 \Rightarrow (N_3) \qquad N_2 \Rightarrow \lambda$$
$$N_6 \Rightarrow N_4 * N_5 \qquad N_3 \Rightarrow N_1 + N_2 \qquad N_1 \Rightarrow \lambda$$
$$N_5 \Rightarrow \lambda$$

For example,

$$S \to A \to B = N_6$$
$$N_6 = B \to B * C = N_4 * N_5 \qquad N_3 = A \to A + B = N_1 + N_2$$
$$N_5 = C \to \lambda \qquad N_2 = B \to C \to \lambda$$
$$N_4 = B \to C \to (A) = (N_3) \qquad N_1 = A \to B \to C \to \lambda$$

The table which shows for each nonterminal character the leftmost terminal characters of its derivatives may be constructed as follows:

(1) For each production $U_1 \to T_1x$ or $U_1 \to U_2T_1x$ $(T_1 \in T, U_2 \in V - T)$, enter T_1 as a LTCD of U_1.

(2) For each production $U_1 \to U_2x$, enter every LTCD of U_2 as a LTCD of U_1.

(3) Repeat Step 2 until, in a finite number of steps, the process converges.

An analogous procedure constructs a table of rightmost terminal characters of the derivatives of each nonterminal character.

A flow chart is shown in Fig. 3.2.4 which performs a syntactic analysis of a string in a precedence language, processing phrases from left to right. This flow chart could be taken as the nucleus of a simple compiler, although other sequences of processing the phrases may potentially yield better coding in many instances.[2]

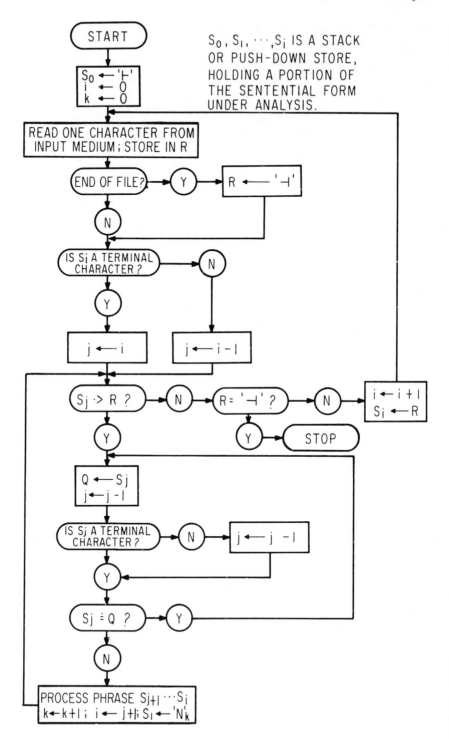

FIGURE 3.2.4

Let us consider several instances of phrase-structure grammars which are not precedence grammars and show how they may be treated as precedence grammars by minor adjustments.

In ALGOL 60,[5] the definition of an identifier (I) is equivalent to

$$I \rightarrow L$$
$$I \rightarrow IL$$
$$I \rightarrow ID$$
$$L \rightarrow a$$
$$L \rightarrow b$$
$$\vdots$$
$$L \rightarrow z$$
$$D \rightarrow 0$$
$$D \rightarrow 1$$
$$\vdots$$
$$D \rightarrow 9$$

Because of the production $I \rightarrow IL$, ALGOL 60 is not an operator language. If, however, the categories L and D are eliminated, we have

$I \rightarrow a$	$I \rightarrow Ia$	$I \rightarrow I0$
$I \rightarrow b$	$I \rightarrow Ib$	$I \rightarrow I1$
$\vdots$	$\vdots$	$\vdots$
$I \rightarrow z$	$I \rightarrow Iz$	$I \rightarrow I9$

This set of productions is consistent with a precedence grammar. It is, however, unwieldy. We may achieve the same effect by the set of productions

$$I \rightarrow \lambda$$
$$I \rightarrow I\lambda$$
$$I \rightarrow I\delta$$

where λ and δ are terminal symbols representing an arbitrary letter and an arbitrary digit, respectively. We speak of λ as a *representative* of the set of letters.

Again, in ALGOL 60, the definition of a **for** statement is

$$\langle \text{for statement} \rangle \rightarrow \langle \text{for clause} \rangle \langle \text{statement} \rangle$$

While this is not consistent with an operator grammar, one may modify the definition of the **for** clause from

$$\langle \text{for clause}\rangle \rightarrow \textbf{for } \langle \text{variable}\rangle := \langle \text{for list}\rangle \textbf{ do}$$

to

$$\langle \text{for clause}\rangle \rightarrow \textbf{for } \langle \text{variable}\rangle := \langle \text{for list}\rangle$$

so that the definition of a **for** statement becomes

$$\langle \text{for statement}\rangle \rightarrow \langle \text{for clause}\rangle \textbf{ do } \langle \text{statement}\rangle$$

which is consistent with a precedence grammar.

A simple formula language may be defined by P_2:

$$S \rightarrow A$$
$$A \rightarrow A - B$$
$$A \rightarrow B$$
$$B \rightarrow B * C$$
$$B \rightarrow C$$
$$C \rightarrow - D$$
$$C \rightarrow D$$
$$D \rightarrow (A)$$
$$D \rightarrow \lambda$$

While P_2 is an operator grammar, both $* \gtrdot -$ and $* \lessdot -$, so that P_2 is not a precedence grammar. If the unary and binary minus signs were distinct characters, however, we would have a precedence grammar P_3, with the

NTC	LTCD	RTCD
S	$-$ $*$ θ $($ λ	$-$ $*$ θ $)$ λ
A	$-$ $*$ θ $($ λ	$-$ $*$ θ $)$ λ
B	$*$ θ $($ λ	$*$ θ $)$ λ
C	θ $($ λ	θ $)$ λ
D	$($ λ	$)$ λ

	$($	λ	θ	$*$	$-$	$)$
$)$				$\gtrdot$	$\gtrdot$	$\gtrdot$
λ				$\gtrdot$	$\gtrdot$	$\gtrdot$
θ	$\lessdot$	$\lessdot$		$\gtrdot$	$\gtrdot$	$\gtrdot$
$*$	$\lessdot$	$\lessdot$	$\lessdot$	$\gtrdot$	$\gtrdot$	$\gtrdot$
$-$	$\lessdot$	$\lessdot$	$\lessdot$	$\lessdot$	$\gtrdot$	$\gtrdot$
$($	$\lessdot$	$\lessdot$	$\lessdot$	$\lessdot$	$\lessdot$	$\doteq$

FIGURE 3.2.5

precedence matrix of Fig. 3.2.5:

$$S \rightarrow A$$
$$A \rightarrow A - B$$
$$A \rightarrow B$$
$$B \rightarrow B * C$$
$$B \rightarrow C$$
$$C \rightarrow \theta D$$
$$C \rightarrow D$$
$$D \rightarrow (A)$$
$$D \rightarrow \lambda$$

We may construct a matrix (Fig. 3.2.6) showing the allowable character pairs of sentences in P_3.

	(	λ	θ	*	$-$	)
)				x	x	x
λ				x	x	x
θ	x	x				
*	x	x	x			
$-$	x	x	x			
(	x	x	x			

FIGURE 3.2.6

In a sentence of P_3, the character preceding any occurrence of $-$ must be) or λ. That preceding any occurrence of θ must be *, $-$, (, or $\vdash$. Since these two sets of characters are disjoint, the characters $-$ and θ may be distinguished by inspection of the preceding character, even when $-$ and θ are represented by the same symbol, as in P_2. A compiler for a language like P_2 might make use of an input program which would at all times remember the last character read, and would change a $-$ to a θ if its predecessor was one of *, $-$, (, or $\vdash$. The remainder of the compiler would then process the precedence language P_3. If a grammar represents the absolute value function by $| x |$, the two uses of the vertical line may be distinguished in the same way.

The determination of the allowable character pairs of the sentential forms of a language proceeds as follows:

(1) For each character X, enter X in a table as a leftmost character of a derivative (LCD) of X.

(2) For each production $U \rightarrow Xy$, enter each LCD of X as a LCD of U.

(3) Repeat Step 2 until in a finite number of steps the process converges.

(4) By a process analogous to steps 1–3, determine the rightmost characters of the derivatives (RCD) of each character.

(5) For each character pair XY which occurs in the string on the right-hand side of a production, if X_1 is a RCD of X and Y_1 a LCD of Y then X_1Y_1 is an allowable character pair in sentential forms of the language. Those allowable character pairs both of which are terminal characters may occur in sentences of the language.

The representation of a precedence matrix requires a table with n^2 entries, where n is the number of terminal characters in V. It is possible, however, in many instances to represent the useful content of the matrix far more compactly. Suppose there are two functions $f(X)$ and $g(X)$ mapping terminal symbols into numbers, such that if $X \lessdot Y$ then $f(X) < g(Y)$; if $X \doteq Y$ then $f(X) = g(Y)$; and if $X \gtrdot Y$ then $f(X) > g(Y)$. Assuming that exactly one of $X \lessdot Y$, $X \doteq Y$, and $X \gtrdot Y$ is true, one may determine which by evaluating and comparing $f(X)$ and $g(Y)$. The tables representing f and g require only $2n$ positions. For example, the precedence matrix of Fig. 3.2.5 may be represented by Fig. 3.2.7.

X	$f(X)$	$g(X)$
)	5	1
λ	5	6
θ	5	6
*	5	4
—	3	2
(	1	6

FIGURE 3.2.7

If such precedence functions exist, we may compute instances of them from the precedence matrix in the following manner:

(1) Initially set $f(X) = g(X) = 1$ for all $X \in T$.

(2) For each instance of $X \gtrdot Y$, if $f(X) \leq g(Y)$ set $f(X)$ equal to $g(Y) + 1$.

(3) For each instance of $X \lessdot Y$, if $f(X) \geq g(Y)$ set $g(Y)$ equal to $f(X) + 1$.

(4) For each instance of $X \doteq Y$, if $f(X) \neq g(Y)$ set the smaller of $f(X)$ and $g(Y)$ equal to the larger.

(5) Iterate Steps 2, 3, and 4 until the process converges. If any value of f or g becomes greater than twice the number of terminal characters in V, the process will never converge, and no pair of functions has the desired qualities.

There are more efficient ways of computing f and g, but the technique given clearly converges only to functions satisfying the desired conditions. In the process of analyzing sentential forms in a precedence language by the algorithm of Fig. 3.2.4, one considers the precedence relations only of terminal characters T_1 and T_2 for which $T_1 T_2$ or $T_1 U_1 T_2$ occurs in some sentential form. Therefore [T9], exactly one of $T_1 \lessdot T_2$, $T_1 \doteq T_2$, and $T_1 \gtrdot T_2$ occurs, according as $f(T_1) < g(T_2), f(T_1) = g(T_2)$, or $f(T_1) > g(T_2)$, respectively.

The existence of a pair of precedence functions representing a precedence matrix seems very unlikely *a priori*, and one readily constructs examples of precedence grammars for which precedence functions of the type described here do not exist. Yet the author has found that insofar as programming languages or natural languages can be represented by precedence grammars, they can also be represented by a pair of precedence functions without doing violence to the intuitive phrase structure of the language. This suggests that the intuitive perception of phrase structure may be based on a mechanism similar to the use of precedence functions.

3.2.5. APPLICATIONS

Several uses for the theory of precedence languages present themselves. Some existing programming languages are, in fact, precedence languages and could be compiled using the flow chart of Fig. 3.2.4 as an analyzer. Probably more existing languages are nearly precedence languages; only for a small number of terminal character pairs does more than one precedence relation hold. The analyzer above could be adapted to test for these special cases, and refer to an appropriate subroutine to resolve each ambiguity.

If a phrase-structure grammar generates ambiguous sentences, the precedence matrix will show terminal character pairs for which more than one precedence relation holds. Such entries in the matrix are guides toward

$f(X)$	Y \ X	; end	;	then	until	else	switch procedure / constant function τ	,	do	op	)	(	[	value / array	step while	:	$\equiv$	$\cap$	$\vee$	ϱ	β	$\llcorner$	π	$\odot$:= if	for comment / begin go to	μ	$\uparrow$ ([*	$_{10}\theta$	λ	δ
22	δ	$\wedge$	$\wedge$	$\wedge$	$\wedge$	$\vee$		$\wedge$	$\vee$	$\wedge$	$\wedge$		$\wedge$		$\wedge$	$\wedge$	$\wedge$	$\wedge$	$\wedge$	$\wedge$		$\wedge$	$\wedge$	$\wedge$		$\wedge$	$\wedge$			$\wedge$
22	λ	$\wedge$	$\wedge$	$\vee$	$\wedge$	$\vee$		$\wedge$	$\vee$	$\wedge$	$\wedge$		$\wedge$		$\wedge$	$\wedge$	$\wedge$	$\wedge$	$\wedge$	$\wedge$		$\wedge$	$\wedge$	$\wedge$		$\wedge$	$\wedge$			$\wedge$
20	*	$\wedge$	$\wedge$	$\wedge$	$\wedge$	$\vee$		$\wedge$	$\vee$	$\wedge$	$\wedge$		$\wedge$		$\wedge$	$\wedge$	$\wedge$	$\wedge$	$\wedge$	$\wedge$		$\wedge$								$\vee$
20	]	$\wedge$	$\wedge$	$\wedge$	$\wedge$	$\wedge$		$\wedge$	$\vee$	$\wedge$	$\wedge$		$\wedge$		$\wedge$	$\wedge$	$\wedge$	$\wedge$	$\wedge$	$\wedge$		$\wedge$		$\wedge$						
20	)	$\wedge$	$\wedge$	$\wedge$	$\wedge$	$\wedge$		$\wedge$	$\vee$	$\wedge$	$\wedge$		$\wedge$		$\wedge$	$\wedge$	$\wedge$	$\wedge$	$\wedge$	$\wedge$		$\wedge$	$\wedge$	$\wedge$						
19	go to	$\wedge$	$\wedge$		$\wedge$	$\vee$																	$\wedge$	$\vee$		$\vee$	$\vee$	$\vee$	$\vee$	$\vee$
18	$_{10}\theta\ \mu\ \uparrow$	$\wedge$	$\wedge$	$\wedge$	$\wedge$	$\wedge$		$\wedge$	$\wedge$	$\wedge$	$\wedge$		$\wedge$		$\wedge$	$\wedge$	$\wedge$	$\wedge$	$\wedge$	$\wedge$		$\wedge$	$\vee$	$\vee$		$\vee$	$\vee$	$\vee$	$\vee$	$\vee$
16	π	$\wedge$	$\wedge$	$\wedge$	$\wedge$	$\wedge$		$\wedge$	$\wedge$	$\wedge$	$\wedge$		$\wedge$		$\wedge$	$\wedge$	$\wedge$	$\wedge$	$\wedge$	$\wedge$		$\wedge$	$\vee$	$\vee$		$\vee$	$\vee$	$\vee$	$\vee$	$\vee$
15	for constant																								$\vee$				$\vee$	$\vee$
15	function																$\equiv$							$\equiv$					$\vee$	$\vee$
14	else				$\wedge$			$\wedge$	$\wedge$	$\wedge$	$\wedge$		$\wedge$	$\wedge$	$\wedge$	$\wedge$	$\vee$	$\wedge$	$\wedge$	$\wedge$		$\vee$	$\vee$	$\vee$	$\vee$	$\vee$	$\vee$	$\vee$	$\vee$	$\vee$
14	ϱ																	$\wedge$	$\wedge$	$\wedge$		$\vee$	$\vee$	$\vee$	$\vee$	$\vee$	$\vee$	$\vee$	$\vee$	$\vee$
12	$\llcorner$	$\wedge$	$\wedge$	$\wedge$		$\wedge$		$\wedge$	$\wedge$	$\wedge$	$\wedge$		$\wedge$		$\wedge$	$\wedge$	$\wedge$	$\wedge$	$\vee$	$\vee$	$\vee$	$\vee$	$\vee$	$\vee$	$\vee$	$\vee$	$\vee$	$\vee$	$\vee$	$\vee$
12	<	$\wedge$	$\wedge$	$\wedge$		$\wedge$		$\wedge$	$\wedge$	$\wedge$	$\wedge$		$\wedge$		$\wedge$	$\wedge$	$\vee$	$\vee$	$\vee$	$\vee$	$\vee$	$\vee$	$\vee$	$\vee$	$\vee$	$\vee$	$\vee$	$\vee$	$\vee$	$\vee$
10	>	$\wedge$	$\wedge$	$\wedge$		$\wedge$		$\wedge$	$\wedge$	$\wedge$	$\wedge$		$\wedge$		$\wedge$	$\wedge$	$\vee$	$\vee$	$\vee$	$\vee$	$\vee$	$\vee$	$\vee$	$\vee$	$\vee$	$\vee$	$\vee$	$\vee$	$\vee$	$\vee$
8	$\cap$	$\wedge$	$\wedge$	$\wedge$		$\wedge$		$\wedge$	$\wedge$	$\wedge$	$\vee$		$\vee$		$\vee$	$\vee$	$\vee$	$\vee$	$\vee$	$\vee$	$\vee$	$\vee$	$\vee$	$\vee$	$\vee$	$\vee$	$\vee$	$\vee$	$\vee$	$\vee$

≡	<	<	<	<	<	<	<	<		<			<		<	<	<	<	<	>						>	>	>		>		>	>	>	6
β																	>	>	>	>						>	>	>		>		>	>	>	12
until	<	<	<	<	<	<	<	<		<			<														>	>							4
while	<	<	<	<	<	<	<	<		<			<	<	<	<	<	<	<	<							>	>							4
comment																														>			>	>	3
end																																			
value	<	<																										=					>	>	3
τ	<	<																					=	=				=					>	>	3
array	<	<			=																							=					>	>	3
do ⊙	<	<			<	<			<	<	<	<																		>			>	>	3
[	<	<	<	<	<	<	<	<		<			<								<				=			=							3
(	<	<	<	<	<	<	<	<		<			<	<	<	<	<	<	<	<						=		=							3
,	<	<	<	<	<	<	<	<		<			<	<	<	<	<	<	<	<	<	<			=	=	=	=					>	>	3
:=	<	<	<	<	<	<	<	<		<	<		<	<	<	<	<	<	<	<		<					=	=		>			>	>	3
switch	<	<				<																											>		2
then	<	<	<	<	<	<	<	<	<	<	<	<	<																	=			>	>	2
step	<	<	<	<	<	<	<	<		<			<																			=			1
if	<	<	<	<	<	<	<	<		<			<	<	<	<	<	<	<	<												=			1
; **begin**	<	<			<	<			<	<	<	<											<						<	<			=	=	1
procedure	<	<				<																											=	=	1
$g(Y)$	21	20	19	19	19	19	19	17	15	15	15	15	15	13	13	13	11	9	7	5	4	4	3	3	3	3	3	3	2	2	1	1	1	1	

FIGURE 3.2.8

detecting the presence of ambiguous sentences, although they do not by themselves prove the grammar to be ambiguous.

Designers of new programming languages might do well to consider precedence languages; the restriction, other things being equal, benefits both the translator and the user of the language. The grammar P_4 shown in Appendix B defines[5] a language closely comparable to ALGOL 60, departing from it only for sufficient reason. Because it contains none of the syntactic ambiguities[6] of ALGOL 60, is much more concise (using 43 nonterminal characters rather than 109), and assigns more natural constructions to several grammatical forms, it might be taken as a model for the eventual successor to ALGOL 60. It is included here because it exemplifies most of the difficulties which may be encountered in analyzing an operator language by precedence techniques.

In the grammar of P_4, the form $U \to x \mid y \mid z$ is an abbreviation for the productions $U \to x$, $U \to y$, and $U \to z$. The form $U \to x\{y\}z$ is an abbreviation for the infinite set of productions $U \to xz$, $U \to xyz$, $U \to xyyz$, $U \to xyyyz$, etc. Only the first and third productions of such a set need be considered in deriving precedence relations. Observe that while the notation $x\{y\}z$ does not increase the class of describable languages, it may reduce the number of productions required by the grammar and is the only way of introducing prime phrases of arbitrarily great length. The form $U \to x\{y\}^a z$ is an abbreviation for the set of productions $U \to xyy \ldots yz$, where the number of occurrences of y is no greater than a.

While P_4 is not an operator grammar, omitting the first seven sets of productions converts it to an operator grammar. The characters λ, δ, β, π, μ, ϱ, and τ are then terminal characters serving as representatives of letters, digits, truth values, signs, multiplying operators, relational operators, and type designators, respectively.

In P_4, the same problem concerning the signs $+$ and $-$ arises as arose in P_2. It may be solved in exactly the same way.

The precedence relations **else** $\gtrdot$: and **else** $\lessdot$: both hold in P_1. In the first instance, the relation applies to the **else** of Production 18 and the colon of Production 27; in the other, the relation applies to the **else** and colon of Productions 40 and 41. The two uses of the colon may be distinguished by counting the preceding left and right brackets; if a colon is preceded by more left brackets than right brackets, it is of the type in Production 27. If an input program distinguishes the two types of colon and the two usages of plus and minus signs, P_4 is a precedence grammar, with the precedence matrix shown in Fig. 3.2.8. In the figure, $\odot$ represents the colon of Productions 36, 40, and 41, and θ represents the π of Production 15.

Fig. 3.2.8 also gives values of the two functions $f(X)$ and $g(Y)$ for P_4; for the precedence relation **array** $\doteq$ [, however, $f(\textbf{array}) < g([)$, so that this case must be detected and treated separately.

These departures from the definition of precedence grammars are inessential; they illustrate liberties which may be taken with the abstract structure at slight cost. In principle, the terminal symbols serving as representatives may be eliminated from the grammar entirely, substituting for each representative all the characters which it may represent. For example, the production

$$\text{factor} \rightarrow \pi \text{ factor}$$

becomes

$$\text{factor} \rightarrow + \text{ factor}$$
$$\text{factor} \rightarrow - \text{ factor}$$

The difference between the precedence relations of the unary and binary plus and minus signs occurs because the unary signs are introduced in the definition of factor, rather than in that of simple arithmetic expression. In ALGOL, FORTRAN, and most other programming languages the two usages of the sign satisfy the same precedence relations. The double use of the vertical line in representing the absolute value function $\mid x \mid$ is, however, an example from conventional mathematical notation of a multiple usage of a character in which the precedence relations satisfied by the character depend upon its context: the immediately preceding character.

The relation **else** $\gtrdot$: may be eliminated by redefining

27 limit pair $\rightarrow$ simple arithmetic expression : arithmetic expression

A slight reformulation of the definition of array declaration results in **array** $\lessdot$[, in accordance with $f(\textbf{array}) < g([)$.

APPENDIX A. The Theory

Proofs follow for most of the properties of phrase-structure grammars (PSG), operator grammars (OG), and precedence grammars (PG) used in the text. Most of the proofs are based on the *Induction Principle* (PSG):

To prove a general proposition of the form $P(x, y)$ for the strings x, y such that $x \Rightarrow y$, it is sufficient to prove $P(x, x)$ and to prove that if $P(x, z)$ and $x \Rightarrow z \rightarrow y$, then $P(x, y)$.

The induction principle may be verified by consideration of the length n of a derivation $(x = x_0 \rightarrow x_1 \rightarrow \cdots \rightarrow x_{n-1} \rightarrow x_n = y)$ of y from x. If $n = 0$ then $x = y$, and it is sufficient to prove $P(x, x)$. If $n > 0$, we may assume the theorem true for the derivation $x \Rightarrow x_{n-1} = z$, which is of length $n - 1$; therefore, in proving $P(x, y)$ we may assume $x \Rightarrow z \rightarrow y$ and $P(x, z)$.

THEOREM 1 (PSG).   *If $x_1x_2 \Rightarrow y$, then there are strings y_1 and y_2 such that $x_1 \Rightarrow y_1$, $x_2 \Rightarrow y_2$, and $y_1 y_2 = y$.*

Proof.   If $y = x_1x_2$, let $y_1 = x_1$ and $y_2 = x_2$. Otherwise, by the induction principle, $x_1x_2 \Rightarrow z \rightarrow y$, and $x_1 \Rightarrow z_1$, $x_2 \Rightarrow z_2$, $z_1z_2 = z$. The relation $z_1z_2 \rightarrow y$ implies one of two situations:

    (1) z_1 takes the form z_3Uz_4 such that $U \rightarrow u$, $y = z_3uz_4z_2$; then $x_1 \Rightarrow z_1 \Rightarrow z_3uz_4 = y_1$, $x_2 \Rightarrow z_2 = y_2$, $y_1 y_2 = y$.

    (2) z_2 takes the form z_3Uz_4, etc.; $x_1 \Rightarrow z_1 = y_1$, $x_2 \Rightarrow z_2 \Rightarrow z_3uz_4 = y_2$, $y_1 y_2 = y$.

COROLLARY 1 (PSG).   *If $x_1x_2 \ldots x_n \Rightarrow y$, then there are strings $y_1, y_2, \ldots, y_n$ such that $x_i \Rightarrow y_i$ ($1 \leq i \leq n$), and $y = y_1 y_2 \ldots y_n$.*

Proof.   By induction on Theorem 1. If a detailed derivation of y from $x_1, x_2, \ldots, x_n$ is given, the strings $y_1, y_2, \ldots, y_n$ are uniquely determined.

THEOREM 2 (PSG).   *If $x \Rightarrow y$ and the initial character of x is terminal, then the initial character of y is terminal.*

Proof.   If $x = y$, the conclusion is immediate. Otherwise, by the induction principle, $x \Rightarrow z \rightarrow y$ where the initial character of z is terminal. The production $U \rightarrow u$ which transforms z into y operates on a nonterminal character U of z, and therefore leaves the initial character unchanged.

COROLLARY 2 (PSG).   *If $x \Rightarrow y$ and the initial character of y is nonterminal, then the initial character of x is nonterminal.*

Proof. Obvious from Theorem 2.

THEOREM 3 (OG).   *If $x \Rightarrow y$ and x nowhere contains two adjacent nonterminal characters, then y nowhere contains two adjacent nonterminal characters.*

Proof.   If $x = y$, the conclusion is immediate. Otherwise, by the induction principle, $x \Rightarrow z \rightarrow y$, and z nowhere contains two adjacent nonterminal characters. Since $z \rightarrow y$, $z = vUw$, $U \rightarrow u$, and $y = vuw$. Neither v nor w contains two adjacent NTC; nor, by the definition of an operator grammar, does U contain two adjacent NTC. Since U is nonterminal, the final character of v and the initial character of w must be terminal; so a pair of adjacent NTC can occur nowhere in vuw.

COROLLARY 3 (OG).   *No sentential form contains two adjacent nonterminal characters.*
    Proof.   Every sentential form is derived from S; apply Theorem 3.

THEOREM 4 (OG).   *If T_1U_1 occurs in a sentential form s, where T_1 is terminal and U_1 is nonterminal, then any phrase of s containing T_1 also contains U_1.*

Proof.   Suppose $s = xyz$ where y is a phrase. Then $S \Rightarrow x'Uz'$, $x' \Rightarrow x$, $U \Rightarrow y$, $z' \Rightarrow z$. If y contains T_1 but not U_1, then U_1 is the initial character of z, and by Corollary 2 the initial character of z' is nonterminal. A pair of adjacent NTC therefore occurs in the sentential form $x'Uz'$, contradicting Corollary 3. If y contains T_1, it then must contain U_1.

COROLLARY 4 (OG).   *If U_1T_1 occurs in a sentential form s ($T_1 \in T$, $U_1 \in V - T$), then any phrase of s containing T_1 also contains U_1.*

Proof.   Similar to the proof of Theorem 4, considering the final character of x'.

THEOREM 5 (OG). *No phrase in a sentential form is immediately preceded or followed by nonterminal characters.*

Proof. If y is a phrase in $xyz = s$ and the initial character of z is nonterminal, then the final character of y is terminal, by Corollary 3. This contradicts Theorem 4. Similarly, the final character of x cannot be nonterminal. Of course, either of x and z may be null strings.

THEOREM 6 (OG). *If $T_1 U_1$ occurs in a sentential form s $(T_1 \in T, U_1 \in V - T)$ and if T_2 is the leftmost terminal character of some derivative v of U_1, then $T_1 \lessdot T_2$.*

Proof. Since s is a sentential form and $s \neq S$, there is a string z for which $S \Rightarrow z \twoheadrightarrow s$. By the induction principle, we may assume the theorem true for the sentential form z. Suppose $z = xUy$, $U \twoheadrightarrow u$, and $s = xuy$. The occurrence of $T_1 U_1$ in s may take four forms:

(1) $T_1 U_1$ occurs in x or y, thus in z; by the induction principle, $T_1 \lessdot T_2$.

(2) $T_1 U_1$ occurs in u, where $U \twoheadrightarrow u$. By the definition of the relation $\lessdot$ itself, $T_1 \lessdot T_2$.

(3) T_1 is the final character of x; U_1 the initial character of $u = U_1 v_1$; $U \Rightarrow U_1 v_1 \Rightarrow v v_1$; T_2 is the leftmost terminal character of a derivative $v v_1$ of U, and $T_1 U$ occurs in z; by the induction principle, $T_1 \lessdot T_2$.

(4) T_1 is the final character of u; U_1 the initial character of y. Then $U U_1$ occurs in the sentential form xUy, contrary to Corollary 3.

COROLLARY 6 (OG). *If $U_1 T_1$ occurs in a sentential form s $(T_1 \in T, U_1 \in V - T)$ and if T_2 is the rightmost terminal character of some derivative v of U_1, then $T_2 \gtrdot T_1$.*

Proof. Apply to Theorem 6 the obvious symmetries of $\lessdot$ and $\gtrdot$.

THEOREM 7 (OG). *If the substring $T_1 U_1 T_2$ occurs in the sentential form s $(T_1 \in T, U_1 \in V - T, T_2 \in T)$, then at least one of the three relations $T_1 \lessdot T_2$, $T_1 \doteq T_2$, or $T_1 \gtrdot T_2$ holds.*

Proof. Since $s \neq S$, we may assume by the induction principle that $S \Rightarrow z \twoheadrightarrow s$ and that the theorem holds for the sentential form z; $z = xUy$, $U \twoheadrightarrow u$, and $s = xuy$. Six cases arise:

(1) $T_1 U_1 T_2$ occurs in x or in y, thus in z; by induction, one of the three relations holds.

(2) $T_1 U_1 T_2$ occurs in u; by the definition of the relation, $T_1 \doteq T_2$.

(3) $T_1 U_1$ is a tail of x; then $U_1 U$ occurs in z, contrary to Corollary 3.

(4) T_1 is a tail of x; two cases arise:

    (4a) $U_1 T_2$ is a head of u, so that T_2 is the leftmost terminal character of a derivative of U. By Theorem 6, $T_1 \lessdot T_2$.

    (4b) $U_1 = u$, and T_2 is a head of y. Then $T_1 U T_2$ occurs in z, and by induction one of the three relations holds.

(5) $T_1 U_1$ is a tail of u, T_2 a head of y. Since u is a derivative of U, application of Corollary 6 yields $T_1 \gtrdot T_2$.

(6) T_1 is a tail of u, $U_1 T_2$ a head of y; then $U U_1$ occurs in z, contrary to Corollary 3.

COROLLARY 7 (OG). *If the substring $T_1 T_2$ occurs in the sentential form S $(T_1 \in T, T_2 \in T)$, then at least one of the three relations $T_1 \lessdot T_2$, $T_1 \doteq T_2$, or $T_1 \gtrdot T_2$ holds.*

Proof. A proof may be modeled upon that of Theorem 7.

THEOREM 8 (OG). *If s is a sentential form containing at least one terminal character, then $\vdash s \dashv$ contains a substring AxC for which $A \lessdot B_1 \doteq B_2 \doteq \cdots \doteq B_n \gtrdot C$ $(n \geq 1)$, where the B_i are the terminal characters of x.*

Proof. By Theorem 7 and Corollary 7, every pair of adjacent terminal characters (whether or not separated by a nonterminal character) satisfies at least one of the three precedence relations; also $\vdash \lessdot T_1$, $T_m \gtrdot \dashv$ where T_1 and T_m are the left- and rightmost terminal characters of s. Let $T_0 = \vdash, T_1, T_2, \ldots, T_m, T_{m+1} = \dashv$ be the terminal characters of s. Let j be the smallest integer for which $T_j \gtrdot T_{j+1}$; such a j exists, since $T_m \gtrdot T_{m+1}$; $1 \leq j \leq m$. Let i be the greatest integer such that $i < j$ and $T_i \lessdot T_{i+1}$; such an i exists, since $T_0 \lessdot T_1$. Now for all k such that $i < k < j$, it is not possible that $T_k \gtrdot T_{k+1}$, by the definition of j; nor can $T_k \lessdot T_{k+1}$, by the definition of i. By elimination, we must have $T_k \doteq T_{k+1}$ $(i < k < j)$, so that the conclusion of the theorem is true in particular for $A = T_i$ and $C = T_{j+1}$.

THEOREM 9 (PG). *If $T_1 U_1 T_2$ or $T_1 T_2$ occurs in the sentential form s $(T_1 \in T, U_1 \in V - T, T_2 \in T)$, then exactly one of the three relations $T_1 \lessdot T_2, T_1 \doteq T_2,$ or $T_1 \gtrdot T_2$ holds.*

Proof. By Theorem 7 or Corollary 7, at least one of the relations holds; by the definition of a precedence grammar, no more than one holds.

THEOREM 10 (PG). *If $T_1 U_1 T_2$ or $T_1 T_2$ occurs in a sentential form s and $T_1 \lessdot T_2$, then there is a phrase in s to which T_2, but not T_1, belongs.*

Proof. There is a derivation $S = s_0 \to s_1 \to \cdots \to s_n = s$ $(n \geq 1)$. Let i be the greatest integer for which T_2 does not occur in s_i $(0 \leq i \leq n - 1)$. Then T_2 occurs in s_{i+1}, and $s_i = xUy$, $U \to u_1 T_2 u_2$, $s_{i+1} = xu_1 T_2 u_2 y$. Three cases arise:

(1) T_1 first occurs in s_{i+1}; then it is the rightmost terminal character of u_1, and $T_1 \doteq T_2$, contradicting $T_1 \lessdot T_2$.

(2) T_1 first occurs in s_j $(j > i + 1)$; then it is the rightmost terminal character of some derivative of u_1, so that $T_1 \gtrdot T_2$ by an application of Corollary 6, contradicting $T_1 \lessdot T_2$.

(3) T_1 already occurs in s_i, so that the phrase of s derived from U contains T_2 but not T_1.

COROLLARY 10 (PG). *If $T_1 U_1 T_2$ or $T_1 T_2$ occurs in a sentential form s and $T_1 \gtrdot T_2$, then there is a phrase in s to which T_1, but not T_2, belongs.*

Proof. Apply the obvious symmetries of $\gtrdot$ and $\lessdot$ to the proof of Theorem 10.

THEOREM 11 (PG). *If $T_1 U_1 T_2$ or $T_1 T_2$ occurs in the sentential form s, and $T_1 \doteq T_2$, then every phrase containing T_1 contains T_2, and every phrase containing T_2 contains T_1.*

Proof. Suppose a phrase z contains T_1 but not T_2. It must also contain U_1 in the first case, by Theorem 4, so that $S \Rightarrow x'Uy', x' \Rightarrow x, U \Rightarrow z, y' \Rightarrow y, xzy = s$, where T_2 is the leftmost character of y and T_1 the rightmost terminal character of z; then $S \Rightarrow xUy \Rightarrow xzy$, and by Corollary 6, $T_1 \gtrdot T_2$, contradicting $T_1 \doteq T_2$. Thus every phrase containing T_1 contains T_2. The converse is obvious by symmetry.

THEOREM 12 (PG). *If x is a phrase whose terminal characters are $T_1, T_2, \ldots, T_n$ $(n \geq 1)$ and $T_i \doteq T_{i+1}$ $(1 \leq i \leq n - 1)$, then x is a prime phrase.*

Proof. Any prime phrase in x contains a terminal character T_i. By Theorem 11, it contains each T_i $(1 \leq i \leq n)$. By Theorem 4 and Corollary 4, it contains all the characters of x. Thus x is a prime phrase.

THEOREM 13 (PG). *If $T_0 x T_{n+1}$ occurs in the sentential form s, where the terminal characters of x are $T_1, T_2, \ldots, T_n$ $(n \geq 1)$, and if $T_0 \lessdot T_1$, $T_n \gtrdot T_{n+1}$, and $T_j \doteq T_{j+1}$ $(1 \leq j \leq n - 1)$, then x is a prime phrase of s.*

Proof. Assume $S = s_0 \to s_i \to \cdots \to s_n = s$. Let i be the greatest integer for which T_1 does not occur in s_i. By Theorem 11, s_i is also the last step in the derivation of s for which T_j does not occur $(1 \leq j \leq n)$. By the proof of Theorem 10, T_0 and T_{n+1} both occur in s_i, so that there is a phrase z containing T_j $(1 \leq j \leq n)$ but not T_0 or T_{n+1}; by Theorem 4 and Corollary 4, z must contain with T_j any adjacent nonterminal characters, so that $z = x$. By Theorem 12, x is a prime phrase.

COROLLARY 13 (PG). *If $T_0 x T_{n+1}$ occurs in $\vdash s \dashv$, where s is a sentential form, and the terminal characters of x are $T_1, T_2, \ldots, T_n$ $(n \geq 1)$, and if $T_0 \lessdot T_1$, $T_n \gtrdot T_{n+1}$, and $T_j \doteq T_{j+1}$ $(1 \leq j \leq n - 1)$, then x is a prime phrase of s.*

Proof. Four cases arise:

(1) $T_0 \neq \vdash$, $T_{n+1} \neq \dashv$; apply Theorem 13.
(2) $T_0 = \vdash$, $T_{n+1} \neq \dashv$; by Corollary 10, there is a phrase containing T_n but not T_{n+1}; by Theorem 11, Theorem 4, and Corollary 4, the phrase contains exactly the characters of x; by Theorem 12, x is a prime phrase of s.
(3) $T_0 \neq \vdash$; $T_{n+1} = \dashv$; similar to (2).
(4) $T_0 = \vdash$, $T_{n+1} = \dashv$; $x = s$, so that x is a phrase; by Theorem 12, it is a prime phrase.

THEOREM 14 (PG). *Every sentential form s either is a nonterminal character or contains a prime phrase.*

Proof. If s is a terminal character, it is itself a prime phrase. If s contains more than one character, then by Corollary 3, it contains a terminal character. By Theorem 8 and Corollary 13, s contains a prime phrase.

APPENDIX B. The Grammar P_4

1. $\lambda \to a \mid b \mid c \mid \cdots \mid y \mid z$
2. $\delta \to 0 \mid 1 \mid \cdots \mid 8 \mid 9$
3. $\beta \to$ **true** $\mid$ **false**
4. $\pi \to + \mid -$
5. $\mu \to \times \mid / \mid \div$
6. $\varrho \to < \mid \leq \mid = \mid \geq \mid > \mid \neq$
7. $\tau \to$ **real** $\mid$ **integer** $\mid$ **Boolean**
8. identifier $\to \lambda \mid$ identifier $\lambda \mid$ identifier δ
9. digit string $\to \delta \mid$ digit string δ
10. literal constant $\to$ digit string $\mid$ digit string $. \mid .$ digit string $\mid$ digit string $.$ digit string
11. subscripted variable $\to$ identifier $[\{$arithmetic expression, $\}$ arithmetic expression$]$
12. variable $\to$ identifier $\mid$ subscripted variable
13. function designator $\to$ identifier $(\{$expression, $\}$ expression$)$
14. primary $\to$ function designator $\mid$ variable $\mid$ literal constant $\mid$ (arithmetic expression)

15. factor → primary | primary ↑ factor | 10 factor | π factor

16. term → factor | term μ factor

17. simple arithmetic expression → term | simple arithmetic expression π term

18. arithmetic expression → simple arithmetic expression | **if** Boolean expression **then** arithmetic expression **else** arithmetic expression

19. relation → arithmetic expression ϱ arithmetic expression | relation ϱ arithmetic expression

20. Boolean primary → β | variable | function designator | relation | (Boolean expression)

21. Boolean secondary → Boolean primary | ¬ Boolean primary

22. conjunction → Boolean secondary | conjunction ∧ Boolean secondary

23. disjunction → conjunction | disjunction ∨ conjunction

24. implication → disjunction | implication ⊃ disjunction

25. Boolean expression → implication | Boolean expression ≡ implication

26. expression → arithmetic expression | Boolean expression

27. limit pair → arithmetic expression : arithmetic expression

28. name part → identifier ({identifier,} identifier)

29. specifier → τ {**value**}¹ {identifier,} identifier | {τ}¹ **array** {identifier,} identifier

30. go statement → **go to** identifier | **go to** identifier [arithmetic expression]

31. assignment → variable := expression | variable := assignment

32. type declaration → τ {identifier,} identifier | **constant** identifier := expression

33. array declaration → {τ}¹ **array** {identifier,} identifier [{limit pair,} limit pair]

34. switch declaration → **switch** name part

35. procedure declaration → **procedure** name part {; specifier} {; statement} **end**

36. function declaration → **function** name part : statement

37. procedure call → identifier ({expression,} expression)

38. compound statement → **begin** {declaration;} {statement;} statement **end**

39. **for** list element → arithmetic expression | arithmetic expression **step** arithmetic expression **until** arithmetic expression | arithmetic expression **while** Boolean expression

40. closed statement → go statement | assignment | procedure call | identifier : {closed statement}¹ | **comment** | compound statement | **for** identifier := {for list element,} for list element **do** closed statement | **if** Boolean expression **then** closed statement **else** closed statement

41. open statement → identifier : open statement | **for** identifier := {for list element,} for list element **do** open statement | **if** Boolean expression **then** closed statement **else** open statement | **if** Boolean expression **then** statement

42. statement → closed statement | open statement

43. declaration → type declaration | array declaration | switch declaration | procedure declaration | function declaration

Remarks. The words **comment** and **end** may be followed by any string not containing a semicolon, **begin, end,** or **else,** without affecting the meaning of the program. Since such strings are typically comments in a natural language, they have the structure assigned them in that language, and cannot be assigned a structure by P_4.

Production 9.   The only literal constants explicitly permitted are digit strings optionally containing a decimal point. The ALGOL 60 constant $123_{10}4$ is ruled out as not in accord with conventional usage; the expression $123 \times_{10}4$, however, is allowed, and it is the intent of the design that all phrases having constant value be evaluated during compilation.

Production 15.   The form $_{10}x$ is intended to mean the same as $10 \uparrow x$. Exponentiation associates from the right, since left association plays no useful role for this operation. As a result, such common forms as $e \uparrow - x \uparrow 2$ may be written without parentheses. Note also the greater freedom allowed the unary minus sign.

Production 19.   Conditions like $1 \leq x < 10$ or $1 < x < y < z$ occur with such frequency that it seems worthwhile to permit the construction.

Production 29.   Type and value declarations in procedures are combined for brevity. Specifiers are required for all parameters.

Production 32.   The constant declaration assigns to an identifier a constant value. The value must be known during translation, and the expression for the constant may therefore contain identifiers only of standard functions and of previous constants. It is not necessary that a type be assigned to a constant; a type specifies a possible set of values and is redundant for an object having a known value.

Production 35, 36.   A procedure declaration plays much the same role as in ALGOL 60, with the restrictions that each formal parameter must be declared in a specifier and that a procedure declaration does not define a function.

A function declaration defines a mathematical function of the values of its parameters. All variables are locally declared within the statement. A function designator is evaluated by assigning the values of its parameters to the corresponding variables in the name part of the function name and executing the statement. The value of the function is then the final value of the variable having the same name.

Functions may be recursive. A function is not recursive if it refers only to functions occurring earlier in the program, none of which are recursive.

REFERENCES

1. Irons, E. T., "A Syntax Directed Compiler for ALGOL 60," *Comm. ACM*, vol. 4 (January 1961), pp. 51–55.

2. Floyd, R. W., "An Algorithm for Coding Efficient Arithmetic Operations," *Comm. ACM*, vol. 4 (January 1961), pp. 42–51.

3. Chomsky, N., "On Certain Formal Properties of Grammars," *Inform. Contr.*, vol. 2 (1959), pp. 137–167, 393–395.

4. Bar-Hillel, Y., Perles, M., and Shamir, E., "On Formal Properties of Simple Phrase Structure Grammars," *Zeit. Phonetik, Sprachwissen. Kommunik.*, vol. 14 (1961), pp. 143–172.

5. Naur, P. (ed.), "Report on the Algorithmic Language ALGOL 60," *Comm. ACM*, vol. 3 (May 1960), pp. 299–314.

6. Conway, M. (letter to the editor), *Comm. ACM*, vol. 4 (October 1961), p. 465.

3.3. A Practical Method for Constructing LR(k) Processors

by A. J. Korenjak

3.3.1. SUMMARY

A practical method for constructing LR(k) processors is developed. These processors are capable of recognizing and parsing an input during a single no-backup scan in a number of steps equal to the length of the input plus the number of steps in its derivation.

The technique presented here is based on the original method described by Knuth, but decreases both the effort required to construct the processor and the size of the processor produced. This procedure involves partitioning the given grammar into a number of smaller parts. If an LR(k) processor can be constructed for each part (using Knuth's algorithm) and if certain conditions relating these individual processors are satisfied, then an LR(k) processor for the entire grammar can be constructed for them. Using this procedure, an LR(1) parser for ALGOL has been obtained. Key words and phrases: LR(k) grammar, syntactic analysis, parser, deterministic language, syntax-directed compiler, language processor, context-free language, ALGOL. CR categories: 4.12, 5.22, 5.23.

EDITOR'S NOTE: This article reproduced by permission of the author and the publisher: *Comm. ACM*, vol. 12, no. 11 (November 1969), pp. 612–623.

3.3.2. INTRODUCTION

The use of formal syntax as the basis of automatically constructed compilers for programming languages has gained wide acceptance in recent years. These applications have, to a great extent, used only the class of context-free languages as a model. For, although features of programming languages, such as the requirement that identifiers be declared before use, require a more powerful descriptive mechanism, these restrictions can be more efficiently handled by other means (e.g., symbol tables) than by using a more powerful language model. In fact, rather than generalizing the context-free model, practical applications have almost exclusively dealt with more restricted language classes.[2] In particular, the majority of the automatically constructed syntax recognizers are based on a subclass of context-free grammars whose strings can be processed in a single left-to-right no-backup scan, using a pushdown stack. This general approach is formally studied in Ref. 3, where the deterministic pushdown automata and the related class of deterministic (context-free) languages are defined. Knuth[4] defines the LR(k) grammars,[†] which have the property that they generate all and only the deterministic languages. (In fact, he shows that the LR(1) grammars also have this "completeness" property with respect to the deterministic languages.) Thus the LR(k) grammars (and, in particular, the LR(1) grammars) are an extremely useful tool for the study of the single-scan, context-free languages.

Knuth has described an algorithm for testing an arbitrary context-free grammar for the LR(k) condition (for any particular value of $k \geq 0$). If it succeeds, it generates a deterministic pushdown automaton which can recognize and parse sentences of the given grammar. However, the effort required to make this check and the size of the processor produced grow very rapidly with the complexity of the grammar.[1] For a very large grammar, such as one describing a syntax for a programming language, the procedure is not practical. In the first part of this paper a practical method, the basis of which is the Knuth algorithm but which will allow us to work with very large grammars, is investigated. This method involves dividing the given grammar into a number of smaller grammars, proving each part is LR(1), using the Knuth algorithm, and concluding that the original grammar is LR(1) if certain conditions relating the parts are satisfied. The second part of the paper applies this method to a grammar for ALGOL and discusses the implementation of the resulting LR(1) processor.

[†] k is a non-negative integer.

3.3.3. DEFINITIONS AND NOTATION

A *vocabulary* V is the union of two disjoint sets of symbols, V_N (the *nonterminal symbols*) and V_T (the *terminal symbols*). For any set of symbols V, the notation V^* is used for the set of all finite-length strings over V, including the empty string, ε; $V^+ \triangleq V^* - \{\varepsilon\}$. For $k \geq 0$, V^k denotes all strings in V^* of length k. Unless otherwise specified, uppercase italic letters $(A, B, C, \ldots)$ are used for nonterminal symbols, lowercase italic letters at the beginning of the alphabet $(a, b, c, \ldots)$ for terminal symbols, lowercase italic letters at the end of the alphabet $(t, u, v, \ldots)$ for strings in V_T^*, and lowercase Greek letters $(\alpha, \beta, \gamma, \ldots)$ for strings in V^*.

A *context-free grammar* G is a 4-tuple:

$$G = (V_N, V_T, \mathscr{P}, Z_0).$$

V_N and V_T are respectively the nonterminal and terminal vocabularies associated with G. $\mathscr{P}$ is a finite set of *productions* (or *rules*) of the form $A \to \omega$; A is called the *subject* of this rule. The set V_N must include all subjects; V_T must include all symbols appearing on the right side of any production that are not members of V_N. The symbol Z_0 is a particular member of V_N, called the *starting symbol*.

If a grammar G includes the rule $A \to \omega$, then for any strings α and β we write $\alpha A \beta \to \alpha \omega \beta$. If $\alpha_1 \to \alpha_2 \to \cdots \to \alpha_n$, $n \geq 1$, we write $\alpha_1 \Rightarrow \alpha_n$, and say that α_n is *derivable from* α_1 or that α_n can be *reduced to* α_1. The sequence $\alpha_1, \alpha_2, \ldots, \alpha_n$ is a *derivation* of α_n from α_1 in G; the sequence $\alpha_n, \alpha_{n-1}, \ldots, \alpha_1$ is a *reduction* of α_n to α_1. If each step of a derivation is of the form $\alpha A t \to \alpha \omega t$, then the derivation is a *rightmost derivation*, since $t \in V_T^*$ and hence the rightmost nonterminal symbol is rewritten at each step; any description of the corresponding reduction is called a *leftmost parse*. If $Z_0 \Rightarrow \omega$ by a rightmost derivation, then ω is a *rightmost sentential form* of G. If $Z_0 \Rightarrow t$ and $t \in V_T^*$, t is a *sentence* of G. The set of all sentences of G is the *language* generated by G, denoted $L(G)$.

3.3.4. LR(k) GRAMMARS AND THE KNUTH ALGORITHM

Although the construction and operation of LR(k) processors has been described in detail by Knuth,[4] to clarify the remainder of this article it is necessary to repeat the formal description. The operation of the processor is described first, followed by the algorithm to construct the *parsing table* that drives it.

For any grammar $G = (V_N, V_T, \mathscr{P}, Z_0)$, number the productions in $\mathscr{P}$ from 1 to π; the pth production is represented by $A_p \to X_{p1} \ldots X_{pn_p}$ $(n_p \geq 0)$. For fixed $k \geq 0$ and Z_0', $\# \notin V$, let $G' = (V_N', V_T', \mathscr{P}', Z_0')$, where $V_N' = V_N \cup \{Z_0'\}$, $V_T' = V_T \cup \{\#\}$ and

$$\mathscr{P}' = \mathscr{P} \cup \{Z_0' \to Z_0 \#^k\}.^\dagger$$

Number the productions of G' as in G, assigning $Z_0 \to Z \#^k$ the number 0. The symbol $\#$ is called the endmarker. G' is called the *k-augmented grammar* associated with G.

If G is LR(k), a *parsing table* $\mathscr{T}(G)$ which describes the LR(k) processor for G can be constructed. $\mathscr{T}(G)$ is composed of a finite number of rows, each of which is associated with a *state* of the processor. A typical row of $\mathscr{T}(G)$, corresponding to a state $\mathscr{S}$, has form[‡] shown in Table 3.3.1:

Table 3.3.1

State Name	Lookahead Strings	Actions	Stack Symbols	Goto States
	y_1	Shift	Y_1	$\mathscr{S}_1$
	.	.	Y_2	$\mathscr{S}_2$
$\mathscr{S}$	.	.	.	.
	.	.	.	.
	y_l	Reduce p	Y_m	$\mathscr{S}_m$

$y_1, \ldots, y_l \in (V_T')^k$ are distinct *lookahead strings* $(l \geq 1)$; $Y_1, \ldots, Y_m \in V$ are distinct *stack symbols* $(m \geq 0)$; $\mathscr{S}_1, \ldots, \mathscr{S}_m$ are *goto states*. The set of lookahead strings is denoted as $L(\mathscr{S})$ and the action associated with each $y \in L(\mathscr{S})$ is denoted as $A_{\mathscr{S}}(y)$. Each action is one of the following: *Shift, Reduce p* $(1 \leq p \leq \pi)$, or *Accept*. The set of stack symbols is denoted $S(\mathscr{S})$ and the goto state associated with each $Y \in S(\mathscr{S})$ is denoted $G_{\mathscr{S}}(Y)$.

Driven by a table $\mathscr{T}(G)$ composed of rows such as these, the LR(k) processor examines an input string from left to right and attempts to reduce it to Z_0—in fact, it does so by attempting to generate its leftmost parse. A two-track pushdown stack is maintained for control purposes. We denote the position of the input tape and the contents of the stack by the notation:

$$\begin{array}{c} \mathscr{S}_0 \; \mathscr{S}_1 \ldots \mathscr{S}_n \\ \bullet \quad X_1 \ldots X_n \end{array} \Big| a_1 \ldots a_k t$$

---

† For any symbol X, X^k denotes the k-fold concatenation of X with itself.
‡ A complete table is shown in Table 3.3.2.

Let the original input string be $xa_1 \ldots a_k t \in V_T^* \#^k$. Then, when the above configuration has been reached, x has been reduced to $X_1 \ldots X_n$, the lookahead string is $a_1 \ldots a_k$, and t is that portion of the input not yet examined. The top track of the pushdown stack contains the state names $\mathscr{S}_0, \ldots, \mathscr{S}_n$; roughly, $\mathscr{S}_n$ represents the possible parses at this point.

The processor operates as follows. A special start state $\mathscr{S}_0$ is initially placed on the stack and the first k symbols of the input string are the initial lookahead string. (The symbol $\bullet$ is just a marker.) Assume the processor has reached the configuration shown above.

First, the lookahead string $a_1 \ldots a_k$ is compared with each of the strings in $L(\mathscr{S}_n)$, causing *exactly one* of four possible actions:

(i) If $A_{\mathscr{S}_n}(a_1 \ldots a_k) = Shift$, a_1 is pushed onto the bottom track of the stack, giving

$$\begin{array}{c} \mathscr{S}_0 \quad \mathscr{S}_1 \ldots \mathscr{S}_n \\ \bullet \quad\; X_1 \ldots X_n a_1 \end{array} \Bigg| a_2 \ldots a_k t$$

(ii) If $A_{\mathscr{S}_n}(a_1 \ldots a_k) = Reduce\ p$, the rightmost n_p items on both tracks of the stack are popped off and A_p is pushed onto the bottom track of the stack, resulting in:

$$\begin{array}{c} \mathscr{S}_0 \mathscr{S}_1 \ldots \mathscr{S}_{n-n_p} \\ \bullet \quad X_1 \ldots X_{n-n_p} A_p \end{array} \Bigg| a_1 \ldots a_k t$$

(iii) If $A_{\mathscr{S}_n}(a_1 \ldots a_k) = Accept$, processing stops and the input is accepted (see below);

(iv) If $a_1 \ldots a_k \notin L(\mathscr{S}_n)$, the input is rejected.

Secondly, if the action was *Shift* or *Reduce p*, a goto state is determined from the parsing table and placed in the empty position at the right end of the top stack track, in the following manner:

(i) If the action was *Shift*, a_1 will be in $S(\mathscr{S}_n)$ and the goto state is $G_{\mathscr{S}_n}(a_1)$;

(ii) If the action was *Reduce p*, $\mathscr{S}_{n-n_p}$ has been exposed; by consulting the $\mathscr{S}_{n-n_p}$ row in the parsing table, the goto state is determined to be $G_{\mathscr{S}_{n-n_p}}(A_p)$.

In either case (after relabeling) the stack again has the form

$$\begin{array}{c} \mathscr{S}_0 \quad \mathscr{S}_1 \ldots \mathscr{S}_n \\ \bullet \quad\; X_1 \ldots X_n \end{array} \Bigg| a_1 \ldots a_k t$$

where $\mathscr{S}_n$ is the goto state just computed. The process is iterated; eventually either the input will be rejected or the special *accepting configuration* will be reached:

$$\begin{array}{c|c} \mathscr{S}_0 \; \mathscr{S}_F & \\ \bullet \quad Z_0 & \#^k \end{array}$$

S_F is the unique state containing the entry $A_{\mathscr{S}_F}(\#^k) = Accept$. No infinite loops are possible, since each move either decreases the length of the input not yet examined or produces another line of the rightmost derivation.

Before proceeding further, it is necessary to explain in some detail the meaning of a state. A *state* is a set of *partial states* of the form $[p, j, w]$, where $0 \leq p \leq \pi$, $0 \leq j \leq n_p$ and $w \in (V_T')^k$. The processor is said to be in the partial state $[p, j, w]$ if, for some string β, the bottom track of the stack is $\bullet \beta X_{p1} \ldots X_{pj}$ and there exists a terminal string t such that $\beta A_p wt$ is a rightmost sentential form of G'. Thus, in scanning from left to right, the processor has made all reductions necessary for a leftmost parse and has reached a point where the first j elements of the pth production are at the top of the stack; w is a k-character terminal string which may appear if the pth production is completed. At any given time, the processor will be in the state composed of all the partial states which fulfill the conditions above; this is the state at the top of the stack.

Before describing the construction of the parsing table, two definitions are needed. The first defines the set of all terminal strings of length k that are prefixes of strings derivable from α. The second is similar, except the derivations involved may not include the application of a rule $A \to \varepsilon$ to a string which begins with A.

3.3.4.1. *Definition*

For a grammar $G = (V_N, V_T, \mathscr{P}, S)$, $\alpha \in V^+$ and $k \geq 0$,

(a) $H(\alpha) = \{t \in V_T^k \mid \exists \beta \in V^* \text{ such that } \alpha \Rightarrow t\beta \text{ in } G\}$;
(b) $H'(\alpha) = \{t \in V_T^k \mid \exists \beta \in V^* \text{ such that } \alpha \Rightarrow t\beta \text{ in } G, \text{ but } \alpha \Rightarrow t\beta$ does *not* contain a step of the form $A\gamma \to \gamma$ (due to $A \to \varepsilon$ in $\mathscr{P}$)}.

Both sets are easily computed from the grammar.

During the construction of the parsing table, a list of states is maintained whose associated rows are yet to be computed. Initially, this list contains the start state,[†] $\mathscr{S}_0 = \{[0, 0, \#^k]\}$; as each row is computed, additional

---

[†] This state does not quite conform to the informal description of a state given above, since $\#^k$ cannot *follow* the rule $Z_0' \to Z_0 \#^k$. However, it does correctly indicate that processing starts at the 0th position of rule 0.

states may be added to the list. Since there is a finite number of possible states, the process will terminate. The entries for a typical row of the table, corresponding to a state $\mathscr{S}$, are determined as follows:

First, we compute a set $\mathscr{S}'$ which is needed to find the table entries for row $\mathscr{S}$. Roughly, $\mathscr{S}'$ adds partial states to $\mathscr{S}$ which represent the introduction of new productions. Formally, $\mathscr{S}'$ is iteratively computed as the smallest set satisfying the equation

$$\mathscr{S}' = \mathscr{S} \cup \{[q, 0, x] \mid \exists [p, j, w] \in \mathscr{S}' \quad \text{such that } j < n_p,$$
$$X_{p(j+1)} = A_q \quad \text{and} \quad x \in H(X_{p(j+2)} \ldots X_{pn_p}w)\}.^\dagger$$

The partial states added to $\mathscr{S}$ in computing $\mathscr{S}'$ indicate the following situation: the processor is in partial state $[p, j, w]$ and the $(j + 1)$-th element of the pth production is the subject of the qth production; thus, the next input symbols may have been derived from A_q according to the qth production.

Second, determine the members of $L(\mathscr{S})$ and their corresponding actions:

(i) If $\exists [p, j, w] \in \mathscr{S}'$ such that $j < n_p$ and

$$y \in H'(X_{p(j+1)} \ldots X_{pn_p}w),$$

then $y \in L(\mathscr{S})$ and $A_{\mathscr{S}}(y) = Shift$, since y allows the possibility of continuing the pth production.

(ii) If $[p, n_p, y] \in \mathscr{S}'$, then $y \in L(\mathscr{S})$ and $A_{\mathscr{S}}(y) = Reduce\ p$, since the entire pth production is on the stack and y can follow the completion of this production.

If the action for any symbol in $L(\mathscr{S})$ is not unique, the algorithm terminates; then G is not LR(k), by the definition below.

Third, compute $S(\mathscr{S})$ and the corresponding goto states:

(i) $S(\mathscr{S}) = \{Y \mid \exists [p, j, w] \in \mathscr{S}' \text{ such that } Y = X_{p(j+1)}\}$;
(ii) For each $Y \in S(\mathscr{S})$,

$$G_{\mathscr{S}}(Y) = \{[p, j + 1, w] \mid \exists [p, j, w] \in \mathscr{S}' \text{ such that } Y \doteq X_{p(j+1)}\}.$$

$\dagger$ For example, to compute $\mathscr{S}'_0$ from $\mathscr{S}_0 = \{[0, 0, \#^k]\}$: at the first iteration, add to $\mathscr{S}_0$ all partial states of the form $[q, 0, \#^k]$, where Z_0 is the subject of the qth rule; successive iterations add all partial states corresponding to the 0th position of rules whose subjects can begin a string derived from Z_0. Thus, $\mathscr{S}'_0$ represents all grammar positions in which the processor might be before the first input symbol is read.

That is, when the processor is in a state containing the partial state $[p, j, w]$ and the $(j + 1)$-th element of the pth production is found, it advances to a state containing the partial state $[p, j + 1, w]$.

Finally, the list of states whose rows must yet be computed is updated by:

(i) Removing the present state, $\mathscr{S}$;

(ii) Adding all those states which appear in the goto column of the row for $\mathscr{S}$ that are not on the list and whose rows have not been computed.

These steps are then repeated for each entry on the list, until it is empty. In order to accept an input string as described above, in the unique state $\mathscr{S}_F$ which contains $[0, 1, \#^k]$, set $A_{\mathscr{S}_F}(\#^k)$ to *Accept*.

This algorithm provides a *definition of* LR(k): a grammar G is said to be LR(k) if, for each state $\mathscr{S}$ in $\mathscr{T}(G)$, each symbol in $L(\mathscr{S})$ has a unique action. Knuth has proved that if G is an LR(k) grammar (for some $k \geq 0$), then $L(G)$ is a deterministic language—that is, $L(G)$ can be recognized by a deterministic pushdown automaton. Since the processor defined by the parsing table is of the pushdown type, it is merely necessary to incorporate the lookahead mechanism into the finite control unit of a canonical pushdown automaton. He has also shown that every deterministic language has an LR(1) grammar.

3.3.5. THE PARTITIONING SCHEME—A SIMPLE CASE

The computation required for Knuth's algorithm increases rapidly with the size and complexity of the grammar and with the value of k. For a grammar G, let $P = \sum_{p=0}^{\pi} n_p$ and $F = T^k$, where T is the size of V'_T; then a bound on the number of states in $\mathscr{T}(G)$ is 2^{PF}. Although the actual number of states is typically smaller, Earley exhibits a class of grammars for which the number of states grows exponentially with grammar size.[1] The partitioning scheme described here attempts to reduce parsing table size by reducing growth reflected in the factor F. In particular, it reduces the number of states whose partial states differ only in their third components. This state reduction decreases the computation required to generate the parsing table in two ways. First, fewer table rows need be computed. Second, certain necessary bookkeeping chores are shortened—e.g., determining whether a goto state is identical to a previously generated state, which is necessary to terminate the Knuth algorithm. Most important, the reduction in table size occurs *during* table generation; it is not achieved by generating the entire Knuth table and eliminating or combining states *a posteriori*.

As the first step, since k is a very strong factor, only LR(1) grammars are considered.[†] From a theoretical point of view, there is no loss of generality, since LR(1) grammars have the same generative capability as LR(k) grammars. More important, this restriction does not seem to be a severe practical limitation. Experience indicates that grammars for most programming languages are LR(1)—or almost so. If a few non-LR(1) situations do arise, the practical solution is not to try to construct an LR(2) processor. In the programming language grammars we have worked with, the few problems encountered have been easily eliminated in one of two ways.

(i) By the preprocessor (lexical analyzer): for example, one problem frequently cited in ALGOL involves the statement prefix "$XYZ :=$". If "$:=$" is treated as two symbols, there may be some problem in correctly parsing "XYZ" with an LR(1) processor. However, there is no good reason for not letting the preprocessor pass the single symbol "$:=$" to the parser. This avoids the problem and probably should be done in any case. Certainly, strings such as **begin** and **end** should be treated as single symbols.

(ii) By making small local changes in the grammar so that it becomes LR(1): A few potential problems in ALGOL were eliminated this way, as mentioned in Section 3.3.8.

If some trouble spots cannot be avoided (perhaps for semantic reasons), it may be necessary for the parser to process these sections in a non-LR(1) manner. (The partitioning scheme seems to be a well-suited framework for such an approach; it is an area for further study.) But it is certainly not generally practical to process significant portions of the input with $k > 1$.

The proposed method of processor construction involves generating the processors for certain LR(1) subgrammars and then combining them to form an LR(1) processor for the entire grammar. To begin with, a very simple case is considered which demonstrates the technique, but avoids the complexities, of the general method. An example is given.

Let $G = (V_N, V_T, \mathscr{P}, Z_0)$ be a large grammar for which we wish to construct an LR(1) processor. Choose a nonterminal Z_1 other than Z_0 and let $\bar{z}_1$ be a new terminal symbol. Let $G_0 = (V_{N_0}, V_{T_0}, \mathscr{P}_0, Z_0)$ be the reduced form[‡] of $(V_N, V_T, \bar{\mathscr{P}}, Z_0)$, where $\bar{\mathscr{P}} = \{Y \rightarrow \bar{\alpha} \mid Y \rightarrow \alpha \in \mathscr{P}$, and $\bar{\alpha}$ is obtained from α by replacing each occurrence of Z_1 by $\bar{z}_1\}$. Let $G_1 = (V_{N_1}, V_{T_1}, \mathscr{P}_1, Z_1)$ be the reduced form of $(V_N, V_T, \mathscr{P}, Z_1)$. Thus

---

[†] However, the partitioning scheme can be generalized to $k > 1$ straightforwardly.

[‡] A grammar is in *reduced form* if all "useless" nonterminals are removed: for each $A \in V_N$, $\exists \alpha, \beta, t$ such that $S \Rightarrow \alpha A \beta \Rightarrow \alpha t \beta$.

G_0 is the reduced form of the grammar obtained from G by replacing every occurrence of the nonterminal symbol Z_1 by the new terminal symbol $\bar{z}_1$, and G_1 is the reduced subgrammar of G which has Z_1 as its starting symbol. Let $G_0' = (V_{N_0}', V_{T_0}', \mathscr{P}_0', Z_0')$ and $G_1' = (V_{N_1}', V_{T_1}', \mathscr{P}_1', Z_1')$ be the 1-augmented grammars associated with G_0 and G_1, with endmarkers $\#_0$ and $\#_1$, respectively. Let the productions of $\mathscr{P}_0$ and $\mathscr{P}_1$ retain the numbering they had in $\mathscr{P}$. The two rules involving endmarkers may both be numbered zero.

Consider a sentence $xz_1 y$ that has a derivation $Z_0 \Rightarrow xZ_1 y \Rightarrow xz_1 y$ in G such that $Z_0 \Rightarrow x\bar{z}_1 y$ in G_0 and $Z_1 \Rightarrow z_1$ in G_1. Assume both G_0 and G_1 are LR(1). Consider the recognition of $xz_1 y$ by an LR(1)-type processor, knowing that both $x\bar{z}_1 y$ and z_1 can be recognized in an LR(1) fashion. The LR(1) recognizer for G might operate in two modes—one for G_0 and the other for G_1. The only difficulty is in ensuring that the master LR(1) processor could determine when to switch between the two modes as it scans $xz_1 y$ from left to right. This requires that the master processor be able to determine that a mode change is to be made on the basis of the state it is in after processing x and the first symbol of z_1.

Similarly, the processor must be able to detect the end of the substring z_1. This can be accomplished if whenever $Z_0' \Rightarrow x\bar{z}_1 at$ in G_0' and $Z_1' \Rightarrow z_1 bu$ in G_1', then $a \neq b$. Otherwise, having seen $xz_1 a$, the processor would not know whether to return to the G_0 mode or to continue to find a longer instance of Z_1 in the G_1 mode.

Rather than formalize these two conditions in terms of the grammar, we describe a method of constructing, if possible, an LR(1) parsing table $\mathscr{T}$ for G from $\mathscr{T}_0 = \mathscr{T}(G_0)$ and $\mathscr{T}_1 = \mathscr{T}(G_1)$. At various points during this construction certain conditions must be met in order to continue. These are sufficient conditions for obtaining the LR(1) parser $\mathscr{T}$. The construction algorithm proceeds by making certain modifications to $\mathscr{T}_0$ and $\mathscr{T}_1$, and then forming $\mathscr{T}$ as the union of the resulting tables.

Consider the left-to-right parsing of the sentence $xz_1 y\#$. The LR(1) tables $\mathscr{T}_0$ and $\mathscr{T}_1$ are available to recognize the strings $x\bar{z}_1 y\#_0$ and $z_1 \#_1$. The composite table $\mathscr{T}$ should start in state $\mathscr{S}_0^0$, the start state of $\mathscr{T}_0$, and proceed to parse x (which may be null) according to $\mathscr{T}_0$ until the initial character of z_1 first becomes the lookahead symbol. The state $\mathscr{S}$ it has reached and all preceding states are in $\mathscr{T}_0$. Since $x\bar{z}_1$ is the prefix of a sentence of $L(G_0')$, $\bar{z}_1 \in L(\mathscr{S})$. However, since the input is $xz_1 y\#$, not $x\bar{z}_1 y\#_0$, $\mathscr{T}$ will see the initial symbol of z_1, not the symbol $\bar{z}_1$. The possible initial symbols of z_1 can be found in S_0^1, the start state of $\mathscr{T}_1$; they are exactly the members of $L(\mathscr{S}_0^1)$. Thus, $L(\mathscr{S})$ should be updated by replacing

$\bar{z}_1$ by $L(\mathscr{S}_0^1)$. The action associated with each of these new symbols depends on $A_{\mathscr{S}}(\bar{z}_1)$. Let b be the member of $L(\mathscr{S}_0^1)$ which is the first symbol of z_1:

(i) If $A_{\mathscr{S}}(\bar{z}_1) = $ *Reduce p*, the action does not affect z_1. Correct parsing of x still requires *Reduce p*, since b now signals the end of rule p for $\mathscr{T}$ just as $\bar{z}_1$ did for $\mathscr{T}_0$. Thus $A_{\mathscr{S}}(b)$ should be set to *Reduce p*.

(ii) If $A_{\mathscr{S}}(\bar{z}_1) = $ *Shift*, processing of z_1 should begin. This would be done in $\mathscr{T}_1$ by S_0^1. To effect this switch to the $\mathscr{T}_1$ mode, $A_{\mathscr{S}}(b)$ should be set to $A_{\mathscr{S}_0^1}(b)$.

These changes should be made to every state $\mathscr{S}$ in $\mathscr{T}_0$ for which $\bar{z}_1 \in L(\mathscr{S})$. In order for the algorithm to proceed, however, the following condition must be met for each such state: if $b \in L(\mathscr{S}) \cap L(\mathscr{S}_0^1)$, then the action assigned to b during the updating of $\mathscr{S}$ must be the same as the action it originally had in $\mathscr{S}$—i.e., no conflicts may be generated.

Before proceeding to modifications in $\mathscr{T}_1$, changes needed in the stack and goto entries of $\mathscr{T}_0$ must be considered. Of the states examined so far, the only ones for which $\bar{z}_1 \in S(\mathscr{S})$ are those for which $A_{\mathscr{S}}(\bar{z}_1) = $ *Shift*. To obtain the correct stack and goto entries for these states, the existing entries must be merged with those for $\mathscr{S}_0^1$, in order to effect the mode change. $S(\mathscr{S})$ must be replaced by $[S(\mathscr{S}) - \{\bar{z}_1\}] \cup S(\mathscr{S}_0^1)$. The goto states corresponding to the new members of $S(\mathscr{S})$ are obtained as follows:

(i) For all $Y \neq Z_1$, $G_{\mathscr{S}}(Y)$ is set to $G_{\mathscr{S}}(Y) \cup G_{\mathscr{S}_0^1}(Y)$.

(ii) $G_{\mathscr{S}}(Z_1)$ is set to $G_{\mathscr{S}}(\bar{z}_1) \cup \tilde{G}_{\mathscr{S}_0^1}(Z_1)$, where $\tilde{G}_{\mathscr{S}_0^1}(Z_1)$ is obtained from the table entry for $G_{\mathscr{S}_0^1}(Z_1)$ by deleting $\#_1$ and its action.

The union operation used on states indicates the formation of a (possibly) *new* state, whose table entries are the "union" of the entires of its members.[†] In (i) above, if $Y \notin S(\mathscr{S})$ before updating, then $G_{\mathscr{S}}(Y)$ is set to $G_{\mathscr{S}_0^1}(Y)$ to allow $\mathscr{S}$ to act like $\mathscr{S}_0^1$ while $\mathscr{T}$ is processing z_1 in the $\mathscr{T}_1$ mode. However, if Y was already in $S(\mathscr{S})$, indicating that Y might also be a continuation of the $\mathscr{T}_0$ mode, then a union state must be formed to allow the processor to follow both paths until the indecision is resolved. In (ii), $G_{\mathscr{S}}(\bar{z}_1)$ indicates that when a Z_1 has been found, processing should return to the $\mathscr{T}_0$ mode, just as if $\bar{z}_1$ had been in the input string. However, if $Z_1 \Rightarrow Z_1\alpha$ in G_1, processing should also continue in the $\mathscr{T}_1$ mode to find a longer instance of Z_1. In this case, $\tilde{G}_{\mathscr{S}_0^1}(Z_1)$ must be added. $\tilde{G}_{\mathscr{S}_0^1}(Z_1)$ is used because $G_{\mathscr{S}_0^1}(Z_1)$ is $\mathscr{S}_F^1$, the accepting state of $\mathscr{T}_1$, and has the entry $A(\#_1) = $ *Accept*. This entry is not needed in the new state, since it indicates that all of z_1 has been reduced to Z_1, in which case the actual lookahead symbol will

---

[†] A detailed description of union state formation appears later.

be a member of $L(G_{\mathscr{S}}(\bar{z}_1))$. If Z_1 cannot generate a string $Z_1\alpha$ with $\alpha \neq \varepsilon$, then $\tilde{G}_{\mathscr{S}_0^1}(Z_1)$ is null and a union state is not actually formed by (ii).

At this point, all updating of $\mathscr{T}_0$ has been completed and the correct transfer of control from the $\mathscr{T}_0$ mode to the $\mathscr{T}_1$ mode has been effected. For the input $xz_1\,y\#$, parsing of z_1 as Z_1 now continues in $\mathscr{T}_1$, since the goto states generated in (i) above (neglecting union states) are in $\mathscr{T}_1$. When the initial character of y is first encountered as the lookahead symbol, $\mathscr{T}$ is in some state $\mathscr{S}$ of $\mathscr{T}_1$ such that $\#_1 \in L(\mathscr{S})$; but the actual lookahead symbol is some member of the set $\mathrm{Follow}_{G_0'}(\bar{z}_1)$.[†] Correct parsing requires that $L(\mathscr{S})$ be updated by replacing $\#_1$ by $\mathrm{Follow}_{G_0'}(\bar{z}_1)$. The action for each new member of $L(\mathscr{S})$ should be set to $A_{\mathscr{S}}(\#_1)$, since any one of these symbols can now signal the end of Z_1, just as $\#_1$ did for $\mathscr{T}_1$. This updating should be done for all states $\mathscr{S}$ in $\mathscr{T}_1$ for which $\#_1 \in L(\mathscr{S})$, except $\mathscr{S}_F^1$. ($\mathscr{S}_F^1$ appears in $\mathscr{T}$ only, if at all, as part of the union state formed in (ii) above; it may be deleted.) As was the case in updating states of $\mathscr{T}_0$, conflicts must not be generated by the symbols which replace $\#_1$. That is, if any symbol b was in $L(\mathscr{S})$ before updating and is also in $\mathrm{Follow}_{G_0'}(\bar{z}_1)$, then $A_{\mathscr{S}}(b)$ is required to have been the same as $A_{\mathscr{S}}(\#_1)$.

Note that replacing $\#_1$ by the entire set $\mathrm{Follow}_{G_0'}(\bar{z}_1)$ may delay the discovery of certain errors in the input string, since, for any particular prefix tz_1 of a sentence, only *some* elements of $\mathrm{Follow}_{G_0'}(\bar{z}_1)$ might follow *this instance* of z_1. However, strings not in $L(G)$ will eventually be rejected by $\mathscr{T}$, since an LR(1) processor reduces a string ω to Y only if $Y \Rightarrow \omega$ and accepts an input only if it is reduced to the starting symbol.

The updating of $\mathscr{T}_0$ and $\mathscr{T}_1$ is now complete, since the switch back to the $\mathscr{T}_0$ mode after z_1 has been reduced to Z_1 has been taken care of: once the reduction to Z_1 has been done, the goto state is computed from the state $\mathscr{S}$ which appears below Z_1 on the stack; but $\mathscr{S}$ is in $\mathscr{T}_0$ and $\bar{z}_1 \in S(\mathscr{S})$, and $G_{\mathscr{S}}(Z_1)$ was computed above. The table $\mathscr{T}$ is the union of the updated $\mathscr{T}_0$ and $\mathscr{T}_1$; its start state is $\mathscr{S}_0^0$ and its accepting state is $\mathscr{S}_F^0$. Occurrences of $\#_0$ should be replaced by $\#$.

3.3.6. AN EXAMPLE

Table 3.3.2 shows a grammar G and its parsing table $\mathscr{K}$, generated by the Knuth algorithm. Its format is as described in Section 3.3.3, except for two additional columns: the partial states of each state are listed under

---

[†] For any grammar G with starting symbol S and any terminal symbol b, $\mathrm{Follow}_G(b)$ $= \{a \mid \exists \alpha,\beta \in V^*$ such that $S \Rightarrow \alpha b a \beta$ in $G\}$.

Table 3.3.2   Grammar G and Parsing Table $\mathscr{K}$

$$G = (\{Z_0, Z_1, A, B, C\}, \{a, b, c, d, e\}, \mathscr{P}, Z_0)$$

1 $Z_0 \to Z_1 A Z_1 B$	5 $B \to c$
2 $Z_1 \to aC$	6 $B \to d$
3 $A \to b$	7 $C \to Ce$
4 $A \to c$	8 $C \to e$

State Name	$\mathscr{S}$	$\mathscr{S}' - \mathscr{S}$	Lookahead Symbol	Action	Stack Symbol	Goto State
$\mathscr{S}_0$	00#	10#	a	Shift	Z_0	$\mathscr{S}_1$
		20bc			Z_1	$\mathscr{S}_2$
					a	$\mathscr{S}_3$
$\mathscr{S}_1$	01#		#	Accept		
$\mathscr{S}_2$	11#	30a	b	Shift	A	$\mathscr{S}_4$
		40a	c	Shift	b	$\mathscr{S}_5$
					c	$\mathscr{S}_6$
$\mathscr{S}_3$	21bc	70bce	e	Shift	C	$\mathscr{S}_7$
		80bce			e	$\mathscr{S}_8$
$\mathscr{S}_4$	12#	20cd	a	Shift	Z_1	$\mathscr{S}_9$
					a	$\mathscr{S}_{10}$
$\mathscr{S}_5$	31a		a	Reduce 3		
$\mathscr{S}_6$	41a		a	Reduce 4		
$\mathscr{S}_7$	22bc		b	Reduce 2	e	$\mathscr{S}_{11}$
	71bce		c	Reduce 2		
			e	Shift		
$\mathscr{S}_8$	81bce		b	Reduce 8		
			c	Reduce 8		
			e	Reduce 8		
$\mathscr{S}_9$	13#	50#	c	Shift	B	$\mathscr{S}_{12}$
		60#	d	Shift	c	$\mathscr{S}_{13}$
					d	$\mathscr{S}_{14}$
$\mathscr{S}_{10}$	21cd	70cde	e	Shift	C	$\mathscr{S}_{15}$
		80cde			e	$\mathscr{S}_{16}$
$\mathscr{S}_{11}$	72bce		b	Reduce 7		
			c	Reduce 7		
			e	Reduce 7		
$\mathscr{S}_{12}$	14#		#	Reduce 1		
$\mathscr{S}_{13}$	51#		#	Reduce 5		
$\mathscr{S}_{14}$	61#		#	Reduce 6		

Table 3.3.2 (*continued*)

State Name	$\mathcal{S}$	$\mathcal{S}' - \mathcal{S}$	Lookahead Symbol	Action	Stack Symbol	Goto State
$\mathcal{S}_{15}$	22cd		c	Reduce 2	e	$\mathcal{S}_{17}$
	71cde		d	Reduce 2		
			e	Shift		
$\mathcal{S}_{16}$	81cde		c	Reduce 8		
			d	Reduce 8		
			e	Reduce 8		
$\mathcal{S}_{17}$	72cde		c	Reduce 7		
			d	Reduce 7		
			e	Reduce 7		

Table 3.3.3. Grammar G_0 and Parsing Table $\mathcal{T}_0$

$$G_0 = (\{Z_0, A, B\}, \{b, c, d\}, \mathcal{P}_0, Z_0)$$

$$
\begin{array}{lll}
1 & Z_0 \rightarrow \bar{z}_1 A \bar{z}_1 B & \quad 5 \quad B \rightarrow c \\
3 & A \rightarrow b & \quad 6 \quad B \rightarrow d \\
4 & \;\;\; \rightarrow c &
\end{array}
$$

State Name	$\mathcal{S}$	$\mathcal{S}' - \mathcal{S}$	Lookahead Symbol	Action	Stack Symbol	Goto State
$\mathcal{S}^0_0$	$00\#_0$	$10\#_0$	$\bar{z}_1$	Shift	Z_0	$\mathcal{S}^0_1$
					$\bar{z}_1$	$\mathcal{S}^0_2$
$\mathcal{S}^0_1$	$01\#_0$		$\#_0$	Accept		
$\mathcal{S}^0_2$	$11\#_0$	$30\bar{z}_1$	b	Shift	A	$\mathcal{S}^0_3$
		$40\bar{z}_1$	c	Shift	b	$\mathcal{S}^0_4$
					c	$\mathcal{S}^0_5$
$\mathcal{S}^0_3$	$12\#_0$		$\bar{z}_1$	Shift	$\bar{z}_1$	$\mathcal{S}^0_6$
$\mathcal{S}^0_4$	$31\bar{z}_1$		$\bar{z}_1$	Reduce 3		
$\mathcal{S}^0_5$	$41\bar{z}_1$		$\bar{z}_1$	Reduce 4		
$\mathcal{S}^0_6$	$13\#_0$	$50\#_0$	c	Shift	B	$\mathcal{S}^0_7$
		$60\#_0$	d	Shift	c	$\mathcal{S}^0_8$
					d	$\mathcal{S}^0_9$
$\mathcal{S}^0_7$	$14\#_0$		$\#_0$	Reduce 1		
$\mathcal{S}^0_8$	$51\#_0$		$\#_0$	Reduce 5		
$\mathcal{S}^0_9$	$61\#_0$		$\#_0$	Reduce 6		

Table 3.3.4. Grammar G_1 and Parsing Table $\mathcal{T}_1$

$$G_1 = (\{Z_1, C\}, \{a, e\}, \mathcal{P}_1, Z_1)$$

$$\begin{array}{ll} 2 & Z_1 \to aC \\ 7 & C \to Ce \\ 8 & C \to e \end{array}$$

State Name	$\mathcal{S}$	$\mathcal{S}' - \mathcal{S}$	Lookahead Symbol	Action	Stack Symbol	Goto State
$\mathcal{S}^1_0$	$00\#_1$	$20\#_1$	a	Shift	Z_1	$\mathcal{S}^1_1$
					a	$\mathcal{S}^1_2$
$\mathcal{S}^1_1$	$01\#_1$		$\#_1$	Accept		
$\mathcal{S}^1_2$	$21\#_1$	$70\#_1 e$	e	Shift	C	$\mathcal{S}^1_3$
		$80\#_1 e$			e	$\mathcal{S}^1_4$
$\mathcal{S}^1_3$	$22\#_1$		$\#_1$	Reduce 2	e	$\mathcal{S}^1_5$
	$71\#_1 e$		e	Shift		
$\mathcal{S}^1_4$	$81\#_1 e$		$\#_1$	Reduce 8		
			e	Reduce 8		
$\mathcal{S}^1_5$	$72\#_1 e$		$\#_1$	Reduce 7		
			e	Reduce 7		

the heading $\mathcal{S}$; the partial states added to $\mathcal{S}$ to form $\mathcal{S}'$ are listed under $\mathcal{S}' - \mathcal{S}$. A compact notation for partial states has been used: "$pjabc$" denotes $\{[p, j, a], [p, j, b], [p, j, c]\}$, etc. Tables 3.3.3 and 3.3.4 show the partition grammars G_0 and G_1 and their respective parsing tables $\mathcal{T}_0$ and $\mathcal{T}_1$, also generated by the Knuth algorithm. Finally, Table 3.3.5 shows the parsing table $\mathcal{T}$ formed from $\mathcal{T}_0$ and $\mathcal{T}_1$.

The parsing table $\mathcal{T}$ has fewer states than $\mathcal{K}$. Very roughly, this savings occurs because $\mathcal{T}$ uses a single closed subroutine to parse all substrings generated by Z_1, whereas $\mathcal{K}$ may use several pieces of in-line code. In this example, once an "a" has been found, indicating that a Z_1 is being sought, $\mathcal{T}$ transfers to the "subroutine" consisting of the states which were originally in $\mathcal{T}_1$—$\mathcal{S}^1_2$, $\mathcal{S}^1_3$, $\mathcal{S}^1_4$, and $\mathcal{S}^1_5$. $\mathcal{T}$ ignores the information that the first occurrence of Z_1 must be followed by b or c and that the second occurrence must be followed by c or d; while in the subroutine, $\mathcal{T}$ allows any of b, c, or d to follow. Only when it exits from the subroutine and returns to the $\mathcal{T}_0$ mode does $\mathcal{T}$ check the validity of this symbol, thereby causing delayed error checking in some cases. On the other hand, $\mathcal{K}$ has two sets of states which search for an occurrence of Z_1 once the initial a has been found—

Table 3.3.5. Parsing Table $\mathscr{T}$ Constructed from $\mathscr{T}_0$ and $\mathscr{T}_1$

$$\text{Follow}_{G_0'}(\bar{z}_1) = \{b, c, d\}$$

State Name	Lookahead Symbol	Action	Stack Symbol	Goto State
$\mathscr{S}_0^0$	a	Shift	Z_0	$\mathscr{S}_1^0$
			Z_1	$\mathscr{S}_2^0 \cup \bar{\mathscr{S}}_1^1 = \mathscr{S}_2^0$
			a	$\mathscr{S}_2^1$
$\mathscr{S}_1^0$	$\#$	Accept		
$\mathscr{S}_2^0$	b	Shift	A	$\mathscr{S}_0^0$
	c	Shift	b	$\mathscr{S}_4^3$
			c	$\mathscr{S}_5^0$
$\mathscr{S}_3^0$	a	Shift	Z_1	$\mathscr{S}_6^0 \cup \bar{\mathscr{S}}_1^1 = \mathscr{S}_6^0$
			a	$\mathscr{S}_2^1$
$\mathscr{S}_4^0$	a	Reduce 3		
$\mathscr{S}_5^0$	a	Reduce 4		
$\mathscr{S}_6^0$	c	Shift	B	$\mathscr{S}_7^0$
	d	Shift	c	$\mathscr{S}_8^0$
			d	$\mathscr{S}_9^0$
$\mathscr{S}_7^0$	$\#$	Reduce 1		
$\mathscr{S}_8^0$	$\#$	Reduce 5		
$\mathscr{S}_9^0$	$\#$	Reduce 6		
$\mathscr{S}_2^1$	e	Shift	C	$\mathscr{S}_3^1$
			e	$\mathscr{S}_4^1$
$\mathscr{S}_3^1$	b	Reduce 2	e	$\mathscr{S}_5^1$
	c	Reduce 2		
	d	Reduce 2		
	e	Shift		
$\mathscr{S}_4^1$	b	Reduce 8		
	c	Reduce 8		
	d	Reduce 8		
	e	Reduce 8		
$\mathscr{S}_5^1$	b	Reduce 7		
	c	Reduce 7		
	d	Reduce 7		
	e	Reduce 7		

$\mathscr{S}_3$, $\mathscr{S}_7$, $\mathscr{S}_8$, $\mathscr{S}_{11}$, and $\mathscr{S}_{10}$, $\mathscr{S}_{15}$, $\mathscr{S}_{16}$, $\mathscr{S}_{17}$.[†] Each of these states stores the information as to which symbols can follow a *particular occurrence* of Z_1. Thus $\mathscr{K}$ checks the validity of the symbol following Z_1 when it first becomes the lookahead symbol and so error checking is immediate.

3.3.7. GENERAL ALGORITHM

The algorithm described in this section generalizes the simple scheme by allowing the grammar to be divided into more than two parts. For $G = (V_N, V_T, \mathscr{P}', Z_0)$, let $Z_1, \ldots, Z_n$ be distinct nonterminals other than Z_0, and let $\bar{z}_0, \ldots, \bar{z}_n$ be new terminal symbols not in V. Number the members of $\mathscr{P}$ from 1 to π. Let $G' = (V'_N, V'_T, \mathscr{P}, Z'_0)$ be the 1-augmented grammar associated with G, and assign the production $Z'_0 \to Z_0 \#$ the number 0. For $0 \leq i \leq n$, let $G_i = (V_{N_i}, V_{T_i}, \mathscr{P}_i, Z_i)$ be the reduced form of $(V_N, \bar{V}_T, \mathscr{P}_i, Z_i)$, where $\bar{V}_T = V_T \cup \{\bar{z}_j \mid 0 \leq f \leq n\}$ and $\mathscr{P}_i = \{A \to \bar{\alpha} \mid A \to \alpha \in \mathscr{P}$ and $\bar{\alpha}$ is obtained from α by replacing every occurrence of Z_j ($f \neq i$) by $\bar{z}_j\}$. Assign the rule $A \to \bar{\alpha}$ in $\mathscr{P}_i$ the number that $A \to \alpha$ has in $\mathscr{P}$. For each i, let $G'_i = (V'_{N_i}, V'_{T_i}, \mathscr{P}'_i, Z'_i)$ be the 1-augmented grammar associated with G_i, with endmarker $\#_i$.

Thus G_0 is analogous to the G_0 of the simple case, and each G_i is similar to the G_1 of the simple case. The composite parsing table $\mathscr{S}$ will operate as follows (it starts in the $\mathscr{S}_0$ mode): When a substring generated by Z_i is encountered, it switches to the $\mathscr{S}_i$ mode; if this substring itself contains a substring generated by Z_j, it will have to switch to the $\mathscr{S}_j$ mode before returning to the $\mathscr{S}_0$ mode. Thus for each pair (i, f) such that $\bar{z}_j \in V_{T_i}$, we must make sure that the master processor is capable of finding the beginning and end of strings generated by Z_j when they are included in strings generated by Z_i. The algorithm for constructing a parsing table $\mathscr{S}$ for G from the tables for the G_i is based on the same reasoning used for the simple case of Section 3.3.5.

3.3.7.1. *Construction Algorithm*

A parsing table $\mathscr{S}_i$ is generated for each G_i using the Knuth algorithm. The following algorithm, if it does not FAIL, will produce an updated version of each $\mathscr{S}_i$. The composite parsing table $\mathscr{S}$ for G is then formed as the union of the resulting tables (and possibly some union states), with

---

[†] In general, each of these sets which is "repeated" in $\mathscr{K}$ is not as large as the "subroutine" in $\mathscr{S}$, which consists of all states in $\mathscr{S}_1$ except $\mathscr{S}_0^1$ and $\mathscr{S}_F^1$.

start state $\mathscr{S}_0^0$ and final state $\mathscr{S}_F^0$. The algorithm is specified by the following two flow charts: MAIN ALGORITHM (Fig. 3.3.1) and SUBROUTINE UPDATE($\mathscr{S}$) (Fig. 3.3.2). No doubt the reader will see a number of ways in which the efficiency of the algorithm could be improved by the addition of various programming switches, some reorganization, etc.; however, the purpose here is to describe the algorithm in the most convenient way.

Box 1: All $\#_0$ entries in $\mathscr{T}_0$ are duplicated with $\#$. This allows $\#_0$ to be treated like the other $\#_j$'s when $\bar{z}_0$ appears in other tables; $\#$ is the actual end marker appended to input strings.

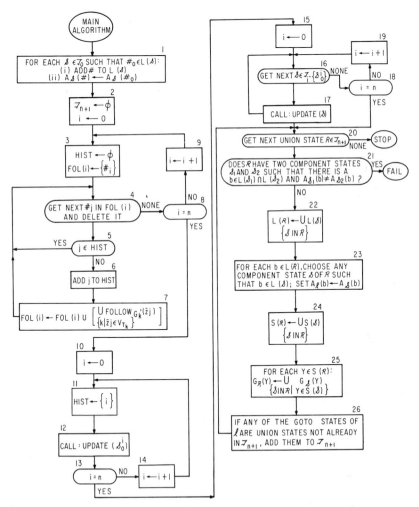

FIGURE 3.3.1

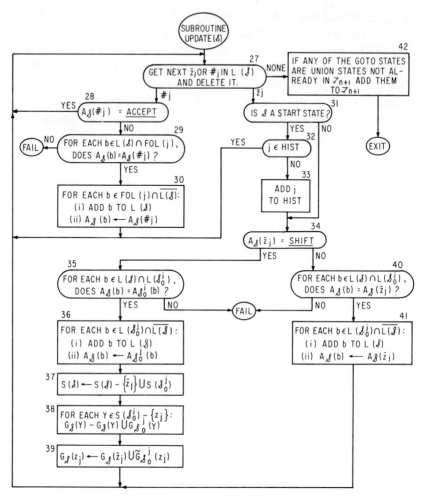

FIGURE 3.3.2

Box 2: This initializes $\mathcal{T}_{n+1}$, the "table" composed of any union states that will be generated.

Boxes 3–9: This loop computes the set FOL(i) for each subgrammar. FOL(i) includes those symbols that could follow instances of Z_i in G', except those that could do so only in the ith subgrammar. It is analogous to $\text{Follow}_{G_0'}(\bar{z}_1)$ in the simple case. The set HIST is used to eliminate looping.

Boxes 11–14: This loop updates the start states by calls to the subroutine UPDATE, which replaces occurrences of any $\bar{z}_j$ or $\#_j$ in these states. Although updating of the start states need not be done in advance, this saves considerable duplication of computation later. HIST is used to guarantee termination of the UPDATE subroutine.

Boxes 16–19: These update the remaining states in the same way.

Boxes 20–26: Some union states may have been created by the calls of UPDATE in boxes 12 or 17. Their table entries are computed in boxes 21–26 by unioning the table entries of their component states. Since the component states have already been updated, no $\bar{z}_j$'s or $\#_j$'s are involved. However, box 21 must check to make sure no lookahead symbol would be assigned conflicting actions by this process. Additional union states may be generated by box 25; these are added to $\mathcal{S}_{n+1}$ if they are not already there. The algorithm terminates when the table entries for each union state have been computed. The notation $\{\mathcal{S} \text{ in } \mathcal{R}\}$ is used to denote the set of component states of $\mathcal{R}$.

The subroutine UPDATE, defined in the flow chart of Fig. 3.3.2, is the heart of the algorithm. It is completely analogous to the updating method used in the simple case; it replaces every occurrence of $\bar{z}_j$ or $\#_j$ by the symbols in V'_T that might actually occur in the same position in a sentence of G'. If no conflicts arise, these new symbols are assigned appropriate actions, and the stack and goto entries are updated accordingly.

Boxes 28–30: If an $\#_j$ has been found in box 27, it should be replaced by the symbols in FOL(j). However, if $\mathcal{S}$ is a final state, the replacement need not be made, since this entry will not appear in table $\mathcal{T}$. Box 29 makes sure conflicting actions will not be assigned to the symbols being added to $L(\mathcal{S})$. Finally, box 30 makes the replacement and assigns $A_{\mathcal{S}}(\#_j)$ to each new symbol, as in the simple case.

Boxes 31–33: If $\mathcal{S}$ is a start state, there is a possibility that even though $\bar{z}_j$ was once deleted from $L(\mathcal{S})$ in box 27, it has since been added to $L(\mathcal{S})$ by boxes 36 or 41 (see below). In this case, to avoid looping, $\bar{z}_j$ is not processed again.

Boxes 35–39: These update $\mathcal{S}$ due to the presence of $\bar{z}_j$ in $L(\mathcal{S})$ with $A_{\mathcal{S}}(\bar{z}_j) = Shift$. In this case, $\bar{z}_j$ is replaced by the symbols in $L(\mathcal{S}_0^j)$, each of which retains the action it had in $\mathcal{S}_0^j$. The updating process fails if any conflicts would be generated. The stack symbols and their goto states are computed in exactly the same way as in the simple case. Note that once the start states have been updated (boxes 11–14), $L(\mathcal{S}_0^j)$ contains no $\bar{z}_k$'s or $\#_k$'s; thus, all symbols added to $L(\mathcal{S})$ in box 36 are in V'_T. On the other hand, during the updating of start states, box 36 (as well as box 41) may introduce additional $\bar{z}_k$'s and $\#_k$'s which must be removed by later execution of box 27. This is why box 32 is needed.

Boxes 40–41:   If the $\bar{z}_j$ in $L(\mathscr{S})$ has the action *Reduce p*, it is replaced by the symbols in $L(\mathscr{S}_0^j)$, which are assigned the action *Reduce p*, if no conflicts arise.

Box 42:   When all $\bar{z}_j$'s and $\#_j$'s have been removed from $L(\mathscr{S})$, the updating is complete. Any new union states which have been created during the updating of $\mathscr{S}$ are added to $\mathscr{T}_{n+1}$. Their table entries are computed later in boxes 20–26.

It should be clear that the additional complexity of the general algorithm is not due to any inherent difference between it and the method used for the simple case. It is only a matter of keeping track of some additional details.

It is shown in Ref. 5 that any grammar for which this algorithm succeeds is LR(1), since the Knuth algorithm would also have succeeded in producing an LR(1) parsing table for G. The converse, however, is not true: there exist LR(1) grammars for which certain partitions will cause the general algorithm to fail.

3.3.8. AN LR(1) GRAMMAR FOR ALGOL

Obtaining a parsing table using the partitioning scheme is somewhat of a trial-and-error process, since a partition must be chosen and the corresponding tables $\mathscr{T}_i$ generated before the updating and merging process can begin. If a particular partition fails to produce an LR(1) parsing table, the entire process may have to be repeated. However, in practical situations the partitioning scheme requires very few iterations. The difficulties that do arise are more often due to non-LR(1) subgrammars than to poor partition choices. Using this scheme, parsers for ALGOL, BASIC, and CDL1[†] have been generated. In this section, the process of producing an LR(1) parser for ALGOL will be briefly described.

ALGOL is defined by a set of Backus Normal Form syntax rules and some additional "semantic" rules.[6] These semantic rules include certain restrictions which imply that the set of all well-formed ALGOL programs is not even context-free, much less deterministic. However, our interest here is in efficient syntax-directed compilation and a language specification that will be useful for this purpose. To this end, we define the structure of ALGOL by a grammar G, given in Ref. 5. G is not identical to the official ALGOL syntax—in fact, it does not define the same set of strings as ALGOL's BNF

[†] The preliminary syntax of a computer description language; there are 350 grammar rules.[7]

rules. But, combined with an appropriate semantic interpretation, it does define the same language as the ALGOL BNF rules together with the ALGOL semantics. It is a matter of shifting the dividing line between syntax and semantics. The main differences are:

1. For convenience and efficiency in applying Knuth's algorithm to various G_i, certain finite sets of basic ALGOL symbols are replaced by a single terminal symbol in G, e.g., *type*, *ad.op*, *digit*, *string.symbol*, etc.

2. In a very few instances changes were made in the ALGOL grammar in order to obtain an LR(1) structure. These changes do not affect the strings generated and do not cause any meaningful change in syntactic structure. For example, the syntax of ⟨string⟩ was changed to eliminate an ambiguity.

3. The symbols *let.string* and *label* are terminal symbols in G. The addition of grammars for these structures would cause no difficulties in proving G to be LR(1), and is omitted for simplicity. Integer labels are not allowed, since an integer appearing as an actual parameter would be syntactically ambiguous: Is it to be parsed as a ⟨designational expression⟩ or as an ⟨arithmetic expression⟩? This restriction is common in ALGOL implementations.

4. The following *terminal* symbols appear in G: *identifier, arithmetic identifier, Boolean identifier, arithmetic array identifier, Boolean array identifier, arithmetic function identifier, Boolean function identifier, switch identifier, procedure identifier*. These symbols (and their interpretation) constitute the only major difference between G and the standard ALGOL syntax. They syntactically reflect certain semantic restrictions on an ALGOL program. Their interpretation (with respect to an ALGOL compiler which is based on G) is as follows: Any string parsable as an ⟨identifier⟩ is to be accepted by the compiler in place of any one of the nine symbols listed above. In the ⟨declaration⟩ subgrammar (the only place where *identifier* appears), successful recognition of such a string will cause a symbol table entry to be made, consisting of the string itself and an attribute indicating how it was declared. The parsing then proceeds as if the symbol *identifier* had been encountered. In all other subgrammars (where only the other eight types of identifiers appear), successful recognition of an ⟨identifier⟩ string in place of one of these symbols will cause the compiler to check the symbol table entry for that string to make sure that its attributes correspond to one of the identifiers allowable in this particular instance. If this check succeeds, parsing continues as if the corresponding terminal symbol had been encountered.

The validity of this interpretation of G depends on the assumption that the compiler framework in which it is embedded is a block-structured symbol table with the necessary identifier entries and their attributes available at the time of use. This is a reasonable assumption, since the ALGOL declaration structure lends itself to this general parsing philosophy. The point is that the relation of G to the official ALGOL syntax is such that an ALGOL compiler could be constructed around the LR(1) parsing table $\mathscr{T}$ for G which will permit particularly efficient processing. The discussion above is meant to justify this point. It is not intended to describe the detailed construction of a compiler.

The initial problem in applying the algorithm is to choose a partition for the given grammar. There are no steadfast rules on how this is to be done. The number of nonterminals chosen, n, is affected by a trade-off in the effort required to complete the two parts of the procedure. A large value of n will result in small subgrammars, to which Knuth's algorithm may be easily applied, but the construction of $\mathscr{T}$ from the $\mathscr{T}_i$ will be more complex. On the other hand, the algorithm is more likely to succeed if n is small. The following guidelines may be useful in determining how to choose the partitioning nonterminals.

1. Each G_i should be small enough so that Knuth's algorithm can be easily applied.

2. Choice of a Z_i whose initial symbols appear infrequently in other parts of the grammar decreases the work required to construct $\mathscr{T}$ and increases the chances of success.

3. Choice of a Z_i which appears in many different parts of the grammar will help to reduce the size of $\mathscr{T}$.

4. Choice of a pair of Z_i, each of which appears in the subgrammar of the other, will markedly decrease the effort needed to apply Knuth's algorithm and will help reduce the size of $\mathscr{T}$.

In the case of a grammar defining the syntax of a programming language, some choices may be rather natural. In the case of grammar G for ALGOL, the choice of ⟨declaration⟩ and ⟨statement⟩ was made first. The initial symbols of ⟨declaration⟩ do not appear in the grammar for ⟨statement⟩. Since ⟨arithmetic expression⟩ and ⟨Boolean expression⟩ are widely used throughout G, they were chosen next. This still left a rather large grammar for ⟨statement⟩; so ⟨actual parameter part⟩ and ⟨designational expression⟩ were chosen. Finally, ⟨simple arithmetic expression⟩ and ⟨simple Boolean⟩ were chosen because of their complex intertwining with ⟨arithmetic expression⟩, and to avoid duplication of the large number of rules defining

⟨simple arithmetic expression⟩ in both ⟨arithmetic expression⟩ and in ⟨Boolean expression⟩.

Once the partition was chosen, the grammar and partitioning non-terminals were used as input to a program which does the following:

1. Forms the subgrammars and applies the Knuth algorithm to each.
2. Updates each $\mathcal{S}_i$ and forms the union states.
3. Encodes the resulting table $\mathcal{S}$ into assembly language format.

The table is then appended to a simple interpreter to form a parser for the given language, in this case ALGOL. Table 3.3.6 indicates the results for ALGOL.

Table 3.3.6

Z_i	Computation Time	Number of States in $\mathcal{S}_i$
⟨program⟩	1	6
⟨unlabeled program⟩	1	15
⟨declaration⟩	4	77
⟨statement⟩	12	110
⟨actual parameter part⟩	2	32
⟨arithmetic expression⟩	1	10
⟨simple arithmetic expression⟩	6	45
⟨Boolean expression⟩	1	15
⟨simple Boolean⟩	5	38
⟨designational expression⟩	2	42
union states	1	53

The following is an example of the savings effected by the partitioning scheme: Instead of treating ⟨simple arithmetic expression⟩ as a $\bar{z}_j$ in the grammar for ⟨arithmetic expression⟩, as was done above, the Knuth algorithm was applied to the ⟨arithmetic expression⟩ grammar directly. (The other $\bar{z}_j$'s were retained.) The result was a parsing table with three times as many states as the old ⟨arithmetic expression⟩ and ⟨simple arithmetic expression⟩ tables combined, and which took nine times as long to generate.

3.3.9. CONCLUSION

LR(k) grammars are useful syntactic descriptors for programming languages because they combine two important features: processing efficiency and wide applicability. The original algorithm given by Knuth for testing a grammar for the LR(k) condition and automatically constructing a parser for its sentences has a serious drawback: It is not practical for large grammars. The partitioning scheme described in this paper significantly reduces the computation required to generate an LR(1) parsing table for a large grammar. In addition, the table it produces is usually smaller than the table that would have been produced if the Knuth algorithm were applied directly.

Knuth has also suggested a way of decreasing the computation time for an LR(k) table. Namely, if a state is generated that is a subset of another state, the latter state can be substituted for the former and the table entries for the former state need not be computed. This shortcut can, of course, be used in conjunction with the partitioning scheme when generating the individual $\mathscr{T}_i$. We have found, however, that the savings is negligible. Knuth also points out that any two states whose parsing action does not conflict can be merged into a single state to cut down on the size of the table. Again, this technique can be applied along with the partitioning method to both the individual $\mathscr{T}_i$ and the final table $\mathscr{T}$.

Additional savings in both time and storage can be obtained by various implementation techniques. For instance, the bottom track of the stack (the track containing vocabulary symbols) is needed only if one of the two kinds of shortcuts suggested by Knuth are used. In that case, when the action *Reduce p* is called for, it is necessary to check whether $X_{p1} \ldots X_{pn_p}$ is at the top of the stack; otherwise, this check is not needed. It is also useful to distinguish between states which have only one action and those with more than one action. In particular, no lookahead symbols need be stored for a state whose only action is *Reduce p*. Whenever the processor is in such a state, it can perform the reduce action without examining the lookahead symbol; delayed error checking will result, but no incorrect strings will be accepted.

A number of problems remain to be studied. Considering the trade-off between the time it takes to form the individual $\mathscr{T}_i$, the time required to update and combine them, and the chances of successfully doing so, how many ways should a grammar be partitioned? What are some reasonable heuristics to guide the choice of the partitioning nonterminals? Although an LR(1) processor (even with delayed error checking) can point to the leftmost unacceptable symbol in a nonsentence, what additional automatic error analysis can be incorporated into the scheme? Perhaps more important, how can error recovery be included? Since the stack contains very detailed information about the input already processed, the possibility of good error processing seems better here than in less formalized processors.

REFERENCES

1. Earley, J., "An Efficient Context-Free Parsing Algorithm." Thesis, Carnegie-Mellon U., Pittsburgh, Pa., Aug., 1968.

2. Feldman, J., and Gries, D., "Translator Writing Systems," *Comm. ACM*, vol. 11, no. 2 (February 1968), pp. 77–113.

3. Ginsburg, S., and Greibach, S. A., "Deterministic Context-Free Languages," *Inform. Contr.*, vol. 9 (December 1966), pp. 620–648.

4. Knuth, D. E., "On the Translation of Languages from Left to Right," *Inform. Contr.*, vol. 8 (December 1965), pp. 607–639.

5. Korenjak, A. J., "Deterministic Language Processing." Thesis, Princeton U., Princeton, N. J., September 1967.

6. Naur, P. (ed.), "Revised Report on the Algorithmic Language ALGOL 60," *Comm. ACM*, vol. 6, no. 1 (January 1963), pp. 1–17.

7. Srinivasan, C. V., "An Introduction to CDL1, A Computer Description Language," Scientific Rep. No. 1, Contract No. AF19(628)4789, RCA Laboratories, Princeton, N. J., September 1967.

4.

RESOURCE ALLOCATION

4.0. OVERVIEW

One may ask what portions of a computer system—hardware and software—are necessary for the execution of an object program and when are they to be allocated. One may also ask how they are to be allocated: statically, before execution truly commences; or dynamically, as execution proceeds; or some combination of the two. Further, one may ask essentially the same questions about the program that is the compiler. Moreover, some languages (ALGOL and PL/I, for example) specifically allow the user to specify both time and manner of allocation. This chapter surveys the allocation of both hardware and software.

Allocation may be defined as the reservation of a specific resource by a process. Resources may be hardware, e.g., disk units, memory, and central processing units; or software, e.g., memory partitions, operating systems, and subsystems. Processes may be human operators or supervisory systems. Allocation of a resource may be made to an operating system, a subsystem or program, a user, a job, or a process alone, or it may be shared among several processes. Once a resource has been allocated, reallocation usually may not be made until the resource has been returned to the operating system.

Hardware allocation is a topic not generally dealt with, as most software

194

systems firmly impose a decision upon the compiler writer. He is provided with a portion of the whole machine for the compiler, usually including the full computational part, a specific amount of memory, and perhaps some limited input/output facilities. The object code is likewise constrained. However, with multiple-processor machines one may have a real choice as to which portions of the computer are to be used and in which order, if not in parallel. Operators now have the facilities for rapidly changing machine configurations; hence the compiler writer must ensure that the compiler is sufficiently flexible to run independent of the specific amount and type of storage available, of input/output facilities attached, and of other possible system attributes.

An object program will always have the choice of how and when to allocate the memory and internal registers of a computer. Most early compilers have allocated memory statically, during the pre-execution initialization phase, and have utilized all internal registers. More recently, with the advent of virtual storage and allocation facilities within high-level languages, the trend has been toward dynamic memory allocation. But, with the exception of the multiple-processor machines, most systems still utilize the full computational hardware.

Software allocation is primarily a system design problem relating to which facilities are provided by the operating system: Such provisions include dynamic relocation and loading of programs, allocation and release memory, input/output devices, system subroutines, and so forth. Again, these questions may be asked for both the object program and the compiler. Unfortunately, literature on resource allocation for compilers is almost nonexistent. An occasional paper will be found, however, that describes how the resources of a specific compiler were reallocated, usually to effect an increase in compiler speed or execution speed, or both.

By far the most readily allocated resource of the two—memory and time—is memory. A complete account of the total memory requirements for the instruction portion of a program is easily made. Usually, an upper bound on the size of the total data requirements may be estimated, and the total amount of memory may then be requested during the loading phase, initialization phase, or both. If the source language provides facilities for the dynamic allocation of storage, then these requests are handed up to the operating system during execution.

One must distinguish between the binding of memory and the allocation of memory. Memory allocation is the reservation of memory. It is usually done in contiguous blocks or segments, or (in paged memory schemes) in pages. Segments and pages appear most commonly in multiples of some power of 2. Memory binding, on the other hand, is the association of program variables or data with specific memory areas. In compilers, binding occurs during the translation process—memory areas are reserved for each variable, each temporary, each data item, and so forth. An additional binding process occurs at load time when the loader assigns each such memory area to a specific core location. One may speak of the time of binding—when the binding is done—for compilers, incremental compilers, and interpreters. In each case, binding is done at translation time, although incremental compilers provide a later binding time than batch compilers, since translation occurs later. In interpreters, binding occurs only during the actual execution of a program. Binding time is important because the later the binding occurs, the more flexible is the compiler system with regard to storage requirements.

The allocation of time is generally implicit. Given a hardware and software environment, each section of a compiler will take some percentage of the total time for the translation of a specific program. Rewriting various sections of a compiler may result in the redistribution of time usage and ideally should result in an increase of overall speed in the translation process. The construction of extremely fast compilers has become increasingly important in recent years, especially within academic environments where the number of jobs submitted has multiplied by several orders of magnitude.

But the optimization of object code for production programs represents, perhaps, even a more important consideration, especially within the business and industrial communities. Object code optimization is a relatively complex subject to which a significant amount of effort has been applied. Many methods developed over the past few years produce more concise and faster code. The application of graph theory to program flow graphs has produced additional savings in the translation of loops. The interested reader is referred to the paper by Beizer in the 1970 Fall Joint Computer Conference, *AFIPS Proc.*, vol. 37. There is, however, no effective way to rigorously optimize a program, nor is there a test for program optimality.

Within the subject area of resource allocation one finds a trade-off common to many aspects of computing: the trade-off between time and space. Given a compiler, a source program, and data, one can utilize a certain amount of time and space during compilation and a certain amount of time and space during execution. If one is willing to increase the size of the compiler and lengthen the amount of time necessary to compile programs by attempting to increase optimization of the object code, the object code may well require less space or may run faster, or both. The reverse is also true. The compiler writer must judge the benefits to be obtained from increased optimization in order to decide when to stop adding to or making changes in the compiler. Many compilers permit the user to select the amount or type of optimization to be imposed on a source program.

What types of optimization are commonly applied to current compilers? Usually, the amount of memory is minimized by the careful production of code. The number of machine registers utilized at any one time is minimized. Computational expressions, both arithmetic and logical, are optimized by several techniques such as factoring, common subexpression evaluation, minimization of the number of storage accesses required, and temporary storage minimization. Redundant instructions are eliminated either by careful code emission or during a cleanup pass over the object program. Loops are optimized by the movement of invariant code out of the loop, the use of registers for loop variables, flow analysis, and other techniques. Array addressing may be optimized whenever elements are accessed in a regular fashion. Source programs as a whole may be subjected to flow analysis.

This chapter is divided into five sections. The first article discusses program optimization and optimization techniques; the second discusses high-speed compilation; the third, identification and modification of inefficient sequences; the fourth, the evaluation of arithmetic expressions; and the fifth, other aspects of resource allocation including index register allocation and storage allocation.

In Article 4.1, Dardan and Heller present a record of their experience in optimizing an already existing ALGOL compiler. They illustrate a way in which one may look for areas of a compiler to optimize and the types of savings which may result.

In Article 4.2, Gear describes techniques for optimizing code in two passes after a preliminary translation into a Polish postfix notation has been made. His discussion lends itself to most algebraic languages.

McKeeman provides in Article 4.3 a concise look at the elimination of redundant instructions. His technique may be either applied within the code-emission portion of a compiler or incorporated into a separate pass.

Article 4.4 by Sethi and Ullman discusses the generation of optimal code for arithmetic expressions. The authors show that their techniques minimize the number of instructions emitted and also minimize the number of storage references.

Holt presents in Article 4.5 a highly informative look at the organization of programs for dynamic storage allocation.

4.1. Compiler Development by Iterative Optimization

by Stephen C. Darden and Steven B. Heller

4.1.1. SUMMARY

The trade-off between straightforward design of software systems and efficiency has traditionally been resolved in favor of efficiency, with considerable effort spent in striving to achieve local optimality for all modules. This article presents an alternative approach which emphasizes transparent design and ease of implementation. Efficiency considerations enter only into overall system organization. High performance is achieved by means of "iterative optimization" of significant modules.

4.1.2. INTRODUCTION

Conventional software development usually involves a brute-force approach to get a workable system. This is then followed by a blanket attempt to try to optimize as much of the system as possible. However, when the performance of a software system is analyzed, it often turns out that much of the code is rarely used while other parts are very frequently used. Consequently, it makes more sense to optimize only those parts of the system that are used frequently. In the case of a typical FORTRAN compiler, only 1

EDITOR'S NOTE: This article reproduced by permission of the authors and the publisher: *Computer Decisions*, vol. 2, no. 10 (October 1970), pp. 29–33.

percent of the code accounted for over 60 percent of the execution time (see Fig. 4.1.1). Because of this concentration, the optimization of only 1 percent of the code, about 100 words, could yield a 50 percent reduction in execution time.

The principle of iterative optimization is that each module of a system can be implemented in a simple, straightforward manner in whatever high-level language is found to be appropriate for the function performed by that module, and then those modules that are important can be redesigned and reimplemented to achieve an optimized system. When the complete system has been integrated and sufficiently debugged, statistical profiles of processor time are compiled for the running system. These results are analyzed to determine which modules warrant an investment to achieve

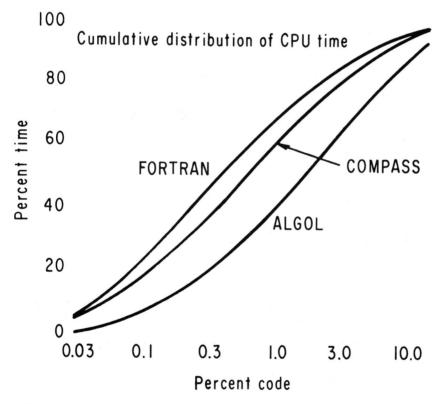

FIGURE 4.1.1 Cumulative distribution of CPU time. For a typical FORTRAN compiler, over 60 percent of the central processor's time is spent in executing only 1 percent of the code. Clearly, that 1 percent of the code is the area to optimize. In fact, 10 percent of the code accounts for 90 percent of the execution time of all the systems tested by the authors. (Reprinted from *Computer Decisions*, October 1970.)

local optimization and how much effort can be justified for each module.

If a statistical profile of the software system's performance can be obtained, either by using a program monitor or a hardware monitor, then the critical parts of the code can be optimized and the system's performance rechecked. If necessary, the procedure can be repeated until it becomes apparent that little improvement in overall performance will result from local code optimization. The total amount of manpower required to complete a system using this philosophy is much less than if the conventional method is used. The resulting system will perform just as fast as one implemented in the conventional way. And, since the technique is easiest to apply when writing in a high-level language, the maintenance and modification of the system become much more straightforward.

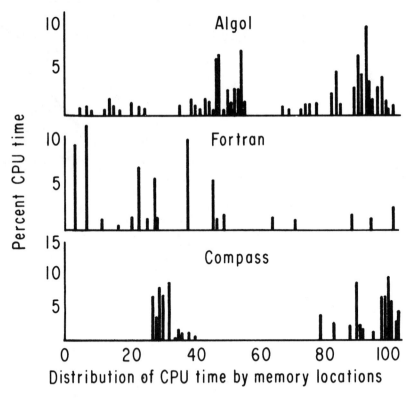

FIGURE 4.1.2   Central processor time distribution. Histograms of the relative frequency of execution of blocks of instruction for an ALGOL compilation, a FORTRAN compilation, and a COMPASS assembly (COMPASS is the CDC 6600 assembler) show that a very small number of modules account for most of the execution time of each system. (Reprinted from *Computer Decisions*, October 1970.)

In the example to be discussed later in some detail, that of the development of an ALGOL compiler, four separate optimizations resulted in a 10 : 1 gain in compile speed. The compiler was developed for a CONTROL DATA 6600 by the authors at the University of Texas.[1] Because the CDC 6600 consists of a large central processor and ten peripheral processors, the program monitoring was done by using one of the peripheral processors. However, the same statistical results (see Fig. 4.1.2) could be obtained either by using trap measurements (code flags that are inserted at points throughout the software system), by using a software monitor, or by using a hardware monitor. An in-depth look at these techniques will be taken later.

The ALGOL compiler that was developed by using this technique of statistical performance measurement and repeated optimization took ap-

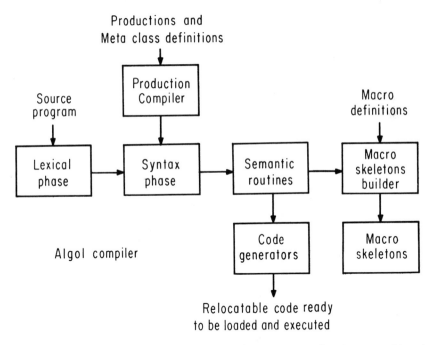

FIGURE 4.1.3 ALGOL compiler organization. The ALGOL compiler that was subjected to repeated optimization was based on a compiler-building system called SERVO. There are three inputs to this compiler: the original source program, a series of macro definitions that generate the machine code for the host computer (in this case a CDC 6600), and a series of semantic definitions generated by a production compiler. The production compiler is a part of the SERVO system that accepts as input a series of rules (called Floyd-Evans productions), a set of symbol definitions, and a set of meta definitions. The output of the production compiler is executable code that becomes the syntax phase of the compiler.

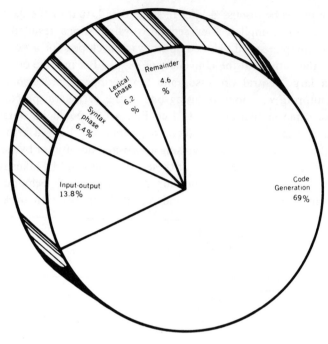

STAGE I

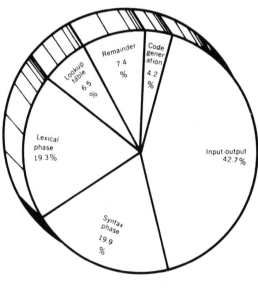

STAGE II

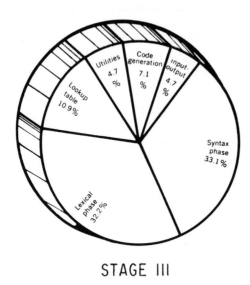

STAGE III

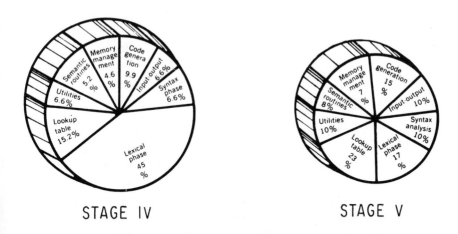

STAGE IV   STAGE V

FIGURE 4.1.4   Repeated optimization changes the shape of a compiler's time distribution. As originally written, 69 percent of an ALGOL compiler's time was spent doing code generation. After optimizing the code-generation section, this time dropped to almost 4 percent (stage II). Applying the technique to the next obvious bottleneck, that of input-output, resulted in further gains in compile speed (stage III). After four optimizations, the compiler's speed had improved by a factor of 10 : 1, yet only 5 percent of the code had been rewritten.

proximately eight man-months to write and tune. It was initially written in FORTRAN and even after repeated optimization the final compiler was still 95 percent written in FORTRAN. The process was aided considerably by using a compiler-writing system developed by the authors called SERVO (see Fig. 4.1.3).[1] This compiler writer uses a set of macro definitions that define the code that can be generated. In this case the SERVO system had macros that would produce code in the assembly language of the CDC 6600. The assembler then has to do the translation to machine code.

It was readily apparent that this was less efficient than generating machine code directly, so the first improvement that was made in the compiler was to rewrite the code-generation section. The time spent in code generation then dropped from 69 percent to about 4 percent (see Fig. 4.1.4).

To eliminate the use of the assembler from the compilation process, the compiler was made to generate the relocatable code itself. Eliminating the assembler from the compilation process proved to be a relatively easy task. Its removal was accomplished by developing a new part of the SERVO system which accepted as input a set of macro definitions and constructed a table of macro skeletons containing such information as where to substitute parameters, what kind of relocation to perform on each instruction, and any word alignment restrictions that an instruction had. A set of variables were added, each with a name corresponding to one of the macro names and containing a pointer to the appropriate skeleton for that macro. These additions resulted in a speed improvement of a factor of 50 in the code generation phase.

4.1.3. OPTIMIZING THE INPUT-OUTPUT

When the compiler's performance was measured again, it was apparent that the input-output routines were taking up a substantial part of the compiler's running time. Figure 4.1.4 shows that, after the optimization of the code generation, 42 percent of system time was spent reading card images and writing the output listing produced by the compiler. The routines comprising this 42 percent were the FORTRAN system run-time routines for formatting and the actual input-output routines of the run-time package. In terms of the source code of the ALGOL compiler, it consisted of one READ statement and one WRITE statement.

It was decided that the generalized FORTRAN input-output statements should be replaced by specialized ones, specific to the needs of the ALGOL system. Thus, a READ and a WRITE routine were written in assembly language. They interfaced to the operating system's input-output facilities directly and had a specialized format appropriate to the requirements of the ALGOL system. These routines took two man-days to design, implement, and check out. When completed, they occupied about 30 words of memory each and improved the performance of the input-output section of the compiler by a factor of 15 over the FORTRAN READ and WRITE statements.

This factor of 15 almost eliminated input-output as a recognizable element (see Fig. 4.1.4). Further performance analysis showed two areas of the compiler that needed optimizing, the syntax phase and the lexical phase. It was obvious that both of these parts of the compiler needed optimization, so parallel projects were initiated to redesign both of them.

4.1.4. SIMPLIFYING THE SYNTAX ANALYSIS

The syntax interpreter was accounting for almost all of the 33 percent of the time spent in syntax analysis. A compiler was in the process of development at that time to generate code which would do the syntax matching directly instead of by an interpreter.[2] It was estimated that a speed improvement of a factor of 10 could be achieved by replacing the interpreter with the machine code generated by this compiler. While the compiler was being completed, work on optimization of the lexical phase continued along a generally more pedestrian line.

The lexical routine was implemented completely in FORTRAN and was about 30 FORTRAN statements in length. It was estimated that a factor of from 2 to 5 in improvement in speed could be achieved by recoding the lexical routine in machine language. This was accomplished in three man-days of effort and resulted in a speed improvement of the lexical routine by a factor of 4. The memory requirement of the resulting recoded routine was about 200 words.

These two parallel projects point out the two extremes to which redesign by iterative optimization can lead. In the case of the production compiler, a system of sufficient generality and usefulness would prove that a fairly large (two man-month effort) was justified. In the case of the lexical routine, a strict recoding was performed. The important point is that both design decisions were made only after sufficient information was available to allow the expected payoffs and expected efforts required to be accurately estimated.

At this point any additional optimization of the ALGOL system was delayed until the production compiler could be installed. An expected improvement of a factor of 10 in the production matching phase would, of course, have a drastic effort on the 33 percent of the time then spent in syntax analysis. It is important to remember that while the development of the production compiler took a significant amount of effort, it is a system generally useful for all language development projects. This compiler has already been used by several other development groups at the University of Texas at Austin.

When the production compiler was completed, it did indeed provide a speed factor of at least 10 over the production interpreter. This resulted in an overall improvement of a factor of 7 for the syntax analysis phase of the ALGOL compiler. The difference between the factors of 7 and 10 is made up by routines included in the syntax analysis phase but unchanged by the replacement of the production interpreter by the production compiler.

It would now seem that the table-searching routines should be the next section of the compiler to come under consideration for optimization. This is not very surprising, since the tables are organized quite simply and searched linearly. The 23 percent of the time being spent in searching tables (mostly linear tables) is now the largest time consumer in the compiler. However, remember that the compiler now compiles ten times faster than the original system. Iterative optimization requires that the expected payoff be justifiable in economic terms, however, and therefore table-searching is currently not being improved. The compiler currently accounts for less than 5 percent of the total time used at the computation center. Considering the unlikely possibility of completely eliminating table-searching, this would result in a saving of only 15 minutes maximum per day. It was judged that even this payoff was not sufficient to warrant any additional work in this area. If the total percentage of time per day spent in compilations should significantly increase, this decision could very well change. For the present, at least, this is a stopping point in the iterative optimization process.

4.1.5. MEASURING PERFORMANCE

The sampling technique used to make the performance measurements for the ALGOL compiler made use of the arrangement of the CDC 6600 as an 11-computer complex consisting of one very large, very fast central processor and 10 small, fairly fast peripheral processors. Each of these peripheral processors has 4096 twelve-bit words of memory which are not directly accessible by any other processor. The individual programs of the peripheral processors reside in their own memory. In addition, a peripheral processor can read and write in the memory of the central processor and can read the instruction counter of the central processor. This ability to read the instruction counter of the central processor provides a convenient way to monitor a running program in order to provide the necessary histograms of central processor usage.

The sampling program is given a range of memory locations to sample. It then divides that range into approximately 500 discrete partitions and allocates two peripheral processor words to each partition. It then samples the central processor instruction counter at 100-microsecond intervals, and, if the central processor is currently active on the job being sampled, it increments the appropriate partition count each time.

Although the sampling technique used in the ALGOL example is specific to the CDC 6600, it appears that this technique is generally applicable on most computer systems. There are three basic techniques that can be used to gather data necessary to produce the histogram: trap measurements (inserting code at planned locations in the problem program or operating system), active measurements (generating timer interrupts to get control after a certain time interval has elapsed), or direct hardware measurement.

The first method, that of inserting code at specific places in the operating system or problem program, has been used primarily on special-purpose measurement tools. They have typically been developed by users and were only applicable to the specific environment for which they were designed. One notable exception was a monitor developed for the General Electric GECOS operating system.[3] This monitor measured both the operating system and the problem program, utilizing traps placed in the operating system.

On many machines, particularly the IBM System/360, the use of the interval-timer interrupt to get control seems to be the easiest and most general method. General programs of this nature have been built both by users and by independent software houses.[†] The most notable of these are probably the packages developed by Boole & Babbage, Inc., of Palo Alto, Calif.

The Boole & Babbage PPE program operates on the 360 in the same partition or region as the problem program. It occupies 4k of memory and generates timer interrupts to sample the program at a 16-millisecond or larger interval. The data gathered are blocked and output to either tape or disk for subsequent analysis. The heart of this later analysis is, of course, a histogram showing the percentage of time spent in various sections of the program.

[†] See "How to Find Bottlenecks in Computer Traffic," *Computer Decisions* (April 1970), p. 44.

The principal disadvantage of this technique is the overhead penalty placed on the system by the generation of the timer interrupts. Two other problems are keeping the program operational when a new version of the operating system is installed and the low number of samples generated by sampling only at a 16-millisecond interval.

An alternative technique is to measure the instruction address counter directly in the hardware device and to build the histogram directly in the hardware unit. This eliminates the overhead of a timer-interrupt tool and relieves the maintenance problem associated with new versions of the operating system. A device of this sort has been developed by Computer Learning and Systems Corporation. This device, called X-ray (Execution Recorder Analyzer) measures the program directly with hardware and builds a histogram directly within the 2000-word memory of the hardware unit. This histogram is then written into a file for later reporting. An additional advantage of this unit is that it can sample at a 100-microsecond interval instead of a 16-millisecond one.

4.1.6. LIMITATIONS OF THE TECHNIQUE

The software development technique of iterative optimization can also be applied in a slightly different manner to programs considered to be input-output bound. The primary extension required to the measurement device to measure input-output activity is to measure the percentage of time input-output is occurring on each particular file. If the concentration of time is largely in a single file, that file should be examined and its organization, accessing method, blocking factor, or device assignment modified to improve its performance. Some programs are of such a nature that the primary design problem is the organization and structure of the files. If this is the case, iterative optimization does not appear to be a useful method of development.

Operating systems represent an area of software development where iterative optimization could be difficult to apply. The time concentrations displayed previously should still occur in an operating system but the sampling program presents some problems. The method of inserting traps into the operating system does not work if the objective is to see where the operating system spends its time. The method of generating timer interrupts causes a problem because many operating systems execute with the timer interrupt disabled, thus not allowing any samples to take place. Hardware measurement of the operating system seems quite feasible, however, and

Table 4.1.1. Stages of Optimization

Stage	Compile Speed (lines/minute)	Code Generation	Input/Output	Syntax Phase	Lexical Phase	Table Lookup	Utilities	Semantics	Memory Management
I. Original compiler	740	69.0	13.8	6.4	6.2	2.1	0.9	0.7	0.6
II. After optimization of code generation by 50 : 1	2300	4.2	42.7	19.9	19.3	6.5	2.8	2.2	1.9
III. After optimization of input-output by 15 : 1	3800	7.1	4.7	33.1	32.2	10.9	4.7	3.7	3.3
IV. After optimization of syntax phase by 7 : 1	5300	9.9	6.6	6.6	45.0	15.2	6.6	5.2	4.6
V. After optimization of lexical phase by 4 : 1	8000	15.2	10.1	10.1	16.6	22.9	10.1	8.0	7.0

the same rules of iterative optimization can be applied from the hardware measurement results.

The memory requirements of systems developed by iterative optimization are generally larger than conventionally developed systems. Most of the final system will still be in the high-level language in which it was originally developed. This means, of course, that the system will be larger than one developed completely in assembly language. It is estimated that the ALGOL compiler previously discussed would be about one-third smaller if it was entirely in assembly language instead of being 90–95 percent in a higher-level language. If the memory requirements of a system are extremely critical, it does not appear that iterative optimization can be usefully applied.

REFERENCES

1. Smith, G. M., "UT-ALGOL Compiler Design Philosophy and Guide to Internal Maintenance." TIMS-1, May 1969, Computation Center, The University of Texas at Austin.

2. Haynes, Herbert R., "An Optimizing Compiler for an Extended Version of the Floyd-Evans Production Language." TRM-12, March 1969, Computation Center, The University of Texas at Austin.

3. Cantrell, H. N., and Ellison, A. L., "Multiprogramming System Performance Measurement and Analysis," *Proc. AFIPS*, vol. 32 (1968), Spring Joint Computer Conference, Spartan Books, New York, pp. 213–221.

4.2. High-Speed Compilation of Efficient Object Code

by C. W. Gear

4.2.1. SUMMARY

A three-pass compiler with the following properties is briefly described: The last two passes scan an intermediate language produced by the preceding pass in essentially the reverse of the order in which it was generated, so that the first pass is the only one which has to read the relatively bulky problem-oriented input. The double scan, one in either direction, performed by the first two passes, allows the compiler to remove locally constant expressions and recursively calculable expressions from loops and to do the important part of common subexpression recognition. Optimization such as the effective use of index registers, although as important, is not discussed, since the object code which would be most efficient is highly machine dependent. The discussion is in terms of a FORTRAN-like language, although the technique is applicable to most algebraic languages.

4.2.2. INTRODUCTION

Existing compilers tend to fall into two classes: those that are relatively fast, very often syntax directed, one- or two-pass programs with either an

---

EDITOR'S NOTE: This article reproduced by permission of the author and the publisher: *Comm. ACM*, vol. 8, no. 8 (August 1965), pp. 483–488.

211

inefficient or an interpretive object code, and those which spend a large amount of time optimizing the object code for the particular machine. Descriptions of the latter do not often appear in print because of their highly machine-dependent nature. (However, descriptions of IBM FORTRAN II[4] and the KDF 9 optimizing ALGOL[3] are available.)

The arguments in favor of this situation are well known. Code checks are run on the fast compiler and then an optimized object is obtained from the other for production.

It has been the experience of this writer that a large number of medium-sized jobs seldom remain unchanged. Before each production run, small changes are made at the source language level. Both because of this and because the source language is a condensed, readily comprehensible representation of the job, it is highly desirable to seek a middle ground with some of the features of both worlds.

The purpose of this report is to describe a method for the high-speed compilation of code which has been rearranged so as to optimize it in terms of the number of basic operations performed. This technique is machine independent. Machine-dependent features, such as index registers, finite length operand stacks, etc., are not discussed.

The object code of a compiler can be made more efficient in a number of ways. They include the location of locally constant expressions or expressions that can be calculated by recursion, location of common subexpressions, and the rearranging of the calculation to facilitate any of these objectives, such that either code can be removed from loop or duplicated coding can be removed. Nonbuffered input from auxiliary storage can also be made more efficient within the operating system by precalling the input package to load a buffer. For example, the FORTRAN statement READ TAPE N, I/O list will cause a wait by the main frame until tape N has been read into a buffer so that it can be copied to the I/O list. This wait can be reduced by calling for the buffer fill earlier.

In order to perform these types of optimization it is necessary to analyze all statements in a neighborhood of a given statement. This neighborhood is the extent of the loop or block of program from which it is desired to remove code. Thus most optimization procedures involve a considerable amount of rescanning, or the construction of very large tables which must be examined more or less at random.

The requirements for high-speed compilation are that a minimum of scans of the entire data be used, and that it not be necessary to refer at random to sections of the program remote from the one being considered, or equivalently, to very large tables containing sections of the program.

For high-speed computer systems now being designed, it is a further advantage to refer to memory in a sequential manner rather than in a highly data-dependent manner, since a larger degree of memory main-frame overlap is then possible using the various look-ahead schemes.

Thus the requirements of high-speed compilation and efficient object code production are somewhat incompatible. Any solution is bound to reflect the assessment of the individual as to the relative importance. This report stresses high-speed compilation; optimization is performed within this constraint. It does not deal with the techniques involved in the standard compilation process, since they are both well known and machine dependent. It only points out additions to the processes which achieve optimization.

4.2.3. AN OUTLINE OF THE PROGRAM

An example will clarify the type of optimization being sought. The following section of a FORTRAN program:

$$\text{DIMENSION A (15,5)}$$
$$\cdots$$
$$\text{DO 1 I} = \text{M1, N1, L1}$$
$$\text{DO 2 J} = \text{M2, N2, L2}$$
$$2 \quad \text{A(I, J)} = \text{A(I, J)} * \text{C} * 15.5 * \text{D} * .5$$
$$1 \quad \text{C} \quad = \text{C} + 1.$$
$$\cdots$$

might compile on a fast "single-pass" compiler as the machine language equivalent of

	Move M1 to I
LOOP1	Move M2 to J
LOOP2	$(J - 1) * 15 + I - 1 + A \rightarrow T1$
	$(J - 1) * 15 + I - 1 + A \rightarrow T2$
	Load indirect from T2
	Multiply by C
	Multiply by 15.5
	Multiply by D
	Multiply by 0.5

Store indirect into T1

$J + L2 \rightarrow J$

Subtract N2 and transfer to LOOP2 if result ≤ 0

$C + 1. \rightarrow C$

$I + L1 \rightarrow I$

Subtract N1 and transfer to LOOP1 if result ≤ 0

. . .

where T1 and T2 are temporary storage cells, and A is the memory cell containing A(1, 1).

A fairly efficient object version is given in the form below:

$L1 \rightarrow X4$

$A - 16 + 15 * M2 + M1 \rightarrow X3$

$L2 * 15 \rightarrow X2$

$D * 7.75 \rightarrow T2$

$M1 \rightarrow I$

Transfer to LOOP1 + 1

LOOP1 $X3 + X4 \rightarrow X3$

$X3 \rightarrow X1$

$T2 * C \rightarrow T1$

$M2 \rightarrow J$

Transfer to LOOP2 + 1

LOOP2 $X1 + X2 \rightarrow X1$

Load indirect from X1

Multiply by T1

Store indirect in X1

$J + L2 \rightarrow J$

Subtract N2 and transfer to LOOP2 if result ≤ 0

$C + 1. \rightarrow C$

$I + L1 \rightarrow I$

Subtract N1 and transfer to LOOP1 if result ≤ 0

The basic steps that were taken in this example are as follows:

(a) The locally constant expression $C * 15.5 * D * .5$ was removed from the inner loop since C and D are not changed in that loop. Since C but not D is changed in the outer loop the $15.5 * D * .5$ part can also be removed from that loop.

(b) The expression $(J + 1) * 15 + I - 1 + A$ was recognized to be recursively calculable in the inner loop by starting at $(M2 - 1) * 15 + 1 - 1 + A$ and adding increments of $15 * L2$. Then the starting expression was also recognized as recursively calculable in the outer loop.

(c) The expression $15.5 * D * .5$ was rearranged to get $D * 7.75$.

(d) The occurrence of the expression $(J - 1) * 15 + I - 1 + A$ twice was recognized.

The first two of these steps may only be taken if the variables concerned are either not changed inside the loop, or are changed in an incremental manner. It is therefore necessary to examine the range of each loop for potential changes. The assumptions made about function or subroutine calls are crucial in this problem. If side effects are allowed, then it is necessary either to tabulate information about the changes effected by each such procedure, or else to assume that everything may be changed and abandon this optimization in any loop containing such a call.

To gather the information required about each loop in the program in a straightforward manner, pass I maintains a stack S_v, each of whose entries is a simple string of variable names. The top level of the stack corresponds to the iterative loop of the program currently being scanned, and lower levels correspond to each of the loops within which the current one is nested. As each statement is scanned, the names of variables which are changed by the statement are added to the top level of S_v. When the end of a loop is reached, the top level contains the string of all changed variables. This string is saved and also added to the second level of S_v, so that when the old top level is discarded, the new top level contains the current set of changed variables for the next outer loop.

Pass I also translates the source input into a more compact internal form where, for example, arithmetic expressions are in a Polish postfix notation. In order not to have to save each of the strings of changed variables in main core, they also are added to the intermediate language output from pass I. They occur at the end of the block to which they refer.

To handle recursive calculation, a second stack S_D (which could be part of S_v) is maintained by pass I. The loop parameters are entered into the top of this stack when they are read so that they can also be moved to the end of the loop where a test can be made to see if the controlled variable or the step quantity is changed inside the loop.

Pass I also performs the syntax checking of the source language, and, for efficiency, it replaces all identifiers by an internal form such as a table address.

Pass II basically scans the output from pass I in reverse order. This makes the string of changed variable names and other loop information available to the program just as the first (in time) statement of a loop is read. Pass II maintains a stack S_v by placing the changed variable string on top of S_v when the end of each loop is entered, and removing it when the beginning of the loop is left. Thus, during the processing of any loop, the top of the stack S_v contains the string of variables changed in that loop. Similarly the top of a stack S_D contains the current loop control parameters. Additional stacks S_L and S_R whose entries are lists are maintained by pass II. These stacks contain lists of strings representing respectively the local constants and recursive increments which are in the process of being moved to the beginning of a loop.

The output of pass II is in a machine language with symbolic addresses. The length of the program being generated can be calculated during the second pass, so that at its completion, variable storage can be assigned. Pass III then produces a relocatable binary object.

The method described below involves operations such as concatenating elements and strings to form larger strings, where these elements or strings are members of stacks. Deliberately, no mention is made of how to mechanize this, since it is highly machine dependent. On some machines it is better to chain everything and not to move elements unless absolutely necessary; on other machines the opposite holds. These tricks of the programmers' trade can easily save or cost a factor of 2 in speed, so a judgment of the method should include an evaluation of their potential value in this problem.

4.2.4. REMOVING LOCALLY CONSTANT SUBEXPRESSIONS

This section indicates the manner in which pass II scans arithmetic expressions in order to locate locally constant subexpressions. The information it has available is contained in the top entry of the stack S_v, which contains a string of changed names. For speed it is convenient on most machines to translate this information so that it is represented by a bit in the name table.

Arithmetic expressions have been translated by pass I into a Polish postfix form. Although the main pass II scan is proceeding backwards, it is more convenient to scan expressions forward. This can be handled either by having pass I reverse the order of the expression or, probably more conveniently, have pass I generate a pointer at the end of an expression indicating the beginning of the expression.

As the Polish postfix form is scanned from left to right, operand names are read and placed in an operand stack S_O. As they are put in this stack they are marked as changed variables or not, depending on whether they appear in the top of S_v or not. When operations are read in from the Polish postfix string they must be compiled. The nature of the compiling action depends on the operands involved. Consider only binary operations. (*n*-ary operations follow the same principle.) If neither of the top two operands in S_O are changed, no code is generated; rather the top two levels are replaced with a single entry representing the combination. For example, if the top two levels are both locally constant variables (LCV) they are replaced by a single locally constant expression LCE. This is mechanized by forming a Polish postfix string consisting of the top two operands followed by the operation, placing this in main store and placing a pointer to it in the stack with the mark LCE. Thus the entries in the operand stack can be any one of the classes:

C	(constant, e.g., 15.5)
LCV	(locally constant variable)
LCE	(locally constant expression)
V	(variable, one that is changed in the loop)

The rules for the combination of these by any binary operations are given in Table 4.2.1.

When the beginning of the loop is reached in the pass II scan, the loop is closed, the top level of S_V discarded, and the Polish postfix assignment statements removed from the top of the S_L stack and compiled to yield the program to generate the local constants. Since these expressions may be partially or wholly local constants in this outer loop, they should be handled in the same manner as pass I generated expressions; that is, all that is necessary is to switch for input from the intermediate language of pass I to this list until it is exhausted. Since the temporary storage name generated for a locally constant expression is not marked as changed, the rules outlined above cause an expression to be removed from all loops in which it does not change.

Table 4.2.1

1st and 2d level Operands of S_O	Action
C –C	Combine at compile time to get new constant.
C –LCV C –LCE LCV–LCV LCV–LCE and LCE–LCE	Form new string consisting of the concatenation of 1st level of S_O, 2nd level of S_O, operation. Single stack entry becomes LCE pointing to this string.
C –V LCV–V V –V	Compile object code directly. Single stack entry becomes V type.
LCE–V	Allocate a temporary storage cell with name T, say. Compile code for T, V, operation. Add "T =" to the end of the string representing the LCE and add this new string to the top level of S_L, the stack of locally constant expressions. The single S_O stack entry becomes V type.

General *n*-ary operations such as functions can be handled by the obvious extension of the process. Indexing is an extension of functions. If the indexing expressions are local constants then the address of the element can be calculated outside of the loop. If in addition no elements of the array are changed, then the element could be part of a larger locally constant expression.

4.2.5. RECURSIVE CALCULATION

Recursive calculation of addresses has been discussed by Samelson and Bauer[5] for ALGOL. Restrictions essentially similar to those of FORTRAN are imposed on the subscripts. The method proposed here is to calculate all expressions recursively where that can be done. If the expression happens to be an index expression, then a compiler for a particular machine can take note of it and use index registers or other features to perform the calculation.

The technique is essentially identical to the one used for identifying local constants. A new type of operand stack entry is defined, the *Step Variable* (sv). This is a variable which is incremented by constant amounts during the execution of a loop. The controlled variable in the loop is of this type provided that neither it nor the step quantity are changed inside the loop. This is the reason for moving the controlled variable name and loop parameters to the end of the loop by the S_D stack mechanism in pass I. As the end of a loop is entered, the new top level is added to the S_D stack, and the loop count mechanism is compiled. If the expression used for the step compiler is a fixed-point constant or local constant, the controlled variable is checked against the changed list. If it is not changed in the loop (except by the loop control), it is flagged in the table as a step variable for the duration of this loop. (If the controlled variable of the next outer loop is also flagged as a step variable, its flag must be turned off until the beginning of the loop has been reached.)

Another type of operand stack entry is defined, a *Step Expression* (SE). An SE is a combination, by addition or subtraction of any two SV's, SE's, LCE's, LCV's, or C's, one of which is an SV or SE, or a combination, by multiplication of an SE or SV with an LCE, LCV, or C type.

Thus a step expression can be expressed in the form LCEA + LCEB * I where I is the step variable and LCEA and LCEB are two C's, LCV's, or LCE's. Since I is being incremented by a locally constant amount, say INC, the value of the step expression can be obtained by starting at LCEA + LCEB * S and incrementing each time by LCEB * INC, where S is the starting value of I.

The procedure is mechanized by marking a variable in the operand stack S_O as an SV if it is so marked in the variable table. When two (or more) operands from S_O are combined which result in an SE, the entry in the stack S_O is so marked, and a pointer is placed there which points to a pair of strings. The first string represents LCEA and the second represents LCEB.

When the operation is an addition (or subtraction), the new lists are formed by concatenating the pairs of strings representing each operand together with a trailing plus (minus) sign. If either of the expressions is simpler than an SE, then its LCEA and LCEB are implied in the obvious way.

When the operation is multiplication of an SE or SV by a C, LCV or LCE, the new LCEA is the string LCEA:

$$\begin{Bmatrix} C \\ LCV \\ LCE \end{Bmatrix} * \text{ and the new LCEB is similarly LCEB} \begin{Bmatrix} C \\ LCV \\ LCE \end{Bmatrix} *.$$

In all other cases involving an SE or SV, some object code is to be compiled. If the operand is either an SV or an SE with its LCEB equal to ± 1, then there is no point to handling it as other than a changed variable (with possibly a locally constant additive LCEA). Apart from these cases, it is necessary to assign a temporary storage cell, say T1, to the SE for the purpose of compiling the current operation. A second temporary storage cell T2 must also be provided for the increment storage. The strings LCEA LCEB S $*$ + T1 = and LCEB INC $*$ T2 = are added to the top list of the stack S_L of locally constant expressions and T1 T2 + T1 = is added to the top of the S_R stack of recursive increments.

When the beginning of the loop is reached in the scan, it is necessary to prepare the incrementing orders by compiling the top level of the S_R stack and then discarding it. The loop is then closed by removing the top level of the S_D stack and compiling the loop initialization plus the transfer around the incrementation orders before compiling the top of the S_L stack.

Just as the multiplication operation has been reduced to successive additions, the exponentiation operation could be reduced to successive multiplications, but this writer feels that it is of doubtful value, both because of rounding error and frequency of occurrence.

4.2.6. REARRANGING THE CALCULATION OF AN EXPRESSION

Whether or not this should be done is open to question numerically. The fact that some compilers work from left to right, others right to left, and still others in some optimizing manner means that if the programmer desires to calculate A + B + C in a specific order, he should indicate it with parentheses, e.g., A + (B + C), if he intends to use the program in more than one installation. In order to indicate the difference between the three expressions A + B + C, A + (B + C), and (A + B) + C in the Polish postfix string, a convention must be used which allows the rearrangement of calculation in the first instance. Such a convention is to allow *n*-ary versions of operands. Thus A + B + C becomes ABC $+_3$. The subscript 3 indicates that + is the summation of the three elements A, B, C. A + (B + C) and (A + B) + C would then uniquely be ABC ++ and AB + C + where the subscript 2 for binary operations has been dropped. In order that this convention also handle the subtraction (and division) operations, the "sign" of the operation is placed over the last element representing that variable. Thus A − B + C is $A\bar{B}C +_3$ while A − (B + C) is ABC $\mp$+ and A + (− B + C) is $A\bar{B}C$ ++. Similarly, A/B $*$ C and A/(B $*$ C) are $A\bar{B}C *_3$ and ABC $\bar{*}*$, respectively.

When the operation $+_3$ in the expression ABC $+_3$ is to be compiled by pass II, the objective is to rearrange the elements so that the minimum of work is done at execution time. This has been discussed in the case of constants by Floyd[1] and Gear.[2] There is a hierarchy of operands that are possible in the stack at any time. This ordering is

Constant

Locally Constant Expression (including Locally Constant Variable)

Step Expression (including Step Variable)

Variable

When an n-ary commutative operation $+_n$ or $*_n$ is encountered by pass II, the top n levels of the operand stack S_O are examined to find all occurrences of constants first (these are combined at compile time) and n is appropriately reduced. If it is not now 1, the remaining levels are examined for LCE's or LCV's. If there are any, they are combined with any constant to give a new LCE. If n still has not been reduced to 1, the search continues for SE's or SV's which can be legitimately combined into SE's. Finally, if n is not 1, code is compiled and the stack entry becomes a variable.

4.2.7. COMMON SUBEXPRESSIONS

Floyd[1] has described one way of locating common subexpressions within a single expression. This method could be extended to a number of expressions within a program segment at a considerable cost in main storage requirements. It seems doubtful that any simple technique can be found to handle this problem without considerable searching and comparing. This writer feels that in general the payoff for the amount of work involved is marginal for the following reasons:

(a) If the common subexpression is very short, e.g., $A + B$ or $A * B$, the gain in execution speed is small, since in most cases a store order to save the result is involved in place of the common arithmetic operation.

(b) If the common subexpression is lengthy, the laziness of the programmer can be relied upon to do the necessary simplification, e.g.,

$$\ldots (A + B) * (C + D)/(E + (A + B) * (C + D)) \ldots$$

is likely to appear as

$$T = (A + B) * (C + D)$$
$$\ldots T/(E + T) \ldots$$

which is a considerable saving in writing.

However, when a feature of the language expresses a fairly involved expression in a simple manner, the recognition of common subexpressions becomes advantageous. Such a case is indexing. For example, the assignment statement for a three-dimensional Gaus-Seidel iteration of the Laplace equation is:

$$A(I, J, K) = (A(I, J, K - 1) + A(I, J, K + 1) +$$
$$A(I, J - 1, K) + A(I, J + 1, K) +$$
$$A(I - 1, J, K) + A(I + 1, J, K))/6.$$

This contains the expression $((K - 1) * N2 + J - 1) * N1 + I - 1 + A$ plus various constants seven times where N1 and N2 are the dimensions of the first two subscripts of A. The method proposed here is not to look for such common subexpressions unless they are either local constants or step functions. If this is done, then each time that a new step function or local constant is generated, it should be compared against the existing set in the top level of S_L before being entered there. A step function contains two local constants. If the step part LCEB agrees with the step part of another step function (the names of these are located in S_R), then only one incremented function is needed, the other can be determined by calculating the difference between the two constant parts LCEA and adding this relocation at the time it is used. If these are identical, so much the better.

In many situations, such as the example above, the two constant parts LCEA of two step functions will only differ by a fixed constant, but this fact will be hidden by the arrangement of the Polish postfix strings representing them. For example, if I is the step variable, and it is being incremented by 1 starting at 1, the LCEA part of A(I, J, K − 1) is

$$K\overline{2} + N2 * J\overline{I} +_3 N1 * 'A' +$$

whereas for

$$A(I + 1, J, K)$$

it is

$$K\overline{I} + N2 * J\overline{I} +_3 N1 * 1'A' +_3$$

where 'A' is the address of A(1, 1, 1). A direct comparison will not easily yield the fact that these differ by $N2 * N1 + 1$.

To aid this recognition, it is proposed that the LCE's be reorganized as they are generated. A suitable form is such that LC's always appear before C's in additive groups. They can easily be rearranged as they are removed from the S_O stack during formation. Additionally when an LCE of the form "LCE, constant, $+$" is multiplied by a constant such as N2, the value of "constant $*$ N2" should be calculated, yielding, say, C_1. The new LCE is then "LCE, N2, $*$, C_1, $+$". In this way, additive constants are moved to the right-hand side of the string (and in an expression like $(I + 3) * 7 + J + 2$ additions are saved). A direct comparison of the LCE's can now be used to determine if they differ only by a constant. If this is so, the second expression can be calculated from the first by simple addition. Whether this is better done outside the loop or at the time of use depends on the machine characteristics.

4.2.8. AUXILIARY STORAGE INPUT

The reverse pass feature of this method can be used to handle this optimizing problem at a simple level. During the first pass, the input statement is moved forward over statements as far as possible such that (a) no transfers into or out of these statements are possible (determined by the nonexistence of statement numbers or control transfers in FORTRAN), (b) no variables used or changed by these statements are in the input list, and (c) none of these statements refers to the same I/O unit.

During the second pass, the call to the buffering program or monitor is moved back to be the first statement of the program segment, that is, immediately following the first transfer into or out of the program.

4.2.9. CONCLUSION

Because the output of one pass is read backwards by the next pass, this method is particularly suited to machines with tapes that can be read in either direction. Disk files or drums are also suitable for the intermediate storage, and can lead to very fast second and third passes.

On a machine with a large main memory many methods of optimization which use large parts of core are feasible. Since the first pass is usually highly input limited, it might be an advantage to use the method outlined above on several programs simultaneously; that is, the compiler program is time-shared by several inputs and auxiliary devices, each using a small piece of memory for data storage.

Partial optimization of the object code in a machine independent fashion is certainly feasible using a small amount of main memory with a reversible auxiliary store. On most machines it is likely that the input time for the source program will dominate the compile speed. Optimization of the use of machine features such as index registers is a harder problem, probably requiring two further passes, one in each direction, since in the proposed compiler, information about which addresses would best be in index registers is not available until pass II, and pass II must generate code whose length can be determined by the end of pass II.

REFERENCES

1. Floyd, R. W., "An Algorithm for Coding Efficient Arithmetic Operations," *Comm. ACM*, vol. 4 (January 1961), p. 42.

2. Gear, C. W., "Optimization of the Address Field Compilation in the ILLIAC II Assembler," *Comput. J.*, vol. 6 (January 1964), p. 332.

3. Huxtable, D. H. R., "On Writing an Optimizing Translator for ALGOL 60," in *Introduction to System Programming*, P. Wegner (ed.), Academic Press, 1964, p. 137.

4. *IBM Systems Manual for* 704 FORTRAN *and* 709 FORTRAN. Appl. Programming Dept., IBM, April, 1960.

5. Samelson, K., and Bauer, F. L., "Sequential Formula Translation," *Comm. ACM*, vol. 3 (February 1960), p. 76.

4.3. Peephole Optimization

by W. M. McKeeman

4.3.1. SUMMARY

Redundant instructions may be discarded during the final stage of compilation by using a simple optimizing technique called peephole optimization. The method is described and examples are given.[†]

4.3.2. INTRODUCTION

Nearly all compilers expend some effort to increase the efficiency of the code they produce. One particularly simple and often neglected technique might be called *peephole optimization*, a method which consists of a local inspection of the object code to identify and modify inefficient sequences of instructions. Several examples are given below. The source language is ALGOL and the object code is given in a simple single-address assembly language; nevertheless, the technique is directly applicable to a wide class of languages and machines.

[†] This work was supported in part by the Office of Naval Research, Contract Nonr. 225(37).

4.3.2.1. *Example 1*

Source code:

$$X := Y;$$
$$Z := X + Z$$

Compiled code:

LDA Y	load the accumulator from Y
STA X	store the accumulator in X
LDA X	load the accumulator from X
ADD Z	add the contents of Z
STA Z	store the accumulator in Z

If the store instruction is nondestructive, the third instruction is redundant and may be discarded. The action may be accomplished by having the subroutine which emits object code check every time it produces an LDA to see if the previous instruction was the corresponding STA and behave accordingly.

4.3.2.2. *Example 2*

Source code:

$$X := Y;$$
$$Z := Z + X$$

This example presents a problem which occurs repeatedly during the translation of arithmetic expressions. A commutative operator, "+", appears in the source code, but straightforward translation leads to less than optimum code. When the optimizing code emitter produces a commutative operator (addition, multiplication, transfer on equality or inequality, logical AND, logical OR, etc.), it must first check the preceding instruction. If that instruction was LDA then the optimizer may choose, if the instruction preceding the LDA was STA, to reorder the commutative operation so as to avoid the LDA, as in Example 1. Having avoided the LDA, the optimizer may check to see if the STA was in fact a store into a temporary location in which case the STA may also be discarded.

4.3.2.3. Example 3

Source code:

$$X := 2.0 \times 3.14159265/360.0 + X;$$
$$\textbf{if } X < 0.0 \textbf{ then } \dots$$

Object code:

LDA $= 2.0$	load the accumulator with the constant 2.0
MUL $= 3.14159265$	multiply by pi
DIV $= 360.0$	divide by 360.0
ADD X	add the contents of X
STA X	store the accumulator in X
LDA X	load the accumulator from X
SUB $= 0.0$	subtract the constant 0.0
TPA $\dots$	transfer on positive accumulator $\dots$

A programmer is often tempted to write an expression involving several constants simply because he does not have the time or facilites to compute the value by hand. If the optimizer, when it produces an arithmetic operation, checks to see if the operation addresses a constant and the preceding instruction is an LDA addressing a constant, then it may simplify the pair to a single LDA addressing the result of the operation on the constants. The optimizer may also discard such nonsense as addition or subtraction of zero and multiplication or division by one. The object code in Example 3 will reduce to:

$$LDA = 0.017453293$$
$$ADD X$$
$$STA X$$
$$TPA \dots$$

Many machines have operations that are convenient in hand coding but difficult to fit into the more general structure of a compiler. Frequently the optimizer can be set to recognize a sequence of instructions as the equivalent of a hardware command and make an appropriate modification in the object code.

There are, however, situations in which the compiled code may not be improved.

4.3.2.4. *Example 4*

Source code:

$$X := Y;$$
$$L: Z := X + Z$$

Even though the object code produced is identical to that of Example 1, the instruction LDA X can be reached via a transfer to the label L and must not be omitted. Similar considerations might be necessary for parameters that cause side effects through the evaluation of a function designator.

These techniques have been used in GOGOL, a translator written by the author for the PDP-1 time sharing system at Stanford. The optimizing code emitting routine consists of about 400 of the 2000 instructions required for the compiler. We have found that the code emitter can see, through a very narrow peephole, enough to make considerable improvement in the object code. The limitation on how well the optimizer will work seems to depend primarily on how much time and space are available for recognizing redundant sequences of instructions.

4.4. The Generation of Optimal Code for Arithmetic Expressions

by *Ravi Sethi and J. D. Ullman*

4.4.1. ABSTRACT

The problem of evaluating arithmetic expressions on a machine with $N \geq 1$ general-purpose registers is considered. It is initially assumed that no algebraic laws apply to the operators and operands in the expression. An algorithm for evaluation of expressions under this assumption is proposed, and it is shown to take the shortest possible number of instructions. It is then assumed that certain operators are commutative or both commutative and associative. In this case a procedure is given for finding an expression equivalent to a given one and having the shortest possible evaluation sequence. It is then shown that the algorithms presented here also minimize the number of storage references in the evaluation.

Key Words and Phrases: arithmetic expressions, associativity, code generation, commutativity, compilers, object-code optimization, register assignment, trees. CR categories: 4.12, 5.24, 5.32.

EDITOR'S NOTE: This article reproduced by permission of the authors and the publisher: *J. ACM*, vol. 17, no. 4 (October 1970), pp. 715–728.

4.4.2. INTRODUCTION

Nakata[1] and Meyers[2] consider the problem of minimizing the number of general registers required to evaluate an arithmetic expression. When only commutative operators like $+$ and $*$ are considered, Redziejowski[3] shows that Nakata's algorithm does give the minimum number of registers.

We consider the somewhat more general problem of minimizing the number of program steps and/or the number of storage references in the evaluation of an expression, given a fixed number of general registers. The algorithms we present exploit the commutative and associative properties of operators, and are at the same time able to cope with noncommutative operators. We assume throughout this article that there are no nontrivial relations between operators and elements. For example, we assume that all elements are distinct, and that laws such as $a * b + a * c = a * (b + c)$ are not applicable. Under the above assumption, the algorithms presented generate optimal sequences of evaluation.

In practice, the associative and commutative laws need not and in most cases do not hold, as machines carry information of finite precision. It is conceivable that the order in which the operators and elements are specified leads to clever use of the available facilities. In such cases, reordering the computation may lead to overflows or underflows. However, most computations are not critically dependent on the order of evaluation—especially as compilers are fairly arbitrary in producing executable code. In these cases, an optimal sequence of evaluation can be arrived at by permuting the specified order of operations, without adversely affecting the accuracy of the result.

In showing that the sequence generated is optimal under the assumed conditions, we show that the algorithms minimize, independently, the number of "clear and adds" into registers and the number of "stores." The number of binary operations cannot be reduced, as the associative and commutative transformations do not change the number of operators in an expression. Later we show that minimizing the number of program steps also minimizes the number of storage references.

In Section 4.4.7 we briefly consider the timing requirements of the algorithms. We indicate, without proof, that the time taken is proportional to n, the number of nodes in the tree for the expression.

The algorithms are designed for a machine with unlimited storage and $N \geq 1$ general registers. The commands permitted are of the following kinds:

1. C(storage) → C(register)
2. C(register) → C(storage)
3. OP[C(register), C(storage)] → C(register)
4. OP[C(register), C(register)] → C(register)

Commands of types 1 and 2 transfer the contents of a storage location to the contents of a register, and vice versa. This makes them the equivalents of the CLear and Add (CLA) and STOre (STO) commands, respectively. Type 3 commands perform an operation on two operands, the first in a register and the second in storage. It is important to note that commands of the type

$$OP[C(storage), C(register)] \to C(register)$$

are not permitted. This restriction is in keeping with the instruction sets of many present-day machines. For example, in a divide operation, the dividend is constrained to be in a register. Permitting commands of this type would have the same effect as making all operators commutative. Commands of type 4 apply an operator to the contents of two registers, leaving the result in a third (not necessarily distinct) register.

An *expression* is a sequence of binary operations on arguments. Arguments are either *initial* (defined externally) or *intermediate* (defined by operations on other arguments) values. Such expressions may be represented by binary trees. Initial values correspond to *leaves* and intermediate values to interior nodes of the tree. Every interior node represents a binary operation on the elements corresponding to its descendants. The value associated with a node can only be computed by applying the corresponding operator to the values of its two descendant subtrees taken in the proper order. Due to commands of type 3, the order in which the descendants are taken is important. Left descendants will be taken to correspond to the first operand and right descendants to the second operand in all commands. Two nodes in a tree are *twins* if they have the same ancestor.

A *program* is a sequence of operations which evaluates an expression when given the initial values in specified storage locations. The program terminates with the value of the entire expression in a register. The *cost* of a computation is the number of program steps required for the computation on the machine described.

Adopting an idea of Nakata[1] and Meyers,[2] we shall *label*[†] each node with

---

[†] Our labels differ from these [Refs. 1 and 2] in order to handle noncommutativity correctly.

a number that turns out to be the minimal number of registers required to evaluate the node without stores. Given a tree, the algorithm defined later in this paper suitably labels it and uses these labels to define a minimal sequence of operations for the machine described.

In the first part of this article, all operations are taken to be noncommutative. This restriction is later relaxed to allow associative and commutative operations.

4.4.3. THE BASIC ALGORITHM

To each node η is assigned a *label* $L(\eta)$, from the bottom up. It should be noted that for the time being all operators are assumed noncommutative:

L1.   If η is a leaf and the left descendant of its ancestor, then $L(\eta) = 1$; if η is the right descendant, then $L(\eta) = 0$;

L2.   If η has descendants with labels l_1 and l_2, then for $l_1 \neq l_2$, $L(\eta) = \max(l_1, l_2)$, and for $l_1 = l_2$, $L(\eta) = l_1 + 1$.

We now give an algorithm for the evaluation of arithmetic expressions using at most N registers. This algorithm is, in fact, the "obvious" top-down algorithm. Significantly, we prove its optimality under the assumptions previously mentioned.

4.4.3.1. *Algorithm 1*

After generating the tree and labeling the nodes:

(1) Apply (2) to the root with registers $b_1, b_2, \ldots, b_N$ available. Routine (2) will evaluate the expression represented by the subtree extending from the node to which it is applied. The result will appear in the lowest numbered register available.

(2) Let η be a node, $L(\eta) = l$ and $l > 0$. Suppose registers $b_m, b_{m+1}, \ldots, b_N$ are available, $1 \leq m \leq N$.

We first treat the case $l = 1$.

(A) If η is a leaf it must be a left descendant. Enter the value of η, which is an initial value, into b_m.

(B) If η is not a leaf its right descendant must be a leaf, else η's label would be at least 2. Apply (2) to its left descendant with registers $b_m, b_{m+1}, \ldots, b_N$ available. The result will appear in b_m. We then evaluate η in one step. The value of the left descendant is in b_m, the right in storage. Return the value in b_m.

Now suppose $l > 1$. Let the descendants of η have labels l_1, l_2.

(C) If $l_1, l_2 \geq N$ apply (2) to the right descendant with registers $b_m, b_{m+1}, \ldots, b_N$ available. Store the value of the right descendant. Apply (2) to the left descendant with registers $b_m, b_{m+1}, \ldots, b_N$ available, leaving the result in b_m. Evaluate η using the value in b_m and the value of the right descendant in storage. Leave the result in b_m.

(D) If $l_1 \neq l_2$, and at least one of l_1, l_2 is less than N, apply (2) to the descendant with the higher label, with registers $b_m, b_{m+1}, \ldots, b_N$ available. Leave the result in b_m. Apply (2) to the other descendant with registers $b_{m+1}, b_{m+2}, \ldots, b_N$ available. The result will appear in b_{m+1}. Evaluate η using the values in b_m and b_{m+1}, and leave the result in b_m. Exception: If the smaller label is 0, do not apply (2), but rather evaluate η using the value in b_m and the value of η's right descendant, which must be a leaf, in storage.

(E) If $l_1 = l_2 < N$, treat the left descendant as the node with the higher label and proceed as above.

Example 1.   Consider the expression $a/(b + c) - d * (e + f)$, whose tree is given in Fig. 4.4.1.

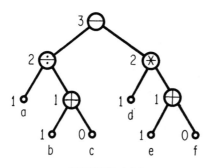

FIGURE 4.4.1

The integers at each node are the labels assigned by the labeling algorithm. Algorithm 1 produces the following code, if $N = 2$.

1. $d \rightarrow \text{reg1}$

2. $e \rightarrow \text{reg2}$

3. $\text{reg2} + f \rightarrow \text{reg2}$

4. $\text{reg1} * \text{reg2} \rightarrow \text{reg1}$

5. $\text{reg1} \rightarrow T$

6. $a \rightarrow \text{reg1}$

7. $b \rightarrow \text{reg2}$

8. $\text{reg2} + c \rightarrow \text{reg2}$

9. $\text{reg1}/\text{reg2} \rightarrow \text{reg1}$

10. $\text{reg1} - T \rightarrow \text{reg1}$

In the above computation instructions 1, 2, 6, and 7 are CLA's. Instruction 5 is a store. The rest are binary arithmetic operations. It is possible to evaluate the given expression using only eight instructions if $*$ is assumed commutative. Example 2 shows this.

Several papers have dealt with the compilation of code for arithmetic expressions and Algorithm 1 can be considered a generalization of some of those ideas. Floyd[4] suggested that the right argument of a noncommutative operation be computed first. Anderson[5] gives an algorithm which starts with an expression, constructs a binary tree, and then produces code for a machine with one register. Given such a machine, the code produced by the algorithm in this paper is essentially the same as the tree code in Ref. 5.

Nakata[1] and Meyers[2] have essentially similar results. As mentioned in Section 4.4.2, the algorithms in this paper are generalizations of these. In Ref. 2 a cost criterion is defined to be *distributive with respect to a given computer* if and only if each program for that computer which evaluates an expression in an optimal way (according to the criterion) also evaluates all subexpressions of that expression in optimal ways (according to the same criterion). The cost of computation defined in Section 4.4.2 is distributive with respect to our machine. When more than one register is involved, distributivity is not obvious, because different numbers of registers may be available to different nodes. The following sequence of lemmas, in effect, proves the distributivity.

We now show that Algorithm 1 produces a minimal cost program when all operators are noncommutative.

LEMMA 1.   *Let Algorithm 1 be started with N registers available. Let r be the number of registers available when routine (2) of Algorithm 1 is applied to a node η. Then: $r = N$ if $L(\eta) > N$; $N \geq r \geq L(\eta)$ if $L(\eta) \leq N$.*

Proof.   We shall prove this lemma by induction on the number of applications of routine (2). The first time routine (2) is applied, it is for the root and all N registers are available.

Let the lemma hold for the first k calls, and let the $(k + 1)$-th call be for node η_1 with r registers available. Let η_1's twin node be η_2 and its ancestor η. Let their labels be l_1, l_2, and l respectively.

Case 1. $l_1 \geq N$. Since $l_1 \geq N$, we have $l \geq N$. As the lemma holds for the application of routine (2) to η, N registers were available then. From (2C), if $l_2 \geq N$, then when routine (2) is applied to η_1, N registers are available and the lemma holds. If $l_2 < N$, then N registers are available for η_1, by (2D).

Case 2. $l_1 < l_2$ and $l_1 < N$. Then from the labeling rules, $l_2 = l$ and $l_1 < l$. The call for η_2 was before the $(k + 1)$-th and r registers were available, $r \geq l_2 = l$. By (2D), the $(k + 1)$-th call occurs with $r - 1$ registers. Since $l_1 < l \leq r$, we have $l_1 \leq r - 1$, and the lemma holds.

Case 3. $l_2 < l_1 < N$. Then $l_1 = l$. The call for η occurred before the $(k + 1)$-th call. Therefore $r \geq L(\eta) = l$. By (2B) or (2D), the $(k + 1)$-th call occurs with r registers and the lemma holds.

Case 4. $l_1 = l_2 < N$. In this case, from the labeling rules $l_1 = l_2 = l - 1$. Since routine (2) was called for η before it was called for η_1, $r \geq l$ registers were available. By (2E), routine (2) is called for η_1 with r or $r - 1$ registers depending on whether η_1 is the left or the right descendant of η respectively. Since $r \geq l$, we have $r - 1 \geq l - 1$, and the lemma holds.

LEMMA 2. *Algorithm 1 evaluates a tree with no stores when as many registers as the label of the root are available.*

Proof. Each interior node represents an operation. To evaluate a node, the algorithm evaluates both its descendants, then applies the operator. Since this is true for all interior nodes in the tree, Algorithm 1 correctly evaluates the expression. With Lemma 1, a simple induction on maximum path length of a tree shows that no stores occur.

LEMMA 3. *For trees with root labels up to 2, the label of the root is a lower bound on the minimum number of registers required to evaluate the tree without any stores.*

Proof. Let l be the label of the root. Then from the labeling rules l is the highest label in the tree. The lemma is trivial for $l = 1$.

Consider a tree in which only the root has a label 2, as in Fig. 4.4.2. For this tree, at least two registers are required. This is because no matter how evaluation proceeds, even if T_1 is a leaf, its value must be in a register when the $*$ operation is performed. Since T_2 is not a leaf, but the result of a computation, its value can only appear in a register, as no stores occur. Therefore at least two registers are required.

FIGURE 4.4.2

Any other case of a tree with a root labeled 2 must contain a subtree of the type just considered, proving the lemma.

LEMMA 4.   *The label of a node is a lower bound on the minimum number of registers required to evaluate the node without any stores.*[†]

Proof.   From Lemma 3 this lemma holds for all labels up to and including 2.

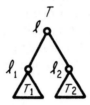

FIGURE 4.4.3

Let T be a smallest tree for which a violation of the hypothesis occurs; then T can be represented by Fig. 4.4.3, where the l's are labels. There are three possibilities for l_1 and l_2:

	l_1	l_2
1	l	$<l$
2	$<l$	l
3	$l-1$	$l-1$

For case 1 (2) the lemma holds; otherwise the left (right) descendant will be a smaller violating tree.

For case 3, when the first command is executed, the value brought into a register is either for tree T_1 or for tree T_2. Since we have assumed that there are no nontrivial relations among operators and elements, the contents of a register at any time can be identified with a partial value in at most one of the subtrees, unless it is the value of the entire tree. If the initial register used is for tree T_1, there must be at least one register used for a partial value of tree T_1 until the final computation. Thus tree T_2 is evaluated using at most $l-2$ registers, providing a contradiction. An analogous argument holds if the first register used is for tree T_2.

[†] This result was proven in Ref. 3 using a similar but not identical labeling scheme and a different computer model. Our proof is more concise and carries over to the model of Ref. 3.

THEOREM 1. *If we assume no nontrivial relations between operators and elements, Algorithm 1 uses the minimum number of registers for the evaluation, with no stores, of an expression.*

Proof. Immediate from Lemmas 2 and 4.

Definitions. Given a number of registers N, we say a node is *major* if both its descendants have labels at least as great as N. We say a node is *minor* if it is a leaf and the left descendant of its ancestor.

LEMMA 5. *The minimum number of stores used in the evaluation of an arithmetic expression with no nontrivial relations among operators and elements is equal to or greater than the number of major nodes in the tree for that expression.*

Proof. We shall prove this lemma by induction on the number of nodes. For the smallest nontrivial tree, Fig. 4.4.4, the lemma is true as there are no major nodes, and no stores are required.

FIGURE 4.4.4

Suppose N registers are available. Let the lemma hold for trees of up to $k - 1$ nodes. The label of a major node must be at least $N + 1$. If the major node could be evaluated without any stores, then a contradiction of Lemma 4 would occur. Therefore, there must be at least one store in a program that evaluates a tree with a major node.

Consider a minimum store program P for a tree T with k nodes and $M \geq 1$ major nodes. When the first store occurs (and we have just shown that there must be one) the value of a subtree S of T is stored in a temporary. Replace S by a leaf to form a new tree T'. Revise P to evaluate T', by deleting those instructions which were a part of the computation of S and treating the temporary as the value of the new leaf. Call the new program P'.

Without loss of generality, we can assume that at least one operation was performed before the store occurred. That is, given any program that causes a store before any operation is performed, there exists a program that performs the same computation with fewer stores. Thus, T' has fewer than k nodes, and the number of stores required for T' is equal to or greater than the number of its major nodes. P evidently has one store more than P'.

We will now show that the number of major nodes of T' is at least $M - 1$. In T, consider the first major node μ preceding S. (If there is none, we are done, as no node of S can be major.) Let the descendant of μ that precedes S (if any) be μ_1. Otherwise, the root of S is μ_1. Let node μ_2 be the twin of μ_1. Since μ is major $L(\mu_1)$, $L(\mu_2) \geq N$. Let $L'(\cdot)$ give the labels in T'.

All nodes preceding S in T have their labels reduced by some amount in T'. It is true that μ may no longer be major, but μ_2 is not affected, so $L'(\mu_2) = L(\mu_2) \geq N$. Since $L'(\mu) \geq L'(\mu_2)$, we have $L'(\mu) \geq N$. Hence nodes preceding μ have labels equal to or greater than N in T'. Since T precedes no major node, if M was the number of major nodes in T, there are at least $M - 1$ major nodes in T'.

By the inductive hypothesis, the number of stores required to evaluate T' is at least $M - 1$. Therefore, P' has at least $M - 1$ stores and P has at least M stores.

LEMMA 6. *If M is the number of major nodes in a tree, then the number of stores in its evaluation by Algorithm 1 is equal to M.*

Proof. Routine (2C) is the only one of (2A)–(2E) which causes a store, and it causes exactly one store with each application. When (2) is applied to a node, routine (2C) is used if and only if the node is major.

LEMMA 7. *The number of CLA's in the evaluation of a tree is at least the number of minor nodes in the tree.*

Proof. We shall prove this lemma by induction on the number of minor nodes. For trees with only one minor node, the lemma is easily seen to hold, as at least one CLA is necessary before evaluation can begin.

Let the lemma hold for trees with up to $k - 1$ minor nodes, and consider the following tree with k minor nodes (Fig. 4.4.5); η_1 is a leaf; $L(\eta_1) = 1$, and η_2 is the root of a subtree with $k - 1$ minor nodes.

To evaluate node η, the value of η_1 must be in a register as it is a left operand. (Note that we are still assuming that all operations are non-

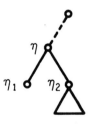

FIGURE 4.4.5

commutative.) Therefore, a CLA must occur for the value of η_1. Since the value of η_1 is not used in evaluating η_2, a program for the total tree which had fewer than k CLA's would yield a program to evaluate η_2 using fewer than $k - 1$ CLA's, contrary to hypothesis.

LEMMA 8. *Algorithm 1 evaluates a tree with as many CLA's as there are minor nodes in the tree.*

Proof. Only routine (2A) is applied to leaves, and only to minor nodes at that. Each application causes a CLA.

THEOREM 2. *For expressions with noncommutative operators and no nontrivial relations between operators and elements, Algorithm 1 produces a minimal cost program for the machine we have described.*

Proof. From Lemmas 5 and 6, the number of stores is minimal. From Lemmas 7 and 8, the number of CLA's is minimal. Each binary operation specified is performed once. Hence, the number of program steps is minimal.

4.4.4. COMMUTATIVE OPERATORS

We have now derived a property of trees, the sum of the number of major and minor nodes, which measures the speed with which its value can be computed. The results of Section 4.4.3 prove our measure to be correct. When certain algebraic transformations are permitted, we are not required to evaluate a given tree, but may evaluate any one of its equivalent trees, obtained by applying the allowed transformations. In this section and Section 4.4.5, we establish procedures for finding a best equivalent tree when the commutative and associative transformations are permitted. Other transformations may make the problem of finding best trees much harder than in the commutative and associative case.

When commutative operators are present, there is a family of trees that compute the same value. Members of this family are derived from each other by interchanging or "flipping" the descendants of commutative nodes. We will select that member of the family of trees that minimizes the highest label in the tree and the number of major and minor nodes.

Looking back, it becomes evident that the only trees for which flipping will help are trees with minor nodes which correspond to commutative operators and have nonleaf right descendants. In such cases, flipping the leaf from the left to the right will reduce its label from 1 to 0, reduce the number of minor nodes, and possibly lead to a reduction in the highest label and/or number of major nodes.

Algorithm 1 may easily be modified to perform the flipping.

4.4.4.1. *Algorithm 2*

1. Generate labels.

2. For all nodes η such that $L(\eta) > 1$, its left descendant is a leaf, and the operator corresponding to η is commutative, flip the descendants so that the leaf is the right descendant (the restriction $L(\eta) > 1$ guards against flipping when both nodes are leaves).

3. Proceed as for Algorithm 1.

Example 2. If Algorithm 2 is used for the expression of Example 1, the expression actually evaluated is $a/(b + c) - (e + f) * d$, whose tree is given in Fig. 4.4.6. The code for this tree is

1. $a \rightarrow \text{reg1}$

2. $b \rightarrow \text{reg2}$

3. $\text{reg2} + c \rightarrow \text{reg2}$

4. $\text{reg1}/\text{reg2} \rightarrow \text{reg1}$

5. $e \rightarrow \text{reg2}$

6. $\text{reg2} + f \rightarrow \text{reg2}$

7. $\text{reg2} * d \rightarrow \text{reg2}$

8. $\text{reg1} - \text{reg2} \rightarrow \text{reg1}$

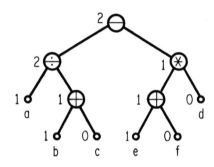

FIGURE 4.4.6

Definitions. Node η_1 in tree T_1 and node η_2 in tree T_2 are *corresponding* nodes if neither is a leaf, and the expressions represented by the subtrees with roots η_1 and η_2 may be obtained from each other by the commutative transformation. Let T_α represent a tree with root α, and let $\eta(T_\alpha, T_\beta)$ represent a tree with root η and left (right) descendant subtrees $T_\alpha(T_\beta)$. If γ is a leaf, we identify γ with T_γ.

LEMMA 9. *Of the family of trees that compute the same result as a given tree, the tree T generated by Algorithm 2 has the minimum number of major nodes, the minimum number of minor nodes, and the label of every nonleaf node in tree T is less than or equal to the label of the corresponding node of any other tree in the family.*

Proof. We shall prove this lemma by induction on the maximum path length P in a tree. For a maximum path length of 1, the lemma is easily seen to hold.

Let it hold for $P \leq k - 1$, and consider a tree generated by Algorithm 2 with $P = k$ and a commutative operator at the root. The tree may be represented by $\eta(T_\alpha, T_\beta)$.

Case 1. β is a nonleaf. Then the other trees in the family may be of either of the following types—$\eta_1(T_{\alpha_1}, T_{\beta_1})$ or $\eta_2(T_{\alpha_2}, T_{\beta_2})$. Here α_1 and α_2 correspond to α, β_1 and β_2 to β, and η_1 to η_2 to η.

As the lemma holds for $P \leq k - 1$, we have $L(\alpha) \leq L(\alpha_1)$, $L(\alpha_2)$ and $L(\alpha_1)$, $L(\beta) \leq L(\beta_1)$, $L(\beta_2)$. Therefore, $L(\eta) \leq L(\eta_1)$, $L(\eta_2)$. If η is major then η_1 and η_2 are also major. Thus, the lemma holds in this case.

Case 2. β is a leaf. Then the other trees in the family are of either of the following types—$\eta_1(\beta_1, T_{\alpha_1})$ or $\eta_2(T_{\alpha_2}, \beta_2)$. The notation here is the same as for case 1. Since β is not a minor node, the number of minor nodes in the generated tree is minimal.

As β is a leaf, $L(\beta) = 0$. However, $L(\beta_1) = 1$ and $L(\beta_2) = 0$. Therefore $L(\beta) \leq L(\beta_1)$, $L(\beta_2)$. As the lemma holds for $P \leq k - 1$, we have $L(\alpha) \leq L(\alpha_1)$, $L(\alpha_2)$. Therefore, just as for case 1, the lemma holds.

THEOREM 3. *Algorithm 2 produces an optimal sequence of evaluation for an expression, on the assumption that there are only commutative and noncommutative operators in the expression and that there are no other nontrivial relations between operators and elements in the expression.*

Proof. The operations performed are STO's, CLA's, and binary operations. By Lemmas 5–9 the number of STO's and CLA's is minimal. Each binary operation specified is performed once. Hence the number of operations is minimal and the sequence of evaluation is optimal.

4.4.5. ASSOCIATIVE OPERATIONS

Exploiting the associative and commutative properties of some operators, we achieve reductions in the register requirements and the time of a computation. The example shown in Fig. 4.4.1, in which both associativity and commutativity hold, illustrates these reductions.

The algorithm presented in this section would produce the tree in Fig. 4.4.7(c) when started out with either of the other trees in Fig. 4.4.7.

It should be noted that the only associative operators we consider are those that are both associative and commutative (a–c). In practice, most operators that are associative are also commutative on integers, reals, etc.[†]

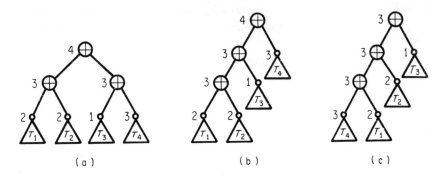

FIGURE 4.4.7

Definitions. An operator is an a-c *operator* if it is both associative and commutative. A *cluster* is a set of nodes in a tree, such that

(1) each node in the set is associated with the same operator,
(2) the branches between nodes in the set form a tree, and
(3) if the operator associated with the set of nodes is not an a-c operator, the set contains only one element.

The *root of a cluster* is the node in the cluster that precedes all other nodes in the cluster. The *ancestor of a cluster* is the ancestor of the root of the cluster. The *descendants of a cluster* are the descendants of the leaves in the cluster. The *descendant subtrees of a cluster* are the subtrees preceded by the descendants of the cluster. A *maximal cluster* is a cluster which is not a proper subset of any other cluster.

Given a binary tree, identify the maximal clusters. It should be clear that these can be found uniquely. Let a maximal cluster C have descendants $\delta_1, \delta_2, \ldots, \delta_m$ and let the root of C be a descendant of maximal cluster A. $\delta_1, \delta_2, \ldots, \delta_m$ are roots of clusters $D_1, D_2, \ldots, D_m$. Generate a tree with node μ in place of cluster C. Let μ have descendants $\delta_1, \delta_2, \ldots, \delta_m$. Proceed from the top down generating a tree with one node per maximal

---

[†] D. M. Ritchie pointed out that the FORTRAN operation SIGN(a, b) is associative but not commutative.

cluster. In the new tree, there is a single node for each maximal cluster in the binary tree. The new tree is called an *associative tree*.

The above definitions have the following motivation. Let T be a binary tree and A its corresponding associative tree. Let T' be derived from T by a single associative or commutative transformation. Then the associative tree A' corresponding to T' can be obtained from A by permuting the descendants of one node of A. That node corresponds to the maximal cluster of T in which the transformation took place. Conversely, any permutation of descendants of a node of A can be mirrored by the application of a sequence of a–c transformations on one cluster of T.

Let F be the family of trees derivable from T by a–c transformations. The problem of finding the member of F yielding the best program by Algorithm 1 is thus broken into two parts. First, using permutations of descendants of the associative nodes, we find the "best" ordering for descendants. Then, from the resulting associative tree, we construct that one of the corresponding binary trees which yields the minimal cost program.

The labeling rules for associative trees are:

LA1. If η is a leaf and the leftmost descendant of its ancestor, then $L(\eta) = 1$. For all other leaves, $L(\eta) = 0$.

LA2. If η has descendants with labels $l_1, l_2, \ldots, l_m$, $l_1 \geq l_2 \geq \cdots \geq l_m$ then $L(\eta) = l_1$ if $l_1 > l_2$, $L(\eta) = l_1 + 1$ if $l_1 = l_2$.

4.4.5.1. *Algorithm 3*

1. Generate a binary tree for the expression. Convert the binary tree to an associative tree.

2. Label the nodes according to the labeling rules for associative trees, and do steps 3 and 4 from the bottom up.

3. At every associative node η, order the descendants by label. Let the new order be $\delta_0, \delta_1, \ldots, \delta_m$ such that $L(\delta_0) \geq L(\delta_1) \geq \cdots \geq L(\delta_m)$. If possible, let δ_0 not be a leaf. Replace the associative node η by m nodes η_i, $1 \leq i \leq m$, such that η_{i+1} is the ancestor of η_i, $1 \leq i < m$. The left descendant of η_{i+1} is η_i and the right descendant is δ_i, $1 \leq i \leq m$. The left and right descendants of η_1 are δ_0 and δ_1 respectively. The ancestor of η is now the ancestor of η_m.

4. If the node η is not associative, proceed as for Algorithm 2.

LEMMA 10. *Let N be the number of available registers. Given a binary tree containing a cluster with m descendant subtrees, r of which have roots with labels greater than or equal to N, the cluster contains at least $r - 1$ major nodes.*

Proof. We shall prove this lemma by induction on the maximum path length P of the subtree dominated by the cluster (i.e., the tree formed by considering the cluster and its descendant subtrees only).

For $P = 1$, the lemma holds trivially. Let the lemma hold for $P < k$, and consider a tree with $P = k$, say $\eta(T_{\eta_1}, T_{\eta_2})$.

If η_1 and η_2 are not in the cluster for η the lemma holds trivially. If only one of η_1 and η_2 is in the cluster, the induction is elementary.

When both η_1 and η_2 are in the cluster there are three possible cases. Let the nodes of the cluster in subtrees T_{η_1} and T_{η_2} have r_1 and r_2 descendant subtrees whose roots have labels greater than or equal to N. The three cases are

1. $r_1 = r_2 = 0$;

2. one of r_1, r_2 is 0;

3. $r_1, r_2 > 0$.

Case 1. Elementary.

Case 2. Without loss of generality, let $r_2 = 0$ and $r_1 = r$. By the inductive hypothesis, the portion of the cluster in subtree T_{η_1} has $r - 1$ major nodes.

Case 3. The lemma holds for the portions of the cluster dominated by η_1 and η_2. Hence they have $r_1 - 1$ and $r_2 - 1$ major nodes, respectively. Since $r_1, r_2 > 0$, $L(\eta_1), L(\eta_2) \geq N$. Hence η is major, and the number of major nodes in the tree is $r_1 + r_2 - 1$. As $r_1 + r_2 = r$, the lemma holds.

LEMMA 11. *Of the family F of binary trees that compute the same result as a given tree, Algorithm 3 generates that tree T which has the minimum register requirements for evaluation without stores and the minimum number of major nodes of all trees in F.*

Proof. We shall prove this lemma by induction on the maximum path length P in the tree T generated by Algorithm 3.

For $P = 0$ or 1 the lemma holds trivially.

Let the theorem hold for $P < k$, and consider a tree with $p = k$ as in Fig. 4.4.8.

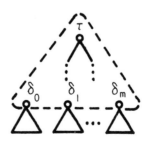

FIGURE 4.4.8

Consider the maximal cluster C defined by the root τ of the tree T. The cluster C has $m + 1$ descendants $\delta_0, \delta_1, \ldots, \delta_m$. The lemma holds for each descendant subtree of the cluster so $L(\delta_i)$, $0 \leq i \leq m$ are minimal and the number of major nodes in each subtree is minimal.

From Lemma 1, if r of the $L(\delta_i)$, $0 \leq i \leq m$ are greater than or equal to N there are at least $r - 1$ major nodes in the cluster C. The reader can show that in Algorithm 3, the cluster produced from C has only $r - 1$ major nodes. The number of major nodes in tree T is therefore minimal.

As for the register requirements, from Algorithm 3, we can assume $L(\delta_i) \geq L(\delta_{i+1})$, $0 \leq i \leq m$.

Case 1. $L(\delta_0) > L(\delta_1)$. Since τ precedes δ_0, $L(\tau) \geq L(\delta_0)$. As in tree T, $L(\tau) = L(\delta_0)$, the label of τ is minimal.

Case 2. $L(\delta_0) = L(\delta_1)$. As $L(\delta_0) = L(\delta_1)$, a node preceding both δ_0 and δ_1 must have a label at least one greater than $L(\delta_0)$. In tree T, $L(\tau) = L(\delta_0) + 1$, so the label of τ is minimal. Any other tree in the family F with the same descendant subtrees must have at least as many major nodes and require at least as many registers as T. From the inductive hypothesis, the same is true of the descendant subtrees themselves. Hence the lemma holds.

THEOREM 4. *Algorithm 3 produces an optimal sequence of evaluation for an expression on the assumption that there are only commutative, noncommutative, and a-c operators in the expression and that there are no other nontrivial relations between operators and elements in the expression.*

Proof. From Lemma 11, the number of STO's is minimized. As Algorithm 2 is applied to the binary tree generated, and hence to the nodes with commutative but not a-c operators, no descendant of a cluster is made a minor node unless all descendants are leaves. The number of CLA's is therefore minimized by Theorem 3.

The number of binary operations performed is equal to the number specified in the expression. (Note that the associative and commutative transformations do not change this number.) Hence, the sequence of evaluation is optimal.

4.4.6. STORAGE REFERENCES

Every time a piece of information is obtained from or placed in storage, a "storage reference" occurs. The information referred to may be an instruction, an initial value, or a piece of temporary storage.

The cost structure we have used so far is not based on the number of storage references during evaluation. However, it is shown in this section that Algorithms 1, 2, and 3 minimize the number of storage references as well as the number of operations.

LEMMA 12.   *Let E be an expression whose tree T has n nodes. Let c be the minimum number of CLA instructions in any program evaluating E and s the minimum number of STO's in any program evaluating E. Then the number of storage references in any program evaluating E is at least $c + n + 3s$.*

Proof.   Let n_0 be the number of nonleaves in T and n_l the number of leaves; $n_0 + n_l = n$. Any program for E has at least $c + n_0 + s$ steps, since n_0 is the number of binary operations to be performed. At least one reference to each initial value in storage must occur, else there would be an identity of the form $E' = E$, where E' was missing at least one of the variables of E. There are n_l initial values. Each time a partial value is stored, a storage reference occurs, and at least s of the values stored are referenced later. (For a value not subsequently referenced need not be stored, and s is a presumed lower bound on the number of storages.) Thus there are at least $n_l + 2s$ storage references involving data. The minimum number of storage references is thus $(c + n_0 + s) + (n_l + 2s) = c + n + 3s$.

THEOREM 5.   *Algorithms 1, 2, and 3 minimize the number of storage references in the evaluation of a given expression.*

Proof.   The programs produced by these algorithms have both the minimum number of CLA's and the minimum number of STO's under their respective assumptions. It is easy to verify that the number of storage references is equal to the lower bound of Lemma 12.

4.4.7. DISCUSSION

For any algorithm to be of practical utility, it must evaluate its object in a reasonable number of steps. The adjective reasonable is not precisely defined, and we will not attempt to do so. We merely state that once the tree has been set up, the algorithms presented in this paper require a number of steps linearly proportional to the number of nodes in the tree.

For Algorithms 1 and 2, the first time each node is visited is when the labeling is done. The second and third visits occur when we travel down from the root to the leaves to determine the order of evaluation, and backtrack, producing the evaluation sequence as we go.

For Algorithm 3, two extra passes occur when the associative tree is constructed, and then remade into a binary tree. Further overhead is introduced by the need to reorder the descendants of the associative nodes. A careful look at the algorithm reveals that it is not necessary to order all the descendants by label. All we need to find is the descendant with the maximum label if it is unique, and two descendants with maximal labels if there is no unique maximum label. This operation can be done in time proportional to the number of nodes involved. The associative node can then be split into binary nodes in linear time. Thus, a slight modification of Algorithm 3 can be done in linear time.

It is easy to modify the algorithms to take into account operations that call for extra registers. An example of such an operation is function invocations which need extra registers for linkages. Labeling rule L2 of Section 4.4.3 has then to be modified.

It can be shown that rule L2 at node η with descendants α and β is equivalent to $L(\eta) = \min\{\max[L(\alpha), L(\beta) + 1], \max[L(\beta), L(\alpha) + 1]\}$.

If the operation at node η requires R registers, then rule L2 may be replaced by $L(\eta) = \max[R, \min\{\max[L(\alpha), L(\beta)+1], \max[L(\beta), L(\alpha)+1]\}]$.

ACKNOWLEDGMENTS

The authors are indebted to A. V. Aho, R. H. Canaday, L. A. Dimino, B. W. Kernighan, M. D. McIlroy, and D. M. Ritchie for helpful discussions and comments.

REFERENCES

1. Nakata, Ikuo, "On Compiling Algorithms for Arithmetic Expressions," *Comm. ACM*, vol. 10, no. 8 (August 1967), pp. 492–494.

2. Meyers, W. J., "Optimization of Computer Code," Unpublished memorandum, G.E. Research Center, Schenectady, N. Y., 1965 (12 pp.).

3. Redziejowski, R. R., "On Arithmetic Expressions and Trees," *Comm. ACM*, vol. 12, no. 2 (February 1969), pp. 81–84.

4. Floyd, R. W., "An Algorithm for Coding Efficient Arithmetic Operations," *Comm. ACM*, vol. 4, no. 1 (January 1961), pp. 42–51.

5. Anderson, J. P., "A Note on Some Compiling Algorithms," *Comm. ACM*, vol. 7, no. 3 (March 1964), pp. 149–150.

4.5. Program Organization and Record Keeping for Dynamic Storage Allocation

by Anatol W. Holt

4.5.1. SUMMARY

The material presented in this paper is part of the design plan of the core allocation portion of the ACSI-MATIC Programming System. Project ACSI-MATIC is concerned with the application of computer techniques to the activities of certain headquarters military intelligence operations of the U.S. Army.

In describing features of organization and record keeping there has been no attempt at completeness, but rather an exploration of the salient aspects of the system to some reasonable level of technical detail.[†]

[†] The developments to which the subject plans pertain are being carried out by the Programming Research Group of the Radio Corporation of America, Astro-Electronics Division, under Army Contract # DA-49-083 OSA-2338. The design plans have been the result of cooperative effort between the RCA Programming Research Group and Applied Data Research, Inc., working under subcontract.

EDITOR'S NOTE: This article reproduced by permission of the author and the publisher: *Comm. ACM*, vol. 4, no. 10 (October 1961), pp. 422–431.

4.5.2. ALLOCATION INTERPRETATION BROADLY
   CHARACTERIZED

As is well known, the translation of pseudocode can be handled in two contrasting ways: (a) the compiling method, and (b) the interpreter method. It is less commonly realized that the function of space allocation (to be more precisely defined below) can also be handled in a corresponding pair of ways.

In the usual compiling method of converting a pseudocode program into fixed machine code there are generally two broad states: (1) translation of the pseudocode into floating machine code (though usually with already built-in assumptions about division into "loads"), followed by (2) space allocation, conversion of floating code into fixed code, and the generation of "read-in" instructions which will bring the program (all at once or in parts) into memory during computation.

Now it is possible to distribute the code-conversion functions summarized under (2) with respect to problem computation, just as the job of converting pseudocode into packets of machine code can be distributed (i.e., the interpreter method). To do so requires that a large total program be broken up into *allocation units*. The program is then performed allocation unit by allocation unit. Whenever the computation requires transition from one such unit to another, the new unit is, at this time, allocated to memory, transformed into absolute code (all at once or piecemeal), and introduced into core prior to being performed. Thus the problem computation and code allocation are intercalated in a manner which justifies the name "allocation interpretation."

The advantages accruing to this manner of performing storage allocation may be summarized as follows:

(1) The manner of performing space allocation for each unit as it comes up can be adjusted to the prevailing conditions in memory at that time. This becomes important whenever the program, data, or computer environment of a given program part cannot be narrowly predicted in advance.

(2) The allocation units generally represent a complete set of space requirements for some period of computation time. Should the memory become very crowded, it is possible to assign some parts of the present unit to space which is still held by other units that have not yet completed their function. The information in memory thus being overlapped must then be dumped to external storage for the duration of the present unit. The dumped information is later restored when the unit to which it belongs

resumes operation. Thus the programmer is effectively working with a flexible amount of memory space.

(3) Only those parts of a program that are actually used in a given computation are ever allocated and assigned to memory. This is important in any problem in which the process chart contains major conditional branches.

4.5.3. DESCRIPTION OF MAJOR SYSTEM FUNCTIONS RELATED TO ALLOCATION INTERPRETATION

Interpretive storage allocation and program control are inextricably linked functions. *Program control* refers here to the bookkeeping involved in sequencing major programmatic entities—call them *programs*—by criteria which will depend in general on (a) the logic of a larger *process* of which these programs are substituent parts, (b) efficiency in the utilization of all equipment parts which are capable of operating in parallel, (c) externally given priorities on a constantly changing collection of waiting tasks. It has become customary to consider the functions of control arising from these different sets of constraints as different, each implemented in some separate way. Control for (a) might be handled by means of a macro-assembly (i.e., not interpretively); control for (b) by means of a special I-O package; control for (c) by means of an operator program. It is possible (and perhaps desirable) to organize matters in such a way that for all these sources of constraint the resultant control actions—program termination, conditional or unconditional interruption, etc.—are expressed and handled in a uniform way. While this will not yet be the case in the ACSI-MATIC Programming System, the system does represent an advance in this direction.

Allocation units are almost invariably also units of control. Requests for new allocations in the course of computation generally come when a new program unit is initiated. The new program's initial estimates for space requirements are scanned, the program caller's estimates of probable use for the program are considered, and some decisions are computed as to what locations in the various storage media may be devoted to the various space-taking portions of the new program. The demand for a shift in control from one program to another demands of the system that a new set of space-taking informational entities belonging to the new program be put "in place." If in any given storage medium—such as core—there is not room enough to provide a "place" for every segment of information, then the "putting in place" will involve *restoring* some segments to memory which since their just-previous use were overwritten. The act of restoring will in turn cause information to be overwritten. Thus shifts in gross control, i.e., from one program unit to another, may involve dumping and restoring. If, in addition, there is at the time of control shift a question of what specific places the newly required information is to occupy, then allocation becomes part of the shift in control.

4.5.4. SOME SPECIFIC ASSUMPTIONS ABOUT PROGRAM STRUCTURE AND ALLOCATION

1. We assume two principal types of events which may require new space allocation: (a) a shift of control to a program copy C_1 (i.e., a program bound by particular parameters specifications) which is entering the computation for the first time, and (b) a request for additional space for some category of information, the request initiated within some program in the form of a special macroinstruction to the control and allocation system. Regarding (a), we assume that the allocation system will in general not attempt to reallocate any part of C_1 which has once been allocated so long as C_1 is still counted as *current*. When it becomes known to the system that C_1 is not required further, then the various parts of C_1 which were used only by it (or any of its consequent programs) can be deleted. It will be possible, however, for a particular program copy, C_2, which has initiated C_1, to indicate that "as many parts as possible" of C_1 are to be considered as no longer allocated to their original locations, with the consequence that on next use all of these parts will be subjected to reallocation.

2. We assume that a program—which is the major allocation unit—may consist of several dump-restore units, called *program phases*. In regard to space, a program is viewed as consisting of some number of space-taking entities which may be required in different combinations in different stages of program operation. When a new program phase is initiated, dumping and restoring may be required, but no new space allocations are performed.

3. For each space-taking entity of the program (such as a reference table, a data set, a section of code, a file, etc.) it is assumed that a particular storage medium is specified as the one in which the entity must be when it is in its "active" position. Suppose, for instance, that the program refers to a matrix. The program may assume that at the time the matrix is being processed it is on disk. The matrix element pick-up code will then include some disk input instructions; alternatively, the code may assume that when the matrix is being processed it is stored in core. The element pick-up code then contains only memory references.

An entity whose active position is in core may be dumped to some other storage medium in the course of program phases which make no reference to it. The present discussion is restricted to the consideration of entities which must be in core when active.

4. Every core-occupying entity may be subdivided into one or more *segments*. Since the segments will be considered as listed in a definite order, the entities are called *sequences*. The subdivision of a sequence into segments is often necessary just to ease its allocation to core when there are already other outstanding space commitments that make unbroken stretches hard to find. Thus, to allocate core locations to a sequence requires the determination of one origin for each of its segments. Some information sets may be segmented because the values were computed step by step with no satisfactory prediction in advance of final size. The program may then add space for this information set a segment at a time.

5. If programs are considered as points connected to one another by lines of initiation, then the resulting structure will form a *tree*. Thus, if program copy C_1 initiates C_2, it is assumed that there is not also another program copy, C_3, which can count as initiator of C_2. To initiate a program copy is to "bring it into being." It is usually connected with some manner of control passage, though not necessarily.

Now the assumption that the lines of initiation form a tree structure implies some restrictions regarding the commonness of subprograms. Program copies C_1 and C_2 cannot refer to a common subprogram unless that program was initiated by some common ancestor of C_1 and C_2, say C_3. It is still possible, however, within the framework of such a system, for the descendants of a program, C_i, to refer to common subprograms the need for which was not anticipated at C_i. To accomplish this the system must attribute a program copy initiation to C_i even though the need is only discovered in the course of executing a descendant of C_i.

4.5.5. THE PROGRAM DESCRIPTION IN RESPECT TO INTRAPROGRAMMATIC STRUCTURE

Programs expected to operate in the environment of a control and allocation system such as those considered here have various special features. For example, all addresses are relative to one of many possible segment origins. When a copy of the program is initiated, the allocation interpreter computes origins for all newly introduced segments, this computation being called *allocation*. After this, the sequences of the program can be *loaded* as required. The loader, as part of its operation, converts all segment-relative addresses into absolute ones. (The loader may also fix addresses or constants which are functions of arbitrarily specified parameters given by the initiating program copy; it is also responsible for putting the appropriately modified segments of constants and program into their proper locations.)

By far the most significant difference between programs which operate without the benefit of a systems environment and programs as presently considered lies in the requirement for a *program description*. This description, which represents the program to the system, is modifiable in the course of computation, just as other parts of internally stored programs are. For instance, when a program sequence is incremented by the addition of a new segment a new record will be added to the program description (in this case, by the system). Further, if during a program's computation an initially unpredicted need for some subprogram should arise, a new record must also be added to the program description (in this case, by the program). The program description is modified both by the system as the status of the program and its parts change and by specific program instructions which notify the system of modifications in program structure.

Our first concern with program descriptions is to consider those parts which describe the program's own elements. Our second concern is to consider those parts which describe relations of this program to its immediate ancestor and to its immediate descendants.

A program description consists first of a *header* which provides some descriptions pertaining to the program as a whole, and then a sequence of tables with each table containing the descriptions of one or another kind of program element. Six such tables are indicated in Fig. 4.5.1, though this is not an exhaustive list. Since we are concerned here only with sequences and allocation of memory to their substituent segments, we are not concerned with many of the description tables which a program description must contain. In particular, for purely intraprogrammatic structure, only tables (2) through (4) need be discussed.

The analysis of a program into phases and sequences is accomplished by associating with each sequence a vector of ones and zeros. The positions of the vector are associated with program phases. If the program is analyzed into p phases, then the first p positions of the vector are corresponded to phases, and that in a name-giving way—i.e., the phase associated with the ith position becomes identified as "phase i" of the program. Assuming that the program has p phases and j is any integer not exceeding p, one may say that the vector, called a *use* vector, associated with sequence σ_i, has value 1

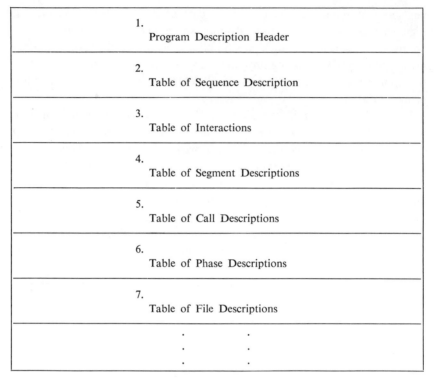

FIGURE 4.5.1   Gross structure of program descriptions.

in position j if and only if σ_i is required to be "in place" whenever control passes to phase j.

To have analyzed a program into s sequences and p phases is to have divided all of the core-held information belonging to the program into s categories with permissions and prohibitions of mutual overlap expressed between them. Two categories of information which are simultaneously required during some phase of the program clearly must occupy disjoint memory locations; conversely, two categories, σ_1 and σ_2, which by their pattern of use are revealed never to be required at the same time may be so assigned that some stretches of memory are allocated to both kinds of information. The consequence of such an allocation is, of course, that whenever the program shifts from a phase requiring σ_1 to a phase requiring σ_2 there must be some rearrangement of memory content—dumping and restoring, or, perhaps, just restoring.

A typical example is shown in Fig. 4.5.2 of how an analysis of a program may be expressed as a breakdown into sequences and phases.

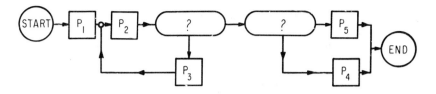

	P$_1$	P$_2$	P$_3$	P$_4$	P$_5$	
σ$_1$	1	0	0	0	0	Main code of P$_1$
σ$_2$	1	1	1	0	0	Input to the program
σ$_3$	1	1	0	0	0	A table referenced by P$_1$ and P$_2$
σ$_4$	0	1	0	0	0	Main code of P$_2$
σ$_5$	0	1	1	1	1	Suboperations common to P$_2$ and P$_3$ as well as program output
σ$_6$	0	0	1	0	0	Main code of P$_3$
σ$_7$	0	0	0	1	0	Main code of P$_4$
σ$_8$	0	0	0	0	1	Main code of P$_5$

FIGURE 4.5.2

Treating the use vectors as rows of a matrix, each column represents the requirements of a particular phase of the program. Per entry to the program, each phase may occur once, more than once, or even less than once. Thus, in the example in Fig. 4.5.2, P_1 occurs exactly once; P_2 and P_3 each occur some number of times, depending on how many times the loop is traversed before loop termination condition prevails; finally, only one of the two phases P_1 and P_5 can occur before the program terminates. These differences are not reflected in the matrix composed of use vectors as shown in Fig. 4.5.2, though we shall shortly consider how they can be represented.

The fineness of the flow chart which is used as a basis for the analysis of a program into sequences and phases is governed by the following considerations. The finer the breakdown (hence the larger the number of sequences and phases), the smaller will be the minimum allotment of space that would still permit the program to operate. The price paid for the possibility of getting along with less space is an increase in systems operations performed per program operation. Each time that there is a transition from one phase to another the system must check whether all the segments belonging to all sequences required for the new phase are intact in memory. If not, restoring and/or loading actions may be required before the program can proceed.

As was mentioned earlier, each sequence consists of an ordered set of segments—one or more. Each sequence description contains an address which tells where its segment descriptions begin (in the table of segment descriptions). The list of segments associated with a sequence may initially be incomplete—indeed, it may be initially empty. Segments may be added to a sequence, one at a time, in the course of problem computation.

In indicating an analysis of a program into sequences and phases sufficiently fine to permit a reasonable condensability of the program, one may well have introduced phase boundaries of quite varying value: value measured by the amount of overlapping which the boundary makes possible (the more, the better), and value measured by the degree to which the computation is slowed down if advantage is taken of the overlapping which the boundary makes possible (the more, the worse). Consider the example illustrated in Fig. 4.5.2. If the P_2–P_3 loop is traversed ten times (order of magnitude) per entrance, then overlapping segments of σ_6 by segments of σ_3 will slow the computation ten times as much as overlapping segments of σ_1 by segments of σ_5. Yet, under some conditions of computation, it may be worthwhile to pay the former heavier price for overlap because the memory has become so crowded. To prevent the heavier price from being paid when it is not necessary, there must be some scheme of indicating preferences (or "rejectabilities") on the use of various phase boundaries which the use vectors introduce.

The task of expressing such preferences is accomplished by means of an additional set of bit vectors, each with a weight number attached. Such a vector-and-weight pair is called an *interaction*. The weight represents the logarithm, base 2, of an estimated frequency of pairwise control transition (directly or indirectly) between phases. The vector identifies two or more phases between which the pairwise frequency of transition is presumed to hold. The identification is accomplished, of course, by the value 1 in positions corresponding to the appropriate phases.

Pairs of phases between which the expected frequency of transition per program execution is one (or near one) need not be governed by an explicit interaction. Occasionally there may be phase pairs between which the expected frequency of transition is much less than one per program execution. Suppose, for example, that the second indicated test in Fig. 4.5.2 would lead ten times more often to the execution of P_4 than P_5. The result is that transition from any phase of the program to P_5 occurs only one-tenth of the time.

Since total interaction between phases is ultimately evaluated by summing all appropriate interactions, the representation of a desired set of results can often be simplified by introducing interactions which cancel part of an effect introduced by another one. Thus, if for the program in Fig. 4.5.2 we add to the assumption about P_4 and P_5 the assumption that P_2 and P_3

interact with weight $+3$ (i.e., eight times round the loop per execution, on the average), we get the representation of approximate interactions for the program (see Fig. 4.5.3).

-3	1	1	1	1	1
$+3$	1	1	1	1	0
$+4$	0	1	1	0	0

FIGURE 4.5.3

We now summarize the principal formal facts so far discussed regarding tables (2) through (4) of Fig. 4.5.1.

1. Each sequence description refers to a use vector and a list of segments.
2. Each interaction consists of a *phase vector* and a weight.

4.5.6. PROGRAM DESCRIPTION IN RESPECT TO INTERPROGRAMMATIC STRUCTURE

We first consider some features of the program description which relate it to its immediate ancestor. Secondly, we consider features of program description relating it to its immediate descendants.

A program copy will normally expect to operate on core-contained information which already existed prior to its initiation. Similarly, program output will normally be accountable to a sequence introduced by its immediate ancestor. It must therefore be possible to provide use vectors for sequences whose segment list lies in some other program description. Formally, the situation is handled in the following way.

Within a program C a sequence σ is identified by the position in the sequence description table where the description of σ is entered. Thus the sequence whose description appears at the ith place is called *sequence i*, denoted σ_i. Now suppose that the first k sequence descriptions concern sequences which are expected to originate in some ancestor of C_1. They will specify use vectors with respect to the phases of C_1 just as in the case of any other sequence description. They will, however, contain no reference to a segment list. Sequences $\sigma_1, \sigma_2, \ldots, \sigma_k$ are, in effect, parameters of C_1 for which specification must be given by the ancestor of C_1. In connection with the call for C_1, the ancestor, C_2, will identify k sequences of C_2 in order: the first specified to correspond to σ_1 of C_1, the second specified to correspond with σ_2, etc. Thus C_2 *passes* k of its sequences to C_1. Of course some of the sequences so passed may have been sequences previously passed to C_2 by its ancestor, etc. Thus a single collection of segments, originally introduced in program copy C_m and there identified as σ_i, may have use-vector representation and name identity in any program copy which is a descendant of C_m. Needless to say, such segments are governed by interactions specified in all of the program descriptions in which they are represented as sequences.

We are now prepared to consider features of program descriptions relating to the initiation of subprograms.

Relative to each program copy to be initiated by program copy C there is a call description, listed in the call description table. Such call descriptions name the program desired and provide access to linking information (including the list of sequences to be passed down) and to the program description of the called copy when once that description has been introduced to memory. Of greatest concern now, however, is the fact that associated with each call description is a phase vector and an interactive weight.

The phase vector specifies relations to be observed in the assignment of segments introduced by the called program copy C_2 (or any of its descendants) relative to the initiating copy C_1. The relations which may be introduced by these vectors are (a) overlap prohibitions, and (b) interactions. Taking the program of Fig. 4.5.2 as C_1 and supposing that it calls on C_2 with associated phase vector

$$0\ 0\ 1\ 0\ 0$$

then: (a) no segments introduced by C_2 or any of its descendants will be assigned to locations which overlap the segments of σ_2, σ_5, and σ_6 of C_1; and (b) all segments of C_2 and descendants will be treated as interacting with the other sequences of C_1 just as the segments of σ_6 are constrained to do. For example, considering the interactions shown in Fig. 4.5.3, the total interactive weight relating the segments of the subprogram C_2 (and below) with the segments of σ_3 and σ_4 of C_1 is $+4$.

Often it may be desired to indicate some specific interaction between the segments of a subprogram and the segments of the initiating program without indicating any prohibitions of overlap. For this purpose a new bit position may be added to all use vectors and phase vectors. Again taking the program of Fig. 4.5.1 as C_1 with interactions as shown in Fig. 4.5.2 as points of departure, suppose one were to modify the table of interactions to become the following:

$$-3 \quad 1\,1\,1\,1\,1\,0$$
$$+3 \quad 1\,1\,1\,1\,0\,0$$
$$+4 \quad 0\,1\,1\,0\,0\,1$$

and suppose the phase vector associated with the call for C_2 becomes

$$0\,0\,0\,0\,0\,1$$

In addition, suppose that the table of use vectors as shown in Fig. 4.5.2 changes only by the effective addition of a 0 at the end of each vector. The result of these changes is the following: (a) no change in the internal relation of C_1 sequences to each other—either in allowed overlaps or in interactions; (b) no prohibitions of overlap between the sequences of C_2 (and below) and the sequences of C_1; (c) interaction weighted $+4$ between C_2 and sequences σ_2 through σ_6 of C_1. Note that in this modified form the last bit position of use and phase vectors of C_1 does not represent a phase, as all other positions do.

The positions which do represent phases really serve two purposes in the course of program control: (a) to specify relations of interaction and overlap prohibition, and (b) to specify which sequences of the program must be restored when a particular phase is activated. Extra bit positions, such as the 6th position introduced above, serve only the first of the two above-mentioned functions.

Next, consider the phase vectors associated with two calls in C_1: a vector for the call on C_2, and another vector for a call on C_3. Each of these vectors specifies overlap and interaction constraints between the branch to which it is attached and the sequences of C_1. But beyond this the two vectors also specify overlap and interaction constraints between the segments of branch C_2 and the segments of branch C_3. Thus a programmer can, if he wishes, call two subprograms which are constrained to occupy nonoverlapping positions, or yet two subprograms which the system will overlap only when it becomes appropriate to pay a penalty which the programmer can fix by means of an interaction.

The weight W associated with the call for C_2 serves as an additive constant to all interactive weights in C_2 and its descendants. In particular, a pair of phases not governed by any explicitly listed interaction (hence with assumed interactive weight of 0) also become burdened by the interactive weight W as a result of having entered the computation via the call for C_2. W makes all interactive weights in the subprogram rise in proportion to the estimated frequency of control passage to C_2 which W represents.

4.5.7. GENERAL FACTS ABOUT SYSTEM RECORDS

We have now presented the principal kinds of information with which the system is provided and on which it can base allocation decisions, to wit:

(1) Permissions and restrictions on sequence overlap, by use vectors. Each program contributes some portion of the total relations which must be taken into account.

(2) Linking information which identifies particular sequences of one program as identical to particular sequences of another.

(3) Interactions which specify costs of sequence overlaps. Again, each program contributes those interactive relations which it can know. The system must take account of all of them.

For the system, records must be so maintained that it is able to form a *global* picture of sequence (and hence segment) relations. What the system is presented with, however, are informational increments, introduced whenever a new program copy is initiated. Program-relative information must somehow become process-relative information—if by *process* one understands a constellation of many programs which jointly lay claim to memory space.

The problem of maintaining records on outstanding memory commitments and announced interactive relations is greatly intensified by the fact that, in addition to new relations being introduced by the initiation of new programs, already outstanding relations must be removed from the total whenever a program copy—usually together with its descendants—is deleted because the function represented is not further required. Thus the entire memory allocation problem is repeated on a small scale for the records required to express the conditions of solution for the large-scale memory allocation problem.

In the system construction which forms the basis for this paper, some special solutions were found to the record maintenance problem. It goes beyond our present scope to describe the matter in full detail, but something of the spirit and the technique can be conveyed. The key point is that means have been found for maintaining virtually all system records—bearing on allocation and control—on a "per program" basis. The information contributed by a program in its description is maintained integrally in one, or at most a few, segments which together constitute a *working copy* of the program description. The global picture is achieved through appropriate linking of entire working program descriptions to each other and similar linking of parts of program descriptions, whenever necessary. The process of adding a new program copy then consists of (1) finding space for the program description, and (2) setting various address connectors which link this description and its parts to all other pertinent descriptions.

Similarly, the process of deleting a program copy involves changing various address connectors in order to "unhook" this description from the various meshes in which it is involved, and then deleting the segments of the program description. One example of this technique will illustrate the point.

Suppose that, as part of each sequence description, one provides space for a *connector*, i.e., an address location. When the program description for C_1 is placed in memory, initial values are computed for these connectors, as follows: If the description of σ_i was placed in computer location b, then the connector is initially set to the value "b."

Next suppose that C_1 initiates program copy C_2 and, through linking information, it is established that σ_5 of C_1 is to coincide with σ_2 of C_2. The two records now become linked by means of connector swapping as illustrated in Fig. 4.5.4.

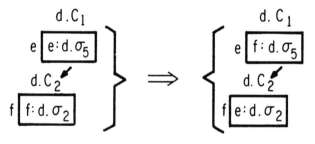

Note: "d.C" means "description of copy,"
"d.σ" means "description of sequence".

FIGURE 4.5.4 Sequence-description linking. *Note*: "d.C" means "description of copy," "d.σ" means "description of sequence."

Next, suppose that C_1 initiates another program copy, C_3 and, again, links its sequence σ_5 with σ_7 of C_3. The link is recorded by swapping. The result, abstracted, is shown in Fig. 4.5.5.

Still a further step in this process produces the result in Fig. 4.5.6.

And quite generally, no matter which program in the tree may initiate a further program and perform an identification of one sequence with another, the link is always realized by connector swapping—which is why

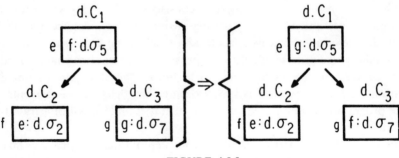

FIGURE 4.5.5

the connectors are called *swap connectors*. The result of this is as follows:
Given an arbitrary sequence in an arbitrary program, suppose one wishes
to know all the relations of overlap constraints in which it participates. For
instance, let this question be asked about σ_7 of C_3 in Fig. 4.5.6. The relations
pertaining to C_3 are expressed at location g of $d.C_3$; further relations are
found at the location to which the connector points, namely h; yet further
ones are found at the location to which the new connector points, namely f;
yet more are found at e. Now there are no more to be found, which the

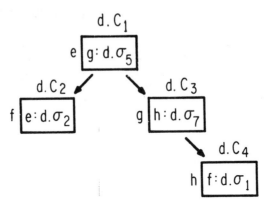

FIGURE 4.5.6

system recognizes by the fact that the next connector points to the location
at which the search began. Thus the connectors form a closed ring, locating
every description which pertains to the sequence in hand. To disconnect a
sequence description, say at location g, from the ring, one must pursue
the connector chain till one locates the description which points to g, in
this case, at location e. There the connector value must be replaced by the
connector value at g.

Swap connectors, similar in principle to the one just described, are used in connecting records in diverse ways. In particular a 2-*connector* system is used to tie program copy descriptions together to form the initiation tree (see assumption 5, Section 4.5.4). This latter connection system is a highly general tree notation which permits very rapid tree modifications—by addition, deletion, node interpolation, etc.—and very rapid tree-scanning operations, both upstream and downstream. The cost per tree node is two fixed-length addresses and a flag bit. All programs operating on trees represented in this way operate without variable storages. This notation and related processing algorithms will be the subject of a forthcoming paper.

4.5.8. SEGMENT RECORDS

Thus far nothing has been said about segment records. To begin with, they contain—as one might expect—segment origin and length. In addition, however, they also contain a pair of swap connectors (i.e., the elements for a 2-connector system) which permit them to be formed into a tree. The semantic basis for connection in the segment tree is inclusion. More exactly, if segment S_1 is assigned memory location b to c, inclusive, and segment S_2 to locations e to f, inclusive, and the $\{e, f\}$ interval is entirely included in the $\{b, c\}$ interval, then S_2 will be treated as a tree descendant of S_1. Thus, the root of the segment tree is a node which represents the entire memory available for assignment.

Fig. 4.5.7 represents a collection of segments assigned to various locations in a 2000-word memory. At each node an origin and a length are

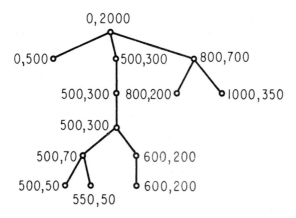

FIGURE 4.5.7

recorded. All segments represented at a given level, taken from left to right, lie at increasing memory locations. In this way two lengths are associated with each node: the length explicitly recorded and the difference between its origin and the origin of its next right neighbor. These two lengths often but not always coincide. It is the length computed by differencing by which the segments form a tree by inclusion.

At origin 500 we see that there are three segments, each 300 words long, exactly overlapping one another. (Obviously they must belong to sequences which are never required to be simultaneously present in memory.) Also at origin 500 we note a segment of size 70, dominating a pair of segments whose lengths sum to 100. Because of our assumption that the segment overlap relations are representable in tree structure, no segment on the same level as (500,70) can be assigned to origin 570 so long as the three segments (500,70), (500,50) and (550,50) represent continuing commitments for memory use.

We are now in a position to summarize the most essential reference relations within and between program descriptions on which the procedure for allocation essentially depends.

1. Program copy descriptions are connected to each other according to lines of call. Thus program descriptions form a tree. This is accomplished by means of a pair of connectors contained in the header. The system has access to the root of the program tree.

2. All sequence descriptions which are meant to refer to the very same set of segments (having become identified with each other through program linking) are connected in a ring.

3. All segment descriptions in current program copy descriptions are connected to each other (by a 2-connector system) to form a tree by the relation of inclusion. The segment tree is rooted at a node to which the allocation system has access. This node represents the entire assignable memory.

4. We shall further assume that any part of a program description is accessible from any other part in the following sense: Given the location of a segment description, $d.S_j$, where S_j belongs to σ_i, we shall suppose it possible to retrieve the location of $d.\sigma_i$; similarly, given the location of $d.\sigma_i$, we shall assume that it is possible to retrieve the location of the header of the program description, etc.

5. Whenever a program copy C_1 passes control to another program copy C_2 which C_1 has initiated, an indicator is set in the header of C_1 which identifies C_2. If and when control returns to C_1 or one of its ancestors, the indicator is reset to "null condition."

4.5.9. LOGIC OF MEMORY EVALUATION FOR ALLOCATION

We now consider the problem of evaluating the memory with respect to a need to find space for a new program copy. The process of space allocation is roughly divided into two major parts: (a) to form a picture of current memory commitments as they affect the allocation of any segment of the new program copy, no matter what its sequence membership may be; and (b) to allocate space to the sequences of this program, one at a time, modifying the picture of memory commitments step by step as new commitments are made.

Step (a) in turn may be subdivided into the following steps: (c) weight distribution on the program tree, and (d) weight distribution on the segment tree.

Let Fig. 4.5.8 be a sample tree of current program copies at the time that a new program copy is to be introduced. The program copy to be initiated is represented by Δ, at the end of the dotted line. Since the event to take place is initiated at node D one may guarantee that, when control last passed from A, it went to B; and when it last passed from B, it went to C; and from C to D. The path $\{A, B, C, D\}$ will be called the current "spine" of the tree. It is guaranteed to be traceable, from the root down, by assumption 5, Section 4.5.4.

In the description of A, constraints of overlap and interaction were expressed between at least five categories of segments: the segments of $A1$ and all of its descendants; the segments of $A2$ and all of its descendants; similarly for $A3$ and for B; finally, the segments of A itself. Furthermore, if the segments of A are categorized into k sequences, then there are recognized, in the description of A, $k + 4$ categories of segments, all told. Each pair of categories is governed by zero or more interactions—namely, all those interactions which have a bit position with value 1 in common with each of the two vectors which describe the two categories of information being considered. We may now sum the weights of all interactions governing each of the pairs: $(A1, B), (A2, B), (A3, B), (\sigma_1, B), \ldots, (\sigma_k, B)$. Each of the $k + 3$ weights thus computed describes the interaction of some category of segments recognized in A, with B and its descendants. If between some

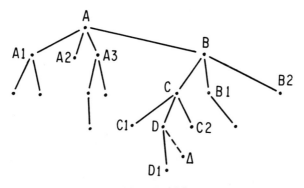

FIGURE 4.5.8

category of segments and B there is absolute prohibition of overlap, this can count as interactive weight ∞.

We now form ordered pairs: one of the above-computed weights followed by a mark which identifies its category. We shall call these pairs *marked weights*. The symbol, $W(A1, B)$, will stand for the marked weight computed by summing the interactions between $A1$ and B. We are now ready to distribute the marked weights computed at A. $W(A1, B)$ is passed to $A1$ and to its two descendants (the "passing down" being accomplished by tree scanning through the 2-connector system). In the header of each program description there is an available field for storing such marked weights. Similarly $W(A2, B)$ is passed to $A2$ and $W(A3, B)$ is passed to $A3$ and its three descendants. Finally, each sequence description of A is marked with its appropriate $W(\sigma_i, B)$.

The above procedure is now repeated at each node on the current spine. A marked weight, $W(X, Y)$, thus becomes attached to every program description in the tree and to every sequence description belonging to programs on the current spine. This completes the distribution of weights on the program tree relative to the allocations next to be performed.

The result of the weight distribution just described is that one or more marked weights now become associated with every segment. If the segment belongs to a sequence introduced at a node on the current spine, then a marked weight will be found in the governing sequence description (see assumption 4, Section 4.5.4); otherwise a marked weight will be found in the governing header.

More than one marked weight may be associated with a segment if the latter belongs to a sequence which has identity in several program descriptions. At each point in the ring of sequence representations (see assumption 2, Section 4.5.4) which apply to this segment, another marked weight is picked up, either from the sequence description itself (if the latter lies at a node on the current spine) or from the governing header. Let us designate the set of marked weights thus associated with a segment S by $\{W_S\}$.

The result of assigning a segment to a location will be to introduce a new node in the segment tree, and this in two possible ways: either (a) zero or more contiguous nodes on some level will be detached from their immediate ancestor, reattached to the new node, and the latter connected to the aforementioned ancestor; or (b) the new node becomes the rightmost descendant at some level. Consider, for example, the assignment of a new segment of size 250 in a memory represented by Fig. 4.5.7. The new segment may be introduced as a new node in the segment tree in any of the locations in Fig. 4.5.9.

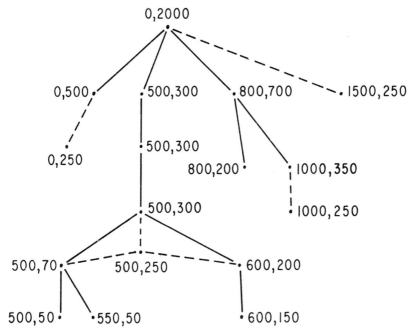

FIGURE 4.5.9 Possible locations for a new segment of size 250.

Considering the cases from left to right we have: (a) zero prior nodes detached, i.e., the new node attached to an old end-point; (b) two prior nodes detached; (c) zero prior nodes detached; (e) new rightmost branch.

Now the values $W_{S_{i,j}}$ can be used to evaluate the merit of a given choice of location. We wish to obtain an estimate for (the logarithm of) the frequency of mutual displacement incurred by a given placement of the new segment. This value is estimated by summing the weights of all segments which are (a) an ancestor (at any level) of the new node, or (b) a descendant (at any level) of the new node. However, in the accumulation of weights, one must use each weight associated with a given category mark once and only once. This may be more accurately stated in the following way: Let N designate a new trial node—corresponding to a trial assignment—and $\{P_N\}$, the set of nodes which are either ancestors or descendants of N. Further, let $\{W(X_a, Y_a)\}$ designate the set of marked weights such that for some P_N there is a W_{P_N} such that $W_{P_N} = W(X_a, Y_a)$. Now, letting $|W(X_a, Y_a)|$ represent the weight value of $W(X_a, Y_a)$, the desired sum is $\sum_a |W(X_a, Y_a)|$.

Why should each marked weight be counted at most once? Consider a segment so assigned that it displaces one other segment of category X.

For ease of visualization, imagine that category X represents a branch off the current spine. A displacement penalty is paid every time that control switches from branch X to the next element down the current spine, or conversely. Having once entered branch X, it makes no difference how many times the segment is required in its place. While computing in branch X, the segment may be restored and dumped arbitrarily many times without affecting the displacement interaction between it and the segment now to be assigned. Similarly, it does not matter how many segments may in course of computation along branch X lay claim to the same space. They will displace each other in some arbitrary pattern. As far as the present assignment is concerned, the only thing that matters is that, with some frequency, the presently proposed segment will be displaced (and will displace) some segment of category X. This argument holds good whether this segment is to overlay adjacent segments, both of category X, or whether it merely overlays two segments of the same category which already displace each other.

Of course the above-mentioned evaluation would be of only academic interest if the values were difficult to compute and the potential locations for segments difficult to identify. It is claimed, however, that the structure of the records as described makes both tasks rapid.

Even being rapid, the tasks cannot be economically performed at too frequent intervals in the course of program computation. Thus new program allocations must be relatively rare events. A program must be large enough—in time and in space—to justify the effort of allocation. Small subroutines such as are the usual subjects of compiling are not suitable candidates for being programs in the above sense. On the other hand, larger processes (such as SORT, UPDATE FILE, MULTIPLY MATRIX, etc.) which are hard to handle by compilation are readily handled by the present technique.

4.5.10. SOME FINAL HEURISTIC CONSIDERATIONS

Thus far we have considered a technique for evaluating an estimate for dump-restore entailed by a proposed memory assignment. There are also general heuristic principals and some specific evaluations possible which will take into account the effect of a proposed assignment on future difficulties of assignment.

1. For a given stretch of memory one may consider the highest node on the program tree at which a segment is recorded which overlaps the stretch. (By "highest node" we mean the node of least depth.) Call this the *level*

of the stretch. In making a new assignment, it is desirable not to raise the level of the stretch to which the assignment is being made; that failing, to raise the level as little as possible. The reader can verify that this principle will tend to reduce the weight which any given stretch accumulates with respect to arbitrarily chosen tree nodes from which to initiate new assignments. This principle may also be viewed as a tendency toward homogeneity, i.e., a tendency for assignments of the same program branch to cluster together rather than scattering widely. This tendency will be opposed, of course, by the dump-restore considerations, since segments of the same branch will tend to have higher interactions than segments of divergent branches.

2. The tendency toward overlapping versus spreading out in accomplishing assignments can be broadly controlled by assigning synthetic interactive weight value to totally free space. The "price" of free space should in general be a function of the amount available before the intended use and the amount available after use. Absolutely free space has special significance for the system, since only it can be used for system records—program descriptions, to mention but one example. Therefore the fund of available totally uncommitted space can never be allowed to run dry.

In general, other broad heuristic principals in memory assignment can be expressed within the present system by differential increments on the weights given to stretches of space. While the weights computed from the segment tree are very much a function of the intended use for which the evaluation is performed, the increments here discussed will be governed by more global considerations.

ACKNOWLEDGMENT

The author wishes to acknowledge the invaluable contribution of Dr. Burnett H. Sams[†] to the process of bringing the above-described designs into being. The author is also indebted to other members of the RCA Astro Programming Research Group for their suggestions and criticisms. Finally, there is an important indebtedness to the U.S. Army Signal Corps, RDL, Fort Monmouth, for sponsoring the work which laid the foundation for the present effort.[‡]

[†] Astro-Electronics Division, Radio Corporation of America, Princeton, N. J.

[‡] Common Programming Language Task of Project ADAR, carried on at the Moore School, University of Pennsylvania. See A. W. Holt, W. J. Turanski, "Automatic Code Translation System," final report, Document No. AD6OURI, Contract No. DA-36-039-sc-75047.

5.

ERRORS—DETECTION AND CORRECTION

5.0. OVERVIEW

The subject of this chapter has, unfortunately, received relatively little attention in the literature, although it certainly does not lack in importance. Perhaps the major reason for this inattention is unavailability of general methods for either error detection or correction. Hopefully, research in this area of computer science will yield significant results in the not too distant future.

Error detection may be divided into two parts: (1) syntactic error detection (that is, detection of errors in the formulation of statements), including spelling errors, keyword errors, illegal constructs, and errors in ordering; and (2) semantic error detection, or detection of errors in the meaning of a program, when a program does not compute what it is intended to compute. Unfortunately, it is impossible to detect semantic errors in general, and it is usually impossible to detect them even when a great deal is known about the specific program. The general problem is theoretically incapable of solution because it may be formally reduced to the unsolvable "halting problem" of recursive function theory and Turing machine theory. (See Minsky, "Computation: Finite and Infinite Machines," or Rogers, "Theory of Recursive Functions and Effective Computability.")

Syntactic errors, on the other hand, may be relatively easy to detect. This is especially true in the case of syntax-directed and table-directed compilers, for a point will be reached in the translation process where an explicit error indication may be found. Compilers using other techniques for translation may find it more difficult to detect syntactic errors.

The correction of errors is an extremely complicated operation. The compiler must not only determine what portions of a statement are in error and the manner in which they are in error, but must also be able to determine what correct statement will produce the results intended by the original statement. Errors in spelling are the most easily corrected, particularly if sufficient care was given to the choice of keywords or reserved words when the source language was designed. Perhaps the next easiest correction occurs with the insertion of statement delimiters (e.g., a semicolon) in free-field languages such as ALGOL and PL/I. But with this approach the correcting compiler may introduce more errors than it corrects. Additional types of correction are applicable, but those available deal with specific statement types or similarly restricted topics.

Another portion of the topic of error detection and correction relates to execution-time rather than compile-time errors. There are two basic approaches to execution-time error detection: Either special error-checking code is included in the object code or a monitor system is provided to supervise the execution continuously. Error correction may be done in either case or not at all. Execution-time errors are of a completely different nature from compile-time errors. They include computational errors such as underflow or overflow, access out of the bounds of arrays, use of uninitialized data, erroneous input/output requests, the destruction of problem data or of program, illegal requests for supervisory system action, and so forth. This subject is even more sparsely documented than that of compile-time errors.

Article 5.1 by Freeman deals with the error detection and correction facilities available in the CORC programming language. CORC is a specially designed language for use by students and those users who are not primarily programmers. The CORC system comprises a translator and an execution-time monitor. More recently, a system that also has excellent compile-time diagnostics and an execution-time monitor, but which does not have extensive error correction facilities, is the WATFIV system developed at the University of Waterloo, Canada.

Article 5.2 by Irons describes a parsing algorithm that detects and corrects syntactic errors. The parser will accept grammars describable in BNF—essentially the class of context-free grammars. When an error is detected, it modifies the source statement by local insertions and deletions until an acceptable parse is obtained.

The concluding article of this chapter, by Moulton and Muller, describes a FORTRAN compiler having extensive error detection and diagnostic facilities. The DITRAN compiler runs in a batch environment and does not require a special execution-time monitor. Rather, it includes execution-time error detection facilities within the object code, sacrificing some execution speed and requiring additional storage in exchange for a more informative system.

5.1. Error Correction in CORC, the Cornell Computing Language

by David N. Freeman

5.1.1. INTRODUCTION

CORC, the Cornell Computing Language, is an experimental compiler language developed at Cornell University. Although derived from FORTRAN and ALGOL, CORC has a radically simpler syntax than either of these, since it was designed to serve university students and faculty. Indeed, most of the users of CORC are "laymen programmers," who intermittently write small programs to solve scientific problems. Their programs contain many errors, as often chargeable to fundamental misunderstandings of the syntax as to "mechanical errors." A major objective of CORC is to reduce the volume of these errors. This objective has been achieved to the following extent: The average rate of reruns for 4500 programs submitted during the fall semester of 1962 was less than 1.1 reruns for each program.

Three features of CORC have enabled it to achieve this low rerun rate:

(1) Inherent simplicity of the syntax
(2) Closed-shop operation of the Cornell Computing Center on CORC programs, including keypunching, machine operation, and submission/ return of card decks

EDITOR'S NOTE: This article reproduced by permission from the author and the publisher: *Proc. AFIPS*, vol. 26 (1964), FJCC, pp. 15–34.

(3) A novel and extensive set of error-correction procedures in the CORC compiler/monitors

The CORC language is briefly described below; it is more fully documented elsewhere.[1] The current paper describes the error-correction procedures in greater detail.

5.1.2. THE CORC LANGUAGE

CORC was designed by a group of faculty and students in the Department of Industrial Engineering and Operations Research at Cornell. This group has coded and tested two similar compiler/monitor systems, one for a medium-scale decimal computer and the other for a large binary computer.

During the definition of the language, the design group surrendered potency to simplicity whenever the choice arose. Certain redundancies have been included in CORC, serving two functions: to facilitate error correction during source-deck scanning, and to aid novice programmers' grasp of compiler-language syntax. Excepting these redundancies, CORC is quite frugal with conventions. For example, all variables and arithmetic expressions are carried in floating-point form, avoiding the confusing notion of "mode." At the same time, programmers are spared all knowledge of floating-point arithmetic.

Each CORC card deck is divided into three required subdecks plus an optional subdeck of data cards:

(a) The *preliminary-description cards* supply heading data for each page of the output listing.

(b) The *dictionary cards* declare all variables used in the program, simple as well as subscripted.

(c) Each *statement card* may have an indefinite number of continuation cards. Statements may bear *labels* having the same formation rules as variables. Continuation cards may not be labeled.

Variables, labels, numbers, reserved words, and special characters comprise the *symbols* of CORC. Each symbol is a certain string of at most 8 nonblank characters. *Numbers* may have up to 12 digits; decimal points may be leading, trailing, or embedded in the numbers. There are 43 *reserved words* in CORC (e.g., LET) and 10 special characters: $+ - * / \$ = ( ) . ,$. The character string defining each label, variable, or reserved word is terminated by the first blank space or special character. The character string defining each number is terminated by the first character that is neither a digit nor a decimal point. Each special character is a distinct symbol. There are 46 *legal characters* in CORC: letters, digits, and special characters.

A subset of the reserved words is the set of 15 *first-words*: LET, IN-CREASE, INC, DECREASE, DEC, GO, STOP, IF, REPEAT, READ, WRITE, TITLE, NOTE, BEGIN, and END. The first symbol in each statement should, if correct, be one of these first-words.

There are eight executable-statement types, plus a NOTE statement for editorial comments on the source-program listing. (NOTE statements may be labeled; in this case, they are compiled like FORTRAN "CONTINUE" statements.) To simplify the description of the statement types, single letters denote entities of the CORC language:

V ...... a variable, simple or subscripted

E ...... an arithmetic expression, as defined in FORTRAN

L ...... a statement label

B ...... a repeatable-block label (see below)

R ...... one of the six relational operators: EQL, NEQ, LSS, LEQ, GTR, and GEQ. A *relational expression* is a predicate comprising two arithmetic expressions separated by a relational operator, e.g., $2 * X$ NEQ 0.9.

The statement types are as follows:

(1) LET $V = E$, and two variants INCREASE V BY E and DECREASE V BY E. (INCREASE may be abbreviated to INC, DECREASE to DEC.)

(2) IF E_1 R E_2
    THEN GO TO L_1
    ELSE GO TO L_2, and two variants

    IF E_{11} R_1 E_{12} IF E_{11} R_1 E_{12}
       AND E_{21} R_2 E_{22} OR E_{21} R_2 E_{22}
       .   .
       .   .
       AND E_{N1} R_N E_{N2} OR E_{N1} R_N E_{N2}
       THEN GO TO L_1 THEN GO TO L_1
       ELSE GO TO L_2 ELSE GO TO L_2.

(3) GO TO L.

(4) STOP, terminating execution of a program.

(5) READ $V_1, V_2, \ldots$, bringing in data cards during the execution phase. Each data card bears a single new value for the corresponding variable.

(6) WRITE V_1, V_2, ..., printing out the variable names, the numerical values of their subscripts for each execution of the WRITE statement, and the numerical values of these variables.

(7) TITLE (message), printing out the remainder of the card and the entire statement fields of any continuation cards.

(8) REPEAT B..., comprising four variants

 (8a) REPEAT B E TIMES,

 (8b) REPEAT B UNTIL E_{11} R_1 E_{12}
 AND E_{21} R_2 E_{22}
 .
 .
 .
 AND E_{N1} R_N E_{N2},

 (8c) REPEAT B UNTIL E_{11} R_1 E_{12}
 OR E_{21} R_2 E_{22}
 .
 .
 .
 OR E_{N1} R_N E_{N2},

 (8d) REPEAT B FOR $V = E_1, E_2, ..., E_i, E_j, E_k)$, ..., where (E_i, E_j, E_k) is an *iteration triple* as in ALGOL.

Closed subroutines—called *repeatable blocks* in CORC—are defined by two *pseudostatements* as follows:

$$B \quad \text{BEGIN}$$
$$\vdots$$
$$B \quad \text{END},$$

where the "B" labels appear in the normal label field. A repeatable block can be inserted anywhere in the subdeck of statement cards; its physical location has no influence on its usage. It can only be entered under control of a REPEAT statement (with a few erroneous-usage exceptions).

Repeatable blocks may be nested to any reasonable depth. Any number of REPEAT statements can call the same block, although the blocks have no dummy-variable calling sequences. All CORC variables are "free variables" in the logical sense, which avoids confusing the novice programmer no less than it hampers the expert programmer.

5.1.3. ERROR ANALYSIS IN CORC

In the CORC compiler/monitor, the author and his colleagues have attempted to raise the number of intelligible error messages and error-repair procedures to a level far above the current state-of-the-art for similar systems. The success of these messages and procedures is measured by three economies: (a) reduced rerun loads, (b) reduced costs of card preparation, and (c) less faculty/student time devoted to tedious analyses of errors.

The detection of each error invokes a message describing the relevant variables, labels, numbers, etc.; why they are erroneous; and what remedial actions are taken by CORC. Exhibiting errors in detail has improved student comprehension of the CORC syntax. Of course certain errors defy detection; e.g., incorrect numerical constants.

A principal tenet of the CORC philosophy is to detect errors as early as possible in

(1) characters within symbols.

(2) symbols within expressions.

(3) expressions within statements, e.g., the left and right sides of an assignment statement.

(4) statements within the sequencing of each program.

An explicit message for each error is printed on the output listing. This listing is the only output document from a CORC program; all programs are compiled and executed, and machine code is never saved on tape or punched cards.

After detecting a statement-card error, CORC always "repairs" the error by one of the two following actions:

(a) CORC refuses to compile a "badly garbled" statement. Instead, CORC replaces it with a source-program "message statement" reminding the programmer of the omitted statement.

(b) CORC edits the contents of a "less badly garbled" statement into intelligible source language. The edited statement is subsequently compiled into machine code.

Errors in cards other than statement cards are repaired by similar techniques.

Thus the machine code produced by CORC is always executable, and compilation-phase and execution-phase error messages are provided for every program. By continuing compilation in the presence of errors, CORC provides diagnostic data simultaneously on structural levels (1)–(4) cited above. By also executing these programs, CORC detects additional errors in program flow, subscript usage, improper function arguments, etc.

The *correction* of a programming error is defined to be the alteration of relevant source-language symbols to what the programmer truly intended. Under this operational definition, many errors are incapable of "correction"; e.g., the programmer may have intended a statement or expression not even offered in CORC. Other errors are capable of "correction" by the programmer himself but by no critic unfamiliar with the complete problem definition; an incorrect numerical constant is again an example.

A third class of errors can be corrected by an intelligent critic after scanning the sourcedeck listing, without recourse to the problem definition. Some errors in this class require a profound use of context to elicit the programmer's true intention. Other errors in this class can be detected and corrected with little use of context, e.g., the omission of a terminal right parenthesis.

The author defines a *corrigible error* to be one whose correction is automatically attempted by the CORC compiler/monitor. Thus this definition is by cases, for a specific version of CORC. CORC may correct one error and fail to correct a second, nearly identical error. Error correction is a fundamentally probabilistic phenomenon; the CORC error-correction procedures attempt to maximize the "expected useful yield" of each program by strategies based on *a priori* probabilities associated with the different errors.[2][†]

The majority of corrigible errors are detected during the scanning of source decks by the CORC compiler. A few corrigible errors are detected during the execution of object programs. For each error, one or more correction procedures have been added to CORC, representing certain investments in core memory and operating speed.

The following paragraph discusses the selection of corrigible errors, and Section 5.1.4 catalogs these errors. The catalog will be somewhat peculiar to the structure of CORC, a population of novice programmers, and the operation of a university computing center. However, the discussion of control-statement errors, arithmetic-expression errors, and misspellings is relevant to most compiler languages.

The author has roughly ranked various error conditions by two criteria: *a priori* probabilities[‡] of their occurrence, and *a priori* probabilities of their correction (if correction is attempted). Correction procedures were designed for some errors, while other chronic errors had such low *a priori* probabilities of correction that only explicit error-detection messages were printed out. For example, omission of a subscript is a common error which is difficult to correct, although easy to detect and "repair." CORC "repairs" a subscript-omission error by supplying a value of 1.

---

† References 2 and 5 also propose probabilistic correction of misspellings.

‡ Probabilities in the sequel are estimates based on human scrutiny of several hundred student programs.

On the other hand, misspellings are common errors whose *a priori* probabilities of correction are high if sophisticated procedures are used. The author hopes to achieve at least 75 percent correction of misspellings with the current procedures; many have not yet been tested in high-volume operation.[3][†]

5.1.4. ERROR CORRECTION DURING SCANNING

First, the general procedures for card scanning will be described. The second, third, and fourth subsections deal with dictionary cards, data cards, and statement cards, respectively. The last subsection describes the error-correction phase which follows scanning, i.e., after the last statement card has been read but before machine code is generated by the compiler.

5.1.4.1. *Card Scanning*

Each CORC source deck should have all cards of one type in a single subdeck:

(1) Type 1, preliminary description cards
(2) Type 5, dictionary cards
(3) Type 0, statement cards
(4) Type 4, data cards (if used)

The *type* of each card is defined by the punch in column 1 (although CORC may attempt to correct the type of a stray source card).

At the beginning of each new source program, CORC scans the card images (usually on magnetic tape) for the next type 1 card, normally a tab card bearing any nonstandard time limit and page limit for this program. (The tab cards are used to divide the decks, facilitating batch processing and other handling.) This scanning procedure skips any extraneous data cards from the previous program deck. If the preceding deck was badly shuffled, misplaced dictionary cards and statement cards will also be skipped.

An indefinite number of type 1 cards may be supplied: CORC inserts data from the first two cards into the page headings of the output listing. This serves to label all output with the processing date and programmer name, avoiding losses in subsequent handling.

The problem identification should be duplicated into each deck; any deviations from this identification generate warning messages. The serializa-

---

[†] Damereau has achieved over 95 percent correction of misspellings in an information-retrieval application.

tion of cards is checked, although no corrective action is taken if the cards are out of sequence. If the serialization is entirely omitted, CORC inserts serial numbers into the print-line image of each card, so that subsequent error messages can reference these print lines without exception.

The general procedure on extraneous or illegal punches is as follows: Illegal punches are uniformly converted to the nonstandard character "$\neq$"; extraneous punches are ignored except in noncompact variable/label fields and in the statement field of type 0 cards, where all single punches are potentially meaningful. Rather than discard illegal punches, CORC reserves the possibility of treating them as misspellings. Likewise, any nonalphabetic first character of a variable/label field must be erroneous and is changed to "$\neq$," furnishing a later opportunity to treat this as a misspelling. All hyphen punches are converted to minus signs during card reading; the keyboard confusion of these two characters is so chronic—and harmless— that CORC even refrains from a warning message.

5.1.4.2. Dictionary Cards

Although the dictionary and data cards are processed in entirely different phases of a CORC program, their formats are identical—with the exception of column 1—and common procedures are used to scan them. As mentioned in the preceding subsection, nonalphabetic first characters are changed to "$\neq$." Embedded special characters are similarly changed with the following exception: Character strings of the form "(I)" or "(I, J)" are omitted. Fixed-column subscript fields have already been provided and students consistently and correctly use them. However, a common student error is to supply redundant parenthesized subscripts in the label field; these are ignored by CORC, although a warning message is supplied.

Non-numeric characters in the subscript fields and the exponent field are changed to "I"s. Vector subscripts can appear in either the first-subscript field or the second-subscript field. These subscripts need not be right-justified in their respective fields. After an array has been defined, subsequent subscripts of excessive magnitude are not used; the corresponding data entries are put into the highest legal cell of the array.

5.1.4.3. Data Cards

All of the foregoing procedures apply with these exceptions: If a data card has its variable field blank or, in the case of subscripted variables, its subscript fields blank, the data can still be entered with a high probability of correcting the omission. Information in the READ statement overrides incorrect or missing entries on the corresponding data cards. CORC insists on exact agreement of the variables and subscripts if warning messages are to be avoided. Symbolic subscripts may be used in READ statements, but their execution-phase values must agree with the numeric subscripts on the type 4 cards.

5.1.4.4. *Statement Cards*

Correction of erroneous statement cards is a complex technique—and the most fruitful of those currently implemented in CORC. Statement cards comprise over 80 percent of student source decks, on the average. Students commit the overwhelming majority of their errors in communicating *imperative* statements to a compiler, rather than *header* statements, *declarative* statements, or *data* cards. Statement-card errors fall into two major categories: those detectable at compilation time and those detectable only at execution time. The second category is discussed in Section 5.1.5. Some of the most useful correction techniques for the first category—tested and modified during the past two years of CORC usage—are described in the following eight subsections.

(1) *Misspellings.*[4,5] At the end of Section 5.1.3, misspellings were cited as a class of errors that both occur frequently and have attractively high *a priori* probabilities for correction. Accordingly, CORC now contains a subroutine that compares any *test word* to any list of words (each entry being denoted a *list word*), determining a "figure of merit" for the match of each list word to the test word. Each figure of merit can be considered as the *a posteriori* probability that the test word is a misspelling of this particular list word. The list word with the highest figure of merit is selected as the spelling of the test word "most likely" to be correct.

Various categories of misspelling are defined in CORC; to each category is assigned an *a priori* probability of occurrence. When the test word and a list word match within the scope of a category, i.e., the test word is some particular misspelling of the list word, the *a priori* probability for this category is added to the figure of merit for this list word. Actually, the figures of merit are integers rather than probabilities; they can be converted to probabilities by the usual normalization, but this is unnecessary—they are used merely to rank the possible misspellings.

All increments used in misspelling analyses reflect the number N of non-blank characters in the test word, as follows: A certain base-value increment is specified for each misspelling; if a match is found, this base value is multiplied by the ratio $N/8$, then added to the corresponding figure of merit.

(a) A *concatenation misspelling* occurs when a delimiting blank is omitted between two symbols; e.g., "LETX..." is a concatenation misspelling of "LET X..." When such a misspelling is detected, any relevant list of words is compared against the concatenated symbol. The increment to the figure of merit for each list word is computed as follows:

(i) If the list word and the test word do not have at least their initial two characters in common, the increment is 0.

(ii) For every consecutive character in common with the list word (after the first character), an increment of 2 is added to the figure of merit. *Example*: Assume that the test word is ENTRYA and that two of the list words are ENT and ENTRY. The corresponding figures of merit are 6 and 10, respectively. The higher figure reflects the more exact agreement of ENTRY to ENTRYA.

(b) Single-character misspellings provide four different increments to the figure of merit, corresponding to mutually exclusive possibilities:

(i) A *keypunch-shift misspelling* occurs when the IBM 026 keypunch is improperly shifted for the proper keystroke, e.g., a "1"-"U" error. There are 14 possible misspellings of this type, corresponding to the 7 letter-number pairs on the keyboard. The special character row, including "0," does not seem susceptible to misspelling analysis, since special characters are always segregated, never embedded in symbols. For each list word which agrees within a single keypunch-shift misspelling with the test word, an increment of $(20N/8)$ is added to the corresponding figure of merit, where N is the number of nonblank characters in the test word.

(ii) An *illegal-character misspelling* occurs either (a) when a variable/label has previously required a "single-letter perturbation" using the character "$\neq$", or (b) when an illegal punch in the card is changed to "$\neq$." Single-letter perturbations are used when the same symbol occurs at both a variable and a label, or when a reserved word is used as a variable or label. In either case, conflicting usage cannot be tolerated, and CORC appends "$\neq$" to the symbol for the current usage. In subsequent searches of the symbol dictionary, one may wish to recognize the original spelling. Thus, for each list word which agrees within a single illegal-character misspelling with the test word, an increment of $(20N/8)$ is added to the corresponding figure of merit, where N is as above. This increment is higher than that for a random misspelling, reflecting the peculiar origins of the character "$\neq$."

(iii) A *resemblance misspelling* occurs whenever any of the following character pairs is confused: "I"-"1," "O" (the letter)-"0" (the number) and "Z"-"2." For each list word which agrees within a single resemblance misspelling with the test word, an increment of $(40N/8)$ is added to the corresponding figure of merit, where N is as above.

(iv) A *random misspelling* occurs when any other single character is mispunched in a symbol. For each list word which agrees within a single random misspelling with the test word, an increment of $(10N/8)$ is added to the corresponding figure of merit, where N is as above.

(c) A *permutation misspelling* provides a single increment to a figure of merit whenever the test word matches the corresponding list word within a pair of adjacent characters, this pair being the same but permuted in the two words; e.g., LTE is a permutation misspelling of LET. For each list word which agrees within a single permutation misspelling with the test word, an increment of $(20N/8)$ is added to the corresponding figure of merit, where N is as above. Other permutations may deserve consideration at some future date, but adjacent-pair permutations seem to have the highest *a priori* occurrence probabilities.

(d) Simple misspellings of the foregoing types have high probabilities of successful correction insofar as the following conditions are met:

(i) The list of words does not contain many nearly identical entries. Otherwise, there will be many reasonable misspelling possibilities from which the program may select only one.

(ii) Neither test words nor list words are single-character symbols. The program excludes such list words from consideration during a misspelling analysis; experience has shown that only a small proportion—perhaps 10 percent—of single-character symbols are successfully corrected.

(iii) Context can be extraordinarily helpful. Associated with each list word is a set of attributes such as the count of its usage in the current program, its function (variable, label, constant, reserved word, etc.), and any peculiar usages already detected (such as being an undeclared variable). Certain misspelling possibilities can be immediately discarded if the context associated with the corresponding list words does not match the context of the test word. For example, if an arithmetic statement is being analyzed, any test for misspelled variables can immediately discard all misspelled label possibilities.

The first two of these three conditions are controlled by the vocabulary of the source-deck programmer; CORC gives far better assistance to programs using only a few variables and labels of highly distinctive spelling with at least three characters apiece.

(e) The increments corresponding to different misspellings were arbitrarily selected; they can be readily raised or lowered as experience indicates. The current values reflect the following observations:

(i) The weakest communication link is between the handwritten coding sheets and their interpretation by the keypunch operator. Hence, the largest increment is assigned to resemblance misspellings.

(ii) In lieu of exact information, permutation misspellings and keypunch-shift misspellings have been judged equally probable.

(iii) Illegal punches in a card image arise from three sources: illegal hole patterns, improper use of a character (e.g., nonalphabetic character beginning a first word, or the duplicate use of a symbol as two entities), and card-reading failures. Lacking other evidence, the author considered the increment to be approximately the same as in (ii).

(iv) Other single-character misspellings seem only half as likely to occur.

Examples of the current CORC misspelling analyses may be found at the end of Subsection 5.1.4.5.

(2) *Subscripts.* Correction attempts for subscript errors have low success probabilities, on the whole. Isolated omission of one or both subscripts seems almost hopeless. CORC edits such an omission by appending "(1)" to a vector variable and "(1, 1)" to a matrix variable. Likewise, if a matrix variable has other than two subscripts, CORC uses primitive editing techniques to produce executable machine code. Excessive commas are changed to "+" signs, and "(E)" is changed to "(E, 1)," where "E" is the arithmetic expression for the first subscript of a matrix variable.

Missing right parentheses are supplied and extra right parentheses are deleted as necessary, although not always correctly.

Definition of new array variables after the dictionary is complete (i.e., after all type 5 cards have been processed) is an attractive—if difficult—error-correction procedure. Most algebraic compilers scan source decks several times; they have a leisurely opportunity to accumulate evidence for undeclared array variables. If such evidence is overwhelming, i.e., if every usage of a certain variable is immediately followed by a parenthesized expression, these compilers could change the status of this variable before the final code-generation scan.

To reduce compilation time, the current version of CORC scans each source statement once and must make an immediate decision when it finds a left parenthesis juxtaposed to a supposedly simple variable. Should "V(...)" be changed to "V*(...)," i.e., implied multiplication, or should it be treated as a subscript (and redesignate "V" as an array variable)? The present error-correction procedure is to encode "V(...)" into the intermediate language without change; special counters for usage as a vector/matrix variable are incremented, depending on one/two parenthesized arguments. At the conclusion of scanning, these usage counters are tested for all "simple" variables. Any variable used preponderantly as a vector variable causes CORC to test for the misspelling of some declared vector variable. Failing this, CORC changes the status of the variable to a vector of 100 cells. Any variable used preponderantly as a matrix variable causes CORC to test for the misspelling of some declared matrix variable. Failing this, CORC changes the status of the variable to a matrix of 2500 cells comprising a 50×50 array.

If a variable is infrequently juxtaposed to parenthesized expressions, CORC treats these juxtapositions as implied multiplications. Deferral of this decision necessitates a procedure for inserting the multiplication operator during the conversion of intermediate language to machine code, together with the appropriate message. This error-correction procedure is one of the few in the code-generation phase. The message appears at the end of the source-deck listing rather than adjacent to the offending card image; the gain in error-correcting power seems to justify deferring the message.

The *a priori* probabilities of omitted array-variable declarations and implied multiplications are both high. Since the two possibilities are mutually exclusive, CORC bases its choice on the percentage occurrence of the ambiguous usage. If the usage is chronic, i.e., comprising more than 50 percent of the total usage of some variable, an undeclared array variable seems more probable. If the ambiguous usage is a small percentage of the total usage, implied multiplication seems more probable.

(3) *Arithmetic and Relational Expressions.* The rules for analyzing and correcting arithmetic expressions are as follows:

(a) Extraneous preceding plus signs are deleted, and preceding minus signs are prefixed by zero, i.e., "$-E$" becomes "$0 - E$."

(b) Thereafter, "$+$," "$-$," "$*$," and "$/$" are all binary operators. If an operand is missing before or after a binary operator, the value "1" is inserted. This merely preserves the coherence of the syntax; to correct this error seems hopeless.

(c) If an expression using two binary operators might be ambiguous (irrespective of the formal syntax), CORC prints out its resolution of the ambiguity; e.g., "A/B * C IS INTERPRETED AS (A/B) * C."

(4) LET, INCREASE-BY, *and* DECREASE-BY. Four components are essential to each correct statement in this category: the first-word, the assigned variable, the middle symbol, and the right-hand-side (RHS) arithmetic expression.

(a) The first-word of the statement has been identified by a generalized prescan of the statement. If "LET" has been omitted but "=" has been found, CORC furnishes the former symbol.

(b) The assigned variable may be subscripted; if so, CORC supplies any missing arguments, commas, and right parentheses when "=" or "BY" terminates the left-hand-side (LHS) of the statement. If other symbols follow the assigned variable but precede "=" or "BY," they are ignored.

(c) "EQU," "EQL," and "EQ" are erroneous but recognizable substitutes for "=."

(d) Any arithmetic expression is legal for the RHS.

(5) GO TO, STOP, *and* IF.

(a) With one exception—(b) just below—all unconditional branches begin with "GO," followed by an optional "TO."

(b) STOP is a complete one-word statement. Also, it may be used in the conditional-branch statement; e.g., "IF ... THEN STOP ELSE GO TO..."

(c) A conditional branch always follows one or more relational expressions in an IF or REPEAT statement. For IF statements, the first incidence of "THEN," "ELSE," "GO," "TO," or "STOP" terminates the last relational expression; missing operands, commas, and right parentheses are then inserted as needed. Thereafter, the two labels are retrieved from any "reasonable" arrangement with two or more of the above five words.

Missing labels are replaced by dummy "next statement" labels, which later inhibit the compilation of machine-code branches. Thus, if an IF statement lacks its second label, the falsity of its predicate during execution will cause no branch. At the end of scanning, certain labels may remain undefined; here also, CORC inhibits the compilation of machine-code branches.

(6) REPEAT

(a) If the repeated label is omitted, e.g., in the statement REPEAT FOR ARG = 2, CORC scans the label field of the following source card. Programmers often place repeatable blocks directly after REPEAT statements using these blocks: Hence, any label on this following card is likely to be the missing repeated label: It is inserted into the REPEAT statement. If no such label is found, CORC creates a dummy label for the repeatable block. During the execution of the program, usage of this erroneous REPEAT statement can be monitored by this dummy label.

(b) If the REPEAT-FOR variant is used, CORC tests for three components in addition to the repeated label:

(i) The bound variable, i.e., ARG in the example in 6(a).

(ii) The character "=" or its erroneous variants "EQU," "EQL," and "EQ."

(iii) Any collection of iteration triples and single arithmetic expressions, separated by commas. In any iteration triple, CORC will supply a single missing argument with value "1."

(c) As in IF statements, an indefinite number of relational expressions can be used in REPEAT-UNTIL statements.

(7) BEGIN *and* END. REPEAT statements and repeatable blocks require consistent spelling of labels and matching BEGIN/END pseudostatements. Through misunderstanding or carelessness, novice programmers commit grievous errors in using REPEAT statements and their blocks. CORC attempts to correct a certain subset of errors whose correction probabilities are attractively high:

(a) If the label of a BEGIN pseudostatement is missing, the preceding and following cards are tested for clues:

(i) If the preceding card was a REPEAT statement using a yet undefined label, this label is supplied to the BEGIN pseudostatement.

(ii) If (i) fails to hold and if the following card is labeled, this label is shifted to the BEGIN pseudostatement.

(iii) Otherwise, a dummy label is supplied, awaiting further clues to the identity of the repeatable block. If such clues never appear, the block is closed by a CORC-supplied END pseudostatement after the last statement card of the deck. Should an unpaired END pseudostatement be subsequently found, the dummy label (on the BEGIN pseudostatement) is changed to match this unpaired END label.

(b) If the label for an END pseudostatement is missing, CORC tests for the existence of a "nest" of unclosed blocks. If so, the label of the innermost unclosed block is used in the current END pseudostatement. Otherwise, the card is ignored.

(c) If the label in an END pseudostatement does not match the label of the innermost unclosed block, the current label is tested against the labels of the entire nest of blocks. If a "crisscross" has occurred, i.e.,

$$A \quad . \quad \text{BEGIN}$$
$$\vdots$$
$$B \quad . \quad \text{BEGIN}$$
$$\vdots$$
$$A \quad \quad \text{END}$$

CORC inserts the END pseudostatement for block B before the current END pseudostatement for block A.

(d) If the preceding test fails, CORC again tests the current label against the nest, looking for a misspelling. If the current label is misspelled, procedure (c) is used. If the misspelling tests fail, CORC ignores the END pseudostatement.

(e) If the student has programmed an apparent recursion, CORC prints a warning message but takes no further action. Although unlikely, there may be a legitimate use for the construction:

$$A \quad \text{BEGIN}$$
$$\vdots$$
$$\text{REPEAT A} \ldots$$
$$\vdots$$
$$A \quad \text{END}$$

In this situation, CORC makes no attempt to preserve the address linkages as a truly recursive routine would require. Thus the program is likely to terminate in an endless loop.

(8) READ *and* WRITE. Only simple or subscripted variables can appear in READ statements. The subscripts can be any arithmetic expressions. If a label appears in the argument list of a WRITE statement, the current count of the label usage will be printed. Constants, reserved words, and special characters are deleted from the argument lists of READ/WRITE statements.

5.1.4.5. *Postscanning Spelling Corrections*

The misspelling of labels and variables is corrected—insofar as CORC is capable—after scanning an entire deck, with the exceptions mentioned in Section 5.1.1.4. After scanning, much usage and context data have been accumulated. CORC attempts to resolve suspicious usages by equating two or more symbols to the same entity.

When the implementation of CORC was originally under study, heavy weight was given to the potential benefits from correcting misspellings. Efficient correction of misspellings seemed to require one of the following similar strategies:

(a) Two or more complete scans of the source deck, the first serving primarily for the collection of data on suspicious usages such as possible misspellings.

(b) Encoding of the source deck into an intermediate language which is tightly packed and substantially irredundant but which also permits re-designation of labels and variables after misspelling analyses.

A third alternative to these strategies was to compile the source deck directly into machine code, and then attempt to repair this code after determining the set of corrigible misspellings. However, this procedure seemed less flexible to use and more difficult to program than the first two strategies; it was rejected from consideration.

The second alternative was selected and appears in both current implementations of CORC. Details of the strategy are as follows:

(a) Each new simple variable entered into the dictionary is paralleled by a *pointer cell* containing the address of a second cell. This address is ordinarily used during machine-code generation to represent the variable in question. Since any misspelled variable is equated to a properly spelled variable *after* scanning but *before* code generation, CORC corrects the misspelling merely by giving the variables identical pointer-cell contents.

(b) Each new array variable is paralleled by a pointer cell containing the base address of the array. As for simple variables, only one pointer cell is changed if this variable is equated to another array variable.

(c) To each label corresponds a pointer cell containing a branch instruction to the appropriate machine location (when the latter becomes defined during the generation of machine code). For an undefined label equated to some other label, its cell is filled with a branch instruction to the pointer cell for the other label. Thus, execution of GO TO LABELA, where LA-BELA is a defined label, requires two machine-language branch instructions; if LABELA is an undefined label equated to LABELB, three machine-language branch instructions are required.

The penalty in compilation speed for using the intermediate language is modest: the average time to complete compilation for CORC programs—after the last statement card has been read—is less than one second; few decks require more than two seconds.

(1) *Correction of Misspelled Labels.* If a label has been referenced but never defined in a label field, it is tested for being a possible misspelling of some defined label. The defined label with the highest figure of merit is selected and the following message is printed:

LABELA IS CHANGED TO LABELB

where LABELA and LABELB are the undefined and defined labels, respectively. If no defined label has a nonzero figure of merit with respect to the undefined label, the following message is printed:

LABELA IS UNDEFINED

Subsequently, all references to this label during the generation of machine language are treated as "next-statement" branches. At execution time, any GO TO or REPEAT statements referencing this label cause the following messages, respectively:

IN STATEMENT_____ ,
GO-TO NOT EXECUTED

IN STATEMENT_____ ,
REPEAT NOT EXECUTED

(2) *Correction of Misspelled Simple Variables*

(a) If an undeclared variable is never used in suspicious juxtaposition to parenthesized expressions (cf. Subsection 5.1.4.4 (2)), CORC attempts to find a declared simple variable meeting the following criteria:

(i) The undeclared variable is a potential misspelling of the declared variable.

(ii) The LHS-RHS usage of the declared variable is complementary to that of the undeclared variable. By LHS-RHS *usage* is meant the following two frequencies: Usage on the LHS of an assignment statement, in a READ statement, or in the initial dictionary (this usage corresponds to assigning the variable a new value); usage on the RHS of an assignment statement, in a relational expression, or in a WRITE statement (this usage corresponds to using the current value of the variable).

The motivation for LHS-RHS analysis is the following: If two variables are spelled almost identically, if one has a null RHS usage and the other a null LHS usage, then the *a priori* probability that the programmer intended a single entity is higher than the probabilities for most alternative misspellings.

CORC does not use LHS-RHS analysis alone to determine the best misspelling possibility. Instead, an increment of 5 is added to the figure of merit of each declared variable whose null usage complements any null usage of the current test word, i.e., undeclared variable. Undeclared variables can be equated only to declared variables, not to other undeclared variables.

(b) If a declared variable has a null RHS usage, it may be an erroneous dictionary spelling of some variable which is thereafter consistently spelled. However, CORC will announce that the dictionary spelling is "correct" in this case, after it detects the misspelling; all "misspelled" incidences of the variable are equated to the declared variable.

(3) *Examples.* Four groups of nearly matching symbols are illustrated in Table 5.1.1. In the first group, the label ABC requires testing for misspelling. The label ABCDE is a concatenation misspelling, figure of merit (FOM) $= 6$. The label ABD is a random misspelling, FOM $= 3$. The label BAC is a permutation misspelling, FOM $= 7$. The label AB$\neq$ is an illegal-character misspelling, FOM $= 7$. Thus, CORC would choose at random between BAC and AB$\neq$ for the defined label to which ABC should be equated.

In this second group, the defined label DEI has FOM $= 15$ with respect to the undefined label DE1.

In the third group, three simple variables have not been declared in the dictionary and require testing for misspelling. One should remember that only declared simple variables, i.e., XYZ and XYU, are eligible for identification with the undeclared variables. With respect to XYV, XYZ has misspelling FOM $= 3$; to this must be added the null-RHS increment of 5, making a total FOM $= 8$. Since XYU has only the misspelling FOM of 3 with respect to XYV, XYV is equated to XYZ.

With respect to YXZ, XYZ has a misspelling FOM of 7, plus the null-RHS increment of 5, making a total FOM of 12: since XYU has a zero FOM for YXZ, CORC equates YXZ to XYZ.

Table 5.1.1. Sample Problems in Postscanning Spelling Corrections

Symbol	Type	Declared/ Defined?	LHS Usage	RHS Usage	Usage as Vector	Usage as Matrix	Total Usage
ABC	label	no					
ABCDE	label	yes					
ABD	label	yes					
BAC	label	yes					
AB≠	label	yes					
DE1	label	no					
DE1	label	yes					
XYZ	simple variable	yes	1	0	0	0	1
XYU	smp. var.	yes	2	1	0	0	3
XYV	smp. var.	no	1	1	0	0	2
YXZ	smp. var.	no	0	1	0	0	1
YXW	smp. var.	no	0	2	0	0	2
GHI	vector variable	yes	2	2	4	0	4
GH1	smp. var.	yes	2	2	4	0	4
GHJ	smp. var.	yes	1	2	2	0	3
GHK	smp. var.	no	2	2	0	0	4

With respect to YXW, neither XYZ nor XYU has a positive FOM; thus, YXW is not equated to a declared variable.

In the fourth group, GH1 was invariably used as a vector variable. Since it is a resemblance misspelling of the declared vector variable GHI, it is equated to this variable and its status changed to a vector. GHJ was used 67 percent of the time as a vector variable; since it is a random misspelling of GHI, it is equated to the latter. GHK has a positive figure of merit with respect to each of the three preceding entries. However, GHK was never used as a vector variable. Since the GHJ and GHI have been set to vector status, GHK can no longer be equated to either of them; it thus remains a distinct, undeclared variable.

5.1.5. ERROR MONITORING DURING EXECUTION

CORC prefaces each compiled statement by a sequence of machine language instructions to monitor object-program flow. Additional "overhead" instructions for monitoring appear in four types of statements: labeled statements, statements containing subscripted variables, REPEAT statements, and READ statements. The monitoring effort has three objectives:

(a) Prevent the object program from overwriting the CORC compiler/ monitor or itself

(b) Continue the execution phase through untested code when the flow of the object program becomes confused (through misuse of REPEAT statements or incomplete GO TO, IF, and REPEAT statements)

(c) Provide explicit diagnostic messages for each error detected at execution time, followed by an unconditional postmortem dump of simple-variable values and other helpful data.[6][†]

5.1.5.1. *The General Monitor*

(1) CORC accumulates a count of all statements executed, *the statement count*. This count is printed in the postmortem dump, together with the number of errors committed during the entire program and the total elapsed time for the program. The statement count has two minor functions: to aid debugging of short programs in conjunction with the "label tallies" (see (3) below), and—looking toward future CORC research—to exhibit the different speeds of execution for various programs, e.g., with/ without heavy subscript usage. The per-statement overhead of the statement count is 13.2 microseconds, comprising a single "tally" instruction.

(2) Before executing each statement, its source-card serial number (converted to a binary integer) is loaded into an index register. Execution-phase messages resulting from this statement retrieve the serial number and print it as an introductory phrase to each message; e.g.,

IN STATEMENT 1234, THE PROGRAM IS STOPPED

Each load-index instruction requires 3.3 microseconds. The percentage of execution time devoted to items (1) and (2) is usually less than 3 percent; see (5) below.

(3) The execution of each labeled statement is tallied, by label. These tallies are printed in the postmortem dump; they show the progress of the program, which branches were never taken, endless loops, etc. Each tally instruction requires 13.2 microseconds.

[†] Many debugging languages such as BUGTRAN (cf. Ref. 6) furnish trace and snapshot information *if requested by the programmer*. CORC furnishes such diagnostic information unconditionally; the overhead instructions cannot be suppressed after programs are debugged.

(4) At each labeled statement, a two-position console switch is interrogated. In the normal position, the switch has no effect on program flow. If set, the switch causes the program to terminate at once, printing the message

> IN STATEMENT _____, THE PROGRAM IS MANUALLY INTERRUPTED

followed by the usual postmortem dump.

Thus, any endless loop can be manually interrupted without stopping the computer, although this is rarely necessary. (Cf. Section 5.1.5.3.) The switch interrogation is required only at labeled statements, since endless loops must include at least one label. Each switch interrogation requires 7.2 microseconds. The percentage of execution time devoted to items (3) and (4) is usually less than 1 percent, as exhibited by the following analysis.

(5) Assuming that 100,000 statements are executed per minute, an average statement requires some 600 microseconds. Since items (1) and (2) aggregate 16.5 microseconds per statement, the overhead for these items is 2.75 percent. Assuming that every fourth statement is labeled, items (3) and (4) are incurred once every 2400 microseconds on the average; since these times aggregate 20.4 microseconds, their overhead is approximately 0.8 percent.

(6) No tracing features are offered in CORC. If a student requires more diagnostic data than are already furnished, he is encouraged to use WRITE and TITLE statements generously. However, he is also warned to print such data compactly:

(a) If two consecutive pages print less than 30 percent of the 14,400 character spaces available (2 pages × 60 lines/page × 120 characters/line), CORC prints out the following message:

> ——TRY TO USE MORE EFFICIENT WRITE AND TITLE STATEMENTS AND AVOID WASTING SO MUCH PAPER——

(b) A page-count limit is set for all normal programs; when this limit is reached, the program is terminated at once.

(7) Each untranslatable source card has been replaced by a TITLE card during scanning, bearing the following message:

> CARD NO. _____ NOT EXECUTED, SINCE UNTRANSLATABLE

These messages remind the programmer of omitted actions during the execution phase.

5.1.5.2. *Monitoring Arithmetic Errors*

CORC uses conventional procedures for arithmetic overflow/underflow errors, but somewhat novel procedures for special-function argument errors. The machine traps of the computer detect overflow/underflow conditions, which are then interpreted into CORC messages:

(1) IN STATEMENT _____, EXPONENT UNDER-FLOW. (CORC zeros the accumulator and proceeds.)

(2) IN STATEMENT _____, EXPONENT OVERFLOW. (CORC sets the accumulator to 1 rather than to some arbitrary, large number. This tends to avoid an immediate sequence of identical messages, allowing the execution phase to survive longer before termination from excessive errors.)

(3) IN STATEMENT _____, DIVISION BY ZERO. ASSUME QUOTIENT OF 1.0

For each special function error, CORC creates an acceptable argument and proceeds, instead of taking drastic action (e.g., immediate program termination) as many monitor systems do.

(4) IN STATEMENT _____, $\begin{Bmatrix} \$ \\ EXP \\ SIN \end{Bmatrix}$ ARGUMENT TOO LARGE. THE RESULT IS SET TO 1.

(5) IN STATEMENT _____, LN 0 YIELDS (or ... LOG 0 YIELDS) 1.

(6) IN STATEMENT _____, $\begin{Bmatrix} LN \\ LOG \\ SQRT \end{Bmatrix}$ OF NEGATIVE ARGUMENT. THE ABSOLUTE VALUE IS USED.

(7) IN STATEMENT _____, ZERO TO NEGATIVE POWER—ASSUME 1.

(8) IN STATEMENT _____, $—NEGATIVE ARGU-MENT. THE RESULT IS SET TO 1.

5.1.5.3. *Terminations*

Two abnormal terminations were discussed in Section 5.1.5.1. Altogether, there are five terminations, caused by the following events:

(1) Console switch set.

(2) Page count limit exceeded.

(3) Time limit exceeded. Overflow of the real-time clock produces a machine trap which is intercepted by CORC. For each program, a time limit (ordinarily of 60 seconds) is set. (The tab cards separating the source decks can bear any nonstandard page count and time limits.[†]) When this time is exhausted, the program is terminated with the following message preceding the postmortem dump:

IN STATEMENT _____, THE TIME IS EXHAUSTED

Endless loops are terminated by this procedure, avoiding the necessity of operator intervention with the console switch.

(4) Error count too high. After each program has been compiled, the total error count is interrogated. When it exceeds 100, then or thereafter, the program is terminated with the appropriate message.

(5) Normal execution of STOP. The message

IN STATEMENT _____, THE PROGRAM IS STOPPED

identifies which STOP statement—possibly of several such statements—has been met. For all terminations, the postmortem dump includes the following:

(a) The final values of all simple variables. Since arrays may comprise thousands of cells, CORC cannot afford paper or machine time to dump them too.

(b) The usage tallies for all labels.

(c) The first 15 (or fewer) data card images.

(d) The error count, statement count, and elapsed time figures.

[†] Ordinarily the tab cards are blank. A special rerun drawer is used for programs which require unusual output volume or running time; the computing center inserts special tab cards with nonstandard page count and time limits before these decks.

5.1.5.4. *Monitoring Subscripted Variables*

One of CORC's most radical innovations is the universal monitoring of subscripts. CORC is attempting to trade execution efficiency for two other desiderata:

(a) Protection of the in-core compiler/monitor against accidental over-writing by student programs

(b) Provision of complete diagnostics on all illegal subscripts: in which statements, for which variables, and the actual erroneous values of the subscripts

CORC's excellent throughput speed has depended on infrequent destruction of the in-core compiler/monitor; in the author's opinion, subscript monitoring is CORC's most important protective feature.

Criterion (b)—full diagnostic information on subscript errors—is also of significance, since erroneous subscript usage comprises at least 30 percent of all execution-phase errors. Students quickly learn that these errors are among the easiest to commit—although they are spared the hardship of their detection and isolation.

Subscript usage is monitored as follows:

(1) Each reference to a subscripted variable incurs a load-index instruction corresponding to the dictionary entry for this variable. If subsequent troubles arise in the subscripts, CORC can retrieve the name and other particulars of the variable by using this index register.

(2) The subscript is an arithmetic expression, whose floating-point value is transmitted in the machine accumulator to a closed subroutine for unfloating numbers.

(3) The latter subroutine checks for a positive, integral subscript.

(a) 0 is changed to 1 with the following message:

IN STATEMENT _____, SUBSCRIPT FOR VARIABLE _____ IS 0. IT IS SET TO 1.

(b) Negative numbers are also changed to 1:

IN STATEMENT _____, SUBSCRIPT FOR VARIABLE _____ IS NEGATIVE. IT IS SET TO 1.

(c) If nonintegral, the subscript is rounded to an integer. If the round-off error is less than 10^{-9}, no error message is incurred; earlier calculations may have introduced small round-off errors into a theoretically exact subscript. If the round-off error exceeds 10^{-9}, the following message appears:

> IN STATEMENT _____, SUBSCRIPT FOR VARIABLE _____ IS NONINTEGRAL. IT IS ROUNDED TO AN INTEGER.

(d) After verifying (or changing to) a positive, integral subscript, the closed subroutine for unfloating subscripts returns control to the size test peculiar to this variable.

(4) The subscript is tested for exceeding the appropriate dimension of the array variable. Thus the first subscript of a matrix variable is tested against the declared maximum number of rows, and the second subscript is tested against the declared maximum number of columns; a vector subscript is tested against its declared maximum number of elements. An excessive value incurs one of the three following messages:

> IN STATEMENT _____, _____ IS THE $\left\{ \begin{array}{c} \text{FIRST} \\ \text{SECOND} \\ \text{VECTOR} \end{array} \right\}$ SUBSCRIPT FOR THE VARIABLE _____. SINCE IT IS EXCESSIVE, IT IS REPLACED BY THE VALUE _____.

The second blank in the message is filled with the current execution-phase value of the subscript. The third and fourth blanks are filled with the variable name and its maximum allowable subscript. This action serves to repair the erroneous subscript but hardly to correct it.

The overhead for each error-free usage of a subscript is 85 microseconds. With obvious waste of effort, this overhead is incurred six times for the statement

$$\text{LET } A(I, J) = B(I, J) + C(I, J)$$

Future versions of CORC may treat such repeated usage of identical subscripts with more sophistication. However, one must remember that "A," "B," and "C" could have different maximum dimensions in this example. A row subscript legal for "A" might be excessive for "B," etc. Also, in statements such as

$$\text{LET } A(I) = A(I + 1)$$

one must corroborate the legal size of "$(I + 1)$" as well as that of "I."

The per-program overhead of subscript monitoring varies between 0 percent and 90 percent of the execution time, as one might guess. An average overhead of 15 percent has been measured for a representative batch of programs.

5.1.5.5. *Monitoring Repeated Blocks*

(1) Each repeatable block is legally used only as a closed subroutine. Hence, the exit instruction from the block—machine code generated by its END pseudostatement—can be used to trap any illegal prior branch to an interior statement of the block. (One cannot enter a block by advancing sequentially through its BEGIN pseudostatement. However, one can illegally branch to an interior statement of a repeatable block from a statement physically outside the block.) When the block is properly entered by a REPEAT statement, the address of the exit instruction is properly set; after the repetitions have been completed, a trap address is set into this exit instruction before the program advances beyond the REPEAT statement.

Thus, program flow can physically leave and re-enter a repeatable block in any complex pattern, as long as the block has been properly "opened" by a REPEAT statement and has not yet been "closed" by completion of the repetitions. In this respect, CORC allows more complex branching than most compilers.

When the exit instruction traps an illegal prior entry, CORC prints the following message:

IN STATEMENT _____, AN ILLEGAL EXIT FROM BLOCK _____ HAS JUST BEEN DETECTED. IN SOME PREVIOUS GO-TO STATEMENT, THE BLOCK WAS ILLE-GALLY ENTERED. THE PROGRAM CONTINUES AFTER THE END STATEMENT OF THIS BLOCK.

(2) To protect against various illegal usages of the bound variable in REPEAT-FOR statements, CORC precalculates the number of repetitions and conceals this count from the repeatable block; the count is fetched, decremented, and tested only by the REPEAT statement. This discussion is amplified in (d) below.

Consider the statement: REPEAT B FOR $V = (E_1, E_2, E_3)$:

(a) If $E_1 = E_3$, the block is executed once.

(b) Otherwise, if E_2 is zero, CORC prints the following message:

IN STATEMENT_____, IN REPEAT-FOR TRIPLE, SEC-
OND ARGUMENT IS 0. THE REPEAT IS EXECUTED
ONCE.

(c) Otherwise, if $(E_3 - E_1)/E_2$ is negative, CORC prints the following
message:

IN STATEMENT _____, IN REPEAT-FOR TRIPLE,
SECOND ARGUMENT HAS WRONG SIGN. THE REPEAT
IS EXECUTED ONCE.

(d) Otherwise, CORC uses the count

$$\left[\frac{E_3 -- E_1}{E_2} \right]$$

to determine the number of repetitions. This count is reduced by 1 for
each iteration, irrespective of the subsequent values of "V," "E_2," or
"E_3." Novice programmers often manipulate "V" inside repeatable blocks;
CORC prevents many potentially endless loops by ignoring this manipulation.

5.1.5.6. *Monitoring Data-Card Input*

The reading and checking of data cards was introduced in Section 5.1.4.
In brief, a READ statement causes the following steps to occur.

(1) A new card is read in; if it is of type 1, CORC assumes it to be the first
card of the next source deck. Thereupon, the following messages appear:

THE INPUT DATA HAS BEEN EXHAUSTED. IN STATE-
MENT _____, CORC SUPPLIES A DATA CARD FOR THE
VARIABLE _____ WITH VALUE 1.0.

Thus, CORC enters a value of 1 for the READ variable and proceeds with
the program; subsequent READ statements incur only the second message
above.

(2) If the new card is neither type 1 nor type 4 (i.e., the correct type),
CORC prints this message:

IN STATEMENT _____, THE CARD IS ASSUMED TO BE
A DATA CARD.

(3) If the new card is type 4—possibly as the result of (2) above—CORC checks the variable field against the variable name in the READ statement. If they disagree, CORC considers the name in the READ statement to be correct; the following message is printed:

> IN STATEMENT _____, THE VARIABLE _____ WAS READ FROM THE CARD. THE VARIABLE IN THE READ STATEMENT WAS _____.

(4) When the variable names have been reconciled, CORC checks for none, one, or two subscripts on the card, as appropriate to the READ variable. Missing or erroneous subscripts incur the following message:

> IN STATEMENT _____, THE SUBSCRIPT (____,____) WAS READ FROM THE CARD. THE SUBSCRIPT IN THE READ STATEMENT WAS (____,____),

or

> IN STATEMENT _____, THE SUBSCRIPT (____) WAS READ FROM THE CARD. THE SUBSCRIPT IN THE READ STATEMENT WAS (_____).

In every case, CORC uses the value in the READ statement.

5.1.6. CONCLUSIONS

5.1.6.1. *Experience in Practice*

Throughout the 1962–1963 academic year, CORC was in "pilot project" status; in 1963–1964 CORC was established as the fundamental computing tool for undergraduate engineering courses at Cornell. In the spring semester of 1964, over 15,000 CORC programs were run, peaking at 2500 programs in one week.

The performance of CORC programmers far surpassed the preceding years' performance by ALGOL programmers at Cornell in such respects as speed of language acquisition, average number of reruns per program, and average completion time for classroom assignments.

Actual processing time can be evaluated from the following figures, which are rough estimates based on last year's experience with CORC programs:

(a) Average processing time (tape/tape configuration)—500 programs per hour

(b) Average machine-code execution rate—100,000 source-language statements per minute, for a random sample of 20 student programs

(c) Average compilation time for CORC programs—less than 2 seconds

(d) Turnaround time for programs—one day or less, with rare exceptions

The author has automated the operation of the compiler/monitor to the following degree: Only a random machine malfunction can cause the computer to halt. Since programming errors cannot produce object code that erroneously diverts control outside the CORC system, the role of the machine operator is merely to mount input tape reels and remove output tapes: The computer console needs almost no attention.

A few error-detection procedures were altered during 1962–1964, primarily to make diagnostic messages increasingly explicit. A new CORC manual was prepared for instructional use in 1963–1964; this manual omitted any catalog of errors, since the author expected that the compiler/monitor systems could describe the errors—and the corresponding remedial actions—in satisfactory detail.

CORC has imposed a modest load on the two computers at Cornell. The computing center is satisfied that neither FORTRAN nor ALGOL can lighten this load, which is rarely as much as 2 hours of CORC runs daily. (FORTRAN and ALGOL systems have greater capability but require more facility in programming. The class of problems for which CORC has been developed would not warrant the expenditure of time required to program in the advanced languages.) In the author's opinion, this small commitment of resources is well justified by the educational value of the CORC project.

5.1.6.2. *Potential Utility of CORC*

The author feels that many universities and technical colleges can profitably utilize CORC for introductory instruction. The designers of CORC are convinced that a simple language is well suited for initial study; many Cornell students have already easily advanced to FORTRAN or ALGOL after mastering CORC.

With respect to the error-detection and error-correction features, CORC demonstrates the modest effort required to furnish intelligible messages and how little core memory and machine time are consumed. Many CORC error-monitoring procedures deserve consideration in future implementations of compiler languages: unconditional counts of statement labels (or statement numbers), source-program citations in diagnostic messages, and brief dumps following all program terminations. The monitoring of subscripts would not be burdensome if the latter were carried as integers—index registers are used in most current compiled codes. Ninety percent of the CORC subscript-usage execution time is devoted to unfloating numbers, and only 10 percent is devoted to testing these numbers for size.

5.1.6.3. *Potential Improvements in CORC*

Four areas for significant improvements in CORC are as follows:

(1) Identification of integer-mode variables by their context. Index registers can then be used for arrays and loop counting as in FORTRAN.

(2) A problem-grading mechanism. Each instructor can assign a scale of penalties for various errors. CORC will process his batch of student programs and assign the appropriate grades.

(3) A permanent file for tabulating errors. Each time that CORC programs are run, an auxiliary output device—paper tape or punched cards—will record the serial number of each error committed. Periodically, these tapes or cards will be summarized. These data will furnish statistical estimates for the *a priori* occurrence probabilities of the errors.

(4) Remote consoles. These are much discussed in current computer literature, and they hold unusual promise for high-volume university operation. Students would type in their programs from keyboards distributed around a campus covering hundreds of acres. Either these programs would interrupt a large computer programmed for real-time entry, or they would be stacked on tape/disk by a satellite computer. Perhaps results could be printed/typed at these remote stations by the satellite computer.

The author and his colleagues are well aware of shortcomings in the language. However, they intend to resist changes which increase the power of the syntax at the expense of linguistic simplicity. Changes on behalf of additional simplicity or clarity are willingly accepted. Continuing efforts will be made to improve the clarity and explicitness of the diagnostic messages so that classroom instruction can be further integrated with output from the computer.

ACKNOWLEDGMENTS

The author is a former student of Professors Conway and Maxwell; he gratefully acknowledges their assistance to the error-correction project. Other contributors were R. Bowen, J. Evans, C. Nugent, J. Rudan, and R. Sanderson.

REFERENCES

1. Conway, R. W., and Maxwell, W. L., "Corc: The Cornell Computing Language," *Comm. ACM*, vol. 6 (1963), p. 317.

2. Damereau, F. J., "A Technique for Computer Detection and Correction of Spelling Errors," *Comm. ACM*, vol. 7 (1964), p. 171.

3. *Ibid.*

4. *Ibid.*

5. Blair, C. R., "A Program for Correcting Spelling Errors," *Inform. and Ctrl.* (March 1960), pp. 60–67.

6. Ferguson, H. E., and Berner, E., "Debugging Systems at the Source Language Level," *Comm. ACM*, vol. 6 (1963), p. 430.

5.2. An Error-Correcting Parse Algorithm

by Edgar T. Irons

5.2.1. INTRODUCTION

During the past few years, research into so-called "Syntax-Directed Compiler" and "Compiler-Compiler" techniques[1-6] has given hope that constructing computer programs for translating formal languages may not be as formidable a task as it once was. However, the glow of the researchers' glee has obscured to a certain extent some very perplexing problems in constructing practical translators for common programming languages. The automatic parsing algorithms indeed simplify compiler construction but contribute little to the production of "optimized" machine code, for example. An equally perplexing problem for many of these parsing algorithms has been what to do about syntactically incorrect object strings. It is common knowledge that most of the ALGOL or FORTRAN "programs" which a compiler sees are syntactically incorrect. All of the parsing algorithms detect the existence of such errors. Many have considerable difficulty pinpointing the location of the error, printing out diagnostic information, and recovering enough to move on to other correct parts of the object string. It is the author's opinion that those algorithms which do the best

EDITOR'S NOTE: This article reproduced by permission of the author and the publisher: *Comm. ACM*, vol. 6, no. 111 (November 1963), pp. 669–673.

job of error recovery are those which are restricted to simpler forms of formal languages.

The algorithm presented here is the outgrowth of an attempt to alleviate some of these difficulties in error detection and recovery. Its general characteristics are as follows:

(1) It will parse strings describable in essentially Backus Normal Form (BNF).[7,8] No automatic parse of the author's acquaintance will work for substantially more complicated languages.

(2) If an incorrect object string is presented to the algorithm, it will make local insertions, deletions, or substitutions in the object string until a syntactically correct string is produced. Many errors made in such a way that the "correction" is clear from context will be corrected. In any event, no matter how garbled the object string is, it will be manipulated until a correct string has been obtained.

(3) The algorithm is relatively efficient. Pilot models indicate that parsing proceeds at the rate of about 100 executed machine instructions per symbol of the object string.

(4) The algorithm is economical of memory space. In particular its intermediate storage requirements are quite restricted.

The essentially novel characteristic of the algorithm is that in parsing the object string (say, from left to right) when a situation arises where more than one parse is possible for the next few symbols *all* possible parses are carried along until a symbol is reached which "selects" one of the parses. The following example will serve to illustrate this principle. The BNF grammar

$$\langle A \rangle ::= ab \qquad \langle D \rangle ::= ce$$
$$\langle B \rangle ::= \langle A \rangle c \qquad \langle E \rangle ::= b\langle D \rangle$$
$$\langle G \rangle ::= \langle B \rangle d \qquad \langle G \rangle ::= a\langle E \rangle$$

assigns the parse

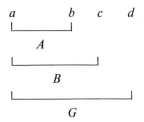

to the string *abcd*, and the parse

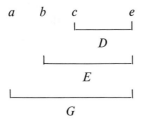

to the string *abce*. This grammar presents a problem to a left-to-right parse because regardless of what string may occur to the left, the parse of *abc* cannot be determined until the next symbol after *c* is encountered.

There are essentially two ways in which this dilemma has been resolved.

(1) The grammar is restricted so that a unique parse for a string *A* is determined by considering only the strings to the left of *A* and one symbol to the right.

(2) The parsing algorithm makes an assumption that one of the possible parses is correct, and if this turns out not to be the case, the algorithm backtracks and tries another parse.

The disadvantage of the first solution is simply that the parsable languages are from a considerably more restricted class than even BNF specified languages.

The disadvantage of the second solution is that in leaving the door open for backtracking, the occurrence of an error requires that a whole host of unexamined alternatives must be examined before it can definitely be established that an error has occurred. Furthermore, when all alternatives *have* been so examined, the matter of deciding which unsatisfied alternative is unsatisfied *because of the error* is somewhat more than hopeless.

In the algorithm presented here, all possible parses are carried along as shown below in the progressing parse of *abce* according to the syntax of the earlier example:

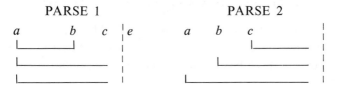

When the symbol *e* is encountered, parse 1 cannot be continued and is dropped, leaving parse 2 as the correct one.

Because the parse proceeds in this way, the location of an error is easily detected, namely, at the point where *no* parses can be continued. Error recovery is then effected by examining the next few symbols in the object string in relation to the syntactic statements concerning the parse "brackets" which have been extended up to the point of error. A more detailed discussion of the error recovery feature will be postponed until a more detailed description of the algorithm has been presented.

5.2.2. THE PARSE ALGORITHM

In order to describe the algorithm we present first the form of the meta language used to specify the parsing and the way in which the statements of the meta language are stored in the machine.

We adopt as meta symbols those used in BNF, namely, $\langle \rangle |$ and $::=$, plus two braces $\{\ \}$. The statements of the meta language take the form of BNF statements with the following restriction: No syntactic variable may occur both as the defined variable (left of the $::=$) and the first defining variable (immediately to the right of the $::=$ or $|$), nor may any set of statements exist such that a variable is defined in terms of itself. For example

$$\langle TERM \rangle ::= \langle TERM \rangle \langle MULT\ OP \rangle \langle PRIMARY \rangle$$

is not allowed, nor are the set of statements

$$\langle A \rangle ::= \langle B \rangle \langle C \rangle$$
$$\langle B \rangle ::= \langle A \rangle \langle D \rangle$$

Having thus stripped BNF of all its recursive power by restriction 1, we add instead an "iterative" power by introducing the meta symbols $\{$ and $\}$ as follows:

Any set of syntactic variables embraced by the braces $\{\ \}$ are specified to occur any number of times in an input string. For example,

$$\langle SUM \rangle ::= \langle TERM \rangle \{\langle MULT\ OP \rangle \langle TERM \rangle\}$$

specifies that a $\langle SUM \rangle$ may consist of a $\langle TERM \rangle$ alone or a $\langle TERM \rangle$ followed by any number of occurrences of the pair $\langle MULT\ OP \rangle \langle TERM \rangle$. A final restriction prohibits a brace from occurring immediately after the $::=$, i.e.,

$$\langle A \rangle ::= \{\langle B \rangle\} \langle C \rangle$$

is not allowed.

Without bogging down in comparisons of this meta language to BNF and others, we assert that as a practical meta language it is essentially as powerful as BNF and furthermore lends itself to somewhat more compact descriptions of languages. To reinforce this point, we present the syntax in our meta language for a part of the arithmetic section of ALGOL 60, which we shall continue to use in later examples.

$$\langle \text{LETTER} \rangle ::= A \mid B \mid C \ldots$$

$$\langle \text{DIGIT} \rangle ::= 0 \mid 1 \mid 1 \mid 2 \ldots$$

1     $\langle \text{IDEN} \rangle ::= \langle \text{LETTER} \rangle \; \{\{\langle \text{LETTER} \rangle\}\{\langle \text{DIGIT} \}\}$
      $\langle \text{ADOP} \rangle ::= + \mid -$
      $\langle \text{MULOP} \rangle ::= * \mid /$

2     $\langle \text{PRIMARY} \rangle ::= \langle \text{IDEN} \rangle \mid (\langle \text{SUM} \rangle)$

3     $\langle \text{FACTOR} \rangle ::= \langle \text{PRIMARY} \rangle \; \{\uparrow \langle \text{PRIMARY} \rangle\}$

4     $\langle \text{TERM} \rangle ::= \langle \text{FACTOR} \rangle \; \{\langle \text{MULOP} \rangle \langle \text{FACTOR} \rangle\}$

5     $\langle \text{SUM} \rangle ::= \langle \text{TERM} \rangle \; \{\langle \text{ADOP} \rangle \langle \text{TERM} \rangle\} \mid$

6     $\langle \text{ADOP} \rangle \langle \text{TERM} \rangle$

The representation in the machine of these statements is designed to facilitate the parsing algorithm. In particular we wish to be able to assign the complete parse (or several of them) to a basic at the first moment it is encountered in the object string. To this end, construct from the syntax statements a "chain" table for each basic symbol as follows

Observing that letter A can be the first symbol of a $\langle \text{LETTER} \rangle$, $\langle \text{IDEN} \rangle$, $\langle \text{PRIMARY} \rangle$, $\langle \text{FACTOR} \rangle$, etc., construct the chain

$$A \leftarrow \langle \text{LETTER} \rangle^0 \leftarrow \langle \text{IDEN} \rangle^{1.1} \leftarrow \langle \text{PRIMARY} \rangle^0$$
$$\uparrow$$
$$\langle \text{SUM} \rangle^{5.1} \rightarrow \langle \text{TERM} \rangle^{4.1} \rightarrow \langle \text{FACTOR} \rangle^{3.1}$$

for each letter. Five other symbols have chains:

$+ \leftarrow \langle \text{ADOP} \rangle^0 \leftarrow \langle \text{SUM} \rangle^{6.1}$

$- \leftarrow \langle \text{ADOP} \rangle^0 \leftarrow \langle \text{SUM} \rangle^{6.1}$

$* \; \leftarrow \langle \text{MULOP} \rangle^0$

$/ \; \leftarrow \langle \text{MULOP} \rangle^0$

$(\; \leftarrow \langle \text{PRIMARY} \rangle^{2.1} \leftarrow \langle \text{FACTOR} \rangle^{3.1} \leftarrow \langle \text{TERM} \rangle^{4.1} \leftarrow \langle \text{SUM} \rangle^{5.1}$

(Although for this example it happens that each link of the chain has only one arrow pointing to it, there may, in general, be several arrows pointing to an element. There may be only one pointing away, however.) A chain for a symbol may be interpreted as indicating that the symbol may begin any syntactic category on its chain. Suppose, for example, we wish to know the parse of a ⟨TERM⟩ beginning with A. It is determined by looking for ⟨TERM⟩ on A's chains, and following the arrows to A to construct

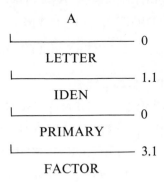

The digits connected to the brackets (copied from the digits in the chain) are called "syntax pointers" and indicate elements of the syntax tree which effectively determine how the brackets may be extended to the right.

The syntax "tree" for our example would be as follows:

Index	Names	Alternates	Successors
0	null		
1.1	⟨LETTER⟩	1.2	1.1
1.2	⟨DIGIT⟩	0	1.1
2.1	⟨SUM⟩		2.2
2.2	)		0
3.1	↑	0	3.2
3.2	⟨PRIMARY⟩		3.1
4.1	⟨MULOP⟩	0	4.2
4.2	⟨FACTOR⟩		4.1
5.1	⟨ADOP⟩	0	5.2
5.2	⟨TERM⟩		5.1
6.1	⟨TERM⟩		0

To interpret the tree, we adopt the following notation

S_i is the *i*th entry (line) of the tree table.

The *alternates* of S_i are $S_i, S_{j_1}, S_{j_2}, \ldots, S_{j_n}$ where S_{j_1} is the alternate for S_i and $S_{j_{p+1}}$ is the alternate for S_{j_p}.

A bracket whose syntax pointer is *i* may be extended right one symbol if the next symbol has any of the alternates of S_i on its chain, *and* if all brackets "under" it can be terminated.

A bracket may be terminated if 0 (or null) is one of alternates of its pointer. Observe that for the parse

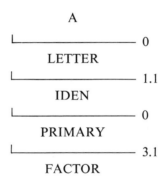

⟨IDEN⟩ may be extended over a ⟨LETTER⟩ or ⟨DIGIT⟩ or since ⟨IDEN⟩ and ⟨PRIMARY⟩ may be terminated, ⟨FACTOR⟩ may be extended over ↑.

Observe that if any bracket is extended;

(1) all brackets "covering" it must be extended as well.

(2) all brackets "under" it must be terminated.

(3) the pointer for the extended bracket becomes the successor of S_i (where *i* was its old pointer).

(4) if it is possible to extend two or more brackets, we must create a new parse for each extension.

Lest the workings of the algorithm be completely obscured by the above description, it is presented more precisely in the following (almost ALGOL) program.

We define the following arrays (with all lower subscript bounds = 1) and variables:

1. The chain for a symbol j:

$CN[i, j]$ is the name of the ith element of the chain for the symbol whose numeric value (under some convenient mapping) is j.

$CS[i, j]$ is the *syntax link* (given as superscript digits in the earlier presentation) for the ith element of the chain for j.

$CP[i, j]$ is the index of the next element in the chain (and $= 0$) if the element is the last, namely, the symbol j.

$NC[j]$ is the number of elements on the chain for j.

2. The syntax tree:

$SN[k]$ is the name of the kth element of the tree table.

$SS[k]$ is the successor for this element.

$SA[k]$ is the immediate alternate (if there is no alternate $SA[k] = 0$) $SN[1]$ is the "null" element).

3. The parses:

N is the number of parses currently existing.

$NP[n]$ is the number of brackets in the nth parse.

$PN[i, j]$ is the *name* of the jth bracket of the ith parse.

$PS[i, j]$ is the *syntax pointer* for the bracket.

$PI[i, j]$ is the index of the first (left most) symbol under the bracket.

Observing that once a bracket has been terminated we no longer need to keep it in the parse table, we may assign the following structure to PN (and corresponding parse vectors): For ith parse, $PN[i, 1]$ is the outermost bracket of the parse. $P[i, 2]$ is the next bracket under it, and so on. $P[i, NP[i]]$ is the "innermost" bracket, namely, the one covering the last parsed symbol.

The algorithm for parsing the "next" (qth) symbol in the object string (call it $O[q]$) is

```
t := N + 1;
for i := 1 step 1 until N do
begin
    for j := NP[i] step − 1 until 1 do
```

```
begin
  for k := 1 step 1 until NC[O[q]] do
  begin
    SW := true;
    l := PS[i, j];
    L2: if CN[k, O[q]] = SN[l] then
    begin
      COPY PARSE (i, j);
      L1: if CP[k] ≠ 0 then
      begin
        j = j + 1;
        PN[t, j] := CN[k];
        PS[t, j] := CS[k];
        PI[t, j] := q;
        k := CP[k];
        go to L1 end;
      t := t + 1 end;
    if l = 1 then SW := false;
    if SA[l] ≠ 0 then begin l := SA[l]; go to L2 end;
  end;
  if SW then go to L3 end;
L3: end
```

The procedure COPYPARSE is defined as follows:

```
procedure COPYPARSE (i, j); value i, j;
begin
  for u := 1 step 1 until j do
  begin
    PN[t, u] := PN[i, u];
    PS[t, u] := PS[i, u];
    PI[t, u] := PI[i, u]; end;
  PS[t, u] := SS[PS[t, u]];
  for u = j + 1 step 1 until NP[i] do
  Output appropriate information about PN[i, u] etc. Such outputs
    specify the final parse.
end
```

After executing these program steps, the parses of the object string lie in $NP[N+1]$, $NP[N+2] \cdots$. They are then moved to $NP[1]$, $NP[2] \cdots$ and the process is repeated for the next symbol in the object string.

As an example of the parsing operation we give a blow-by-blow description of the parse of

$$AB * (C + D)$$

according to the syntax of our example. The final parse is

A	B	*	(	C	+	D	)

LETTER LETTER MULOP (LETTER ADOP LETTER)

IDEN   IDEN   IDEN

PRIMARY   PRIMARY   PRIMARY

FACTOR   FACTOR   FACTOR

                         TERM   TERM

                              SUM

                            PRIMARY

                            FACTOR

                              TERM

                              SUM

The chain for A is

i	$CN[i, \text{‘A’}]$	$CS[i, \text{‘A’}]$	$CP[i, \text{‘A’}]$
1	A	0	0
2	letter	1	1
3	iden	2	2
4	primary	4	3
5	factor	6	4
6	term	8	5
7	sum	10	6

The complete syntax tree is

i	$SN[i]$	$SA[i]$	$SS[i]$
1	null	0	0
2	letter	3	2
3	digit	1	2
4	sum	0	5
5	)	0	1
6	↑	1	7
7	primary	0	6
8	mulop	1	9
9	factor	0	8
10	adop	1	11
11	term	0	10
12	term	0	1

The parse (there is only one at all times for this example) is (we abbreviate the syntactic names by their first letter)

$$PN[i], \; PS[i]$$

O/i	10	9	8	7	6	5	4	3	2	1
A					L, 1	I, 2	P, 1	F, 6	T, 8	S, 10
B					L, 1	I, 2	P, 1	F, 6	T, 8	S, 10
*								M, 1	T, 9	S, 10
(							P, 4	F, 6	T, 8	S, 10
C	L, 1	I, 2	P, 1	F, 6	T, 8	S, 10	P, 5	F, 6	T, 8	S, 10
+					A, 12	S, 11	P, 5	F, 6	T, 8	S, 10
D	L, 1	I, 2	P, 1	F, 6	T, 8	S, 10	P, 5	F, 6	T, 8	S, 10
)							P, 1	F, 6	T, 8	S, 10

The output of the program is simply a list of brackets equivalent to the pictorial parse diagram given earlier.

5.2.3. ERROR-CORRECTION ALGORITHM

An error in the object string will cause all parses to disappear at or shortly after the error. In this event the following actions are taken:

1. A list is compiled of all the syntactic elements or basic symbols which

might be called for after the error point. The list consists of all elements of *SN* named by the syntax pointers of all brackets in all parses (just before the error point) and all successors and alternates of these SN elements.

2. The symbols at and after the error point are examined one by one and discarded until one is found which (a) occurs on the list of 1, or (b) has an element on its chain which occurs on the list of 1.

3. The bracket from (1) which is selected in (2) is examined in relation to the parses to determine a string of basic symbols which, when inserted at the error point, will allow the parse to continue at least one symbol past the inserted string.

4. The string of (3) is inserted into the object string at the error point and the parse is continued. The parse is forced to cover the complete input string by initializing the parse with a "program" bracket which requires a special symbol (to be inserted at the end of input string) for its termination.

The pilot model used to verify these algorithms used the syntax productions of Fig. 5.2.1 to produce the parse and error diagnostic shown in Fig. 5.2.2.

An interesting side effect of the parse algorithm is that ambiguous strings for a set of productions are easily detected, since they will cause the occurrence of two or more *identical* parses in PN at the end of the ambiguous string. Such occurrences cause all but one of the parses to be dropped and the printing of appropriate diagnostic information.

5.2.4. APPLICATIONS

The most important application of the error-correcting parse algorithm is to compiler construction. The error correction feature will allow compilers using this technique to compile and run an error-ridden program to obtain a maximum of diagnostic information in one try on a machine. The success of the CORC compiler testifies to the merits of this mode of operation. We reiterate the earlier statement that constructing a good compiler is still far from being a trivial task; output code optimization and "self-defining" or declarative languages are just two areas which still present difficulties in compiler construction which are not solved by (indeed are partly outside the scope of) automatic parsing techniques. The error-correcting parse will, however, remove some of the burdens of programming a good compiler.

Syntax rules

1. Metavariables are enclosed in parentheses.

2. No vertical bar allowed.

3. Use + and — for left and right braces respectively.

4. The following rules provide for inserting basic symbols ( ) + — '

use 'L for (

use 'R for)

use 'P for '

use 'A for +

use 'S for —

5. Assignments are to the right rather than to the left.

I.E. (A)(B) = (C) means an A concatenated with a B forms a C.

Productions for figure 5.2.2

(SL) = (PG)	S = (LT)
A = (LT)	T = (LT)
B = (LT)	U = (LT)
C = (LT)	V = (LT)
D = (LT)	W = (LT)
E = (LT)	X = (LT)
F = (LT)	Y = (LT)
G = (LT)	Z = (LT)
H = (LT)	'A = (AO)
I = (LT)	'S = (AO)
J = (LT)	* = (MO)
K = (LT)	/ = (MO)
L = (LT)	(LT) + (LT) — = (PR)
M = (LT)	'L(SU) 'R = (PR)
N = (LT)	(PR) + (MO)(PR) — = (TM)
O = (LT)	(TM) + (AO)(TM) — = (SU)
P = (LT)	(LT) + (LT) — = (SU) = (ST)
Q = (LT)	(ST) + ; (ST) — = (SL)
R = (LT)	

FIGURE 5.2.1

A second area of application which may have some importance in the future is in the area of pattern recognition. One of the biggest problems in pattern recognition devices is their lack of ability to capitalize as the human reader does on the wealth of contextual information contained in many patterns of interest. A combination of the error-correcting parse and a pattern-recognizing device which, for example, might offer several in-

Input string

; (RE = − V21) (∗ XM; +X = A + F; X − + HT . (R) ∗ ST; EN

Diagnostics

In col 01 of card 001 replaces ; (
In col 06 of card 001 replaces −
In col 08 of card 001 + replaces 21)
In col 12 of card 001 I) replaces
In col 16 of card 001 replaces +
In col 24 of card 001 = replaces − +
In col 28 of card 001 + replaces
In col 01 of card 002 = I replaces

Parse

R	0, 0	LSSP	;	0, 0	SP
E	0, 0	LSSP	X	0, 0	LSSP
=	0, 0	SSP	=	0, 0	SSP
V	0, 0	LPTSSSP	H	0, 0	LPTSSSP
+	0, 0	ASSSP	T	0, 0	LPTSSSP
(	0, 0	PTSSSP	+	0, 0	ASSSP
I	0, 0	LPTSPTSSSP	(	0, 0	PTSSSP
)	0, 0	PTSSSP	R	0, 0	LPTSPTSSSP
∗	0, 0	MTSSSP	)	0, 0	PTSSSP
X	0, 0	LPTSSSP	∗	0, 0	MTSSSP
M	0, 0	LPTSSSP	S	0, 0	LPTSSSP
;	0, 0	SP	T	0, 0	LPTSSSP
X	0, 0	LSSP	;	0, 0	SP
=	0, 0	SSP	E	0, 0	LSSP
A	0, 0	LPTSSSP	N	0, 0	LSSP
+	0, 0	ASSSP	=	0, 0	SSP
F	0, 0	LPTSSSP	I	0, 0	LPTSSSP

FIGURE 5.2.2

terpretations of a pattern and weight for each, might produce an effective device for reading and interpreting names on forms, information in journals, and the like. At the very least, we might hope to allow a programmer to present his handwritten XGOL program to the computer, thus avoiding the very serious restrictions of cardpunch and typewriter character sets.

REFERENCES

1. Irons, E. T., "A Syntax Directed Compiler for ALGOL 60," *Comm. ACM*, vol. 4 (1961), pp. 51–55.

2. ——— "Towards More Versatile Mechanical Translators." (To be published.)

3. ——— "The Structure and Use of the Syntax Directed Compiler," *Ann. Rev. in Autom. Programming*, vol. 3, pp. 207–228.

4. Paul, M., "A General Processor for Certain Formal Languages," in *Symbol Languages in Data Processing*. Gordon and Breach, London, 1962, pp. 65–74.

5. Eickel, J., Paul, M., Bauer, F. L., and Samuelson, K., "A Syntax Controlled Generator of Formal Language Processor." Institut für Angew. Mat. der Univ. Mainz., September 1962.

6. Brooker, R. A., MacCallum, I., Morris, D., and Rohl, J. S., "The Compiler Compiler," *Ann. Rev. Autom. Programming*, vol. 3, pp. 229–271.

7. Backus, J. W., "The Syntax and Semantics of the Proposed International Algebraic Language of the Zurich ACM-GAMM Conf. Proc. Internat. Conf. Inform. Process., UNESCO (June 1959), pp. 125–132.

8. Naur, Peter (ed.), "Report on the Algorithmic Language ALGOL 60," *Comm. ACM*, vol. 3 (1960), pp. 299–314.

5.3. DITRAN—A Compiler Emphasizing Diagnostics

by P. G. Moulton and M. E. Muller

5.3.1. SUMMARY

DITRAN (DIagnostic forTRAN) is an implementation of ASA Basic FORTRAN with rather extensive error-checking capabilities both at compilation time and during execution of a program. The need for improved diagnostic capabilities and some objectives to be met by any compiler are discussed. Attention is given to the design and implementation of DITRAN and the particular techniques employed to provide the diagnostic features. The handling of error messages by a general macro approach is described. Special features which provide teaching aids for use by instructors are noted.

5.3.2. INTRODUCTION

Much of the attention given to compiling techniques for algebraic languages has been directed toward producing more efficient object code, automating the process of writing a compiler, and incorporating new features into the programming source languages. An area which has not

EDITOR'S NOTE: This article reproduced by permission of the authors and the publisher: *Comm. ACM*, vol. 10, no. 1 (January 1967), pp. 45–52.

320

received comparable emphasis is that of developing techniques to improve the diagnostic capabilities of compilers. This lack of emphasis may be in part due to the fact that the usual specifications of a programming language exclude or give little attention to the need of diagnostic capabilities, for example, the specification of ASA Basic FORTRAN or ASA FORTRAN.[1] In this paper CSC is described—the results of a compiler project undertaken at the University of Wisconsin Computing Center (UWCC).

DITRAN (DIagnostic FORtran) is a FORTRAN compiler and operating system which provides extended diagnostic capabilities, both at compilation and execution time. One of the purposes in presenting this paper is to outline some of the design features of DITRAN which, when combined with some known algebraic compiling techniques, make it possible to achieve a high degree of success in the detection and analysis of compile time and execution time errors.

DITRAN achieves many of its diagnostic capabilities by extending the notion of a storage unit by associating with each unit a vector of values which describes the status of a variable or array element during the execution of a program. Another purpose of this paper is to discuss, in general, some of the standards or objectives that ought to be set for the diagnostic capabilities of any compiler.

DITRAN was written for the CDC 1604 and was put into operation at the UWCC in the summer of 1965. DITRAN has now received considerable use and the success with DITRAN supports the belief that more attention to this area of compiler development can provide worthwhile dividends. Although DITRAN operates as a compile-and-go batch-processing system, many of the techniques employed to maintain information required for diagnostic capabilities ought to be of particular use in an interactive environment involving man and computer via an input-output device.

5.3.3. BACKGROUND AND OBJECTIVES

Manufacturer-supplied FORTRAN compilers normally provide rather efficient object code, provide flexible interaction with the operating systems, and have many sophisticated programming features. However, they are inadequate for the needs presented in the area of finding and correcting errors as quickly as possible. In many instances, the description of an error condition lacks resolution and offers the user little assistance in removing the error other than indicating the statement in which the error occurs. A more serious inadequacy is that many error descriptions are given in terms not understandable to a FORTRAN programmer. For example: (1) Several types of compilation time errors are passed on to the assembly phase and emerge as assembly errors which are quite often difficult for the user to associate with his source program, or (2) execution time errors are presented in terms of absolute or relative core locations and machine instructions, all of which are of little or no value to the FORTRAN programmer. Perhaps the most serious inadequacy of the compilers is the inability to detect some error conditions. These conditions are prohibited by FORTRAN manuals, but the compilers produce no messages for these errors. At execution time, these errors produce undefined results usually dependent upon the residual contents of storage locations of which the programmer is unaware and over which he has no control; for example: subscripting beyond the limits of an array, accessing an entity which has not been assigned a value, or performing real arithmetic on type integer data assigned to a type real entity through an I/O operation or through equivalence associations.

In a university, a large portion of the users of a computing facility are students learning programming and graduate students or research investigators who are not full-time programmers but are faced with the need of using the computer as an educational or research tool. For this group, in particular, the concern of finding and correcting errors in their programs as quickly as possible outweighs the need for efficient object code and sophisticated programming features. Programs submitted by this group generally involve a rather small amount of computer run time and have rather short useful lives. The ratio of machine time used for program check-out to that used for production is quite high. The interests of this group of users presented a need for a compiler which would provide a maximum of diagnostic information to the programmer in order to shorten the check-out time.

DITRAN was developed to provide a compiler with extensive diagnostic capabilities. It appeared that developing this compiler would increase the service of the computing facility in several areas. By providing more complete diagnostic information on all errors encountered, the compiler would aid in reducing the number of runs required to check out a program and thus would reduce the time to complete a project. It would also reduce the level of experience required to begin using the computer, and thus increase the availability of the facility to a larger number of users. Finally, by helping students and programmers correct errors without resource to an instructor or consultant, DITRAN would increase the utility of the facility for educational functions.

5.3.4. DIAGNOSTICS

As noted in Section 5.3.2, the ASA specifications for FORTRAN or Basic FORTRAN include no requirements of minimum diagnostic capabilities. The word "diagnostic" is used here as in the dictionary sense of meaning the *detection and analysis* of errors or defects. (By detection is meant the discovery of the existence of an error condition; by analysis, the determination of the location and context of an error and a description of the type of error which has been detected.) Diagnostic capabilities do not include the automatic treatment or correction of the errors which have been detected and analyzed. Some work has been done on error-correcting compiling techniques which will alter a defective expression into one which can be compiled and executed.[2] Perhaps the most notable in terms of our objectives is the CORC compiler.[3,4] However, it did not seem clear that the techniques of CORC could be implemented with comparable success for a language as complex and powerful as FORTRAN.

It has been brought to our attention that the existence of several ALGOL compilers provides excellent diagnostic features.[13,15] The Burroughs B5500 system provides many of the checks through the use of hardware features.[14] The problems encountered in error checking differ somewhat between ALGOL and FORTRAN; an example is the checking and maintenance of the definitional status of entities needed in FORTRAN (see the example in Section 5.3.8). Two FORTRAN systems incorporating extensive diagnostic features are QUIKTRAN[10,11] and FORGO.[12] QUICKTRAN is an interpretive system developed with different operational objectives than those set for DITRAN. FORGO is a diagnostic compiler for a somewhat restricted FORTRAN on a small scale computer (IBM 1620).

When considering all of the error conditions which may occur within a program, one class for which the compiler can assume very limited responsibility is that of logical errors. A logical error occurs when a statement or sequence of statements is well formed, can be compiled and executed, but does not perform according to the intention of the programmer. Obviously, these errors are much less susceptible to detection by a compiler. At best, the compiler can be provided with a capability to search for a set of suspicious conditions which, being encountered, will generate warnings. Examples are a variable being defined, but never referenced, and a statement to which control of execution can never pass. For the programmer himself to measure the performance of the program against his intentions, routines to trace control of the program and assignment of values to entities during execution can be provided.

5.3.5. DITRAN DIAGNOSTIC OBJECTIVES

The development of DITRAN has met the following diagnostic objectives:

(1) All errors other than logical errors are to be detected and described to the programmer. This means that any condition prohibited by the specifications of the language or any condition prohibited by the machine implementation must be detected and not allowed to produce some undefined result. An example of such a case is the handling of the definitional status of variables at execution time. The ASA specifications are quite explicit about the conditions under which an entity becomes defined or undefined during the execution of a program. However, except for DITRAN, we have not seen any system which would check for all possible violations of these rules; for example, in most systems, a reference to an undefined entity would produce an undefined result.

(2) All compilation and execution diagnostic messages and descriptions of errors are to be in terms of the source language. This means that all references to storage locations are given in terms of the symbolic names of the source program and that all references to program locations are given in terms of statement labels or, if a statement is not labeled, its position with respect to the last labeled statement. A corollary to this objective is that the compiler isolates the programmer from any errors detected by the operating system so that they may be described by DITRAN in terms of the source language. In order to do this, DITRAN must either detect the error condition before the operating system does, or intercept the message output by the operating system and provide an understandable interpretation to the programmer.

(3) The formation of error messages and the analysis of errors are to be made in such a way that they will provide the user with as much information as possible, giving him direct cues aiding the correction of errors. This requires that more than the mere indication of the presence of an error is needed; ideally a suggested correction might be presented.

(4) As many errors as possible are to be detected during compilation. Since most compilation errors inhibit execution, to delay detection of an error until execution time can waste an additional run if that error could have been detected during compilation. An example of such a case is to defer checking FORMAT statements until execution time.

(5) Provision is to be made for the use of diagnostic routines for tracing control of execution of a program and auditing the assignment of values to variables. Although these routines themselves have not yet been implemented,

the linkages have been provided by the compiler to be sufficient to allow these routines to describe the conditions they must handle in terms of the source language program.

5.3.6. THE FORTRAN LANGUAGE LEVEL OF DITRAN

With the exception of a few additions, the FORTRAN language implemented is that specified for ASA Basic FORTRAN.[1] This choice was made for several reasons. First, the language seemed adequate for the needs of the students and inexperienced programmers. Furthermore, many of the features not available in Basic FORTRAN are features which have been found to be sources of error for the inexperienced user much more often than they have been employed as useful programming tools. Examples are mixed mode arithmetic, alteration of the parameters of a DO within its range, and unrestricted entry into the range of a DO. Restriction of these features has eliminated many sources of error with minor cost in terms of programming power. Secondly, the language is compatible with the other FORTRAN compilers in use at the UWCC. This would allow a program once written and checked out under DITRAN to be run on a production basis under the standard compilers. Also, a programmer familiar with DITRAN could advance to the other compilers with little difficulty. Third, the selection of Basic FORTRAN made it possible to meet the time limits set on design and implementation of DITRAN.

The additions made to Basic FORTRAN permit (1) arrays of three dimensions, (2) six character identifiers, (3) alphanumeric information via A-field descriptors and Hollerith literals, and (4) free-format I/O operations. The free-format I/O permits instructors to assign problems with I/O operations and yet defer the presentation of FORMAT statements until the students have gained some experience.

5.3.7. OPERATIONAL AND ENVIRONMENTAL REQUIREMENTS

In order for the compiler to be used efficiently and to be available to the users within the normal computing center operating procedures, DITRAN operates under the standard operating system in use. However, in order to provide the required execution time error checking, DITRAN itself must provide many of the functions of a resident operating system.

The error checking performed during execution was achieved at the expense of program execution time and available storage. For example, the error checking at execution time associated with the normal operation of assigning an arithmetic value to an entity requires many associated checks and the maintenance of additional control information. In addition to storing the value into a storage unit, the following checks must be made. First the entity is checked for any restrictions such as being the active parameter of a DO. If any other entities are associated with the first entity via COMMON or EQUIVALENCE, they are also checked for restrictions. Then, if no restrictions are encountered, a bit is set to indicate that the entity is defined. If an entity associated with the first entity is of the same type, its definitional status is set to "defined"; if an associated entity is of a different type, it is set "undefined" so that any reference to it will produce an error message. Obviously, such checking takes time and also storage for the control information. Although the decision had been made to accept any necessary increase in execution time in order to obtain the necessary diagnostic capabilities, it also seemed reasonable to attempt to offset this by an increase in compilation speed at the cost of additional execution time and less available storage if necessary.

The additional execution time is not expected to be serious. First, since most programs can initially be expected to contain errors detected during compilation and those with no compilation errors can be expected to have small execution time requirements, there seems little point in spending time to produce the most efficient object code. Secondly, any program to be used on a production basis where execution time is important can be written and checked out under DITRAN and then compiled and used under the other compilers. With regard to storage usage, it seemed reasonable to assume that the programs for which DITRAN was designed would have modest storage requirements; storage was not considered a problem. The following initial limits on the capacity (which can be modified as the need arises) might give some indication of the size of program which may be handled:

500 statements/program unit

512 identifiers/program unit

250 constants/program

 25 formal parameters/subprogram

 20 subprograms/program

 24 DO statements in a single DO nest

 10 function references in a single nest.

The present core requirements of DITRAN, including all of its library routines (see below) and messages (see Section 5.3.9) are 13,700 words of storage. Thus a program of modest size using DITRAN can include an array of about 8,000 elements.

DITRAN has reached its goals by compiling directly to core and remaining in memory during execution of a program or batch of programs. Several recent efforts at developing fast batch-processing FORTRAN compilers corroborate this approach.[5,6,16] Remaining in core without hardware memory protection presented the additional requirement that the system protect itself from being damaged by the user. However, such damage could only occur as the result of an error in the program; and such an error should be detected by DITRAN whether or not it endangered the compiler. In fact, hardware memory protection alone would not have been adequate to the needs for diagnostic capabilities. At best, an interrupt would be given, but no explanation of the error, such as subscripting beyond the limits of an array. While memory protection could detect some instances of such errors, the subscript limits of three-dimensional arrays can be exceeded in the second or third subscripts while remaining within the limits of the linearly stored array. However, with additional sophistication of memory addressing, it is possible to detect such errors with hardware, as is demonstrated by the Burroughs B5500, which does, in fact, perform multidimensional subscript checking at the hardware level.[14]

In order to realize the complete diagnostic and operational objectives of DITRAN, general access to the system library tape has been eliminated; the standard set of FORTRAN functions is retained in core with the compiler. This means that general routines such as a matrix inversion subroutine are not automatically available to DITRAN users because such routines do not perform the necessary error checking and are thus basically incompatible with DITRAN. However, routines other than the standard set of library functions can be introduced either as FORTRAN subprograms for a particular program or, as noted in Section 5.3.11, as specifically designated FORTRAN subprograms inserted at the beginning of a batch run and made available as library routines in core to subsequent programs in the batch. While this approach may be adequate for a teaching situation, in general it represents a compromise between making the general library available to the more advanced programmer and the economic requirements of the time allotted to the development of DITRAN. An approach such as redeveloping all of the library routines to perform the necessary error checking was not taken in the hope that future developments could lead to a more economical solution.

5.3.8. DESIGN AND IMPLEMENTATION—USE OF STORAGE UNIT VECTORS

The basic compilation techniques used by DITRAN are standard techniques well described in the literature, implemented to allow the diagnostic capabilities. The compilation of arithmetic expressions is by the standard precedence technique.[7,8] One other algorithm taken directly from the literature is that for processing EQUIVALENCE statements.[9] All compilation is done directly to core with no intermediate language.

One feature of DITRAN which is quite different from standard compilers is the structure of storage units for each variable and each array element. To detect and handle execution time errors and to describe them in terms of the source program, a storage unit is treated as a vector with the following additional components.

(1) *Definitional Status Control.* This indicator allows the determination of whether an entity is defined or undefined. Accessing an undefined entity produces an error message.

(2) *Type Control.* This indicator allows the determination of whether an entity is type integer or type real. This control allows DITRAN to check for type conflicts in I/O operations. It further allows setting an entity undefined when an entity of different type associated by means of EQUIVALENCE or COMMON becomes defined.

(3) *Restriction Control.* This indicator allows determining if an entity is the index or parameter of a DO or a constant or arithmetic expression used in a calling sequence. This indicator is checked before an entity is defined. An attempt to define a DO index or parameter or a constant expression produces an error message.

(4) *Array/Variable Control.* This indicator allows determination of whether the storage unit is associated with a variable or an array element. For a variable this component indicates that the preceding word in storage is the identifier to be used in any execution time diagnostic concerning use of that variable. If the storage unit is an array element, this component indicates that a search backwards for a negative zero separator between array control blocks (see below) is necessary to retrieve the array identifier and compute the subscript of the array element concerned.

(5) *Association Control.* This component links to the next entity in the equivalence class if the entity is associated with any other entity by means of EQUIVALENCE or COMMON statements. For a group of entities sharing a common storage unit, these links form a closed loop. This allows

protection of restricted entities across equivalence associations and allows proper maintenance of definitional status across equivalences.

An example of the maintenance of the definitional status across equivalences is given by the sequence

$$\text{EQUIVALENCE } (A, I)$$
$$A = 0.$$
$$B = A$$
$$I = 1$$
$$J = I$$
$$5 \quad C = A$$

in which A is type real and I is type integer. This sequence would execute correctly up to statement 5, at which point A would be undefined for the following reason: Whenever two entities of different type are associated by means of COMMON or EQUIVALENCE, the definition of one of the entities causes the status of the other entity to become undefined. Thus, in the sequence above, the definition of the type integer entity I would cause the status of the associated entity A, of different type, to become undefined, and as such, A cannot be referenced to define C as specified in statement 5. Similar checking is performed across associations effected by COMMON statements. For example, the sequence

$$\text{COMMON A}$$
$$A = 10.$$
$$\text{CALL FX}$$
$$\vdots$$
$$\text{SUBROUTINE FX}$$
$$\text{COMMON I}$$
$$1 \quad \text{DO } 10 \text{ J} = I, 25$$

would produce an error at statement 1 of subroutine FX at which point variable I would be undefined as a result of the associated entity A, of different type, having been defined in the calling program unit.

(6) DO *Nest Control.* This component is a counter used to determine when an entity is no longer the active parameter of a DO in the case of

nested DO's. A counter is needed, since variables may be shared parameters to many DO statements in a single nest.

As control passes into the nest, this component is incremented by one for each DO entered; as control passes out of the nest, this component is decremented.

The restriction placed upon the variable as a parameter of an active DO cannot be removed until the outermost DO of which it is a parameter has been satisfied or left by a branch of control. For example, in the following sequence of a nest of two DO's, the restriction on M as a parameter of the DO at statement 2 can be removed upon completion of the range from statement 2 to statement 5:

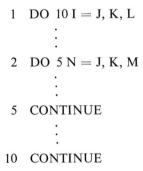

However, at this point the restrictions on variables J and K must be retained, since they are parameters of the outer DO at statement 1.

Any branch of control by means of an IF or a GOTO statement from inside the range of a DO to a statement outside of the range is routed through a routine which releases the restriction on the index of the DO while leaving its status "defined," decrements the DO nest counter of any variable parameter of the DO, and releases the restriction on any parameter for which the counter becomes zero. Normal completion of a DO produces the same effect except that the status of the index is set to "undefined."

(7) *Address Control of Signed Numeric Value.* This component contains an indirect address which permits all references to the numeric value of the entity to be made indirectly through this component. Therefore entities equivalenced by COMMON or EQUIVALENCE may have separate control vectors and yet share the same storage area.

(8) *Identifier Control.* For variables, the symbolic name is stored as a component of the value vector. This allows any reference to the variable to be made in terms of the source-language identifiers.

For each array, a control block is constructed which contains the symbolic name of the array together with the declared limits on the subscripts. All subscript expressions within an array reference are compared against these limits.

Figures 5.3.1, 5.3.2, and 5.3.3 illustrate the structure of storage units

Control Part Components:

C_1: Definitional Status $\qquad$ C_5: Association

C_2: Type $\qquad$ C_6: DO Nest

C_3: Restrictions $\qquad$ C_7: Address

C_4: Array/Variable $\qquad$ C_8: Identifier

FIGURE 5.3.1 Storage control for variable.

Array Control Block Items

A. Identifier $\qquad$ D. First Dimension Limit

B. Number of Dimensions $\qquad$ E. Second Dimension Limit

C. Total Number of Elements* $\qquad$ F. Third Dimension Limit

* This item equals the product of items D, E and F; it is a useful redundancy.

Element Control Part Components: C_1–C_7 same as in Fig. 5.3.1.

FIGURE 5.3.2 Storage control for array.

which consist of a control part and an information part. In each figure, dotted lines represent the linkage of the control part to the information part via the address component to emphasize that the two parts are not necessarily contiguous in core. From Fig. 5.3.1, one can see that a storage unit for a variable consists of a two-word control part and a one-word information part. As illustrated in Fig. 5.3.2, the storage structure of an array consists of an array control block and storage units for the array elements. The storage units for each array element consist of a one-word control part and a one-word information part. Illustrated in Fig. 5.3.3 are the association linkages for the case in which several entities are equivalenced and share a common information part of their storage units.

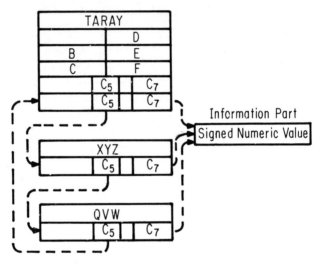

FIGURE 5.3.3   Association linkages for equivalence class specified by EQUIVALENCE (XYZ, TARAY(2), QVW).

In order to be able to specify to a programmer the statement within his program at which any specific execution-time error occurs, several tables are constructed during compilation for use by the execution-time error routines. These tables contain, for each program unit, entries specifying the symbolic name of that program unit, the core locations occupied, the location of the entry point, and the location of a secondary table for that program unit. This secondary table contains the core locations of each statement within that unit and the label of the statement. Unlabeled statements are referenced by their position with respect to the last labeled statement. The first statement of a program unit is referenced as "STATEMENT

0." A compiler-generated line number, as in many compiler systems, was not used in order to spare students concern with elements not in the source language.

When the absolute core location of the instructions producing an execution-time error is known, the program unit containing those instructions can be determined from these tables and the source location within the program unit from the corresponding secondary table. If the program unit is a subprogram, the absolute location of the call to the subprogram can be found in the entry point, and thus the source location of the call determined. This allows execution-time error messages to be followed by a source-language trace of control back to the main program.

Following is an example in which the main program ALPHA has called subprogram BETA from the third statement beyond the statement labeled "10" and BETA has called GAMMA from the fifth statement beyond the statement labeled "20." The indicated error has occurred in GAMMA at the statement labeled "100." The error message is generated as

VARIABLE XYZ REFERENCED BUT NOT DEFINED
IN PROGRAM UNIT GAMMA AT STATEMENT 100

CALL BY BETA AT STATEMENT 20 + 5

CALL BY ALPHA AT STATEMENT 10 + 3

5.3.9. MACRO APPROACH TO MESSAGE HANDLING

At present DITRAN has a repertoire of 300 messages. To facilitate changing the diagnostic messages, the messages have been implemented as macros called by DITRAN as needed rather than storing each message in its output format. The PUFFT system[5] appears to use a similar approach encoded directly into the compiler rather than maintained by a separate program. A macro is described as a skeletal message in which special characters specify the location into which parameters are to be inserted. For example, the skeletal message

STATEMENT $ IN RANGE OF DO AT $

could be the macro for indicating the errors detected when a branch of control will enter the range of a previously compiled DO. When it is discovered during the compilation of the range of a DO that a previously compiled branch of control may enter the range of the DO, the message elicited is

'THE RANGE OF THIS DO MAY BE ENTERED FROM
STATEMENT $'

When an error is detected and a message is to be output, DITRAN calls
the message-handling routine with an index associated with the error and
the location of a calling sequence containing the parameters and indication
of the parameter types (e.g., statement label, integer value, variable name).
The message-handling routine then uses tables to associate a skeletal message with the detected error. The parameters are then converted from the
indicated parameter format into the output format and inserted into the
skeletal message.

In the above example, the first parameter might have been a binary
representation of the statement label 132. This would have been converted
to BCD and inserted into the message. The second parameter might have
been an absolute core location of the beginning of the DO. This location
would be located in the statement tables and a phrase such as "STATE-
MENT 100 + 5" inserted into the output message to indicate that the DO
began five statements after the statement labeled 100, the closest labeled
statement. The message output would then be

STATEMENT 132 IN RANGE OF DO AT STATEMENT
100 + 5

By changing the form of the macro for a given error, the output message
for that error can be altered without making any changes to DITRAN. For
example, the above skeletal message could be changed to

THE BRANCH TO STATEMENT $ WILL ILLEGALLY
ENTER THE RANGE OF THE DO BEGINNING AT $

The output message would then be

THE BRANCH TO STATEMENT 132 WILL ILLEGALLY
ENTER THE RANGE OF THE DO BEGINNING AT
STATEMENT 100 + 5

A general ancillary program has been developed to housekeep the messages, maintain linkages with the compiler, and provide ease of modifying
the messages without altering DITRAN. This program creates a block of
skeletal messages together with a routine for converting the parameters

of the macro calls into the specified output format. This block of messages and set of routines is then made available to the compiler as a subroutine. This support program is expected to be of value to any compilers or large systems requiring the maintenance of a large body of messages.

5.3.10. MONITORING THE PERFORMANCE OF DITRAN

To monitor the performance and use of DITRAN, a performance record is written on the system-accounting medium for each program submitted to DITRAN. The contents of this record include:

- user and run identification
- memory requirements of the program
- size of program
- number of statements of each type
- information describing the size of system tables needed during compilation
- library functions referenced
- compilation time
- execution time
- number of records input and output during execution
- a code describing conditions of termination
- number of errors in each of 21 categories.

An analysis of this information should help in identifying those areas where improvement of compiler performance should be of greatest value. One area of special interest is the identification of the types of errors most frequently made by the users. Having identified these errors, we can make an effort to instruct users or to improve the diagnostics in order to provide stronger cues to aid the correction of errors. The error counts in the compiler performance record are distributed into the following categories:

Batch-control errors

- errors in batch-control cards or instructor-supplied routines

Compilation time errors associated with

- statement format or sequence
- subscripts
- arithmetic expressions
- FORMAT statements

- I/O statements
- reference and definition of entities
- compiler limits for which compilation is terminated
- statement format punctuation
- identifiers
- DO statements
- GOTO and IF statements
- storage allocation
- system control and limits

Execution time errors associated with

- arithmetic faults
- computed GOTO operations
- I/O operations
- reference and definition of entities
- library function parameters
- subprogram references
- system control and limits.

5.3.11. INSTRUCTORS USE OF DITRAN

Since a major part of the effort of developing DITRAN was directed toward improving the effectiveness of the computing facility for students, it seemed appropriate to include the following features to aid the instructors.

One feature allows batch processing to save machine time and permit the instructor to assign more problems within the time allocated for a given course. DITRAN will process a batch-control card specifying time and I/O limits to be imposed on each program in the batch, and then remain in core while compiling and executing each program in the batch.

So that the instructor may provide data for the student programs in a run, DITRAN allows him to insert specifically designated FORTRAN programs at the beginning of a run to write tape files which may be referenced as read-only files by the student programs in the run. This allows the instructor to prepare the input data at the time of the run and provides a common data file which cannot be altered by the student programs.

Another feature of DITRAN allows the instructor to supply SUBROUTINE or FUNCTION subprograms at the beginning of a run, which may be referenced as library routines by the student programs in the remainder of the batch.

At the end of the batch run, the instructor receives a performance log of each program in the batch, which indicates compilation time, execution time, and a code indicating the reason for termination. Also a batch summary is provided which indicates the number of errors in each of the 21 categories noted above and the number of programs containing errors of each type. This should help the instructor identify any particular problem area which might require additional attention in class.

5.3.12. EXPERIENCE WITH DITRAN

DITRAN was initially used in the summer of 1965 and then in the fall semester of 1965 by an introductory programming course with an enrollment of about 180 students. During the fall semester, about 10,000 programs were submitted by these students. DITRAN has performed quite successfully and very few problems have been encountered. The instructors and teaching assistants have reported quite favorably on the effectiveness of the diagnostic capabilities.

DITRAN is being used by the Department of Computer Sciences in numerical analysis courses as well as in introductory programming courses. It has also been placed on the standard library and made available to all users of the computing facility.

A review of a sample of the information collected in the performance records has provided some interesting results. Table 5.3.1 presents a summary of this information from the performance records collected for student programs submitted for two Department of Computer Sciences courses during a three-month period. One of the courses was an introductory programming course with an enrollment of 151 students; the other, an introductory numerical analysis course with an enrollment of 83 students. One observation which might be of interest in this summary is the distribution of execution-time errors which appear to justify the emphasis placed in this area.

A shortcoming of the performance-reporting system is that the present procedures for submitting runs do not collect and retain enough information to trace the history of a student's trial runs for a particular problem assignment. Although such information would be extremely valuable, obtaining it would present the impractical requirement that each student accurately report details of each of his runs (such as assignment number, trial number, and purpose of trial) in reaching the solution of each assignment.

Table 5.3.1. Summary of Performance Record Data
Sample of March, April, May 1966

A summary of information collected from the performance records for student programs
submitted for two Department of Computer Sciences courses

Number of students	234	Total number of programs	5158
Number of batch runs	208	Average number programs per batch	25

Average compilation time per program	3 seconds
Average execution time per program	3 seconds
Average core requirements per program	793 words
Average number of statements per program	38

Distribution of statements (percent of total):

Arithmetic assignment	45.6	END	3.1
WRITE	9.1	READ	3.0
DO	8.5	DIMENSION	3.0
IF	7.4	CONTINUE	2.7
GOTO	4.9	All others	7.9
FORMAT	4.8		

Number of programs with compilation errors	1859
Average number of compilation errors per program	3.8

Distribution of compilation time errors (percent of total number of compilation errors):

Arithmetic assignment	26.0	I/O statements	5.6
Statement format and sequence	22.0	Reference and definition	5.4
Identifiers	14.8	FORMAT statements	4.6
DO statements	6.8	GOTO, IF statements	2.4
General punctuation	6.6	All others	5.8

Number of programs with execution errors (not including errors for exceeding the execution time limit)   1699

Distribution of execution time errors (percent of total no. of execution errors):

I/O operations	64.2	Arithmetic faults	3.5
Reference and definition	31.3	All others	1.0

A very successful feature of DITRAN's performance has been the speed at which batched programs can be processed. The compilation speed is quite good—about 1000 statements per minute. At this rate under the batch mode, the average student jobs are run in 2 or 3 seconds. This is an improvement by a factor of about 10 over the standard compiler under the standard operating system.

ACKNOWLEDGMENTS

The authors wish to acknowledge the many suggestions contributed by the staffs of the Department of Computer Sciences and the Computing Center of the University of Wisconsin, and express appreciation to Professors C. H. Davidson and E. C. Koenig for their encouragement and patience with the use of DITRAN in their programming course in the fall semester of 1965. Furthermore, Professor Davidson has offered particularly valuable suggestions based upon his experience with the development and use of FORGO.

REFERENCES

1. "FORTRAN vs. Basic FORTRAN," *Comm. ACM*, vol. 7, no. 10 (October 1964), pp. 592–625.

2. Irons, E. T., "An Error Correcting Parse Algorithm," *Comm. ACM*, vol. 6, no. 11 (November 1963), pp. 669–673.

3. Conway, R. W., and Maxwell, W. L., "CORC: The Cornell Computing Language," *Comm. ACM*, vol. 6, no. 6 (June 1963), pp. 317–321.

4. Freeman, D. N., "Error Corrections in CORC," *Proc. AFIPS* (1964), Fall Joint Comput. Conf., Vol. 26, pp. 15–34.

5. Rosen, S., Spurgeon, R. A., and Donnelly, J. K., "PUFFT—The Purdue University Fast FORTRAN Translator," *Comm. ACM*, vol. 8, no. 11 (November 1965), pp. 661–666.

6. "Fast FORTRAN—Preliminary Reference Manual," Michigan State U., East Lansing, Mich., September 1965.

7. Floyd, R. W., "Syntactic Analysis and Operator Precedence," *J. ACM*, vol. 10, no. 3 (October 1963), pp. 316–333.

8. Graham, R. M., "Bounded Context Translation," *Proc. AFIPS* (1964), Spring Joint Comput. Conf., Vol. 25, pp. 17–29.

9. Galler, B. A., and Fisher, M. J., "An Improved Equivalence Algorithm," *Comm. ACM*, vol. 7, no. 5 (May 1964), pp. 301–303.

10. Dunn, T. M., and Morrissey, J. H., "Remote Computing—An Experimental System, Part 1: External Specifications," *Proc. AFIPS* (1964), Spring Joint Comput. Conf., vol. 25, pp. 413–423.

11. Keller, J. M., Strum, E. C., and Yang, G. H., "Remote Computing—An Experimental System, Part 2: Internal Design," *Proc. AFIPS* (1964), Spring Joint Comput. Conf., vol. 25, pp. 424–443.

12. McClure, C. W., Sanderson, K., and Davis, J., "FORGO (Load and Go FORTRAN)," COMMON Program Library 1620-02.0.008, IBM Data Processing Program Information Dept., Hawthorne, N. Y.

13. "The Burroughs B5500 Extended ALGOL Reference Manual," Manual 1020872, Burroughs Corp., Detroit, Mich., March 1966.

14. "The Burroughs B5500 Reference Manual," Manual 1021326, Burroughs Corp., Detroit, Mich., May 1965.

15. Randell, B., and Russell, L. J., ALGOL 60 *Implementation*. Academic Press, New York, 1964.

16. Shantz, P. W. *et al.*, "WATFOR: The University of Waterloo FORTRAN IV Compiler," *Comm. ACM*, vol. 10, no. 1 (January 1967), pp. 41–44.

6.

COMPILER IMPLEMENTATION

6.0. OVERVIEW

This chapter includes several articles on implemented compilers, mostly of ALGOL-like compilers. There are two reasons for the choice of ALGOL: These compilers are the most frequently documented in the literature, and the techniques described are sufficiently general that they apply to most compilers.

The second reason for the inclusion of these articles is that it is only within such literature that one finds discussions of the organization of compilers. This extremely important subject has been seemingly ignored in the literature.

The "publish or perish" syndrome may be partially responsible for the large number of ALGOL compilers described in the literature. The choice of ALGOL over other languages may be due to its nature as a relatively clean language, the ease with which it can be formally described, and the sufficient complexity of its structure to provide some challenge to the implementor (e.g., recursive procedures, block structure, and dynamic allocation). This syndrome may be also partially responsible for the usually high quality of such papers. Moreover, within the nonacademic community one finds greater management pressure on production of working systems than on publication of descriptive papers.

This chapter opens with two general articles on the structure of languages. The first, by Perlis, discusses the relationships among programming languages, data structures, and syntax. Article 6.2 by Raphael covers two major points: It identifies the major components of programming languages and discusses the factors influencing their inclusion in a language system.

Article 6.3, a discussion by Gries, Paul, and Wiehle, describes some specific techniques used in implementing the ALCOR ALGOL compiler.

This is followed by Article 6.4 by Evans, which describes an ALGOL translator implemented at the Carnegie Institute of Technology. The article discusses the basic concepts used in the compiler and gives a thorough explanation of its operation on a subset of ALGOL consisting of assignment statements, conditional statements, and expressions.

6.1. The Synthesis of Algorithmic Systems

by Alan J. Perlis

6.1.1. INTRODUCTION

Both knowledge and wisdom extend man's reach. Knowledge led to computers, wisdom to chopsticks. Unfortunately, our association is over-involved with the former. The latter will have to wait for a more sublime day.

On what does and will the fame of Turing rest? That he proved a theorem showing that for a general computing device—later dubbed a "Turing machine"—there existed functions which it could not compute? I doubt it. More likely it rests on the model he invented and employed—his formal mechanism.

This model has captured the imagination and mobilized the thoughts of a generation of scientists. It has provided a basis for arguments leading to theories. His model has proved so useful that its generated activity has been distributed not only in mathematics, but through several technologies as well. The arguments that have been employed are not always formal and the consequent creations not all abstract. Indeed a most fruitful consequence of the Turing machine has been with the creation, study, and computation of functions which are computable, i.e., in computer programming.

EDITOR'S NOTE: This article reproduced with the permission of the author and the publisher: *J. ACM*, vol. 14, no. 1 (January 1967), pp. 1–9.

This is not surprising, since computers can compute so much more than we yet know how to specify.

I am sure that all will agree that this model has been enormously valuable. History will forgive me for not devoting any attention in this lecture[†] to the effect which Turing had on the development of the general-purpose digital computer, which has further accelerated our involvement with the theory and practice of computation.

Since the appearance of Turing's model there have, of course, been others which have concerned and benefited us in computing. I think, however, that only one has had an effect as great as Turing's—the formal mechanism called ALGOL. Many will immediately disagree, pointing out that too few of us have understood it or used it. While such has, unhappily, been the case, it is not the point. The impulse given by ALGOL to the development of research in computer science is relevant while the number of adherents is not. ALGOL, too, has mobilized our thoughts and has provided us with a basis for our arguments.

I have long puzzled over why ALGOL has been such a useful model in our field. Perhaps some of the reasons are:

(a) its international sponsorship;

(b) the clarity of description in print of its syntax;

(c) the natural way it combines important programmatic features of assembly and subroutine programming;

(d) the fact that the language is naturally decomposable so that one may suggest and define rather extensive modifications to parts of the language without destroying its impressive harmony of structure and notation. There is an appreciated substance to the phrase "ALGOL-like" which is often used in arguments about programming, languages, and computation. ALGOL appears to be a durable model, and even flourishes under surgery—be it explorative, plastic, or amputative;

(e) the fact that it is tantalizingly inappropriate for many tasks we wish to program.

Of one thing I am sure: ALGOL does not owe its magic to its process of birth; by committee. Thus, we should not be disappointed when eggs, similarly fertilized, hatch duller models. These latter, while illuminating impressive improvements over ALGOL, bring on only a yawn from our

[†] See *First ACM Turing Lecture*, presented at the 21st ACM National Conference, August 1966.

collective imaginations. These may be improvements over ALGOL, but they are not successors as models.

Naturally we should and do put to good use the improvements they offer to rectify the weakness of ALGOL. And we should also ponder why they fail to stimulate our creative energies. Why, we should ask, will computer science research, even computer practice, work but not leap forward under their influence? I do **not pretend** to know the whole answer, but I am sure that an important **part of their** dullness comes from focusing attention on the wrong weakness of ALGOL.

6.1.2. THE SYNTHESIS OF LANGUAGE AND DATA STRUCTURES

We know that we design a language to simplify the expression of an unbounded number of algorithms created by an important class of problems. The design should be performed only when the algorithms for this class impose, or are likely to impose, after some cultivation, considerable traffic on computers as well as considerable composition time by programmers using existing languages. The language, then, must reduce the cost of a set of transactions to pay its cost of design, maintenance, and improvement.

Successor languages come into being from a variety of causes:

(a) The correction of an error or omission or superfluity in a given language *exposes* a natural redesign which yields a superior language.

(b) The correction of an error or omission or superfluity in a given language *requires* a redesign to produce a useful language.

(c) From any two existing languages a third can usually be created which (i) contains the facilities of both in an integrated form, and (ii) requires a grammar and evaluation rules less complicated than the collective grammar and evaluation rules of both.

With the above in mind, where might one commence in synthesizing a successor model which will not only improve the commerce with machines but will focus our attention on important problems within computation itself?

I believe the natural starting point must be the organization and classifying of data. It is, to say the least, difficult to create an algorithm without knowing the nature of its data. When we attempt to represent an algorithm in a programming language, we must know the representation of the algorithm's data in that language before we can hope to do a useful computation.

Since our successor is to be a general programming language, it should possess general data structures. Depending on how you look at it, this is neither as hard nor as easy as you might think. How should this possession be arranged? Let us see what has been done in the languages we already have. There the approach has been as follows:

(a) A few "primitive" data structures (e.g., integers, reals, arrays homogeneous in type, lists, strings, and files) are defined into the language.

(b) On these structures a "sufficient" set of operations (e.g., arithmetic, logical, extractive, assignment, and combinational) is provided.

(c) Any other data structure is considered to be nonprimitive and must be represented in terms of primitive ones. The inherent organization in the nonprimitive structures is explicitly provided for by operations over the primitive data, e.g., the relationship between the real and imaginary parts of a complex number by real arithmetic.

(d) The "sufficient" set of operations for these nonprimitive data structures is organized as procedures.

This process of extension cannot be faulted. Every programming language must permit its facile use, for ultimately it is always required. However, if this process of extension is too extensively used, algorithms often fail to exhibit a clarity of structure which they really possess. Even worse, they tend to execute more slowly than necessary. The former weakness arises because the language was defined the wrong way for the algorithm, while the latter exists because the language forces overorganization in the data and requires administration during execution that could have been done once prior to execution of the algorithm. In both cases, variables have been bound at the wrong time by the syntax and the evaluation rules.

I think that all of us are aware that our languages have not had enough data types. Certainly, in our successor model we should not attempt to remedy this shortcoming by adding a few more, e.g., a limited number of new types and a general catchall structure.

Our experience with the definition of functions should have told us what to do—not to concentrate on a complete set of defined functions at the level of general use, but to provide within the language the structures and control from which the efficient definition and use of functions within programs would follow.

Consequently, we should focus our attention in our successor model on providing the means for defining data structures. But this is not of itself enough. The "sufficient" set of accompanying operations, the contexts in which they occur, and their evaluation rules must also then be given within the program for which the data structures are specified.

A list of some of the capabilities that must be provided for data structures would include:

(a) structure definition

(b) assignment of a structure to an identifier, i.e., giving the identifier information cells

(c) rules for naming the parts, given the structure

(d) assignment of values to the cells attached to an identifier

(e) rules for referencing the identifier's attached cells

(f) rules of combination, copy, and erasure both of structure and cell contents

These capabilities are certainly now provided in limited form in most languages, but usually in too fixed a way within their syntax and evaluation rules.

We know that the designers of a language cannot fix how much information will reside in structure and how much in the data carried within a structure. Each program must be permitted its natural choice to achieve a desired balance between time and storage. We know there is no single way to represent arrays or list structures or strings or files or combinations of them. The choice depends on

(a) the frequency of access;

(b) the frequency of structure changes in which given data are embedded, e.g., appending to a file new record structures or bordering arrays;

(c) the cost of unnecessary bulk in computer storage requirements;

(d) the cost of unnecessary time in accessing data; and

(e) the importance of an algorithmic representation capable of orderly growth so that clarity of structure always exists.

These choices, goodness knows, are difficult for a programmer to make. They are certainly impossible to make at the design level.

Data structures cannot be created out of thin air. Indeed the method we customarily employ is the use of a background machine with fixed, primitive data structures. These structures are those identified with real computers, though the background machine might be more abstract as far as the defining of data structures is concerned. Once the background machine is chosen, additional structure as required by our definitions must be represented as data, i.e., as a name or pointer to a structure. Not all pointers reference the same kind of structure. Since segments of a program are themselves structures, pointers such as "procedure identifier contents of (x)" establish a class of variables whose values are procedure names.

6.1.3. CONSTANTS AND VARIABLES

Truly, the flexibility of a language is measured by that which programmers may be permitted to vary, either in composition or in execution. The systematic development of variability in language is a central problem in programming and hence in the design of our successor. Always our experience presents us with special cases from which we establish the definition of new variables. Each new experience focuses our attention on the need for more generality. Time sharing is one of our new experiences that is likely to become a habit. Time sharing focuses our attention on the management of our systems and the management by programmers of their texts before, during, and after execution. Interaction with program will become increasingly flexible, and our successor must not make this difficult to achieve. The vision we have of conversational programming takes in much more than rapid turnaround time and convenient debugging aids; our most interesting programs are never wrong and never final. As programmers we must isolate that which is new with conversational programming before we can hope to provide an appropriate language model for it. I contend that what is new is the requirement to make variable in our languages what we previously had taken as fixed. I do not refer to new data classes now, but to variables whose values are programs or parts of programs, syntax or parts of syntax, and regimes of control.

Most of our attention is now paid to the development of systems for managing files which improve the administration of the overall system. Relatively little is focused on improving the management of a computation. Whereas the former can be done outside the languages in which we write our programs, for the latter we must improve our control over variability within the programming language we use to solve our problems.

In the processing of a program text an occurrence of a segment of texts may appear in the text once but be executed more than once. This raises the need to identify both constancy and variability. We generally take that which has the form of being variable and make it constant by a process of initialization; and we often permit this process itself to be subject to replication. This process of initialization is a fundamental one and our successor must have a methodical way of treating it.

Let us consider some instances of initialization and variability in ALGOL:

(a) *Entry to a Block*. On entry to a block declarations make initializations, but only about some properties of identifiers. Thus, **integer** *x* initializes the property of being an integer, but it is not possible to initialize the value of *x* as something that will not change during the scope of the block. The declaration **procedure** P $(\ldots)$; $\ldots$; emphatically initializes the identifier P, but it is not possible to change it in the block. **array** A $[1 : n, 1 : m]$ is assigned an initial structure. It is not possible to initialize the values of its cells, or to vary the structure attached to the identifier A.

(b) FOR *Statement*. These expressions, which I will call the "step and until" elements, cannot be initialized.

(c) *Procedure Declaration*. This is an initialization of the procedure identifier. On a procedure call, its formal parameters are initialized as procedure identifiers are, and they may even be initialized as to value. However, different calls establish different initializations of the formal parameter identifiers but not different initialization patterns of the values.

The choice permitted in ALGOL in the binding of form and value to identifiers has been considered adequate. However, if we look at the operations of assignment of form, evaluation of form and initialization as important functions to be rationally specified in a language, we might find ALGOL to be limited and even capricious in its available choices. We should expect the successor to be far less arbitrary and limited.

Let me give a trivial example. In the FOR statement the use of a construct such as **value** E, where E is an expression, as a step element would signal the initialization of the expression E. **value** is a kind of operator that controls the binding of value to a form. There is a natural scope attached to each application of the operator.

I have mentioned that procedure identifiers are initialized through declaration. Then the attachment of procedure to identifier can be changed by assignment. I have already mentioned how this can be done by means of pointers. There are, of course, other ways. The simplest is not to change the identifier at all, but rather to have a selection index that picks a procedure out of a set. The initialization now defines an array of forms, e.g., **procedure array** P $[1 : k](f_1, f_2, \ldots, f_j)$; $\ldots$ **begin** $\ldots$ **end**; $\ldots$; **begin** $\ldots$ **end**; the call P $[i](a_1, a_2, \ldots, a_j)$ would select the *i*th procedure body for execution. Or one could define a **procedure switch** P := A, B, C and procedure designational expressions so that the above call would select the *i*th procedure designational expression for execution. The above approaches are too static for some applications and they lack an important property of assignment, the ability to determine when an assigned form is no longer accessible so that its storage may be otherwise used. A possible application for such procedures, i.e., ones that are dynamically assigned, is as generators. Suppose we have a procedure for computing (a) $\sum_{k=0}^{N} C_k(N)X^k$ as an approximation to some function (b) $f(x) = \sum_{k=0}^{\infty} C_k X^k$, when the integer N is specified. Now, once having found the $C_k(N)$, we are merely interested in evaluating (a) for different values of x. We might then wish to define a procedure which prepares (a) from (b). This procedure, on its initial execution, assigns, either to itself or to some other identifier, the procedure which computes (a). Subsequent calls on that identifier will only yield this created computation. Such dynamic assignment raises a number of attractive possibilities:

(a) Some of the storage for the program can be released as a consequence of the second assignment.

(b) Data storage can be assigned as the **own** of the procedure identifier whose declaration or definition is created.

(c) The initial call can modify the resultant definition, e.g., call by name or call by value of a formal parameter in the initial call will affect the kind of definition obtained.

It is easy to see that the point I am getting at is the necessity of attaching a uniform approach to initialization and the variation of form and value attached to identifiers. This is a requirement of the computation process. As such our successor language must possess a general way of commanding the actions of initialization and variation for its classes of identifiers.

One of the actions we wish to perform in conversational programming is the systematic, or controlled, modification of values of data and text, as distinguished from the unsystematic modification which occurs in debugging. The performance of such actions clearly implies that certain pieces of a text are understood to be variable. Again we accomplish this by declaration, by initialization, and by assignment. Thus we may write, in a block heading, the declarations

> **real** x, s;
> **arithmetic expression** t, u;

In the accompanying text the occurrence of $s := x + t$; causes the value of the arithmetic expression assigned to t, e.g., by input, to be added to that of x and the result assigned as the value of s. We observe that t may have been entered and stored as a form. The operation $+$ can then only be accomplished after a suitable transfer function shall have been applied. The fact that a partial translation of the expression is all that can be done at the classical "translate time" should not deter us. It is time that we began to face the problems of partial translation in a systematic way. The natural pieces of text which can be variable are those identified by the syntactic units of the language.

It is somewhat more difficult to arrange for unpremeditated variation of programs. Here the major problems are the identification of the text to be varied in the original text, and how to find its correspondent under the translation process in the text actually being evaluated. It is easy to say: Execute the original text interpretively. But it is through intermediate solutions lying between translation and interpretation that the satisfactory balance of costs is to be found. I should like to express a point of view in the next section which may shed some light on achieving this balance as each program requires it.

6.1.4. DATA STRUCTURE AND SYNTAX

Even though list structures and recursive control will not play a central role in our successor language, it will owe a great deal to LISP. This language induces humorous arguments among programmers, often being damned and praised for the same feature. I should only like to point out here that its description consciously reveals the proper components of language definition with more clarity than any language I know of. The description of LISP includes not only its syntax, but the representation of its syntax as a data structure of the language, and the representation of the environment data structure also as a data structure of the language. Actually the description hedges somewhat on the latter description, but not in any fundamental way. From the foregoing descriptions it becomes possible to give a description of the evaluation process as a LISP program using a few primitive functions. While this completeness of description is possible with other languages, it is not generally thought of as part of their defining description.

An examination of ALGOL shows that its data structures are not appropriate for representing ALGOL texts, at least not in a way appropriate for descriptions of the language's evaluation scheme. The same remark may be made about its inappropriateness for describing the environmental data structure of ALGOL programs.

I regard it as critical that our successor language achieve the balance of possessing the data structures appropriate to representing syntax and environment so that the evaluation process can be clearly stated in the language.

Why is it so important to give such a description? Is it merely to attach to the language the elegant property of "closure" so that bootstrapping can be organized? Hardly. It is the key to the systematic construction of programming systems capable of conversational computing.

A programming language has a syntax and a set of evaluation rules. They are connected through the representation of programs as data to which the evaluation rules apply. This data structure is the internal or evaluation directed syntax of the language. We compose programs in the external syntax which, for the purposes of human communication, we fix. The internal syntax is generally assumed to be so translator and machine dependent that it is almost never described in the literature. Usually there is a translation process which takes text from an external to an internal syntax representation. Actually the variation in the internal description is more fundamentally associated with the evaluation rules than the machine on which it is to be executed. The choice of evaluation rules depends in a critical way on the binding time of the variables of the language.

This points out an approach to the organization of evaluation useful in the case of texts which change. Since the internal data structure reflects the variability of the text being processed, let the translation process choose the appropriate internal representation of the syntax, and a general evaluator select specific evaluation rules on the basis of the syntax structure chosen. Thus we must give clues in the external syntax which indicate the variable. For example, the occurrence of **arithmetic expression** t; **real** u, v; and the statement $u := v/3 * t$; indicates the possibility of a different internal syntax for $v/3$ and the value of t. It should be pointed out that t behaves very much like an ALGOL formal parameter. However, the control over assignment is less regimented. I think this merely points out that formal-actual assignments are independent of the closed subroutine concept and that they have been united in the procedure construct as a way of specifying the scope of an initialization.

In the case of unpremeditated change a knowledge of the internal syntax structure makes possible the least amount of retranslation and alteration of the evaluation rules when text is varied.

Since one has to examine and construct the data structures and evaluation rules entirely in some language, it seems reasonable that it be in the source language itself. One may define as the target of translation an internal syntax whose character strings are a subset of those permitted in the source language. Such a syntax, if chosen to be close to machine code, can then be evaluated by rules which are very much like those of a machine.

While I have spoken glibly about variability attached to the identifiers of the language, I have said nothing about the variability of control. We do not really have a way of describing control, so we cannot declare its regimes. We should expect our successor to have the kinds of control that ALGOL has—and more. Parallel operation is one kind of control about which much study is being done. Another one just beginning to appear in languages is the distributed control, which I will call monitoring. Process A continuously monitors process B so that when B attains a certain state, A intervenes to control the future activity of the process. The control within A could be written **when** P **then** S; P is a predicate which is always, within some defining scope, under test. Whenever P is **true**, the computation under surveillance is interrupted and S is executed. We wish to mechanize this construct by testing P whenever an action has been performed which could possibly make P **true**, but not otherwise. We must, then, in defining the language, the environment, and the evaluation rules, include the states which can be monitored during execution. From these primitive states others can be constructed by programming. With a knowledge of these primitive states, arrangement for splicing in testing at possible points can be done even before the specific predicates are defined within a program. We may then troubleshoot our programs without disturbing the programs themselves.

6.1.5. VARIATION OF THE SYNTAX

Within the confines of a single language an astonishing amount of variability is attainable. Still, all experience tells us that our changing needs will place increasing pressure on the language itself to change. The precise nature of these changes cannot be anticipated by designers, since they are the consequence of programs yet to be written for problems not yet solved. Ironically, it is the most useful and successful languages that are most subject to this pressure for change. Fortunately, the early kind of variation to be expected is somewhat predictable. Thus, in scientific computing the representation and arithmetic of numbers varies, but the nature of expressions does not change except through their operands and operators. The variation in syntax from these sources is quite easily taken care of. In effect, the syntax and evaluation rules of arithmetic expression are left undefined in the language. Instead, syntax and evaluation rules are provided in the language for programming the definition of arithmetic expression, and for setting the scope of such definitions.

The only real difficulty in this one-night-stand language definition game is the specification of the evaluation rules. They must be given with care. For example, in introducing this way the arithmetic of matrices, the evaluation of matrix expressions should be careful of the use of temporary storage and not perform unnecessary iterations.

A natural technique to employ in the use of definitions is to start with a language X, consider the definitions as enlarging the syntax to that of a language X', and give the evaluation rules as a reduction process which reduces any text in X' to an equivalent one in X.

It should be remarked that the variation of the syntax requires a representation of the syntax, preferably as a data structure of X itself.

6.1.6. CONCLUSION

Programming languages are built around the variable—its operations, control, and data structures. Since these are concepts common to all programming, general language must focus on their orderly development. While we owe a great debt to Turing for his simple model, which also focused on the important concepts, we do not hesitate to operate with more sophisticated machines and data than he found necessary. Programmers should never be satisfied with languages which permit them to program everything, but to program nothing of interest easily. Our progress, then, is measured by the balance we achieve between efficiency and generality. As the nature of our involvement with computation changes—and it does— the appropriate description of language changes, our emphasis shifts. I feel that our successor model will show such a change. Computer science is a restless infant and its progress depends as much on shifts in point of view as on the orderly development of our current concepts.

None of the ideas presented here are new; they are just forgotten from time to time.

I wish to thank the Association for the privilege of delivering this first Turing lecture. And what better way is there to end this lecture than to say that if Turing were here today he would say things differently in a lecture named differently.

6.2. The Structure of Programming Languages

by Bertram Raphael

6.2.1. SUMMARY

In this paper the major components of every programming language are identified as: (1) the elementary program statement, (2) mechanisms for linking elementary statements together, (3) the means by which a program can obtain data inputs. Several alternative forms of each of these components are also described, compared, and evaluated. Many examples, frequently from list-processing languages, illustrate the forms described.

The advantages, disadvantages, and factors influencing the choice of a form of component for a language are discussed, and the paper concludes with the suggestion that programming languages evolve toward one which will permit all the most convenient ways of structuring programs, organizing systems, and referencing data.

6.2.2. INTRODUCTION

The way in which a programming language is structured can strongly affect the efficiency and modus operandi of a programmer. The three purposes of this paper are (1) to identify the major components of pro-

EDITOR'S NOTE: This article reproduced by permission of the author and the publisher: *Comm. ACM*, vol. 9, no. 2 (February 1966), pp. 67–71.

gramming languages, (2) to describe alternative forms available for implementing each of these components, and (3) to compare and evaluate the various forms.

The computing community has tried to attach to certain programming languages such ill-defined labels as *imperative, declarative,* and *implicit.* This paper, while avoiding discussion of the semantics and applicability of those particular terms, attempts to analyze some of the underlying concepts in the structure and use of a language.

Some form of each of the following components is present in every programming language: an elementary program statement, a mechanism for linking one elementary program statement to another or to a group of other statements, and a means by which the program can obtain data inputs. Several factors, such as the nature of the operating system and the kind of problem to be solved, influence the relative desirability of various forms of these components of programming languages. In this paper the alternative forms for these components are discussed.

The examples are drawn largely from various languages for symbol manipulation (sometimes called "list-processing languages"). List languages have been chosen because list processing is relatively new; none of the forms for the components of list languages has as yet been established as "standard" even in an informal sense. Instead, a variety of interesting languages having different forms are available. Consequently, list languages are a rich source of illustrative material.

6.2.3. ELEMENTARY PROGRAM STATEMENTS

Elementary program statements can usually be classified as either *commands, requirements,* or *implicit specifications.* A *command* is an imperative statement that commands the action to be taken without saying anything at all about what effect will thereby be achieved. A *requirement* describes the effect to be achieved without saying anything at all about the actions to be taken in achieving the effect, nor requiring that the programmer know how the effect will be achieved. An *implicit specification* is similar to a *requirement,* but the programmer must know something about what actions will be taken to achieve the desired effect.

6.2.3.1. *Commands*

The elementary statements of conventional assembly languages are imperative; they command that certain computations be performed, or that data be moved, or that tests be made. Thus, the terminology "order code" or "instruction set" is used to refer to the repertoire of operations of a computer. For example, the statement CLA X is manifestly a command.

In the list-processing language IPL-V,[1] the elementary statements are imperatives. They command certain symbols to be manipulated. For example, the statement 30 W1 is the imperative, "Pop-up the stack cell named W1."

The elementary program statements of most conventional programming languages are exclusively commands. Recently, languages have emerged whose elementary statements are statements of requirements or implicit specification statements. Programs having such statements offer outstanding advantages in many situations. However, these programs still require the use of commands. For example, the most natural way to specify when and under what conditions an input/output operation should take place is simply to *command* it to take place at the right time and under the right conditions. Notice the roundabout and inelegant mechanisms necessary to handle input/output in languages not having commands: In LISP1.5,[2] "pseudofunctions" are evaluated for their side effects, such as a "print" operation, and their true values are ignored; in SNOBOL,[3] data can be output only by the awkward mechanism of requiring it to be part of the special string named SYSPOT.

6.2.3.2. Statements of Requirements

One way of describing a computer[†] is by its transfer characteristics. Data are fed in, certain transformations of the data take place, and results are spewed out. One does not have to give a sequence of commands that would carry out the transformation. Instead, one may express the transfer function to be executed by the program by presenting only general descriptions of acceptable data as well as descriptions of the results into which the data are to be transformed. Simon[4] has called these descriptions the input and output *state descriptions* of the computer.

The elementary statements of some programming languages consist of statements, in this state description form, of the *requirements* of the program. Some examples may be found in the program generator languages described in Young's[5] paper. The report generator feature of SIMSCRIPT[6] is a similar example.

The pattern match and rearrangement statements of the COMIT[7] and

---

[†] By "computer" is meant the combination of a particular program running on a particular EDP machine.

SNOBOL languages are also statements of requirements. They assert that if a data string is of a certain specified form, then it is to be transformed into a string with a different specified form (without specifying the procedure by which this transformation is carried out). The compiler creates both the tests to determine whether the statement is applicable to particular data strings, and the program that carries out the desired transformation.

Let us define *program* for a moment in a narrow sense as a sequence of commands. Then compilers for languages whose elementary statements are commands are program *translators*; they translate the source-language program into the object-language program. Compilers for statements of requirements, on the other hand, are program *writers*; they create commands that bring about the required states.

The statement of requirements for solving differential equations could consist of descriptions of how to recognize both a differential equation and its solution. The compiler would then have to write a program (sequence of commands) for transforming the equation into the solution. Unfortunately, we do not now know how to write such general program-writing programs. However, less ambitious, yet useful program-writing programs *are* within our reach.

For instance, in a sample of text a linguist can arrange to separate verb roots from their endings by writing an appropriate SNOBOL or COMIT program. He need merely specify the input state—i.e., tell how to recognize verbs and their roots and specify the required output state—that each root is separated from its ending by a space. He need never know just what procedures are followed in achieving the separation.

6.2.3.3. Implicit Specification

Some programming languages have elementary statements that are neither commands nor simple statements nor requirements. In order to understand the effects of such statements the programmer must be aware of unstated constraints or interpretation procedures. I call such statements *implicit specifications* of the actions of the program.

Of course the distinction between a *command* and an *implicit specification* is not clear cut. Here, any command is considered implicit to the extent that the action it produces is not apparent without further explanation.

Indirectly addressed instructions and "execute" instructions are familiar examples of implicit specification statements; they require unusual evaluation procedures of which the programmer must be aware. (These special evaluation procedures are carried out by special hardware.)

Lisp[2] programs are always executed by means of an implicit mechanism called the EVAL operator. The programmer must know that the elements of his program statement will be evaluated in a certain (recursive) order, and he must understand the effect of evaluating each element of an elementary program statement. On the other hand, he does not have to understand the nature of the evaluation mechanism (which, incidentally, may itself conveniently be expressed in LISP).

COGENT[8] is a language in which some program statements implicitly specify production rules for a phrase-structure grammar. Implicit evaluation procedures construct or analyze certain list structures in accordance with those grammatical rules.

Naturally, the more computation done implicitly by the programming system, the less left for the programmer to worry about. Since the implicit procedure generally performs a task that would otherwise be difficult or awkward to define, it is a great boon to the programmer. However, when an implicit evaluation procedure is an intrinsic part of a programming system and cannot be "turned off" when it is not needed, it can cause the programmer troublesome difficulties.

In LISP, the elementary program statements are either definitions of functions or applications of functions to arguments. When a program is executed, the implicit EVAL operator always maintains control as it goes about its task of evaluating expressions by applying functions to arguments. Occasionally a LISP programmer desires to describe an action (such as the modification of the property list of an atomic symbol) that is awkward to couch in the standard terms "arguments," "functions" and "evaluations." The omnipresence of the EVAL operator then actually encumbers the programming task. To get around this problem, most LISP systems offer an alternate means called the PROG feature, for structuring programs. In the PROG mode, LISP becomes a language of simple sequential commands.

6.2.4. SUBPROGRAM LINKAGE

The utility of subroutines was recognized early in the development of computer programming. A (closed) subroutine reduces the storage requirements for a program, since the single copy of the subroutine may be used in several parts of the higher-level program. In addition, the subroutine provides a convenient building block that can assist a programmer in organizing a complex program.

Psychologists have shown that a human being can contemplate at most about seven discrete objects at any one time. In designing a system involving more than seven program segments, the programmer can either use complex flow charts and focus his attention on a small part of a highly connected network at one time, or he can build a hierarchical structure containing independent units, each of which has only a small number of subunits and which can thus be "debugged" independently of the rest of the structure. The feasibility of building such a hierarchical structure depends largely upon the manner in which subroutines must be constructed and executed.

Some languages have provisions for identifying a group of elementary program statements as a logical block—e.g., with BEGIN and END statement brackets as in ALGOL. In this section we are concerned with relations between logical blocks rather than with the internal structure of a block.

6.2.4.1. *Explicit Call*

Most well-known programming languages require subroutines to be identified as special kinds of entities, both when constructed and when used. TSX SUBR,4 and CALL SUBR(ARG) are typical examples of explicit subroutine calls. In each case the subroutine SUBR must itself know how and where to find its arguments, where to put its results, and how to get back to the calling program. Subroutine calls in COMIT,[7] a language of requirement statements for string manipulations, are handled by simple transfers of control, but only after a return location has been put in some standard place. Usually, a single pushdown list is used for all subroutine returns. As in the FAP and FORTRAN cases, the subprograms know how to get back to the calling program.

Minor differences in immediate convenience have major effects on overall programming habits. Subroutines of the conventional type described above are usually used to eliminate duplicate copies of programming code. They are infrequently used as a mental aid in organizing systems, because to use them in this way would require extra linkages and more complicated coding and loading procedures. We have all seen flow charts of programs that are virtually unreadable and unmodifiable because they do not have a hierarchical structure.

6.2.4.2. *Execute Calls*

By an "execute call" is meant a subroutine call which is syntactically indistinguishable from the basic instructions of a programming language.

For example, an assembly-language programmer uses macroinstructions in exactly the same way as he does the basic instructions of the language. Macroinstructions generate "open" subroutines; that is, a new copy of the instructions in the macrodefinition is inserted at each use. Thus macros do not save space the way closed subroutines do. Their purpose is strictly to reduce the burden on the programmer of keeping track of "lower level" details.

IPL-V instructions are of four kinds: data transmission, storage-cell pushdown and popup, branch, and execute. There is no special subroutine entry or exit mechanism; none is needed. The argument of an execute instruction may be either (1) the name of any of approximately 100 built-in programs (to perform list processing, arithmetic, input/output, and other operations), or (2) the name of any IPL program (including the one in which the execute statement occurs). Arguments and results are transmitted according to conventions which are independent of how the program unit being executed fits into the larger program system. Any program may be used as either a main program or a subroutine. Each program simply runs to termination, at which time the system executive knows where to go next (by using a pushdown stack as a conventional program counter).

IPL-V programmers rarely write routines (program units) having more than about 20 lines of code. Newell's recent version of GPS[9] has over 30,000 lines arranged as many short routines. The problems of organizing systems like GPS would be tremendously difficult were it not for the ease with which short program segments may be written independently of each other and then plugged into an appropriate part of a hierarchical structure.

6.2.4.3. *Function Composition*

The mathematical idea of "function" has been carried over into programming to mean a subroutine that calculates a single number, the "value" of the function. Function calls may be nested to achieve the effect of mathematical function "composition." In FORTRAN, for example,

$$X = SIN(MAX(X1, ABS(X2)))$$

generates a hierarchical set of subroutine calls. The result of each subroutine execution is transmitted to its calling program in a standard way for all "function" subprograms.

The basic element of a LISP 1.5 program is the *function*; no other kind of main or subprogram is used. A LISP function call is similar to an IPL subprogram execute call in that a LISP function may call any function, including itself, simply by writing the name (or definition) of the called function at the appropriate place in the definition of the calling function. Functions are thus convenient organizational units of large LISP programs.

Most conventional programmers flow-chart before they code. However, the author knows of no experienced LISP or IPL-V programmer who uses flow charts. They may first code either the highest- or the lowest-level routines, and they may code extremely short or moderately short routines. But these programmers use the routines themselves as flow charts, thereby eliminating a time-consuming step in the programming process. For example, the highest-level function in a program for symbolic differentiation of a function y with respect to a variable x would be defined in LISP 1.5 approximately as follows:

$$\textit{diff}\,[\,y;\,x] = [\textbf{if}\ \textit{constant}\ [\,y]\ \textbf{then}\ 0;$$
$$\textbf{else if}\ \textit{variable}\ [\,y]\ \textbf{then}\ \textit{vardiff}\,[\,y;\,x];$$
$$\textbf{else if}\ \textit{algebraic}\ [\,y]\ \textbf{then}\ \textit{algdiff}\,[\,y;\,x];$$
$$\textbf{else if}\ \textit{trigonometric}\ [\,y]\ \textbf{then}\ \textit{trigdiff}\,[\,y;\,x];$$
$$\textbf{else}\ \textit{otherdiff}\,[\,y;\,x]]$$

where *constant*, *variable*, *vardiff*, etc., are other LISP functions. Note that the program serves as its own flow chart because of the ease with which subfunctions are used.

6.2.5. INPUTS TO ROUTINES

The peculiar ways and means of referencing data influence the modus operandi and efficiency of the programmer. The three principal ways of getting inputs for routines are (1) by referring to the data themselves; (2) by referring to the data by a "name," usually associated with its address; and (3) by referring to data implicitly by means of values of variables or values of functions of other data.

6.2.5.1. Direct Data

The assembly-language pseudo-ops, OCT and BCD, and the FORTRAN-type H format version are familiar examples of the inclusion of data themselves in programs. The value of the LISP expression (QUOTE, (A,

B, C)) is the list (A, B, C). Similarly, one may define the same string of symbols in SNOBOL, and give it the name LIST, by the statement

$$\text{LIST} = \text{``(A, B, C)''}$$

6.2.5.2. *Reference by Name*

In the FAP "CLA X" or FORTRAN "Z = X + C", the letter X is the *name* of the desired data item and is identified in a symbol table with the storage location of the data. In IPL-V and in SLIP,[10] most of the basic list-processing routines or functions have symbols naming list structures as their inputs. Here a name is identified in a symbol table as a pointer to the head of the list.

6.2.5.3. *Implicit Reference*

The "dummy variables" in a FORTRAN subprogram are implicit data items; neither the values nor the locations of the data are known when the program to manipulate the data is written.

In LISP programs *all* data are defined implicitly by dummy variables. A program is a set of defined subfunctions. At execution time, direct data are provided to the system's top-level functions.

6.2.5.4. *Discussion*

Data names in programs are analogous to proper names in ordinary discourse: Sometimes they are essential, at other times they are superfluous, and occasionally they are confusing.

In ordinary discourse, one can use a pronoun such as "he" to refer to an antecedent. Also, one can identify a person by his description rather than by his name. When one says, "The Prime Minister of England," one refers to the current officeholder, whatever his name may be. Programs in FORTRAN or FAP, or in IPL, SLIP, or COMIT, can frequently refer to data items only by their proper names. Thus the programmer must make up names for each immediate computational result in order to be able to refer to it later. In LISP, on the other hand, intermediate data structures do not have names. All data transmission is handled automatically as specified implicitly in intermediate function definitions. Since the need to make up explicit names takes some of the programmer's attention and provides an opportunity for errors, one might expect LISP's completely implicit data transmission philosophy to be an unmitigated blessing.

Unfortunately, the naming problem is a two-edged sword. All large LISP programs with which the author is familiar—including Slagle's calculus integration,[11] Evans' geometry analogy solver,[12] and Raphael's question answerer[13]—make extensive use of inconvenient pseudofunctions and features of the LISP system for the sole purpose of *introducing* the ability to access intermediate data by their names. For complex symbolic data processing, treating each program segment as an independent mathematical function is not sufficient. One must also have names for entry points into "permanent" data structures that various subprograms manipulate.

The ability to use different levels of data reference can enhance the flexibility of using named data. In IPL-V, an elementary program statement can contain the data themselves, the name of a cell containing the data, or, for an additional level of indirectness, the name of a cell containing the name of the cell containing the data. These various ways of getting at inputs to routines have proved to be quite useful as well as confusing.

An on-line test-manipulation system being developed at SRI[14] provides another example of the importance of naming. The ability to identify a segment of text by its label in a standard hierarchical outline arrangement is a key feature of this system. Here, not only does the label name the text, but also the characters in the label specify the relative location of the text. An implicit naming scheme could not have this desirable property. The next version of this text manipulation system may be written in SNOBOL 3,[15] which is well suited for analyzing the characters in a string name as well as for utilizing a hierarchical program structure.

6.2.6. FACTORS INFLUENCING THE STRUCTURE OF A LANGUAGE

Thus far, different kinds of elementary program statements and various ways of linking subroutines and of referencing data have been discussed. Let us now mention some factors influencing the choice of these components in a programming language.

6.2.6.1. *Environment*

The mode of use of a computer influences the choice of language components. Batch, job-shop computer operation requires the minimizing of computer running time. On-line "conversational" operation, whether for a single user on a small computer or for a time-sharing system, requires the optimization of other parameters. The job mix also influences language choice. The users of the MIT time-sharing system[16] are research-oriented. Their system uses MAD as its principal compiler language, rather than FORTRAN, because for these users it is advantageous to have a fast compiler and a more sophisticated language at the expense of an inefficient object code. The SRI CDC-3100 will have a special fast assembler that compiles nonrelocatable code because of its special advantages for use in an on-line system with symbolic debugging capability.

6.2.6.2. *Storage Allocation*

How to control free storage is a major problem for designers of symbol manipulation systems. One must decide (1) the precise form of the storage control mechanism, and (2) how much control should be exercised over the mechanism by the program.

A "free storage list" of linked cells is the basis of most dynamic storage allocation schemes. Cells are generally removed from this list as they are needed by the processes of the language. Several methods have been used for returning unneeded cells to the free storage list. Cells may be returned under program control, automatically as they are abandoned, or periodically by "garbage collection." The reference-count scheme used by SLIP is a clever compromise between continuous and periodic reclamation of free cells. A "garbage collector" might simply construct a linked list, or it might compress the list into a contiguous block of storage (by any of several available schemes). Choice of the storage-allocation mechanisms depends upon the programming language to be used and, to some extent, upon the application to which the program will be put.

6.2.6.3. *Escape Mechanisms*

No matter how general or powerful a programming language seems to be, some user is bound to come up with a task that is awkward to perform with any of the available components. Therefore it is important to provide "escape mechanisms" with which the user may enhance the language.

The easiest escape mechanism provides the ability to write special-purpose machine-language subroutines that can be called from within the language. Of course some sort of subroutine-calling mechanism must be inherent in the language before externally written subroutines may be used. Thus, for example, machine-language subroutines are convenient to use in

SNOBOL 3 as a by-product of the new facility to define and use SNOBOL "function" subprograms.

A more elegant—and more difficult to implement—escape mechanism is the ability for the programmer to actually extend the *syntax* of a language. This is possible if the behavior of a compiler is influenced by a syntactic description of the language being compiled. The author is of the understanding that the proposed LISP II[17] language will have a feature of this kind.

6.2.7. CONCLUSIONS

We have seen that several apparently mutually exclusive features of programming languages all have their advantages. Names are sometimes useful handles by which to reference data items, and sometimes the compulsory use of names is inconvenient; subroutines should be usable implicitly through function composition or execute calls, yet it should be possible to define special-purpose subroutines explicitly; and the elementary statements of programs are most conveniently specified, in various situations, as commands, requirements, or implicit specification statements. How are we to resolve these issues?

One might think that a suitable subset of desirable components could be selected for any one "problem-oriented" language. But if this were done, programmers who wished to widen their scopes would have to learn a variety of "foreign" languages. Furthermore, as more difficult and more interesting problems are attacked, larger varieties of components are generally needed than would be available in any standard set.

Embedding one language within another[18] offers one solution, although frequently this has the drawback of compounding the minor disadvantages of the embedded and the embedding languages. One observes a more direct approach to more powerful languages in the evolution of existing systems: FORTRAN I to ALGOL, or LISP 1 to LISP 1.55.[19] Each sequence represents the progression toward a language containing more of the desirable components and alternatives discussed above. A quite ambitious language currently being implemented is LISP II,[17] which resembles a marriage of ALGOL, LISP 1.5, and COMIT, and includes provisions for automatic storage allocation and escape mechanisms.

Assembly languages have already evolved to the point where they are fairly standardized (because useful components have been generally identified and provided, rather than because any committee has established "standards"). A machine-language programmer can now switch from one manufacturer's digital computer to another's and, although the instruction sets will differ, the structure of the assembly language, the pseudo-ops, and the macroprogramming facilities will be pretty much the same. Hopefully, before too many more years elapse, problem-oriented languages for symbol manipulation as well as for scientific and business application will reach a similar state. The most convenient ways of structuring programs, organizing systems, and referencing data will become generally recognized and available. Perhaps, then, those of us primarily interested in *using* computers can stop worrying about the terminology and the nature of computer language design.

REFERENCES

1. Newell, A. (ed.), *Information Processing Language V Manual.*, Prentice-Hall, Englewood Cliffs, N.J., 1961.

2. McCarthy, J., *et al.*, *LISP1.5 Programmer's Manual.*, MIT Press, Cambridge, Mass., 1963.

3. Farber, D. J., *et al.*, "SNOBOL, A String Manipulation Language," *J. ACM*, vol. 11, no. 2 (January 1964), pp. 21–30.

4. Simon, H. A., "Experiments with a Heuristic Compiler," *J. ACM*, vol. 10, no. 4 (October 1963), pp. 493–506.

5. Young, J. W., Jr., "Non-procedural Languages—A Tutorial." Presented at ACM So. Calif. Chapters, 7th, Ann. Tech. Symp., March 1965.

6. Markowitz, H. M., *et al.*, *SIMSCRIPT—A Simulation Programming Language*, Prentice-Hall, Englewood Cliffs, N.J., 1963.

7. MIT Research Laboratory of Electronics and Computation Center. COMIT *Programmer's Reference Manual.* MIT Press, Cambridge, Mass., 1961.

8. Reynolds, J. C., COGENT *Programming Manual.*, ANL-7022, Argonne Nat. Lab., 1965.

9. Newell, A., *et al.*, "Report on a General Problem-Solving Program," Proc. Int. Conf. on Information Processing, Paris, UNESCO House, 1959.

10. Weizenbaum, J., "Symmetric List Processor," *Comm. ACM*, vol. 6, no. 9 (September 1963), pp. 524–544.

11. Slagle, J. R., "A Heuristic Program that Solves Symbolic Integration Problems in Freshman Calculus," *J. ACM*, vol. 10, no. 4 (October 1963), pp. 507–520.

12. Evans, T. G., "A Heuristic Program to Solve Geometric-Analogy Problems," Proc. 1964 Spring Joint Comput. Conf., vol. 25, Spartan Books, Washington, D.C., (May 1964), pp. 327–328.

13. Raphael, B., "A Computer Program which Understands," Proc. 1964 Fall Joint Comput. Conf., vol. 26, October 1964.

14. Engelbart, D. C., "Augmenting Human Intellect: Experiments, Concepts, and Possibilities," Sum. Rep., AF49(638)-638)-1064, SRI Proj. 3578, Stanford Res. Inst., Menlo Park, Calif., March 1965.

15. Farber, D. J., *et al.*, "Snobol 3," Bell Telephone Labs., Holmdel, N.J. (Unpublished.)

16. Corbató, F. J., *et al.*, *The Compatible Time-Sharing System—A Programmer's Guide*. MIT Press, Cambridge, Mass., 1963.

17. Levin, M., *et al.*, "Lisp II Project.," Tech. Mem. Ser. 2260, Systems Development Corp., Santa Monica, Calif., 1965.

18. Bobrow, D. G., and Weizenbaum, J., "List Processing and Extension of Language Facility by Embedding," *IEEE Trans.* *EC-13*, 4 (August 1964), pp. 395–400.

19. Wooldridge, D., Jr., "The New lisp System (lisp1.55)," Artif. Intel. Proj. Memo 13, Stanford U., February 1964.

6.3. Some Techniques Used in the ALCOR ILLINOIS 7090

by D. Gries, M. Paul, and H. R. Wiehle

6.3.1. SUMMARY

An ALGOL compiler has been written by the ALCOR group for the IBM 7090. Some little-known but significant techniques in compiler writing, together with organizational details of this compiler, are described. Timing estimates and an indication of compiler requirements are also given.

6.3.2. INTRODUCTION

6.3.2.1. *The Project*

ALCOR ILLINOIS is an ALGOL compiler written for the IBM 7090. Work on the compiler was begun at the Digital Computer Laboratory, University of Illinois,[†] in June 1962 as a joint project by this University, the Mainz Institute for Applied Mathematics, and the Rechenzentrum, Munich Institute of Technology.[‡] The directors of these institutes felt a responsibility

[†] This project was partly supported by the Deutsche Forschungsgemeinschaft.

[‡] Department of Computer Science. The 7090/1401 system at the University of Illinois used in this development was partially supported by the National Science Foundation under Grant No. NSF-GP-700.

EDITOR'S NOTE: This article reproduced by permission of authors and the publisher: *Comm. ACM*, vol. 8, no. 8 (August 1965), pp. 496–500.

to make ALGOL available as a practical language to their students and to a wider public, and therefore initiated the task since at that time the manufacturer was not going to provide an ALGOL compiler for the 7090. In January 1963 the work was partly transferred to the Rechenzentrum, Munich Institute of Technology, and by May 1963 the main parts of the compiler had been programmed and checked. The field-test phase was entered in November 1963, and in July 1964 the compiler was given a final release.

The language of the ALCOR ILLINOIS 7090 is ALGOL with the exception of **own**. Input and output are temporarily controlled by standard input and output procedures under a FORTRAN-like format, described in Ref. 5. As an introduction to ALGOL (with the exception of input-output) and as a manual, Ref. 11 can be used.

6.3.2.2. *Historical Background*

The ALCOR (meaning ALgol COnverteR) group, formed in 1958, is a cooperative group of computing centers and computing manufacturers interested in automatic translating. From its beginning, it has based its language decoding (text analysis) on a sequential translation technique using the well-known cellar principle and state-transition matrix developed by Bauer and Samelson,[4] and has based its run-time organization on principles of dynamic storage allocation and subroutine linkage introduced mainly by Rutishauser.[10] This group has built over ten ALGOL compilers, the ALCOR ILLINOIS 7090 being one of the latest and most modern ones. This group is continually doing research in improving and developing techniques for formal language translation and in the development of programming languages.

6.3.2.3. *Aims*

In contrast to the other compilers built by the ALCOR group, this was to be the first one built for a very fast machine with a big and homogeneous storage. The authors could therefore concentrate on refinements of the translation techniques used. Restrictions on the language earlier imposed by slow, small machines were no longer necessary, and methods were developed to implement all features. There was no limitation on the size of the compiler itself. Other problems, however, presented themselves, one being the necessity for a compiler which could easily be embedded in the numerous 7090 operating systems.

Basically, the successful techniques developed by the ALCOR group, which emphasize a fast object program, a good syntax checker, and a short translation time, are used.

6.3.2.4. *Organization of the Compiler*

Text analysis is preferably performed using the cellar principle and a state-transition automata with a one-sided tape (the cellar). A complete syntax check can be accomplished through the use of a complete transition matrix, including the necessary means for synchronization in case of syntactical errors. On the other hand, a system of priorities of the states and incoming symbols[2,9] is simpler and more lucid. However, it requires a correct program. The solution is as follows:

Pass 1 performs the usual mapping of the source program symbols into an internal representation and generates a few lists needed by the syntax checker.

Pass 2, using a complete transition matrix, performs a complete syntax check without actually translating. However, it creates lists of all necessary information needed for the actual translation, and transfers control to the next pass only if the source program is correct.

Pass 3, the actual translator, working only on correct programs and using the lists already produced, can use the priority method and devote much space and effort to produce efficient object programs.

Pass 4 does final address calculation and relocation.

6.3.2.5. *Use of Storage Space*

One of the ways in which translation time can be held down is to keep tape movement to a minimum. Since the source program must be read, processed, and modified by each pass, it should be kept in memory as much as possible. With program buffers of 1000 words (each word containing 5 ALGOL symbols), a program of 150 to 200 cards needs no intermediary tape; while compiling a program of 500 cards, at most 5 or 6 records are written and read.

One problem with a compiler is the number of lists to be stored. In order to minimize translation time, these lists must be kept in memory, even if this limits the size of programs which can be translated. This is no real restriction, since a program can be split up into code procedures. With an available storage of 32K words, the ALCOR ILLINOIS 7090 limits the number of different identifiers within an ALGOL program to 3000, FOR loops to 400, blocks to 500, and the number of constants to 700. These limits are large enough to accommodate most programs and small enough so that no list (except the ALGOL program itself) has to be put on tape. Many lists become obsolete from pass to pass, and the space is then used for other purposes. Due to this, the final object program buffer has 4000 words. The compiler itself has a total of 26,000 instructions and uses $70,000_8$ locations in memory.

6.3.2.6. *Remarks*

Since the main compiling techniques of the ALCOR group have become well known and widely used, this discussion is limited to a few significant but little-known points. Questions of run-time organization are mentioned in connection with Pass 3 (the object program generator), the most important being the use of linear address incrementing, whenever possible, in FOR loops.

6.3.3. PASS 1

The first pass has two main objectives. The first is to change all ALGOL symbols into a 7-bit representation while discarding blanks and comments (except in strings). The other is to produce a list, called the ID-list, of all formal parameters, labels, and variables. This list is necessary for a good, fast syntax check. It must be in a form which is easy to search, since (1) every identifier can occur before it is declared, and (2) for each occurrence of an identifier the syntax checker must find it in the ID-list and check it. At the end of pass 2, this list will contain all information about each identifier (e.g., type, kind, number of subscripts, formal parameter or not). In order to prevent duplication of effort between pass 1 and pass 2, pass 1 inserts into the ID-list only the name and, implicitly, the block number. This has the additional advantage that the pass 1 state-transition matrix is very small, since only block structure and declarations must be analyzed. For instance, expressions may be entirely skipped; no states are necessary for "+", "*", and so on.

Experience has shown that a very efficient way to organize the ID-list is by "block number," where a block has block number n if it is the nth block to be statically opened. For reasons explained later, each FOR loop and each procedure is also technically counted as a block (with the formal parameters being the only identifiers belonging to the artificially created procedure block). Two lists are actually produced. The first, called the block list, contains in the ith location (corresponding to block i) the triple (surrounding block number, address of ID-list for block i, number of identifiers in block i).

In addition, blocks 0 and −1 exist and surround all blocks. Block 0 contains all standard procedures, with complete information about them. The compiler can be changed easily to add or delete standard procedures by changing this list in pass 1. Block −1 is empty and will be used by pass 2 for a list of all undeclared identifiers, to aid in continuing after errors. The second list, the ID-list itself, contains for each block the identifiers and labels declared in that block. Figure 6.3.1 illustrates the formation of the lists for the following program:

```
begin integer procedure B(C);
        integer C; B := C * A;
    integer A, C, D;
    A := C := 2;
    for D := 1 step 1 until C do LABE:
        begin integer E;
            E := B(D) + A; A := E;
        end;
    for D := 1 step 1 until C do PRINT (D, A * D);
    end
```

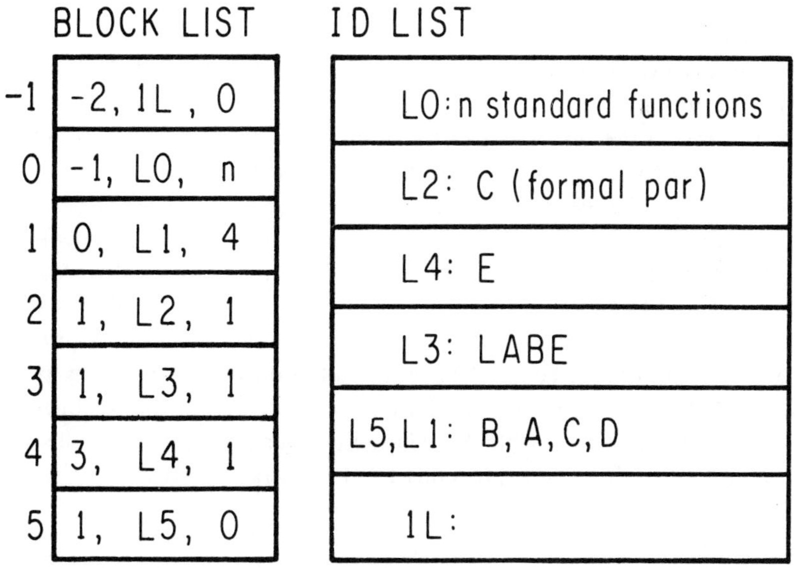

BLOCK LIST   ID LIST

−1	−2, 1L , 0
0	−1, L0, n
1	0, L1, 4
2	1, L2, 1
3	1, L3, 1
4	3, L4, 1
5	1, L5, 0

L0: n standard functions
L2: C (formal par)
L4: E
L3: LABE
L5,L1: B, A, C, D
1L:

FIGURE 6.3.1

Notice that the identifier list is not ordered by block number, but by the order in which the blocks are closed. This makes no difference to pass 2 and is easier to generate.

6.3.4. PASS 2

Pass 2 performs a complete syntax check. The method (state-transition matrix with one stack as in pass 1) is not discussed here. Practical and theoretical explanations can be found in Refs. 1 and 4.

There are some jobs which pass 2 can easily do in order to simplify pass 3 and help optimize the object program.

6.3.4.1. *ID and Block Lists*

One important job is to replace each identifier in the program by the entry number of the identifier in the ID-list. (The nth identifier in the list has entry number n). Pass 3 uses this number directly in order to find an identifier in the list; no search of the list is required. The identifier list can then be shortened at the end of pass 2 by deleting the name of each identifier, leaving more room in memory for other lists (especially the object program to be produced). Another operation easily performed is the calculation of addresses of variables for the object program. Since all information for each identifier will then be in the ID-list, pass 2 deletes all specifications and all declarations except procedures, switch, and array declarations from the source program.

Returning to the discussion of the ID-list, one sees that its form allows efficient searching. The subroutine LUIL (Look Up in ID-List), given in Fig. 6.3.2 with the identifier and block number B as parameters, performs this search. This one subroutine can be used for all occurrences of identifiers except in declarations and specifications. It also automatically tests for jumps into a FOR loop from outside. Such a use of a label causes it to be undefined, since a FOR loop is technically treated as a block. Declarations and specifications can be handled by the addition of another entry point, LUIL 1, which searches only in block number B, due to the treatment of procedure declarations as blocks. The only other problem is the checking of variables occurring in expressions E_i of an array declaration

$$\textbf{array } A[E_1 : E_2, \ldots, E_{2n-1} : E_{2n}]$$

These variables must be declared in surrounding blocks. This check is accomplished by the following:

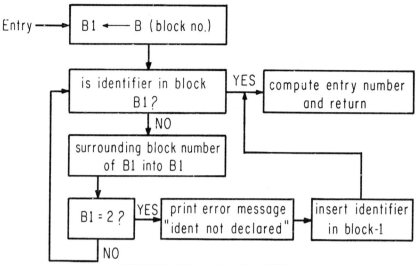

FIGURE 6.3.2 Subroutine LUIL.

(a) When [of an array declaration is pushed into the cellar: (1) the current block number is saved in an auxiliary location; (2) the surrounding block number is put into the current block number location.

(b) At the end of the array declaration, ( ] encounters the [in cellar): (1) the current block number is restored in the current block number location.

The need for counters and pointers to indicate which variables have been used in which blocks as array limits has been eliminated.

Another consequence of the block structured ID-list is the simplicity of the "block entry" and "block close" subroutines. They consist merely of pushing the actual block number into the cellar and inserting the new one, and restoring the old block number, respectively. This method is simpler than those used by some other authors.[3]

6.3.4.2. *Linear Address Incrementing*

Linear address incrementing is a term used for a special type of optimization of array-element address calculation in FOR loops.

Let a loop be

$$\textbf{for } I := E1 \textbf{ step } E2 \textbf{ until } E3 \textbf{ do } \textstyle\sum ;$$

and A[E] be an array element occurring in the statement $\sum$. If E is linear in the loop variable I, then A[E] can be written as A[aI + b] where a and b

are (integer) expressions which do not change in the loop, and

$$\text{address } (A[a(I + E2) + b]) = \text{address } (A[a(I) + b]) + a * E2$$

Upon entering the loop, address $(A[a * E1 + b])$ and the value $a * E2$ are calculated and stored. Then each time the loop is repeated, $a * E2$ is added to the address.

Due to a questionable generality in ALGOL 60, the program must be checked thoroughly to make sure that I and E2 do not change during execution of the loop, and to determine just which array elements are linear in the loop variable. Further time and storage space in the object program can be saved by making identity checks of array elements (e.g., with respect to equal initial addresses and address increments) in pass 2. More information is contained in Refs. 4 and 8. For an exact description of its use in the ALCOR ILLINOIS 7090, see Refs. 5 and 7.

In order that pass 3 can perform this optimization in the object program, pass 2 must produce a list of FOR loops in which linear address incrementing is used and must test each array element for linearity in the loop variable. This can complicate pass 2 if incorporated directly into it, since at each step of analyzation of an expression, a test must be made to see if it is in a subscript expression, and if so, a jump to a subroutine which tests for linearity must be executed.

It would therefore seem logical to have an extra pass (linearity checker) to check for linear address incrementing, but this would increase the translation time, since the source program would be read and processed again.

The solution to the problem is to run both parts—the syntax checker and the linearity checker—*separately, but simultaneously*. Each one has its own set of subroutines and can be programmed separately, but they use common lists and locations. The syntax checker processes a source-program symbol and passes it on to the linearity checker. When it is finished with one symbol, it reads the next symbol and jumps to the syntax checker. This technique could be used to run any number of separate passes which can run parallel. What is saved is the bookkeeping which must accompany each pass, and the corresponding time involved.

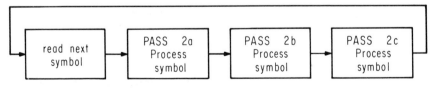

FIGURE 6.3.3

Figure 6.3.3 gives a simplified flow chart for running three passes together. In order to save time, the linearity checker is in action only when necessary. This requires connections between the two parts at the following points:

(1) **for** is the symbol just read.

(2) $a[$ (beginning of an array element).

(3) $a($ (procedure or function call).

(4) $a :=$ (where a is of type integer).

(5) end of a **for** loop.

6.3.5. PASS 3

Pass 3, operating only with correct programs, uses a list of priorities assigned to the ALGOL symbols, together with two cellars. This method, described in Refs. 2 and 9, is not discussed here. The optimization through the use of linear address incrementing also needs no further discussion, although it is the most effective type of optimization.[4,5,7,8] Instead, we discuss the use of dynamic storage allocation during execution and its relation to recursive procedures.

6.3.5.1. *Storage for Blocks and Arrays*

In ALGOL, arrays must be handled dynamically, since the bounds of an array may only be determined at run time. Therefore the program must have a mechanism for reserving and releasing storage. The usual method is to think of free storage as a stack. There exists one location, DFSL (Dynamic Free Storage Location), which always contains the address of the first (lowest) free location. When a new block is entered, the block saves the contents of DFSL in an auxiliary location. An array declaration needing n locations causes locations $\langle DFSL \rangle$ through $\langle DFSL \rangle + n - 1$ to be reserved for it and $\langle DFSL \rangle$ to be changed to $\langle DFSL \rangle + n$. ($\langle A \rangle$ means contents of location A). The problem is that at every exit from the block, the old value of DFSL, which was saved upon entry, must be restored in order to save storage space, since the arrays declared in the block are no longer needed. This causes complications in the compiler and in the object program, especially if an exit leaves more than one block at a time.

A simple device, introduced by K. Samelson, eliminates the need for any reinitialization when leaving a block. Define the outermost block to be block number 0. An inner block has block number n if the immediately surrounding block has block number $n - 1$. The block number is then the level of nesting within other blocks. To each block number b there exists a location $DFSL_b$.

Upon entering a block with number b, the instructions $\langle DFSL_{b-1} \rangle \rightarrow DFSL_b$ are executed. An array declaration declared in block b, needing n locations, causes the locations $\langle DFSL_b \rangle$ to $\langle DFSL_b \rangle + n - 1$ to be reserved, and $\langle DFSL_b \rangle$ to be increased by n. It is obvious that no extra work is required when leaving a block, since each block with number b uses only $DFSL_b$ to indicate storage reserved for it, and not a universal DFSL.

6.3.5.2. *Procedures*

Let the main program be called hierarchy 0, and each procedure hierarchy $n + 1$, if it is declared in a hierarchy of order n. The hierarchy number is then the level of nesting of procedures. Each procedure has a fixed number of locations (called FFS, for free-fixed storage) associated with it—simple variables declared in it, formal parameters, auxiliary locations, etc.

In order to save space, it is desirable that locations for an FFS be reserved only when the procedure is being executed. This means, however, that the variables be easily relocatable, since the storage space is dynamically allocated. If a procedure call takes place in block b, $\langle DFSL_b \rangle$ are given as a parameter to the procedure. The procedure, having m locations in its FFS, takes locations $\langle DFSL_b \rangle$ to $\langle DFSL_b \rangle + m - 1$ for its FFS, and inserts the value $\langle DFSL_b \rangle + m$ in its own DFSL location. Every variable and location in the FFS of a hierarchy is then defined by the pair (A, STR), where A is its absolute position in the FFS, and STR (stack reference) is the relocatable beginning of the FFS. Upon entry to a procedure from block b, STR is clearly equal to $\langle DFSL_b \rangle$.

It is obvious that all procedures can be made recursive if every piece of information which depends upon the call is saved in the FFS. Each time the procedure is entered, space is again reserved for the FFS of the procedure.

We do not wish to go into details of just which information must be saved. In order to indicate how to make this as efficient as possible, we give a few practical techniques. When in a certain procedure, an index register can be used to contain its stack reference. The relocation is performed once and for all at the beginning of the procedure by loading the index register with the stack reference, and using this index register as a tag to each instruction referencing the FFS. Hierarchy 0—the main program—

cannot be recursive and must always be in memory. It is therefore given absolute locations for its FFS. A detailed description can be found in Ref. 7.

6.3.6. PASS 4

This pass does final relocation and puts the program onto a tape in the equivalent form of relocatable binary cards. It also does final address calculation, in order to handle forward references to labels, switches, and procedures. Error messages are also printed by this pass, from a list containing all necessary information (card number, error number, state of the matrix when the error occurred, etc.) made up by pass 2.

6.3.7. PARAMETERIZATION OF THE COMPILER

The existence of numerous systems used on the IBM 7090 made it worthwhile to parameterize the ALCOR ILLINOIS 7090. The compiler has about 50 parameters, representing most connections between the compiler and a system. Examples are tape numbers, locations to be used by the compiler, and positioning of the system tape after compilation. An installation fills in the list of parameters according to its needs,[6] punches them on cards, and inserts them in the front of each pass. The passes are then assembled, producing absolute binary cards ready for use.

6.3.8. CONCLUDING REMARKS

As of this date, the ALCOR ILLINOIS 7090 has been distributed to over 10 installations and embedded in 3 different systems. Wider use is expected. A confirmation of the efficiency of the techniques used is the speed of translation. A program of 20–50 cards compiles in less than 10 seconds (including the 2.7 seconds overhead to read the compiler from tape). One program of 2700 cards, produced by duplicating a single program many times and surrounding the result by a **BEGIN** and **END**, took 75 seconds to compile. In the few tests made, object programs were 1.2 to 2.2 times slower than a corresponding FORTRAN program, the higher of the factors resulting from a program in which mostly integers were used, the lower in the calculation of the determinant of a 50×50 matrix. Barth, Institute of Technology Darmstadt, programmed and tested a mathematical algorithm in FORTRAN and ALGOL. The program was about 550 cards long. Results are listed in Fig. 6.3.4.

ALCOR ILLINOIS 7090   FORTRAN II   SHARE 7090 ALGOL

	A	B	FORTRAN II	SHARE 7090 ALGOL
Compilation time plus loading time (sec)	37	37	260	330
Factor (using ALCOR ILLINOIS as 1)	I	I	7.0	8.9
execution time (sec)	320	420	190	630
Factor	I	1.3	.59	1.9
total time (sec)	357	457	450	960
Factor	I	1.4	1.4	2.7

A with linear address incrementing
B without linear address incrementing

FIGURE 6.3.4

REFERENCES

1. Eickel, J., Paul, M., Bauer, F. L., and Samelson, K., "A Syntax Controlled Generator of Formal Language Processors," *Comm. ACM*, vol. 6 (August 1963), pp. 451–455.

2. Floyd, R. W., "Syntactic Analysis and Operator Precedence," *J. ACM*, vol. 10 (July 1963), pp. 316–333.

3. Lietzke, M. P., "A Method of Syntax-Checking ALGOL 60," *Comm. ACM*, vol. 7 (August 1964), pp. 475–478.

4. Samelson, K., and Bauer, F. L., "Sequential Formula Translation," *Comm. ACM*, vol. 3 (February 1960), pp. 76–83.

5. Bayer, R., Murphree, E., Jr., and Gries, D., *User's Manual for the* ALCOR ILLINOIS *7090* ALGOL-*60 Translator* (2d ed.). U. of Illinois, September 1964.

6. Gries, D., Paul, M., and Wiehle, H. R., "ALCOR ILLINOIS 7090—An ALGOL compiler for the IBM 7090." Rep. 6415, Rechenzentrum der Tech. Hochsch., München, 1964.

7. ——— "The Object Program Produced by the ALCOR ILLINOIS 7090 compiler." Rep. 6412, Rechenzentrum der Tech. Hochsch., München, 1964.

8. Hill, U., Langmaack, H., Schwarz, H. R., and Seegmüller, G., "Efficient Handling of Subscripted Variables in ALGOL 60 Compilers," Proc. 1962 Rome Symposium on Symbolic Languages in Data Processing. Gordon and Breach, New York, 1962, pp. 311–340.

9. Paul, M., "A General Processor for Certain Formal Languages," Proc. 1962 Rome Symposium on Symbolic Languages in Data Processing. Gordon and Breach, New York, 1962, pp. 65–74.

10. Waldburger, H., "Gebrauchsanleitung für die ERMETH," Institut für angew. Mathematik der ETH, Zürich, 1959.

11. Baumann, R., Feliciano, M., Bauer, F. L., and Samelson, K., *Introduction to* ALGOL. Prentice-Hall, Englewood Cliffs, N.J., 1964.

6.4. An ALGOL 60 Compiler

by Arthur Evans, Jr.

6.4.1. INTRODUCTION

The internal operation of an ALGOL translator now running at Carnegie Institute of Technology will be discussed in detail. The discussion will be predicated on the assumption that the reader is an experienced programmer and is familiar with ALGOL-60 (although not necessarily an ALGOL specialist). The purpose of the article is to give the experienced programmer the information he needs so that he will know how the translator works.†

It is difficult in an article such as this one to give proper credit to sources. We have made free use of all knowledge and information available to us. Of course there is very little new in the programming world. With little difficulty, it can be shown that the translation technique used is very much the same as that described by Samelson and Bauer in 1960.[1] The production

† The research reported here was supported in part by the Advanced Research Projects Agency of the Office of the Secretary of Defense (SD-146). The paper was originally presented at the 18th Annual Meeting of the Association for Computing Machinery, Denver, Colorado, August 1963.
EDITOR'S NOTE: This article reproduced by permission of the author and the Association for Computing Machinery, and the publisher: *Annual Review of Automatic Programming*, vol. 4, Pergamon Press Ltd., Oxford, England, 1964; distributed by the Macmillan Company, New York.

language used to formulate Phase I is based on a notation devised by Robert W. Floyd.[2] The compiling technique used in Phase II is similar to that developed at the University of Michigan by Graham, Arden, and Galler[3] as used in the GAT translator on the 650.

6.4.2. PRELIMINARIES

This section consists of five parts that discuss the concepts needed for an understanding of the rest of the paper. In the first subsection (6.4.2.1) the source and target languages will be named and described, as will certain intermediate languages. In Section 6.4.2.2 the three parts of the translator will be explained briefly to give an overall picture of the translation process. In Section 6.4.2.3 the idea of Polish postfix notation will be defined and discussed. Section 6.4.2.4 will discuss the need for and nature of the symbol table in the translator. Finally, Section 6.4.2.5 will discuss the stack concept and explain how it is realized in this translator.

6.4.2.1. *The Languages* L_o , L_o' , L_i , *and* L_t ; L_p *and* L_p'

The subject of this article is a translator that translates ALGOL source code into machine language for execution on a computer. In the course of this discussion we will be considering several additional languages. It is therefore expedient to define now each of these languages and to give each of them a name. These names will then be used uniquely in the following discussion with a hopeful increase in clarity.

The first language is the *source language* and will be referred to as L_o. Obviously, L_o is ALGOL (modified slightly to suit the requirements at Carnegie Tech. and the hardware requirements of our computer). We will be translating into machine code, which will be referred to as L_t (target language). Thus our translator may be regarded as a transformation from L_o to L_t. We may represent the translator as an operator T and write

$$T(L_o) \to L_t$$

As we will see, there are several stages through which the translation process goes in affecting this transformation. In particular, there is an *intermediate language* produced, called *postfix*, which will be referred to as L_i. More will be said about postfix later. Further, we will see another language called L_o' which is very similar to L_o. Indeed, we will usually ignore the distinction between L_o and L_o'. In connection with the languages we will have certain translators. T is the entire translator for L_o to L_t.

We also have T_s, T_1, and T_2, as follows:

$$T_s(L_o) \rightarrow L'_o$$
$$T_1(L'_o) \rightarrow L_i$$
$$T_2(L_i) \rightarrow L_t$$

An alternate way to write is

$$L_o \underset{T_s}{\rightarrow} L'_o \underset{T_1}{\rightarrow} L_i \underset{T_2}{\rightarrow} L_t$$

In addition to the four languages referred to above, we will be concerned with two other languages. It will be seen that one part of the translator itself (T_1) has been written in a special language designed expressly for this purpose. This language is a production language modeled after a notation developed by Robert Floyd.[2] It will be referred to as L_p—production language. In addition to L_p we will have L'_p, the internal representation of the production language. A processor T_m translates L_p to L'_p. Schematically,

$$T_m(L_p) \rightarrow L'_p$$

or

$$L_p \underset{T_m}{\rightarrow} L'_p$$

6.4.2.2. The Subscan, Phase I and Phase II

It has proved expedient in writing the ALGOL translator to write it in three sections: subscan, Phase I, and Phase II. These are the T_s, T_1, and T_2 referred to above. The subscan reads the source code L_o from 80-column punched cards and transforms it to the intermediate form L'_o. This translation consists of looking up all identifiers, control words, and punctuation marks in suitable tables. The output L'_o is a string of integers—the coded representation of the source code. Since there is an exact one-to-one correspondence in both order and form between L_o and L'_o, the existence of the subscan (and of L'_o) will usually be ignored in what follows. The output of the subscan is processed by Phase I. The effect of Phase I is to translate L_o (that is, L'_o) into the intermediate language L_i. The output of Phase I consists of essentially the same characters as the input, but the characters have been reordered. The same representation of the characters is used in L_i as was used in L'_o. Phase II takes the L_i produced by Phase I and generates a machine code, L_t. At the completion of the execution of Phase II, the compiled program will be in core almost ready to execute. Before execution, however, there is a final step involving the filling in of certain undefined addresses.

We thus have three routines to consider: a subscan, Phase I, and Phase II. It develops that we may consider each of these routines independently of the other two, since the only communication between them is in terms of their output. That is, with only very few exceptions, all information created by the subscan which is needed by either Phase I or Phase II is contained in L_0'. The subscan creates no tables which are needed by the other two routines. Similarly, the only information needed by Phase II is that produced as L_i by Phase I. Again, Phase I produces no tables needed later. Thus it would be possible to have the three parts of the translator in core at different times, with the two intermediate outputs being stored, say, on magnetic tape. The Carnegie Tech. translator is not organized that way, since we have adequate core space to keep the entire translator in memory at one time. This point is mentioned at this time, however, to emphasize the extent to which the three parts of the translator are separate. There are two tables created by the subscan which are used later and thus are exceptions. The abcon table becomes part of the running program, and the symbol table may also be kept until run time to provide source language diagnostics.

In what follows, particularly in the discussion of Phase I, the phrase "create the character such-and-such in the output string" will frequently be used. We must remember that Phase I is a transformation process which translates L_0 into L_i. The quoted phrase means that another character is to be appended to the string L_i which has been created so far. The mechanism of this creation is not material in this discussion. If the entire translator is in core at the same time (as it is in our case), the mechanism is to supply the character to Phase II so that Phase II may process it. If the intermediate language L_i is to be stored on magnetic tape, then the phrase means that the character created is to be added to the tape record. All that need concern us is that Phase I creates a string of characters which Phase II will look at in the same order in which they were created.

6.4.2.3. *Postfix Notation*

Before we can discuss Phase I it will be necessary to describe what is meant by the term "postfix." In an expression such as A + B the operator "+" is between the two operands A and B. This notation is referred to as *infix*. *Prefix* notation is nothing more complex than putting the operator before its two operands rather than between, like this: +AB. It is known that "+" is a binary operator (that is, it has two operands) and the notation then means that the two operands of $+$ are those immediately following the occurrence of $+$. Postfix notation is just the opposite: The two operands of a given operator precede it rather than follow it. Thus, we would have AB$+$. In what follows we will be concerned only with infix notation and postfix, never prefix. Now let us consider a more complex example:

$$Y \leftarrow A * (B + C) \uparrow D + E$$

This is a simple assignment statement in ALGOL written in infix notation. (In this article and in our translator the symbol $\leftarrow$ will always be used in place of $:=$ as in the ALGOL report.) The postfix representation of the above assignment statement is as follows:

$$Y \; A \; B \; C + D \uparrow * E + \leftarrow$$

There are several points to be noted about the postfix. First, it is a parenthesis-free notation, since the order of operation is implied by the order that the symbols appear. It should also be noted that the same identifiers appear in the postfix as in the infix and in the same order. Similarly, the same operators appear that appeared in the infix but *not* in the same order. The translation from infix to postfix thus consists merely of reordering the operators of the input string.

6.4.2.4. *Symbol Table*

Traditionally, there are two aspects to the translation from problem-oriented algebraic languages to machine languages. These may be referred to as *formula translation* and *assembly*. The operation of formula translation consists of scanning the statements of the source code and determining the constituent parts (terms, factors, etc.). On the basis of this analysis it is determined which types of machine operations are to be compiled and in what order. The assembly process refers to the storage allocation and assignment of machine locations for both compiled code and program data. In the early translators these two phases were completely separated and many of these translators produced assembly language code as their output. Thus, for example, FORTRAN translated into SAP, which was then assembled into machine language. In most of the modern translators (including the one to be described) these two aspects of translation are merged inextricably into one program. Nonetheless, it is convenient for expository purposes to consider these two phases separately, even though the work is being done more or less at the same time.

Basic to all translation and assembly schemes is the idea of a *symbol*

table. By a *symbol* we mean an identifier used by the program writer in his
source code. For example, in the statement

$$X \leftarrow Y * (3 + Z)$$

the entities X, Y, and Z are identifiers. The number 3 is an absolute constant
(abcon) or a literal whose value is known at compile time. As each identifier
is read in by the translator, it is looked up in the symbol table. Here, by
"look up" we mean the following operation: We visualize a table of "sufficient" length which is cleared before translation. As each identifier is encountered, a routine looks to see if that identifier is in the table. If it is,
the result of the routine is the location of the identifier relative to the
beginning of the table. If not, it is appended to the end of the table and,
again, the output of the look-up routine is the location in the table. We may
regard the routine that looks up symbols in the symbol table as a routine
to encode the symbols into integers. That is, we may visualize that the
routine transforms each symbol into an integer, where the integer is the
location of the symbol in the table. In all cases, the transformation will be
unique and reversible, since each symbol can give rise to only one integer
and will give rise in all cases to the same integer. Further, one could do the
reverse operation, since (given the integer) it is trivial to get the symbol.
(We will not consider now the process of handling symbols which are too
long to be stored in one computer word, since this is not essential to an
understanding of the translator.)

Associated in some sense with the symbol table is another table, the
equivalent table. The equivalent table is of the same length as the symbol
table, containing one entry for each entry in the symbol table. It contains,
for each symbol, certain information regarding that symbol. For example,
if the symbol is an identifier of one of the problem variables, the information
in the equivalent table will give this fact, state whether the identifier is
real, integer, or Boolean, and indicate in which block head the identifier
was declared. Further, the equivalent table will contain information leading
to the machine address assigned to the variable. The Kth entry in the symbol
table will contain an internal representation for the Kth symbol encountered,
and the Kth entry in the equivalent table will contain its type information.

It is frequently the case in assemblers or translators that the symbol table
and the equivalent table are created at more or less the same time by the
same routine. In the present system these two tables are created at different
times by different routines. All that is important is that information is
placed in the equivalent table before it is needed by any other routine. It
will be seen that this condition is met.

It is clear that the block structure of ALGOL, which permits the re-use in a different context of a given identifier, causes serious problems in the maintenance of the symbol and equivalence tables. Although a variety of ways are known to handle this problem, we will refrain from discussing here the pros and cons of these ways. We will assume in what follows that a given identifier appears with only one meaning in a given ALGOL program. This assumption will effect none of the discussion that follows except that which pertains to the construction of the equivalent table, only a very minor part of the translator.

6.4.2.5. *The Stack*

The use of a stack for temporary storage during translation is basic to almost all modern translators. The stack provides for the convenient storage of information needed on a last-in-first-out basis. Although there are several techniques known for the realization of a stack in a digital computer, the method selected in the present translator is one of the simpler ones. We have a (sufficient) block of contiguous storage in memory and a pointer initialized to point to the first location of the block. The operation of stacking an element consists of storing it into that location in the block to which the pointer points and then incrementing the pointer by one. The operation of unstacking consists of decrementing the pointer by one and of making available the contents of that location to which the pointer now points. It can be easily seen that this scheme results in the last-in-first-out operation mentioned. (It is assumed here, of course, that each item of information occupies precisely one computer word.) All of this process may be clarified somewhat by the following example. The sequence of operations

```
STACK      A
STACK      B
STACK      C
UNSTACK
STACK      D
UNSTACK
UNSTACK
STACK      E
UNSTACK
UNSTACK
```

will have the effect of reordering the string A B C D E to the new order C D B E A.

6.4.3. THE SUBSCAN

The subscan is that portion of the translator referred to previously as T_s, which translates the source string L_0 punched on 80-column cards (or equivalent input medium) into the intermediate language L_0'. In the nature of things, much that goes on in the subscan is machine dependent. The problem here has to do with the representation of the ALGOL text on punched cards. It is an unfortunate aspect of punched cards that they are not blessed with underlining or with an adequate alphabet. There are several approaches to getting around the problem of underlining. The one chosen here (and, indeed, the usual approach) is to treat the words which appear in bold face type in the ALGOL report as reserved identifiers. Thus, for example, the programmer may not have a problem-variable name **begin**, since **begin** punched in a card will be interpreted as the ALGOL delimiter. He may, however, have a variable named BEGINNING. The effect, then, is that the symbol table starts at the beginning of translation with certain identifiers already in it: To wit, all English words appearing in bold face type in the ALGOL report, plus a few others added by Carnegie Tech. In addition, it has proved expedient to include in the symbol table all punctuation and delimiters represented by special characters. These include, for example, $+$, $-$, etc. The actual details of this process are all unimportant; the effect is all that counts. Here the effect of the subscan is that the source string L_0 is replaced by an equivalent string L_0' containing only integers, each integer representing a single character in L_0. As was mentioned above, we will usually ignore the existence of L_0'.

Since so much of the subscan is machine dependent, no further details of its operation will be given here. Instead, a few general comments will be made about it. The subscan creates two tables: the symbol table and the abcon table. Each identifier containing six characters or less is stored in one machine location in the symbol table. If the identifier has between seven and ten characters, it takes two locations in the symbol table; when it has more than ten characters, all characters beyond the tenth are stored in a special table located elsewhere. The second word of the symbol table entry then contains a link to the special table. All characters in a symbol are considered, regardless of the length of the symbol. Thus, for example, we will distinguish between two 50-character identifiers differing only in the fiftieth character. (Of course the translation process will be slowed down noticeably if the user uses very many such identifiers.) Although the symbol table is used by no other part of the translator, it continues to be available through running time to provide diagnostics in source language.

The abcon table contains an entry for each constant or literal used by the programmer. This table becomes part of the object program at run time.

6.4.4. PHASE I

We now will consider the operation of Phase I. As has been described, Phase I transforms an input string L'_0 created by the subscan into an output string L_i consisting of essentially the same characters, but reordered. For the most part, the transformation done by Phase I may be described as a conversion from infix to postfix notation. This description is not too accurate, however, since much that goes on in ALGOL cannot conveniently be termed infix; similarly, the Phase I output corresponding to this part of ALGOL is not really postfix. In addition, in procedure calls, in subscripting and elsewhere, it has proved expedient to produce a form which cannot rightly be called either infix or postfix but which is useful.

The characters appearing as input to Phase I include all characters in the ALGOL language and no other characters. Here the term *character* refers to a single item of punctuation (such as $+$ or $-$), a single reserved word, or a single identifier. The term *identifier* in this context includes abcons, since Phase I does not distinguish between constants and variables in its decision-making process but lumps all such operands together into a single indistinguishable category. The output string L_i from Phase I consists of essentially all characters which may appear in L_0, plus quite a few more characters. The governing principle used in selecting these characters and determining their meaning has been that Phase II is to have no recognition problem whatsoever. To the maximum extent possible, a given character is to have a unique meaning to Phase II, regardless of when it is encountered. (Putting it differently, the output from Phase I will never contain syntactic errors. Thus Phase II need do no checking but may operate on a given character as soon as it receives it.) Thus Phase I must do the work of distinguishing between different meanings given to the same character in ALGOL. For example, the character "," has several different meanings in ALGOL, depending on what kind of list it is separating. For each of these different meanings a different character is used in L_i.

The internal operation of Phase I will be discussed in some detail later on. Briefly, however, it is a conventional type of translator in which the hierarchy values of the various operators are used to control the order of execution of the operations. Consider, for example, the four expressions given below:

	Expression	*Postfix*
1.	A + B * C	ABC * +
2.	A * B + C	AB * C +
3.	(A + B) * C	AB + C *
4.	A * (B + C)	ABC + *

Lines 1 and 2 show the effect of hierarchy. Multiplication is considered of higher hierarchy than is addition. Thus, in line 1 we cannot create the plus in the output string until we have created the times. The reason is that we know that the multiplication must be executed first and that the right operand of + is the result of the multiplication. The effect, then, is that the operator with higher hierarchy must be compiled first. Just the opposite occurs in the second line. When multiplication is followed by addition, it is clear that the right operand of multiply is merely B. Thus we can create times in the output string immediately when plus is encountered on the input string. Lines 3 and 4 merely show how the normal hierarchy rules can be circumvented by suitable addition of parentheses. Clearly, parentheses form a special case and must be handled specially.

As was mentioned earlier in this paper, a special language called "Production Language" has been created for the purpose of describing Phase I. Before we can explain the operation of Phase I, we must describe the production language L_p. In the nature of things, a compiler is a program in which most of the work done consists of making decisions based on asking suitable questions about the last character scanned and the state of the translator as determined by the characters which have been scanned recently. Thus, a flow chart for a compiler usually has more decision boxes than action boxes. It is expedient, therefore, to attempt to develop a notation in which it is convenient to describe and program the decision-making processes involved. The language used is derived from a notation developed by R. W. Floyd. Floyd described[4] an algorithm for the translation of arithmetic expressions. This paper consists of about five pages of flow charts accompanied by three or four more pages of explanatory text. Later the same year, Floyd published[2] another description of the same algorithm. However, Floyd had developed a formalism for the algorithm which was the reason for existence of the later article. The formalism permitted a description in a very concise form of a process which had been described otherwise in a very lengthy series of flow charts. It is somewhat interesting to note that Floyd's sole reason for developing the formalism was to permit him to describe more concisely a process which had been formulated in a different manner. The notation developed by Floyd has come to be referred to as "Floyd productions."

At Carnegie Tech. it has proved to be expedient to modify Floyd's notation in several nontrivial ways, both to meet the demands of the character set of the computer available and for various aesthetic and philosophical reasons which were deemed appropriate. The result is a programming language rather than a notation. The emphasis in the previous sentence is on the word *programming*. Almost by definition, a programming language is one which can be run on a computer. The important thing here is that we were able to develop a language which we could run on the computer in which it was convenient and natural to express the algorithm of Phase I. It is, of course, necessary that the phrase "a language which can be run on a computer" be explained. Production language runs on the computer just as does FORTRAN, in the sense that in each case we have a mechanism to translate the language that the programmer writes into a form acceptable by the computer's hardware. For FORTRAN we have a FORTRAN translator; for production language we have a loader and an interpreter.

We will now define the production language L_p. For concreteness and to provide a workable example, we will consider a somewhat modified subset of all of the productions. This subset will be capable of translating assignment statements into postfix. Its abilities include the processing of subscripted variables, procedure calls, and conditional arithmetic or Boolean expressions. These productions are listed in Table 6.4.1, to which reference is made in the following discussion.

L_p will be defined first by example. Look at line 22 about halfway down Table 6.4.1 with the label E3 in the second column. The meaning of this line is as follows: "If the top element in the stack is the symbol] and if the second element is the symbol [, then delete these two elements from the stack, create the character] in the output string, scan a new character, and consider next the production whose label is E3A." This meaning may be deduced as follows: The first vertical bar (|) indicates the top of the stack. The characters immediately to its left represent the elements which we are looking for in the stack. The fact that a symbol → appears immediately to the right of the | indicates that the stack is to be transformed into the form indicated just to the left of the next |. Since on this line there are no characters to the left of that |, we conclude that the two brackets are to be deleted. The fact that we are to create] in the output string is quite clear from the message OUTPUT]. The field containing this message is the *action field* containing the *operation* OUTPUT with the *parameter*]. The next field is the *link* field. The "∗" indicates that a new character is to be

Table 6.4.1. Productions

No	State	S1	S2			→	S3	→₂	S4			Alt	Action	Next
1	E1B		-	|					|		ERROR 0	Q1
2	E1A		+	|	→				|			*E1C
3			-	|	→	NG			|			*E1C
4	E1		-	|					|			*E1B
5	E1C		I	|	→				|		OUT	*E2
6			(	|	→	E(			|			*E1A
7			IF	|					|			*E1
8			<SG>	|					|		ERROR 1	Q1
9	E2		(	|					|		OUTPUT (	*E1A
10			[	|					|		OUT	*E1A
11	E2A		<OP>	|					|		COMPILE	E2B
12			←	|					|		OUTPUT LOG	E5
13			,	|					|		COMPILE ←|	E11
14			]	|					|		COMPILE	E3
15			THEN	|					|		COMPILE ←|	E21
16			ELSE	|					|		COMPILE	E25
17			;	|					|		COMPILE ←|	E30
18			)	|					|		COMPILE	E6
19			<SG>	|					|		ERROR 2	Q1
20	E2B		<AR>	|					|			*E1C
21			<SG>	|					|			*E1A
22	E3	[	]	|	→				|		OUTPUT]	*E3A
23			<SG>	|					|		ERROR 3	Q1
24	E3A	(	,	|	→	(			|		OUTPUT LOC	EA11
25		(	)	|	→				|		OUTPUT LOC	EA6
26			←	|					|		OUTPUT LOC	E5
27			<SG>	|					|			E2A
28	E5	| →	←	|	→	|→	←←		|			*E1A
29		←←	←	|					|			*E1A
30		←	←	|					|			*E1A
31			<SG>	|					|		ERROR 4	Q1
32	E6	E(	)	|	→				|			*E2A
33		(	)	|	→				|	EA6	OUTPUT)	*E2A
34			<SG>	|					|		ERROR 5	Q1
35	E11	(	,	|	→	(			|	EA11	OUTPUT ,	*E1A
36		[	,	|	→	[			|		OUTPUT AR.	*E1A
37			<SG>	|					|		ERROR 6	Q1
38	E21	IF	THEN	|	→	THEN			|		OUTPUT IF	*E1A
39			<SG>	|					|		ERROR 7	Q1
40	E25	THEN	ELSE	|	→	ELSE			|		OUTPUT THEN	*E1A
41			<SG>	|					|		ERROR 8	Q1
42	E30	|→	;	|	→	|→			|		OUTPUT ←|	
43											HALT	
44			<SG>	|					|		ERROR 9	Q1
45										Q1	HALT	

scanned, and the fact that we are to consider next the production named E3A is again clear.

Let us look now at production E3A on line 24. It is interpreted as follows: "If the top character in the stack is comma and if the second character in the stack is (, then delete the comma from the top of stack, create the character LOC in the output string, and consider next the production EA11." A character enclosed in the special brackets $\langle \cdots \rangle$ is considered as a meta character. The definitions of the meta characters used in the assignment statement productions are given in Table 6.4.3. The meta character $\langle SG \rangle$, however, is a special case recognized by the translator, and stands for "any character whatsoever." Look now at line 23: It is apparent that if we ever reach this line, we will get a match, since the line says, "If the top character in the stack is anything at all, then. . . ." The action on this line indicates that an error in source code has been detected and that error message number 3 is to be produced on the output printer. Attention next is to go to that production whose name is Q1. The production labeled E2A about a fourth of the way down the column in Table 6.4.1 may be interpreted as follows: "If the top character in the stack is a member of the meta linguistic class $\langle OP \rangle$, then do the action COMPILE and consider next that production labeled E2B." The operation COMPILE is as follows: Associated with each operator is a hierarchy value as given in Table 6.4.4. The operation of COMPILE consists of comparing the hierarchy of the top element in the stack with that of the second element in the stack. If the top element has higher hierarchy than the second element, the operation terminates. If the top element has a hierarchy which is less than or equal to the hierarchy of the second element, an instance of the second element is created in the output string and the second element is deleted from the stack. The operation is then repeated on the (new) second element of the stack. In some lines, the operation COMPILE has a parameter. This means that instead of using the hierarchy of the top element of the stack to compare with the hierarchy of the second element, instead the hierarchy of the character appearing to the right of COMPILE is to be used. In this case, the top element of the stack is ignored.

Three other actions must be described. The action OUTPUT will always have a parameter. The effect will be to create an instance of that parameter in the output string. The action OUT will never have a parameter. The effect will always be to create in the output string the last character which was scanned from the input string. Although this will in general be the character at the top of the stack, it will not be in the case where the last character scanned was an identifier. In that case the character in the top of the stack is I. OUT, however, will produce the actual identifier scanned rather than an instance of I. A final action that must be mentioned is HALT. Its effect is obvious.

It is fairly clear that the productions as described are representative of a computer language. The leftmost field contains a label for the production. As is usual in assembly languages, this field may be blank if the production is never referred to elsewhere. The next four fields contain a representation of the (up to) top four characters in the stack. If any of these fields is blank, it indicates that we are not concerned with the corresponding stack entry. Next, there will be a | if the card represents a production card. If the symbol → appears immediately to the right of the |, the next three columns represent the form into which the stack is to be transformed. To the right of the next | is another label field which may be used to label an action. Next comes the action field with, perhaps, a parameter. The last column may contain a star, indicating SCAN, and will contain the label of the production to which attention is to go next. As a special case, the last field may be blank. In that case, it is assumed that the next card does not contain a production (and therefore, will not have |'s in the columns which normally contain this symbol), but will contain only an action and a link. An example of this may be found on the third line from the bottom of the table.

It is appropriate now to consider, at least briefly, the internal representation of the production language in the computer. Remember that we refer to the production language as L_p and its internal representation as L_p'. Note now Table 6.4.2. This table contains the representation of the *interpretation list* for each production. The production code actually exists in memory as two tables. The first table, called the production table, consists of all the information to the left of the leftmost vertical bar in Table 6.4.1. It can be seen that this information is precisely that which is scanned to find a match. Associated with each line in the production table is a link to a location in the interpretation list. The interpretation list may be regarded as containing code for a very simple one-address computer. Look, for example, at line 40, labeled E25 in Table 6.4.1. The corresponding line in the interpretation list in Table 6.4.2 contains five sections: The first, NSTK, stands for unstack. The meaning of NSTK 2 is to delete the top two elements of the stack. Next the character **else** is stacked. Note that the effect of these two operations is to give precisely the stack change indicated in the production line. Next the character **then** is created in the output string, and finally we scan a new character and go to E1A. The internal representation L_p' is precisely the production table and the inter-

Table 6.4.2. Interpretation List

#							
1	ERRO		NEXT Q1				
2	NSTK	1	SCAN	NEXT E1C			
3	NSTK	1	STAK NG	SCAN	NEXT E1C		
4	SCAN		NEXT E1B				
5	NSTK	1	OUT	SCAN	NEXT E2		
6	NSTK	1	STAK (	SCAN	NEXT E1A		
7	SCAN		NEXT E1				
8	ERRO	1	NEXT Q1				
9	OUTP (		SCAN	NEXT E1A			
10	OUT		SCAN	NEXT E1A			
11	COMP		NEXT E2B				
12	OUTP LOC		NEXT E5				
13	COMP ←|		NEXT E11				
14	COMP		NEXT E3				
15	COMP ←|		NEXT E21				
16	COMP		NEXT E25				
17	COMP ←|		E30				
18	COMP		NEXT E6				
19	ERRO	2	NEXT Q1				
20	SCAN		NEXT E1C				
21	SCAN		NEXT E1A				
22	NSTK	2	OUTP]	SCAN	NEXT E3A		
23	ERRO	3	NEXT Q1				
24	NSTK	2	STAK (	OUTP LOC	NEXT EA11		
25	NSTK	2	OUTP LOC	NEXT EA6			
26	OUTP LOC		NEXT E5				
27	NEXT E2A						
28	NSTK	2	STAK |→	STAK ←←	SCAN	NEXT E1A	
29	SCAN		NEXT E1A				
30	SCAN		NEXT E1A				
31	ERRO	4	NEXT Q1				
32	NSTK	2	SCAN	NEXT E2A			
33	NSTK	2	OUTP)	SCAN	NEXT E2A		
34	ERRO	5	NEXT Q1				
35	NSTK	2	STAK (	OUTP ,	SCAN	NEXT E1A	
36	NSTK	2	STAK [	OUTP AR.	SCAN	NEXT E1A	
37	ERRO	6	NEXT Q1				
38	NSTK	2	STAK THEN	OUTP IF	SCAN	NEXT E1A	
39	ERRO	7	NEXT Q1				
40	NSTK	2	STAK ELSE	OUTP THEN	SCAN	NEXT E1A	
41	ERRO	8	NEXT Q1				
42	NSTK	2	STAK |→	OUTP ←|	HALT		
43							
44	ERRO	9	NEXT Q1				
45	HALT						

pretation list. The translator T_m is no more than a loader to create these two tables from the productions as punched on cards.

Now that the *form* of the productions has been explained, we are in a position to discuss the algorithm they define. We will continue to discuss the assignment statement productions of Table 6.4.1. We will assume that each input assignment statement is delimited on the left by two instances of the left terminator symbol $| \rightarrow$ and on the right by a semicolon. The operation of translation consists of reading the characters from the source statement, one character at a time. As each character is read, the translator decides on the basis of that character and of certain preceding characters what action to take. In general, the actions will consist of storing information in a stack for later branching, of creating characters in the output string, and of scanning new characters. Phase I maintains a stack containing only operators and special internal symbols created by Phase I which are more or less equivalent to operators. Operands are never stacked. When a character is scanned, the effect is to stack the new character. An apparent contradiction results from what was said above, since it was stated that only operators may appear in the stack whereas it is clearly the case that the new character may be an operand (an identifier). It will be seen, however, that the productions are written in such a way that whenever an identifier is scanned, it is immediately created in the output string. Actually, all that is put in the stack is a special character (called I) which stands for "identifier." The identifier itself is stored in a special location where it is available to the routine which creates characters in the output string.

Let us consider an explicit example, the same one used by Floyd:[2]

$$X \leftarrow Y \uparrow Z * (U + V)$$

We assume that the stack has been initialized to contain two left terminator symbols, $| \rightarrow$, and that the initial X has already been scanned and stacked. Look now at Table 6.4.5. Each line of this table represents a snapshot trace of the state of the stack when a character is created in the output string. The rightmost column of the table indicates the characters of the output string. The column to its immediate left shows the last character which was scanned. The leftmost column of the table indicates the last production to which attention was transferred, and the remainder of the table indicates the contents of the stack. Before explaining the translation process as revealed by this example, we will discuss various details.

Note that the new character LOC, which has not before been mentioned, appears in the output string. LOC is a unary operator which indicates that we are concerned with the *location* of its operand rather than its value. The idea here has to do with the fact that the two instances of X in the statement

$$X \leftarrow X + 1$$

have a different meaning. The X to the left of the left arrow refers to a location and the X to the right refers to the value of X. The postfix code produced for this statement would be

$$X \text{ LOC } X \text{ } 1 \text{ } + \text{ } \leftarrow\leftarrow$$

The symbol $\leftarrow\leftarrow$ is also a new one. Consider the legal ALGOL assignment statement

$$X \leftarrow Y \leftarrow Z + 1$$

The postfix produced would be

$$X \text{ LOC } Y \text{ LOC } Z \text{ } 1 \text{ } + \text{ } \leftarrow \text{ } \leftarrow\leftarrow$$

Here, $\leftarrow$ is a binary operator which has the effect of storing the value of the second operand into the location given by the first operand. The operator has a value: the value of the right operand. (What this means in a computer representation is that it is assumed that the value just stored is still available in the accumulator.) The operator $\leftarrow\leftarrow$ is also a binary operator whose effect is the same as for left arrow except that it is assumed that the operator has no value. (In the computer, the value in the accumulator is to be ignored.) The idea here is that the two instances of $\leftarrow$ in the original assignment statement have different meanings, depending on whether or not the value will continue to be needed. Since one of the design criteria was that Phase II was to have as little decision making to do as possible, it is therefore desirable to introduce new notation and new symbols to reduce the problems of Phase II. Other such conventions will be seen in the following discussion.

Let us now consider some more aspects of the language. No satisfactory representation of subscripted variables could be found which could be called postfix. The decision which was finally made can best be shown by example. Consider the statement

$$A[I, J] \leftarrow B[K, L]$$

The postfix representation of this statement is

$$A \text{ [} I \text{ AR, } J \text{] LOC } B \text{ [} K \text{ AR, } L \text{] } \leftarrow\leftarrow$$

The operator] is an *n*-ary operator, with the number of parameters indicated by the number of elements between it and the last left bracket preceding. (It will be seen that subscripted elements appearing in subscripts will cause no problems.) The symbol "AR" is a separator used to separate the subscript positions. Note the use again of LOC to indicate that the location rather than the value of A[I, J] is desired.

Subroutine calls are handled in a similar way. The symbols (and) are used in the postfix string just as are [and]. Here,) is an *n*-ary operator whose parameters are delimited on the left by the (. The symbol used as a separator between actual parameters is comma. Again, note how we are adhering to the principles stated above in giving a different postfix character for ambiguous meanings of a given source string character. Here we are using comma for one meaning of "," and "AR," for another.

Let us now consider conditional arithmetic expressions. Let β stand for any Boolean expression and let ε_1 and ε_2 be arithmetic expressions. Further, let the notation $\{X\}$ stand for "the postfix representation of X," for any X. Then the arithmetic expression

$$\textbf{if } \beta \textbf{ then } \varepsilon_1 \textbf{ else } \varepsilon_2$$

will be translated to the postfix form

$$\{\beta\} \textbf{ if } \{\varepsilon_1\} \textbf{ then } \{\varepsilon_2\} \textbf{ else}$$

Thus, **if** is a unary operator whose operand is a Boolean expression, and **then** and **else** are both binary operators.

We are now in a position to resume discussion of the statement

$$X \leftarrow Y \uparrow Z * (U + V)$$

which was first mentioned earlier. Noting Table 6.4.5 containing the trace printout of the translation of this statement, let us look carefully at just what is going on. We start with the first production of Table 6.4.1 and look for a match. Remember that we have the identifier X and two left terminators in the stack. (Actually, as was mentioned, it is not X which is in the stack but rather the internal symbol I. X is stored in a temporary location where it will be available to the action OUT.) The first production on which we will find a match is on line 5. In this case, we are looking for an I as the top element in the stack and we are not concerned with any other element in the stack. The production indicates that the I is to be deleted and the action OUT is to be performed, creating an instance of the identifier X in the output string. We next scan a new character (which will be left arrow) and turn our attention to production E2. In this case we will get a match at line 12. We create an instance of LOC in the output string, and without scanning a new character, turn our attention to E5. Here we get a match on the first production at which we look, line 28. The effect is to replace the ← by ←←← and then to scan a new character and go to E1A. The new character will be the identifier Y, which, after a match at line 5, we will create in the output string. We scan a new character and go to E2. The new character is ↑. We get a match at line 11, since ↑ is a member of the meta-linguistic class ⟨OP⟩ (see Table 6.4.3). We are told that we are now to

Table 6.4.3. Meta Characters

P>	←	<		>		~<		~>		=		v		≠		+		−		*		/		↑		∧
R>	←	+		−		*		/		↑															

compile. The hierarchy of ↑ as given in Table 6.4.4 is 24, and the hierarchy of ←←← is 8. Since the top element of the stack has higher hierarchy than the second element, we terminate the compile operation, having done nothing. We now go to E2B. Since ↑ is a member of the metalinguistic class ⟨AR⟩, we get a match immediately, scan a new character, and go to E1C. The new character is Z, which we will process as before and continue with a new character at E2. The new character is "*", and we again do the operation of COMPILE. The hierarchy of "*" is 20. Since ↑ has a higher hierarchy, we create an instance of ↑ in the output string and delete ↑ from the stack. We then do COMPILE again. We now find that left terminator has a lower hierarchy than "*" so we terminate the operation. It is left as an exercise for the reader to follow the operation of the translator through the rest of the statement. He may check his calculation with Table 6.4.5, showing the condition of the stack each time a character is created in the output string.

A few more words about the productions of Table 6.4.1 are appropriate. Basically, the translator is usually in one of two states, as represented by

Table 6.4.4. Hierarchies

24	↑				
22	*NG*				
20	*	/			
18	+	-			
16	<	>	~<	~>	= ≠
14	~				
12	∧				
10	∨				
8	←	←←			
6	*ELSE*				
4	,				
2	)	]			
0	←|				
-2	*IF*				
-4	*THEN*				
-6	[	*E(*	(		
-8	|→	*FOR*			

scanning at E1 (or E1A, E1B, or E1C) or at E2 (or E2A). At E1 the system is expecting an operand; at E2 it is expecting an operator. In ALGOL, the usual operand will be an identifier. However, it is also possible that the identifier will be preceded by a unary operator; that the operand will be a parenthesized expression; or that the operand will be a conditional expression starting with IF. Note that it is just these possibilities which are checked for. At E2, we will have just scanned an operand and we will be expecting an operator. However, an operand may also be followed by),], **then**, **else**, or ;. Again, these possibilities are all checked for. The difference between E2 and E2A arises from the fact that an identifier may be followed by a (or a [, indicating "subroutine call" or "subscripted variable," respectively. If the operand just scanned was not an identifier but was a parenthesized expression or a subscripted variable, then it may not be followed by a (or a [, but must be followed instead by one of the other possibilities. Thus, a match at line 5 leads to E2 while we go to E2A following the scanning of a parenthesized expression or a subscripted variable. (Note the links of lines 27, 32, and 33.)

Table 6.4.5.   Production Traces

```
                         X ← Y ↑ Z * ( U + V ) ;

LABEL                      S T A C K                 SCANNED   OUTPUT

E1B                                      |→  |→      | X         X
E2                              |→  |→  ←            | ←         LOC
E1A                             |→  |→  ←←           | Y         Y
E1C                     |→  |→  ←←  ↑                | Z         Z
E2          |→   |→   ←←   ↑    *                    | *         ↑
F1A                     |→  |→  ←←  *   E(           | U         U
E1C          |→   |→   ←←   *    E(   +              | V         V
E2    |→   |→   ←←   *    E(    +    )               | )         +
E2A                     |→  |→  ←←  *   ;            | ;         *
E2A                     |→  |→  ←←  ;                | ;         ←←
E30                                      |→  |→      | ;         ←|
```

```
                  Y ← A - IF P = Q THEN B ↑ C ELSE W * Z ;

LABEL                      S T A C K                 SCANNED   OUTPUT

E1B                                      |→  |→      | Y         Y
E2                              |→  |→  ←            | ←         LOC
E1A                             |→  |→  ←←           | A         A
E1          |→   |→   ←←    -    IF                  | P         P
E1A    |→  |→   |→   ←←    -    IF   =               | Q         Q
E2    |→   |→   ←←    -    IF   =   THEN             | THEN      =
F21             |→   |→   ←←    -   THEN             | THEN      IF
E1A             |→   |→   ←←    -   THEN             | B         B
E1C        |→   |→   ←←    -    THEN  ↑              | C         C
E2    |→   |→   ←←    -    THEN  ↑   ELSE            | ELSE      ↑
E25             |→   |→   ←←    -   ELSE             | ELSE      THEN
E1A             |→   |→   ←←    -   ELSE             | W         W
E1C        |→   |→   ←←    -    ELSE  *              | Z         Z
E2    |→   |→   ←←    -    ELSE  *   ;               | ;         *
E2         |→   |→   ←←    -    ELSE  ;              | ;         ELSE
E2              |→   |→   ←←    -   ;                | ;         -
E2                       |→   |→   ←←   ;            | ;         ←←
E30                                      |→  |→      | ;         ←|
```

The character (has two meanings in the language: It may be used as a bracket to indicate explicitly order of evaluation or as a bracket to delimit the arguments of a subroutine. In the first case, it will be encountered by the translator immediately after an operator; i.e., when an operand is expected. In this context, it will be encountered at E1 on line 6. The second meaning will occur immediately after scanning an identifier, when an operator is expected. In this context, it will be scanned at E2. It is thus easy for the translator to recognize which type of left parenthesis it has encountered. To keep track of this fact, the left parenthesis, which is used for the first meaning, will be replaced in the stack by the symbol "E(" which is a mnemonic for "expressional left-parenthesis." The replacement takes place on line 6. "E(", then, is an internal symbol of the translator created to ease the recognition problem. Now note the occurrence of right parentheses in the productions. A match for a right parenthesis will occur at line 18 after E2, when an operator is expected. The operation COMPILE is done with the hierarchy of the right parenthesis. The effect will be to remove from the top of the stack all operators which have been stacked (and not removed) since the last left parenthesis. We then turn our attention to production E6. If the second character in the stack is "E(", then the two parentheses are deleted from the stack, a new character is scanned, and we go to E2A. The effect, then, is that we have completely forgotten about the occurrence of the parenthesized expression, since we have processed it in its entirety. If, on the other hand, the second character in the stack is "(", the right parenthesis terminates a subroutine call. In that case, we create in the output string an instance of the character) and continue as before. In all other cases, a syntactic error has been detected. We give error message 5 and terminate.

Let us now consider comma. A comma is recognized on line 13 after E2 when an operator is expected. We compile with the hierarchy of right terminator (right terminator has hierarchy 0) and continue at E11. If the second character in the stack is left parenthesis, the comma separates parameter positions in a subroutine call. In that case the comma is deleted from the stack, an instance of comma is created in the output string, and we continue at E1A after scanning a new character. If the second character in the stack is left bracket, the comma separates subscript positions. In that case we create AR in the output string and continue as above.

Let us now consider right bracket. A match on right bracket is obtained on line 14 after E2 where we expect an operator. We compile to remove from the stack all operators which were part of the subscript position and continue at E3. It must now be the case that the second character in the stack is a left bracket. If so, we delete both brackets from the stack, create an instance of right bracket in the output string, scan a new character, and continue at E3A. If not, a syntactic error has been detected. If the new character is a comma and the previous character in the stack was a left parenthesis, the subscripted variable was an entire actual parameter to a procedure. In that case we are interested in the location of the subscripted variable rather than its value, since we must provide for the case where the parameter is called by name at run time. To indicate this, the symbol LOC is created in the output string. The link on this line is EA11. This is a new situation, not covered before in the article, since there is no production with the label EA11. On the other hand, we will find an instance of EA11 in the column just to the right of the rightmost vertical bar, on line 35. The effect, then, is that after creating LOC in the output string, we are to go to the interpretation list action labeled EA11. This tells us to create an instance of comma in the output string and then to go to E1A after scanning a new character. Let us continue now with our discussion of the match after E3A. If the new character scanned is a right parenthesis and the previous character was a left parenthesis, the subscripted variable is again an entire actual parameter to a procedure call. (In this case it is the last parameter.) We again create an instance of LOC in the output string and continue at EA6 as before. Finally, if the next scanned is left arrow, we again create an instance of LOC in the output string and continue at E5. In all other cases, we continue at E2A, expecting an operator.

There are several extra productions added to the table. The production E1B provides for the occurrence of two successive instances of the ¬ symbol. We can reach E1B only after getting a match at line 4. E1A is the usual entry after scanning an operator when an operand is expected. At E1A, the unary operators are legal. Immediately after scanning an arithmetic unary operator (plus or minus) we may not have another such. Therefore, matches for these cases lead to E1C. A plus encountered as a unary operator (i.e., when an operand was expected) is merely deleted from the stack and ignored. A minus is replaced in the stack by the symbol "NG." It is imperative in interpreting the postfix that each operator have a unique meaning. It would be very difficult, if not impossible, for Phase II to distinguish between the two meanings of minus if the same symbol were used in the postfix for both. It is for this reason that "NG" is stacked rather than minus when it is recognized that minus is a unary operator. Here, as usual, we are following the principle of saving information when it is available so that it can be used later when it is no longer available.

Let us now look at the details of the handling of **if**, **then**, and **else**.

(Remember that we are considering here only assignment statements. Thus we are not concerned with the use of these three operators in connection with conditional statements but merely with their use in conditional expressions.) **if** indicates the beginning of an operand and is recognized at E1. We see that the **if** is merely left in the stack and we continue, expecting another operand. Both **then** and **else** are encountered when an operator is expected below E2. After **then** is encountered, we compile with the hierarchy of ←| to remove from the stack all operators encountered since the last **if** and continue at production E21. At this time, it must be a case that the **if** is the second element in the stack. If it is, we delete it, leaving **then** in the stack, and create an instance of **if** in the output string. We continue at E1A, scanning a new character. Again, when we encounter **else** we compile with its hierarchy (i.e., 6). The effect will be to compile all operators other than parentheses or comma. In particular, we will not compile **then**. We continue then at E25, expecting that the second element in the stack is **then**. A little thought on the part of the reader will show that the result here is exactly that which we said we would give.

Finally, we must consider the end of translation. A semicolon would be encountered when an operator was expected at E2. We would compile with hierarchy of ←| (i.e., 0) and continue at E30. At that time, the left terminator should be the second element in the stack and the semicolon the top. We create an instance of ←| in the output string and halt.

One might ask what would give rise to the various possible error conditions. A few words will be said about each. Error 0 indicates the occurrence of two consecutive ¬ symbols. Error 1 indicates an illegal character encountered when an operand was expected. An example might be A ↑—B. (This construction is illegal according to the ALGOL report and will be recognized as illegal by the set of productions now being described. In the actual translator as used at Carnegie Tech., such constructions will be accepted as legal.) Error 2 will be indicated when an operator is expected and not found. An example might be a missing multiply. Error 3 indicates that a right bracket does not have a matching left bracket in the stack as expected. This might be caused by a right bracket occurring without a left bracket or by more left parentheses than right parentheses in the subscript expression. Error 4 indicates an illegal use of left arrow. This would be caused by a left arrow appearing in any context other than as part of a left part list in an assignment statement. Error 5 will be given when a right parenthesis does not have a matching left parenthesis. This might be caused by more right parentheses than left parentheses in the assignment statement or between an **if** and a **then** or between a **then** and an **else**. Error 6 indicates the use of a comma other than as a delimiter of subscript positions or parameter positions. Error 7 indicates a **then** not properly preceded by an **if**. It might be caused by more left parentheses or left brackets than right between the **if** and the **then**. Similarly, Error 8 indicates an **else** not properly preceded by a **then**. Finally, Error 9 indicates that characters remain in the stack when semicolon is encountered. These characters could only be left parenthesis, left bracket, **if** or **then**.

6.4.5. PHASE II

We will now consider briefly the operation of Phase II. The effect of Phase II is to transform the intermediate postfix string L_i into machine language L_t. Let us consider an example. The assignment statement

$$Y \leftarrow (A + B) * (C + D)$$

will be translated by Phase I to

$$Y \text{ LOC } A \ B + C \ D + * \leftarrow \leftarrow$$

The resulting machine code should look something like that given below. Here we are visualizing a hypothetical one-address computer (which may look familiar) in which CLA is the operation code for "clear and add," STO is "store," and ADD and MPY stand for addition and multiplication, respectively.

CLA	A
ADD	B
STO	TEMP1
CLA	C
ADD	D
MPY	TEMP1
STO	Y

Note that the operators appear to have been compiled in the same order in which they appear in the postfix but that the operands have had their order changed. Remember that in Phase I the operands appeared in the output in the same order as in the input but the operators had their order changed. In this sense the examples given are typical and indicative of the operation of Phase I and Phase II. Phase I reorders the operators so that the eventual machine code will do the right thing in the right order to match the hierarchy and other precedence rules of the source language. In Phase II the operands are reordered as appropriate for economization of storage into temporaries.

Phase II operates using a single stack. In this case, however, the stack contains only operands and never operators. Whenever Phase II encounters an operand in the source string, it puts it into the stack. When an *n*-ary operator is encountered, code is compiled, utilizing the top *n* positions of the stack. For example, when + is encountered, the code to produce the sum of the top two elements of the stack is compiled. These two elements are deleted from the stack and a symbol is stacked, indicating that the result is in the accumulator. If at any time Phase II has to compile new code when there is already a result in the accumulator, and if further the new code does not use this result, it will compile the appropriate store into a temporary. Let us consider again the above example. We are translating the postfix string

$$Y \text{ LOC } A \ B + C \ D + * \leftarrow\leftarrow$$

Phase II will stack the symbol Y. The operator LOC will cause the symbol to be marked in the stack as being a location rather than a value. Then A and B will be stacked. When + is encountered, the code

$$\begin{array}{ll} \text{CLA} & \text{A} \\ \text{ADD} & \text{B} \end{array}$$

will be compiled, A and B will be deleted from the stack, and the accumulator symbol ACC will be stacked. Next, C and D will be stacked. When the next + is encountered, the routine will note that it needs the accumulator for the next calculation and that it is already in use. It will therefore compile

$$\text{STO} \qquad \text{TEMP1}$$

and replace the accumulator symbol in the stack by the symbol TEMP1. Then it will compile

$$\begin{array}{ll} \text{CLA} & \text{C} \\ \text{ADD} & \text{D} \end{array}$$

and delete C and D from the stack, stacking again the accumulator symbol. When the "*" is encountered, the top two elements in the stack will be

ACC and TEMP1. Therefore, the only code that need be compiled is

MPY   TEMP1

TEMP1 and ACC are deleted from the stack and ACC is restacked. When the ←←← is encountered, the top of the stack is ACC and the second element is Y. Thus we compile

STO   Y

It is unfortunate that we have no formalism similar to the production language appropriate to describe the algorithm of Phase II. Phase II is a collection of machine code which can be described in no better way than by giving flow charts. Flow charts for complex processes are usually either sufficiently detailed that they are unreadable or so clear that they are uninformative. The Phase II flow charts are no exception. In any case, however, the effect of the algorithm is to compile code for one particular machine—the Control Data G-20. Although a very similar algorithm could be used on any other one-address computer, it is certainly the case that the algorithm would have to be modified. For example, on the G-20, no distinction need be made in doing accesses between integer and floating point variables. The G-20 has opcodes for REVERSE DIVIDE and for REVERSE SUBTRACT, a great blessing to the compiler writer. A large unsolved problem, which we are now working on, is that of devising a formalism suitable for representing the translation from postfix to machine code. Ideally, the notation would permit the object computer to be described formally. Its properties would then appear only as table entries rather than as an inextricable part of the code of Phase II as they do now. It should only be added that the algorithm used in Phase II is modeled loosely after an algorithm devised at the University of Michigan and used in the GAT translator on the IBM 650 and the MAD translator on the IBM 704. This algorithm has been described briefly in Ref. 3.

REFERENCES

1. Samelson, K., and Bauer, F. L., "Sequential Formula Translation," *Comm. ACM*, **3**, 76 (1960).
2. Floyd, R. W., "A Descriptive Language for Symbol Manipulation," *J. ACM*, **8**, 579 (1961).
3. Arden, B. W., Galler, B. A., and Graham, R. M., "The Internal Organization of the MAD Translator," *Comm. ACM*, **4**, 28 (1961).
4. Floyd, R. W., "An Algorithm for Coding Efficient Arithmetic Operations," *Comm. ACM*, **4**, 42 (1961).

7.

DETAILS OF COMPILER
CONSTRUCTION

7.0. OVERVIEW

This chapter is concerned with a number of specific techniques used in the construction of compilers. Compiler implementation, as are most other system implementation endeavors today, is usually a group effort coordinating the work of several individuals. First, the overall design is decided upon, and then modules are designed which perform each of the functions necessary to realize the overall translator.

Decisions must be made—whether the compiler is to be syntax directed, what type of syntax analyzer is to be used (if any, or the alternative process if not), the amount and types of optimization to be made, and how resources are to be allocated for both the compiler and the generated code. Restrictions in machine environment or systems environment will influence the design of some modules, especially those relating to storage management and input/output facilities.

This chapter, then, presents specific techniques to be used in the implementation of such modules. Article 7.1 by Elson and Rake is concerned with the subject of generating optimized code for complex, high-level programming languages. The authors chose PL/I as their source language and the IBM System/360 for their target machine. The techniques they present, however, are sufficiently general so as to be applicable to a wide variety of computers and almost arbitrary source languages.

Article 7.2 by Samelson and Bauer describes a common technique for the translation of independent statements—the "last-in-first-out" (or LIFO) stack. This algorithm is known by various other names, among which are the "cellar algorithm" and the "railway shunt algorithm." The LIFO technique particularly lends itself to the translation of computational statements; however, it is sufficiently powerful so that when slightly extended, it is adequate for the translation of a large subset of the ALGOL programming language.

Address calculation is the subject of Article 7.3 by Ingerman; a piece of code that produces an address is termed a "thunk." Ingerman's motivation for devising this technique was the need for a more general technique for implementing procedure calls.

Irons and Feurzeig discuss in Article 7.4 the implementation of recursive procedures in ALGOL 60. They refer to Ingerman's article and utilize several types of thunks in their presentation.

7.1. Code-Generation Technique for Large-Language Compilers

by M. Elson and S. T. Rake

7.1.1. SUMMARY

A solution is proposed to the problem of optimizing code generation by a large-language compiler. A high-level definitional language is used to define the code mappings, and an interpreter executes the routines in this language during the one-pass, text-driven, code-generation phase. The technique might also be applied to extendable languages and shared-component compilers.

7.1.2. INTRODUCTION

The design of an optimizing compiler for a large and rich language poses problems beyond those of sheer size and cost. One of the most serious is that the wealth and variety of the language makes it possible to express the same logical function in terms of many different source constructs. The choice may be based on naturalness of language use; program readability; ease of debugging; compile-time or object-time; space-versus-time trade-offs, or programmer whimsicality.

EDITOR'S NOTE: This article reproduced by permission of the authors and the publisher: *IBM System J.*, vol. 9, no. 3 (1970), pp. 166–188.

The problem is compounded when the target machine of the compiler is one as rich in function as the IBM System/360.[1] Again, there are many ways of expressing the same function. And if the source language is designed to be highly machine-independent, there is, naturally, no simple set of mappings between source and target constructs. The problem of optimizing in this environment is most strongly felt at code-generation time, when the mapping must be effected from a source-oriented text to a target-oriented one.

This article describes a solution to this problem, in terms of a code-generation phase that features a high-level, special-purpose, code-generation language, and total context sensitivity, unlimited special casing, and a paging mechanism necessary because of the resultant phase size. The phase was developed as part of an experimental optimizing compiler.

In this paper, PL/I is used as an example source language,[2] and System/360 machine code is used because it is the particular target language for which the technique was developed. However, application of the ideas presented presuppose implementation of a language designed to be machine-independent, but do not presuppose PL/I source language or System/360 target language. The code-generation language was parameterized for different System/360 models, but not for radically different machine languages. The authors feel, however, that modifications to the language and its use might easily be made to accommodate different machine architectures.

We first describe our solution to the code-generation problem, and then demonstrate the solution with a prototype compiler.

7.1.3. THE CODE-GENERATION PROBLEM

7.1.3.1. *Worst-Case Code*

The semantics of PL/I are highly context-sensitive, so that worst-case code generation is a more severe problem than with simpler languages. For example, the worst-case and best-possible code that could be generated from the PL/I source statements

$$\text{DCL (C1, C2) CHAR (10) VAR;}$$

$$\text{I} = \text{LENGTH (C1} \parallel \text{C2);}$$

are shown in Table 7.1.1. The table shows how local context-free code generation can destroy the meaning of the original source statement and then generate the only code possible. The meaning of the statement is—

Table 7.1.1. Naive and Context-Sensitive Code Generation

	Naive		Context-Sensitive	
	LA	1,WS1.1		
	L	2,DV..C1		
	LH	3,DV..C1+6	LH	14,DV..C1+6
	LTR	0,3	AH	14,DV..C2+6
	BC	8,CL.1	ST	14,I
	BCTR	3,0		
	EX	3,C..048C		
	AR	1,0		
CL.1	EQU	*		
	L	2,DV..C2		
	IC	3,DV..C2+6		
	LTR	3,3		
	BC	8,CL.2		
	AR	0,3		
	BCTR	3,0		
	EX	3,C..048C		
CL.2	EQU	*		
	STH	D,TMPDV..0480+6		
	L	14,DV..TMP..0444		
	L	15,TMPDV..0480		
	LH	8,TMPDV..0480+6		
	STH	8,DV..TMP..0444+6		
	LTR	8,8		
	BC	8,CL.3		
	BCTR	8,0		
CL.3	EQU	*		
	LH	14,DV..TMP..0444+6		
	ST	14,I		

place in I the length of the result of concatenating C1 and C2—*not* concatenate C1 and C2 and then take the length of the result. The difference is only marginal in appearance, but as can be seen from the code generated, is significant.

7.1.3.2. Source Statement Choices

The example illustrates another problem. A programmer is usually unaware of how a compiler processes the statements he includes in his source program. If the above statement had been written in some other manner, the code generated might have been considerably improved. For example, the statement

$$I = \text{LENGTH (C1 } \| \text{ C2);}$$

results in poor code; the statement

$$I = \text{LENGTH (C1) } + \text{ LENGTH (C2);}$$

results in the best possible code.

7.1.3.3. *Compiler Size*

Another problem is evident from studies that indicate that about 15 times as much code-generation logic is needed for unoptimized full PL/I as for optimized full FORTRAN. It was felt that, with the use of standard techniques, about 50 times as much would be needed for optimized PL/I as for optimized FORTRAN.

7.1.3.4. *Optimization Problems*

Multipass generators cause information to be lost between passes. Multipass code generators are function driven; i.e., during each pass, code is generated for a given set of functions and the passes are performed in a set order. Unless a large amount of information is retained, one phase is aware only of the data from a previous phase that it is to process; it is not aware of the use to be made later of its results. The amount of information carried around to allow communication from phase to phase is enormous for a large language.

Code in multipass generators is usually generated from the inside out. A suitable form of internal text for multipass generation is triples, or a similar structure. The triples express the relationships among the different parts of the source statement. They generally are ordered so that the innermost part of any expression occurs first. As code is generated by succeeding phases, the triples are replaced by sequences of computer instructions. The problem is that unless the triples are manipulated in some way, the innermost part of an expression forces requirements on the outer parts. The consequences can be seen from the example in Table 7.1.1.

7.1.3.5. *Extendability*

Additions to the language may require a new phase or an extensive addition to an existing phase, adding to the communication problem within the compiler. Several phases may be affected by a language change. When the compiler is first written, this is not a serious problem; however, as time passes, the introduction of new code makes it increasingly difficult to identify the areas affected by even the simplest change.

7.1.3.6. *Number of Cases*

Code generation for a large language must deal with a great many cases. The most innocent looking statement can have enormous ramifications, which, in turn, can lead to an enormous number of different strings of code. For example, consider the PL/I statement A = B, where A and B are both floating-point scalars. The possible implications are shown in Table 7.1.2.

Table 7.1.2. Implications of A = B in PL/I

Precision	A single B single		A single B double		A double B single		A double B double	
Both aligned	L	R,B	L	R,B	SDR	R,R	LD	R,B
	ST	R,A	ST	R,A	LE	R,B	STD	R,A
					STD	R,A		
Both unaligned					MVC	A(4),B		
					XC	A+4(4),A+4		
A unaligned					MVC	A(4),B		
					XC	A+4(4),A+4		
B unaligned					MVC	WKSPC(4),B		
					SDR	R,R		
					LE	R,WKSPC		
					STD	R,A		
Either unaligned	MVC A(4),B		MVC A(4),B				MVC A(8),B	

Table 7.1.2 does not include cases for complex numbers, for extended precision, nor where there is an expression on the right-hand side of the equal sign. It ignores multiple targets on the left of the assignment operator, and addressing problems are not considered. Cases specified are for time optimization, but cases for space optimization are not given. The optimization is for an IBM System/360, Model 65. Other computer models require

different code for best object-time performance. As this indicates, the problem is one of sheer size. The number of cases is huge in every part of the language.

7.1.3.7. *The Solution*

The solution we saw to the problems posed by a multipass system was to have a single-pass code-generation phase. The single-pass phase allows code generation to be text-driven, which means that the text governs the order of code generation. The problem of inside-out generation was solved by the use of tree structures to represent the source text and by an outside-in order of scanning the trees.

The solution involved developing a definitional language that allows all cases to be defined. The definitions were then executed at compile time to generate the correct code.

A prototype compiler was designed and written to determine the validity of the techniques. A paging system was required to remain within the 100K-byte main storage space that was one of the design constraints for the prototype compiler.

7.1.4. THE PROTOTYPE COMPILER

In the prototype compiler, the functions performed in the code-generation phase are separated from the functions performed in other phases. There are five major sections in the compiler.

The front end creates trees and the required dictionary entries from the source program. It is necessary to expose addressing and subscript calculations as well as aggregate operations for code generation. A preoptimizer phase therefore expands the trees to show all such operations. Constant expressions are also evaluated. Following this phase, the trees are optimized by the cross optimizer, which performs the function of global optimization.

The code-generation phase accepts trees as input and produces pseudocode as output. Pseudocode differs from machine code in having symbolic registers, symbolic references to data, and symbolic references to labels in the pseudocode.

The prototype has a skeleton back-end for storage allocation, register allocation, and final assembly. The register allocation function involves replacing symbolic registers with absolute registers, resolving register conflicts, and inserting store or load instructions as required. The prototype final assembly section produces only an object listing.

7.1.5. TREE TEXT

Table 7.1.1 demonstrates a requirement for optimization at code-generation time—the context in which a program operand is to be used must be
understood before that operand is evaluated. With this ground rule in
mind, several common data formats can serve as input to the code-generation phase. As an example, consider again the expression LENGTH
(C1 ‖ C2) but in the following possible text forms:

1. Reverse Polish form

$$\text{C1 C2 ‖ LENGTH}$$

2. Standard Polish form

$$\text{LENGTH ‖ C1 C2}$$

3. Multiaddress code with named results

$$\text{CONCAT } t_1 \text{ C1 C2}$$
$$\text{LENGTH } t_2\ t_1$$

4. Multiaddress code with implicit instruction results

(a)   CONCAT C1 C2
(b)   LENGTH 1

5. Trees (see Fig. 7.1.1).

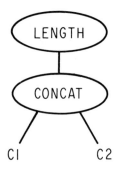

FIGURE 7.1.1   Tree representation.

These forms have much in common. Number 1 is derived from number 5 by a top-down, left-right tree walk; numbers 3 and 4 are derived from 1 by stacking operands left to right and then unstacking and producing code when an operator is encountered; numbers 3 and 4 are derived from 2 by stacking operators and operands separately and unstacking both, and then producing code when all of an operator's operands have been encountered. In addition, each of these derivations is logically reversible. However, the issue here is not one of logical equivalence but of practical case of processing. Bearing in mind the above ground rule, consider now a reasonable order for investigating the expression.

1. Invoke the length processor.

2. Invoke the concatenation processor. (Normally, it returns both a result and an indication of the length of that result. In this case, however, it is told to return only the length.)

3. Invoke data reference processors for C1 and then C2, telling each to return only the object time location of the length.

4. Return the object time locations of the lengths to the concatenation processor.

5. Generate the add of the lengths.

6. Return the location of the result to the length processor.

7. Return this value as the result.

In considering the above data formats for this kind of processing order, a striking implementation difficulty can be seen with both numbers 1 and 2. Whether the scanning order is forwards or backwards, it is difficult to find all of an operator's immediate operands. They are not adjacent, but separated by arbitrary distances; the location of one operand depends upon the full content of the other. Form number 3 has the same problem to a lesser degree; the scan entails investigating first operands of prior operators. Numbers 4 and 5 both give immediate access to operands. The usual hardware imposition of a single-dimensional addressable store implies the same internal storage requirements for the two. They differ then only in external representation and in the fact that using number 4 requires a bottom-up processing order to establish the context. In addition, number 5 seems to provide a more intuitive means of associating an operator with its operands diagrammatically. Thus we used number 5.

7.1.5.1. *Interrogating Trees*

A large set of utility routines are provided to interrogate the trees at code-generation time. These routines are also used throughout earlier portions of the compiler to build, modify, and interrogate trees. Figure 7.1.2 gives a general idea of the complexity. It shows the complete tree for

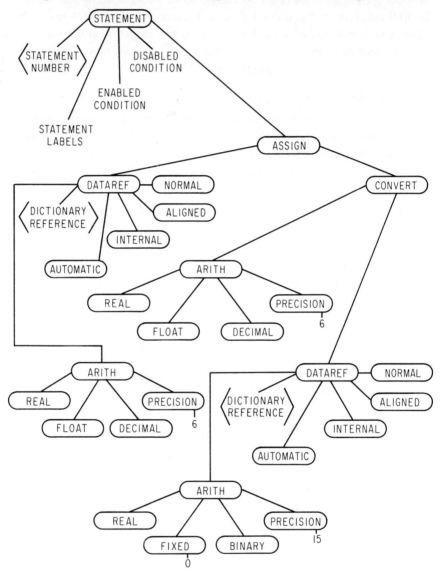

FIGURE 7.1.2 Tree for assignment statement $X = 1$.

the assignment statement X = I, where both X and I are undeclared, thus acquiring the usual PL/I default characteristics.

The most important thing to note here is that all attribute information is retained in the text. During code generation, it is never necessary to interrogate the dictionary to produce code.

7.1.6. THE CODE-GENERATION MECHANISM

The production of pseudoinstructions at code-generation time is carried out by a set of routines called OPGEN macrodefinitions (OMD's). They are written in our generate coding language (GCL), pretranslated into a compressed internal form, and stored in a library as part of the compiler. They are invoked and interpreted as needed during code generation.

An OMD area is provided in main storage, and OMD's are paged into this area as required during execution. The paging mechanism is invoked when a GCL LINK command (bring in a new OMD) or an RTN command (return control to the LINKing OMD) is executed. An OMD need be in storage only while it is being executed. At any other time, it may be overwritten if the space is required. OMD's are read-only, so they need never be written out. Each (possibly recursive) invocation of an OMD involves a new allocation of dynamic work space, which must remain active until that invocation is terminated.

The input data for the code-generation phase is the abstract tree text produced by the front end and the optimizer. The OMD's scan this text and produce from it the pseudoinstructions, which subsequently become input to the register-allocation phase.

The compile-time flow of control is best illustrated by a simple example, as shown in Fig. 7.1.2. The text trees are being processed one by one. Processing has just been completed for a statement, which we shall assume is GOTO X.

OPGEN, the interpreter for the OMD's, normally is a slave to the OMD's. It brings in a new OMD to be interpreted only when a LINK or RTN statement in a currently active OMD is executed. The only time that OPGEN initiates an action is when the OMD's have finished processing a statement. OPGEN then brings in the next statement tree, stores a pointer to the top node (which is always the STATEMENT node), brings in the OMD for handling this node (the @ STATEMENT OMD), and begins interpreting this OMD. (@ is a special marker indicating that the following name is an OMD name.)

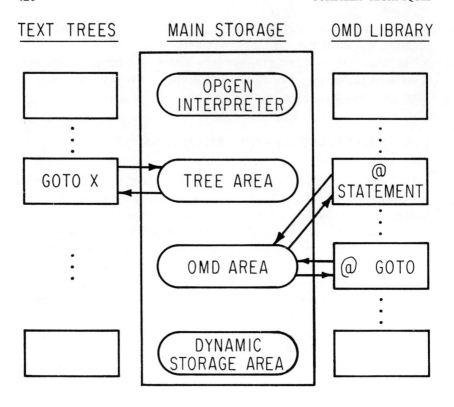

TEXT TREES   MAIN STORAGE   OMD LIBRARY

THE TREE FOR GOTO X
LOOKS LIKE THIS:

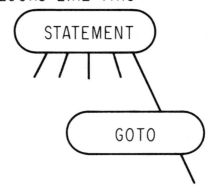

DICTIONARY REFERENCE FOR X

FIGURE 7.1.3 Processing statement GOTO X.

In the case shown in Fig. 7.1.3, the OMD analyzes its first four arguments, possibly generating some code indicated by them. Eventually

LINK ARG(5)

is executed (the OMD representing the fifth argument of the STATEMENT node).

The OMD @ GOTO is now brought in and interpreted. It eventually generates the instruction

BC 15, X

which goes into the pseudoinstruction file, and issues an RTN statement. OPGEN stores another node pointer, checks that the @ STATEMENT is in main storage, and resumes interpretation of the @ STATEMENT from the point following the LINK. After some cleaning up, the @ STATE-MENT issues a RTN, and OPGEN knows that processing for this statement has been completed. It then brings in the next tree and the cycle is repeated.

As is indicated in the above example, there is a direct relation between node names in the text trees and names of the corresponding OMD's for processing those nodes. When a blind link is made (as in LINK ARG (5)), the indicated node is found, and the OMD invoked is that of the same name as the node name, but prefixed by the symbol @. All OMD names, in fact, begin with @, whether or not they correspond to node names.

7.1.7. GENERATE CODING LANGUAGE

It became evident that some type of definition of the various cases to be generated was required. If this definitional language could then be executed in some way (compiled and either executed or interpreted), the definition of special cases could proceed together with the design and coding of the code-generation phase. Thus the generate coding language was developed.

7.1.7.1. *Language Features*

The following description of GCL is intended to convey the spirit of the language, which has the following characteristics:

- The language is procedural, with control passing from statement to statement unless an IF, GOTO, or subroutine call statement is encountered.

- Each OMD can reserve local storage (cells) for the duration of its execution.
- Facilities are provided for obtaining from trees the information needed to generate code.
- A subroutine call facility with argument-passing capabilities is provided.
- Complex expressions can be evaluated.
- A table look-up function allows information to be extracted from arrays of up to 256 dimensions.
- Code skeletons can be generated for all nonprivileged System/360 instructions.

7.1.7.2. Procedural Characteristic

In GCL, the form for the IF statement is

IF (expression) true label, false label

The expression is evaluated. If a true (nonzero) result is obtained, control is passed to the true label; if a false (zero) result is obtained, control is passed to the false label. The true and false labels are optional, implying that no special action is required if that condition arises.

GOTO acts as a FORTRAN GOTO, but with the extra ability to GOTO label variables (see Section 7.1.7.3).

Control is passed from one OMD to another by use of the LINK and RTN statements, which are described in Section 7.1.7.5 on subroutine calls.

7.1.7.3. Local Storage

An item with the CELL attribute is a four-byte item that may be declared in any OMD that requires it. Cells are local to the OMD and are reallocated if the OMD is invoked recursively. A cell can hold many types of items, which can vary dynamically when the OMD is being executed.

Consider the following example of the use of a cell:

```
            DCL       C CELL
            SET       C = LABEL
            GOTO      C
              .
              .
              .
    LABEL ···
```

The GOTO passes control to whatever OMD label is held in cell C. In the sequence

```
DCL     PQ CELL
SET     PQ = 1
SET     PQ = 1.3584 − 5
```

PQ can hold both integers and floating-point numbers.

Another use of cell is shown in the sequence

```
DCL     XY CELL
SET     XY = @ PLUS
LINK    XY
```

Execution of the LINK statement passes control to the PLUS OMD.

Cells can also contain compiler-generated labels to be inserted into the pseudocode, symbolic registers to be inserted into skeletons, 32-bit strings to hold switches, and packed decimal constants of up to five digits.

In addition to the cells, a long cell or string is provided. This type of storage is used when dealing with values that will not fit into four bytes, such as long floating-point constants, long decimal constants, character string constants, edit masks for conversion from numeric to character, etc. They are used exactly the same as cells, and in our implementation had a maximum length of 50 bytes. Use of the string facility is exemplified by

```
DCL     S STRING
SET     S = X'2021204B'
SET     S = S ‖ X'20'
```

Another type of cell is provided for the entire code-generation phase. Such cells are thus known to all OMD's and are never dynamically reallocated.

7.1.7.4. *Tree Analysis*

To understand how a set of OMD's scans a tree and generates the correct code for that tree, it is important to understand the working of the cursor. The cursor is a pointer to the current node in the tree and can be altered by execution of certain statements. Before each tree is processed, the cursor is set to the top node.

Information is extracted from the tree by use of attribute expressions, whose evaluations result in indications of presence or absence of specified nodes (Fig. 7.1.4). An attribute expression is a sequence of node references (node names or argument indices) separated by any of the search specification symbols . , ; or —. Evaluation of such an expression proceeds as follows: The first node reference, which must be an argument index, is evaluated, and the cursor is pushed to this location relative to the old cursor position. If this action is impossible (the node indicated by the old cursor position had fewer arguments than the index of the one requested), then evaluation

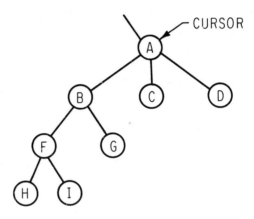

FIGURE 7.1.4   Attribute expression tree.

ceases and the value false (integer 0) is the expression result. Otherwise the next search symbol and the following node reference are examined. If the node reference is an argument index, the cursor is pushed as before, and the search symbol disregarded. But, if the reference is a node name, an attempt is made to push the cursor to the indicated node, if found, in a manner depending upon the search symbol. A period indicates that only immediate arguments of the current node are to be examined; a colon indicates that only the current node itself is to be examined; an underscore indicates that all descendants of the current node are to be examined. This process continues until either a search fails (expression false) or the expression is completed successfully (expression true). At completion of evaluation, the cursor is returned to its position prior to the expression evaluation.

For example, consider the tree in Fig. 7.1.4, with the cursor initially as shown. Let us look at several attribute expressions.

- ARG(2):C   (true)
  ARG(2), which is the node C, is examined to determine whether its name is C.

- ARG(2).X or ARG(2)—X   (false)
  C has no descendants, so clearly these are false.

- ARG(1):B. ARG(1).H   (true)
  ARG(1) is examined and is named B. The cursor is then pushed to
  B's first argument and from this point (F) immediate arguments of
  the current node (F) are examined. One of them is H.

- ARG(1)—I   (true)
  All descendants of B are checked. I is such a descendant.

The VALUE keyword allows values to be extracted from the tree.
Consider the tree in Fig. 7.1.5. The notation $\langle\ \rangle$ indicates a value in the
tree as opposed to a node. The attribute expression

$$ARG(1).ARG(1).VALUE$$

returns the value 6. The VALUE keyword is essential to pick up scales and
precisions.

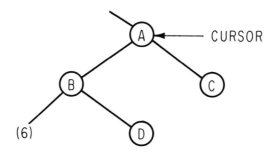

FIGURE 7.1.5   Tree containing a value.

7.1.7.5. *Subroutine Calls*

GCL allows OMD's to pass control from one to another by use of the
LINK statement. When the RTN statement in the LINKed to OMD is
encountered, control is passed to the statement following the LINK. The
position of the cursor in the tree is not altered.

A second type of LINK allows the tree to specify which OMD is invoked.
Consider the tree shown in Fig. 7.1.6. The statement

$$LINK\ ARG(2)$$

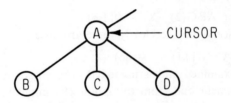

FIGURE 7.1.6 OMD-linking tree.

causes the OMD corresponding to the node C to be invoked. The cursor is positioned at node C. When the OMD @ C has been executed and returns control to the calling OMD, the cursor is repositioned to node A. This type of blind linking is used to analyze the shape of the tree while actually generating code.

In either type of LINK statement, it is possible to pass arguments to the invoked OMD. The statement

$$\text{LINK} \ @ \ \text{CONMPY} \ (A, B, C, D, E)$$

passes to the CONMPY OMD the items a, b, c, d, e. The items are passed by name so that the invoked OMD can pass back results. The invoked OMD must have a similar parameter list. Thus,

LINK @ CONMPY (A,B,C,D,E,)

                    START @ CONMPY (P,Q,R,S,T)
                    .
                    .
                    .
                    END

A limited variable-length parameter list capability is provided, whereby a call to an OMD may have any number of arguments not greater than the number of parameters indicated in the OMD. The items that can be passed in an argument list include: cells, strings, registers, OMD names, and parameters. Results must be returned in cells or strings.

7.1.7.6. *Expressions*

The language allows expressions that include all of the PL/I operators, as well as exclusive or ('?'). For example, the following expressions are allowed:

DCL (X,Y,Z,P,Q) CELL, S STRING

SET X = Y**2 = (P > 4 | Q < 2)*Z

SET S = S || X'20'

Logical expressions are evaluated to give an integer result (1 or 0). A limited amount of conversion is allowed:

$$\text{SET X} = 1.0E0$$

$$\text{SET X} = \text{X} + 1$$

Built-in functions include one called BIT, which tests the referenced bit in a cell and returns a true or false indication, depending on whether it is 1 or 0. The statement

$$\text{IF (BIT(X,5))T,F}$$

tests bit 5 of cell X and branches to T if bit 5 is a 1.

7.1.7.7. *Table Look-up*

The table look-up facility allows an item to be extracted from a table that can have up to 256 dimensions. The look-up is performed in response to the LOOK statement. For example, in the statement

LOOK error label, result cell, table name (arguments)

error label is the OMD label to which control is passed if the arguments do not specify a member of the table. The result cell will contain the item extracted from the table. Table name is the OMD label of the table being used in this LOOK statement.

In the simplest case of table look-up, the expressions serve as indices, so that the look-up acts as an array element reference. In more complex cases, the evaluated expressions may be tree node names, and the indexing is done by matching these names against the named table projections (rows, columns, etc.) In the simple case, a table is specified as follows:

Table Name: TBL (dimension 1, dimension 2, etc.) type ARRAY item 1, item 2, etc.

Type: Describes the length of each item in the array.

Dimension: 1, 2, etc., give the size of each dimension.

Item: 1, 2, etc., are the elements of the array in row major order.

The LOOK statement allows a multiple choice to be made in one statement. As an example:

```
        DCL      (X,Y,)CELL
        LOOK     ERROR,X,CONTBL(Y)
        GOTO     X
*GENERATE CODE TO MULTIPLY BY ONE
ONE
           .
           .
           .
*GENERATE CODE TO MULTIPLY BY TWO
TWO
           .
           .
           .
CONTROL TBL (6)REF
               ARRAY   ONE,TWO,THREE,FOUR,FIVE,SIX
```

Cell Y contains the constant by which a variable is to be multiplied. The LOOK extracts the OMD label from the table of the particular section of the OMD that will generate the required code. A similar effect can be achieved by a series of IF statements:

```
        IF (Y = 1)ONE
        IF (Y = 2)TWO
           .
           .
```

Many different types of items can be held in a table: floating-point constants, integers, symbolic registers, OMD labels, or OMD names.

7.1.7.8. Skeletons

Code skeletons are similar in format to System/360 assembler language. When a skeleton is encountered in an OMD, it is inserted into the output file as pseudocode. The registers used by the various skeletons must be declared. Thus the statements

```
        DCL R REG(FIXED)
        AR R,R
```

cause an AR skeleton to be generated with symbolic registers.

It is possible to generate code with absolute registers if these are required. The statements

```
        DCL RO REG(FIXED,ABS(0)),R REG(FIXED)
        LR   RO,R
```

cause an LR pseudoinstruction to be generated that loads absolute register 0 from a symbolic register.

In skeletons that require offsets and lengths, expressions can specify the required values. For example,

$$\text{MVC} \quad \text{OFF*4} = 1(\text{L} = (\text{L} > 6)\text{*4} = 1,\text{R}),1(\text{R})$$

It is possible to replace a register in a skeleton by a cell containing a register. Thus

$$\begin{array}{ll} \text{DCL} & \text{R REG(FIXED),X CELL} \\ \text{SET} & \text{X} = \text{R} \\ \text{AR} & \text{X,X} \end{array}$$

If a skeleton refers to data in storage and the address of the storage is not known at code-generation time, the base and offset fields can be replaced by a cell containing the dictionary reference of the data. A later phase adds the addressability code. Thus the statement

$$\text{DCL} \quad \text{X CELL, R REG(FIXED)}$$

is followed by code to pick the dictionary reference from the tree and then by

$$\text{L} \quad \text{R,0(X)}$$

7.1.7.9. *The Interpreter*

The execution of GCL could proceed in either of two ways—translate and interpret, or compile and execute. It was decided to translate and interpret for several reasons. The translation process can be kept fairly simple. The translator takes GCL source code and compacts it in a one-for-one manner. Expressions are translated into reverse Polish notation.

To compile and execute would require a second compiler with its associated problems of housekeeping, module linkages, etc. Having an interpreter with all executable code in one place made the compiler easier to debug and more reliable. Also, because of the more compact interpreter code, it conserved main storage space.

7.1.8. CODE-GENERATION EXAMPLES

Two examples of GCL code illustrate the code-generation process. The first example, in Table 7.1.3, is of the complete OMD for doing floating-point assignment. It is presented to give the flavor of GCL and to indicate the relative ease of generating code for the many cases.

Table 7.1.3.   Floating-Point Assignment

@FLOATASSIGN OMD

```
START @FLOATASSIGN
DCL (GOPT, LLEN, RLEN, WKCELL, RATR, LATR, LO, LB, LI, LL, LR, RO,
    RB, RI, RR, RL, WKCELL) CELL, GPR REG (FIXED)
*CHECK GLOBAL CELL WHICH HAS COMPILER OPTIONS
    IF (BIT (GOPT, OPTT) = 0 | BIT(GOPT,MG5) = 0), OK
    MSG '@FLOATASSIGN OPTIMIZED ONLY FOR MOD 65, TIME OPTION'
*FIND BYTE LENGTHS OF SOURCE AND TARGET
*@FLOATLENGTH UTILITY EXPECTS CURSOR AT PARENT OF ARITH NODE
OK PUSH ARG (1)
    LINK @FLOATLENGTH (LLEN)
    POP
    PUSH ARG (2)
    LINK @FLOATLENGTH (RLEN)
    POP
    IF(LLEN = 16 | RLEN = 16), NOT16
    MSG 'DOUBLE DOUBLE LENGTH NOT SUPPORTED BY @FLOATASSIGN'
    RTN
NOT16 IF (ARG(1), COMPLEX | ARG (2), ARG(1), COMPLEX), NOTCPX
    MSG 'COMPLEX NOT SUPPORTED BY @FLOATASSIGN'
    RTN
NOTCPX SET LALN = 2 − ARG(1). UNALIGNED
    SET RALN = 2 − ARG(2). UNALIGNED
*NOW DO TABLE LOOK UP AND GO TO RESULT LABEL TO
*SET UP REQUIREMENTS FOR SOURCE RESULT, DEPENDING
*ON LENGTHS AND ALIGNMENTS
    LOOK ERR1, WKCELL, TBL1(LALN, LLEN 4, RALN, RLEN 4)
    GO TO WKCELL
ERR1 MSG 'ERROR IN TBL1 LOOK UP IN @FLOATASSIGN'
    RTN
*FOLLOWING ARE THE RESULT LABELS OF LOOK UP
*TARGET 4 BYTES ALIGNED, SOURCE ALIGNED. ASK FOR
*RX REFERENCE OR FLOATING REGISTER
RXFR1 SET RATR = M'F0001000'
    GOTO LRX
*8 - BYTE RESULT NEEDED IN FLOATING REGISTER, SO SOURCE
*WILL DO SDR, LE or LD or MVC(4), SDR, LE
FRFW1 SET RATR = M '30000000'
*GET ADDRESSABILITY OF TARGET AS RX or RS REFERENCE
```

Table 7.1.3 (*continued*)

```
LRX SET LATR = M 'C0000000'
    GOTO LINK
*REQUEST BOTH SOURCE AND TARGET AS RS REFERENCES
*SINCE MVC WILL BE DONE
RS1 SET RATR = M '40000000'
    SET LATR = M '40000000'
*NOW LINK TO EACH ARGUMENT
*STANDARD CALLING SEQUENCE HAS BIT ATTRIBUTE CELL,
*OFFSET, BASE, INDEX, LENGTH, AND ONE EXTRA CELL
*FOR SPECIAL USE IN SOME CONTEXTS
LINK LINK ARG(1) (LATR, LO, LB, LI, LL, LR)
    LINK ARG(2) (RATR, RO, RB, RI, RL, RR)
*NOW DO LOOK UP AS BEFORE, BUT THIS TIME TO
*DECIDE WHERE TO GO TO FINISH WORK
 LOOK ERR2, WKCELL, TBL2 (LALN, LLEN/4, RALN, RLEN/4)
 GOTO WKCELL
ERR2 MSG 'ERROR IN TBL2 LOOK UP IN @FLOATASSIGN'
    RTN
*FOLLOWING ARE THE VARIOUS LABELS RESULTING
*FROM THE LOOKUP
*SOURCE IS EITHER RX (IF DATA REFERENCE) OR FLOATING
*REGISTER (IF EXPRESSION). IT HAS SET RATR TO INDICATE WHICH
RXFR2 IF (BIT (RATR, RXREF) | BIT (RATR, RSREF)) LST
*IN FLOAT REGISTER GIVEN IN RB FIELD
    STE RB, LO (LI, LB)
    RTN
*IN CORE
LST L GPR, RO (RI, RB)
    ST GPR, LO (LI, LB)
    RTN
*DOUBLE LENGTH RESULT IN REGISTER, TARGET ALIGNED
FRFUL2 STD RB, LO (LI, LB)
    RTN
*TARGET IS SHORT FLOAT, EITHER IS UNALIGNED.
*SOURCE WAS RETURNED AS RS REFERENCE
RS24 MVC LO (4, LB), RO (RB)
    RTN
*TARGET IS LONG FLOAT UNALIGNED, SOURCE LONG
*FLOAT RS REFERENCE
```

Table 7.1.3. (*continued*)

RS28 MVC LO (8, LB), RO (RB)
   RTN
*TARGET LONG FLOAT UNALIGNED, SOURCE SHORT FLOAT
*RS REFERENCE
RS24XC MVC LO (4, LB), RO (RB)
   XC LO + 4 (4, LB), LO + 4 (LB)
   RTN
*FOLLOWING ARE THE TWO TABLES, GIVEN IN
*ROW MAJOR ORDER
TBL1 TBL (2, 2, 2, 2) REF
   ARRY   RXFR1, RXFR1, RS1, RS1, FRFUL1, FRFUL1, FRFUL1, RS1, RS1
       RS1, RS1, RS1, RS1, RS1, RS1, RS1
TBL2 TBL (2, 2, 2, 2) REF
   ARRY   RXFR2, RXFR2, RS4, RS4, FRFUL2, FRFUL2, FRFUL2, RS28,
       RS24, RS24, RS24, RS24, RS24XC, RS28, RS24SC, RS28
   END

This example also illustrates some GCL coding conventions crucial to exploitation of the code-generation philosophy. The outside-in processing order automatically gives most of the context-sensitivity required. In general, it is not further required that the OMD for a node be given the identity of an argument node. If this information is needed for special cases, the OMD can, of course, determine it. But otherwise, it is able blindly to link to an argument node. Thus common-parameter passing conventions must be used and respected within certain contexts. A common convention for all calls to expression node OMD's was used in the prototype. The first parameter is an attribute cell giving details of its requirements for location, length, alignment, etc., of the argument result. The subsequent parameters detail those specified in the first. Often the caller requests any of several alternative result conditions; in such cases, the called routine modifies the parameters to indicate which alternative has been used as most convenient.

The second example, in Table 7.1.4, shows the ease of the required context-dependent generation, which results from the outside-in processing order. This technique requires that the OMD for a certain node pass down certain requirements to the OMD's for processing its argument nodes. For example, @ ASSIGN may preallocate a target location for an argument's result, require a certain alignment, request RX or RS storage references, or any variety of register, etc. In this case, @ ASSIGN is asking that only a length be returned.

Table 7.1.4. Length Determination

START @ LENGTHBIF (ATR, P, B, I, L, ML)

*SET BIT TO INDICATE ONLY A LENGTH REQUIRED
SET ATR = ATR | M '00000001'
LINK ARG (2) (ATR, O, B, I, L, ML)
END
START @CONCAT (ATR, O, B, I, L, ML)
.
.
.

IF (BIT (ATR, LONLY)), NORM

*SPECIAL CASE IF LENGTH ONLY REQUIRED

*ASK FIRST OPERAND TO PUT LENGTH IN REGISTER
SET LATR = M '06004000'
LINK ARG(2) (LATR, LO, B, LI, LL, LML)

*ASK SECOND OPERAND FR IN EITHER REGISTER OR STORAGE
SET RATR = M 'C6000000'
LINK ARG(3) (RATR, RO, RB, RI, RL, RML)
IF (BIT (RATR, EGPR) | BIT (RATR, OGPR)) RR

*SECOND OPERAND IN STORAGE
AH B, RO (RI, RB)
RTN

*SECOND OPERAND IN REGISTER
RR AR B, RB
RTN
.
.
.

END

7.1.8.1. *Floating-Point Assignment*

When @ FLOATASSIGN is invoked, the tree looks as shown in Fig. 7.1.7. The sample tree in the section on tree text gives a representative tree for this case in more detail.

The GCL cursor is pointing at the ASSIGN node. Prior to this invocation, control had passed to the @ STATEMENT OMD, which then stated LINK ARG(5). This action brought in the @ ASSIGN OMD and positioned the cursor at ASSIGN. The instruction @ ASSIGN is a driver OMD that investigates the types of its arguments, and then calls the appropriate assignment routine for the data types found. In this case, it calls @ FLOAT-ASSIGN, leaving the cursor positioned at ASSIGN.

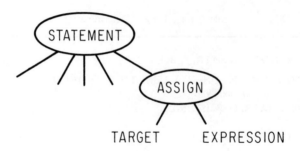

FIGURE 7.1.7   Floating-point assignment.

The length built-in function is trivial because of the outside-in processing order followed during code generation. The @ LENGTHBIF OMD simply passes to its argument expression a preassigned bit on the first argument, indicating that only the length of the result is desired, not its value. The tree for the example is shown in Fig. 7.1.8. Cl and C2 may, in general, be string expressions. The following recursive definition of the result of the length bit for CONCAT holds for the various possible nodes under it: @ CONCAT simply invokes its two arguments with the same bit on to indicate that only a length is required. These arguments return their result lengths as requested. @ CONCAT subsequently adds those lengths and returns this result to its caller (in this case, @ LENGTH).

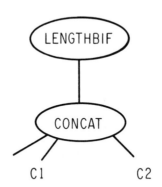

FIGURE 7.1.8   Length function.

The outside-in processing order ensures that no matter how complicated the argument may be, no processing is performed except that necessary to establish the length of the ultimate argument to @ LENGTH. The immediate argument OMD to @ LENGTH passes down to each argument the fact that only a length is required. Ultimately, no result expressions are evaluated, only their lengths.

This example is typical of the value of the outside-in processing order. Every operand in a statement is evaluated only as required by its context.

7.1.9. COMPILE-TIME CHARACTERISTICS

Using a trace facility supplied by GCL, we obtained the following statistics: each PL/I statement results in 300 GCL statement executions; 33 GCL statement executions result in one line of pseudocode; thus, each PL/I statement results in nine lines of pseudocode.

Twenty OMD's were involved for each PL/I statement. Forty percent of all OMD's invoked were found to already be in main storage.

There were 211 OMD's, totaling 102,000 bytes of GCL code. Average length of an OMD was 482 bytes, the longest being 3800 bytes. Since it was estimated that this represented one-third of the code-generation phase of a PL/I compiler, a complete compiler code-generation phase would have required 600 OMD's totaling 300,000 bytes.

The compile time appeared to be slow, particularly in the code-generation phase, although no compile times are available. However, we believe that the interpreter and the OMD loader could be recoded so as to significantly reduce their size and their execution times.

Another area for improvement is the design of the prototype OMD loader. When called, the loader checks first to determine if the required OMD is already in main storage. If not, it checks for available unused storage space in the OMD area. If there is none, it simply displaces an OMD in main storage, taking up the least space sufficient for the new OMD. More sophisticated techniques are available and could be used to advantage.

Displacement priorities should be statistically established, based on frequency of execution and size of the OMD's. Possible preloading techniques should be investigated. If a certain OMD always, or usually, calls a certain other OMD, then loading of the second OMD should accompany loading of the first.

At this time, effectiveness of these techniques cannot be quantified. The OMD structure, however, did obey the following two encouraging generalities: Frequency of execution of the various OMD's varied widely, with a small number (@ STATEMENT, @ DATAREF, and several others) requiring most of the execution and most of the loader invocations—which should make a priority scheme effective. Many predictable OMD call trees were found, a result both of the OMD structuring and of the source language itself. Large high-level languages are not so modular that text-driven processing need imply totally unpredictable process sequencing. The pre-loading technique, therefore, should also be exploited.

7.1.10. SUMMARY COMMENT

The authors believe that using the high-level language (GCL) for code generation has advantages in terms of extendability, flexibility, and reliability.

7.1.10.1. *Extendable Compiler*

The code-generation techniques are highly relevant to an extendable language definition system. In most such systems, definition of a new type of statement or language element involves two specifications: the information required to parse the new language element and integrate its syntax with surrounding language elements; and definition of the semantics of the new element, in terms of the compiler base language.

The second requirement means that the base language must theoretically have all power required, since all extensions are ultimately reduced to the base language. With the introduction of languages like PL/I, it becomes apparent that the base language required to extend to PL/I is very close to PL/I itself. Even if it were theoretically possible to extend a FORTRAN type of base to PL/I level, its efficiency would be doubtful.

This code-generation technique lends itself to a new kind of definition mechanism. A new language element might be defined in terms of its syntax and of the form the trees take when the element occurs in a source program. The trees might contain new nodes never before used. Where new nodes appear, new OMD's are written and entered into the system automatically, causing the semantics of the new element to be defined precisely in a language very close to machine code (in this case, pseudocode).

This possibility obviates the requirement of theoretical adequacy of the base language and makes it possible to define new language with efficient implementation. The authors believe that if this system of code generation is adopted by extendable language compilers, their efforts are likely to lead to considerable success.

7.1.10.2. *Language Changes*

One of the problems encountered by a compiler for a new language is that the semantics of the language elements tend to change. Keeping up with these changes can be very expensive and time consuming. Much of the compiler alteration occurs at the code-generation phase, since it is there that the new definition of the language element is finally realized. The authors believe that a code-generation scheme like the one described would allow language changes to be made easily and at small cost. OMD's can be added to a system almost *ad infinitum*.

7.1.10.3. *Reliability*

When writing an optimizing compiler for a large language, two types of reliability become necessary. The writer must ensure that the compiler is bug-free and produces code that works. All cases must be covered with equal care to avoid leaving traps and pitfalls.

The experience gained during the coding of the code-generation stage of the prototype indicated that OMD's are easily debugged, requiring an average of three machine runs to check and debug. It was easy to think about the special cases involved because the problem was to identify the special cases, rather than code the phase so as to generate the required code. Since coding time was so trivial, effort could be spent on ensuring that all cases were covered and all pitfalls removed.

7.1.10.4. *Shared-Component Compilers*

The technique described is a step toward providing a common component for the code-generation process. The tree-text format, tree analysis, GCL (including its translator and interpreter), and the paging mechanism are all language-independent and might serve as common tools for use in other compilers. Producing the code-generation phase for a new compiler this way, then, would require only the writing of OMD's needed for that language. It is probable that if one has available the complete set of OMD's for a language as rich as PL/I, a large number could be lifted intact and used in new compilers for other languages.

ACKNOWLEDGMENTS

The authors wish particularly to thank Dick Sites for his contribution to our code-generation design and development. Helpful suggestions were also received from the other compiler designers: Ray Larner, Tom Peters, Dave J. G. Reid, and Eric Souers.

REFERENCES

1. Blaauw, G. A., and Brooks, F. P., Jr., "The Structure of System/360: Part I, Outline of the Logical Structure," *IBM Systems Journal*, vol. 3, nos. 2 and 3 (1964), pp. 119–135.

2. IBM SYSTEM/*360 Operating System*: PL/I *F Language Reference Manual*, C28-8201. International Business Machines Corporation, Data Processing Division, White Plains, New York.

7.2. Sequential Formula Translation

by K. Samelson and F. L. Bauer

7.2.1. ABSTRACT

The syntax of an algorithmic language such as ALGOL is conveniently described as a sequence of states indicated by an element called cellar. Transitions are controlled by admissible state-symbol pairs which may be represented by a transition matrix. This description of syntax furnishes at the same time an extremely simple rule for translating into machine programs statements in the algorithmic language. Sequential treatment, however, is not feasible in the case of certain optimizing processes such as recursive address calculation.

7.2.2. ORIGIN AND DEVELOPMENT OF FORMULA TRANSLATION

In consequence of the rapid development of automatic data processing during the last decade, a considerable number of different makes of automatic computers are produced today. In spite of all differences with regard to construction and order code, practically all present-day computers possess

EDITOR'S NOTE: This article reproduced by permission of the authors and the publisher: *Comm. ACM*, vol. 3, no. 2 (February 1960), pp. 76–83. Originally published in *Elektronische Rechenanlagen*, vol. 1 (1959), pp. 176–182.

two common characteristics commonly considered to be technological in origin. These are

(1) breakdown of storage into a serially numbered sequence of words of fixed length, and

(2) as a consequence of (1), breakdown of the program into a sequence of independent elements of fixed form (instructions) which are interpreted sequentially by the control unit.

These two characteristics are the main reason for the well-known inconvenience of programming resulting in a high error frequency, since they require (1) introducing, with the concept of computable address and the necessarily ensuing address calculation, a programming element extraneous to any problem to be solved on the computer; and (2) atomizing the entire program in an unusual and uneconomical manner. The resulting programs normally are illegible to anybody but (maybe) the programmer himself.

Efforts to eliminate duplications and routine work in programming by means of the computer itself started very early.[1,8,9] They led to the development of assembling and compiling systems working with pseudoinstructions, symbolic addresses, subroutines, and library programs.[10]

Rutishauser[4] was first in recognizing that an effective solution of the programming problem requires introducing conventional notation (commonly called "problem-oriented language" today) into programming and having the computer do all subsequent phases of translation work. His proposal, published in 1952,[5] and the subsequent work of Böhm[14] found no immediate response. The first large-scale programming systems with formula translating features, PACT[3] and FORTRAN,[2] were developed as late as 1955. Methods used, however, were not published at that time.

At about the same time the computer group at the Technische Hochschule in Munich, fully acquainted with Rutishauser's ideas, started discussions of the subject of formula translation. However, interest was centered on methods feasible for computers far inferior in capacity and speed to, say, the IBM 704. For this purpose a sequential translating technique based on independent previous investigation[6,13] was developed.

Since 1957, work was continued within the framework of today's ZMMD (Zürich-Munich-Mainz-Darmstadt) group. The basic aim was development of a common language (and translator system) for different computers. This finally led to the creation of a joint committee of the ACM and the GAMM, which in 1958 proposed a common algorithmic language—ALGOL.[11,12]

In the meantime the structure of the translator of the ZMMD group was frozen, and coding of the system (called ALCOR = ALgol CONverteR) for the computers involved (ERMETH Zürich, PERM Munich, z 22/2002 Mainz, 650/DERA Darmstadt) and for a number of computers in cooperating scientific institutions in Austria, Germany, and Denmark was begun. Pilot models of the translator have been working satisfactorily in Mainz, Munich, and Zürich since the fall of 1958.[15–17]

The entire ALCOR project is nearing completion now. Therefore, it seems advisable to give a description of the underlying principle of sequential translation, which differs considerably from Rutishauser's original proposal,[5] as well as from the methods used in FORTRAN.[7] However, certain features of the system, although for a rather restricted language, are already contained in the work of Böhm.[14] Detailed plans describing the system in a machine-independent, reproducible form are being completed in Mainz and will be made available to scientific institutions willing to adopt the system.

7.2.3. SEQUENTIAL TRANSLATION AND THE PRINCIPLE OF "LAST-IN-FIRST-OUT"

The statements formulated in an algorithmic language such as ALGOL are sequences of symbols composed of one or several characters of a basic alphabet. This composition of symbols, however, is trivial, and depends to a certain degree on technical data such as the writing device employed. *Therefore, we shall subsequently disregard the difference between symbols and characters, and consider the symbols as introduced to be the elements of the alphabet of the language.*[†] Since we are using the ALGOL notation, this concerns mainly identifiers 1, numbers N, and verbally defined delimiters such as **go to**, **if**, etc.

The sequence of symbols of a formula program (in the usual interpretation) represents an operating rule. However, symbol-wise sequential transformation of this rule into machine instructions is not possible, since the syntax of the conventional arithmetic notation contains precedence rules ("$\times$" before "$+$") and parentheses prescribing an ordering of operations differing from the sequence of symbols.

Therefore it is necessary during translation to pass by certain symbols as not being evaluable and to find and evaluate these at some later time depending on the subsequent symbol sequence. Rutishauser with his "parentheses mountain range" has given the principle of solution. However, his method of evaluation by repeatedly reading forward and backward is

---

[†] Italics introduced by editor.

inconvenient and time consuming. The problem of making available at the proper moment information previously postponed as not evaluable is extremely simplified by means of a principle which may be called the principle of "last-in-first-out," which can be used whenever the structure of the symbol sequence is of a bracketing character.

The principle means that all incoming (source) information given by symbols which cannot immediately be evaluated is introduced, in the sequence of first appearance, into a special storage called "symbols cellar," where at any given time only the element introduced last (the highest level of the cellar) is of immediate consequence and need be available. Each new symbol of source information is, in turn, compared to the momentarily highest cellar symbol. These two symbols in conjunction determine the evaluation (if possible) of the highest cellar symbol by generation of an appropriate machine instruction and the new state of the cellar by eliminating the old highest symbol and/or introducing the new symbol as the case may be.

In the language of the theory of automata the principle may be formulated as follows: The contents of the symbols cellar determines a state which, in effect, at any given time depends on the highest element only, and the new symbol of source information plus state determine output (of machine instructions) and successor state. The essential feature, however, is the ordered latent-state structure induced by the contents of the cellar.

7.2.4. EVALUATION OF SIMPLE ARITHMETIC EXPRESSIONS

The most important case of bracketed structures is given by the arithmetic expressions, which for this reason will be treated extensively. However, in order to keep the essential features free of annoying details, we shall introduce some simplifications:

(1) We exclude, for the moment, subscripted variables I[E, E, ..., E] and functions I(P, P, ..., P), and the use of the symbols + and − as unary operators (+a, −b).

(2) To the symbols cellar determining syntactical states we add a second cellar (called numbers cellar H) with the same last-in-first-out principle where all elements introduced are numerical values of variables or expressions, and which may be said to define interpretive states. [†] This numbers cellar will be part of the resulting program.

[†] Concretely, this may be considered to be a limited high-speed buffer storage with an access time negligible in comparison to that of the main working storage.

Under these assumptions, any identifier is a variable which is the name of a number, and therefore corresponds to some storage address determined by the translator as in usual symbolic address systems. Numbers N within expressions must be stored by the translators, and replaced by their respective addresses. Therefore they need not be treated separately.

The evaluation of expressions by the last-in-first-out principle now proceeds in the following way:

(A) Every identifier I upon appearance generates a transfer of the contents of the corresponding storage location into the momentarily highest location η_h of numbers cellar H, where "generates" means that the translator joins the corresponding instructions to the machine program already generated.

Let $\sqcap$ be the designation of the storage locations into which new instructions of the generated program go, and let K_1 be the machine instruction $I \Rightarrow \eta_h$ (transfer instruction with address I corresponding to the variable abbreviated by I, and address η_h giving the highest location of H). The operations executed by the translator are then

$$I: h + 1 \Rightarrow h; \ K_1 \Rightarrow \sqcap; \ \text{read } \chi;$$

where h is a counter contained in the translator which always shows the currently highest location of numbers cellar H, and "read χ" means that the next source symbol χ is to be read.

(B) The other symbols $+ - \times / ( )$ admissible in expressions are upon appearance tested against the highest symbol ξ_s of the symbols cellar, where the initial state is s = 0, cellar empty (ϕ). Each pair of source symbol and cellar symbol causes a certain sequence of operations to be executed by the translator. Some (but not all) of these sequences contain generation of machine instructions designated K_ξ and of the form

$$K_\xi: \ \eta_{h-1}\xi\eta_h \Rightarrow \eta_{h-1}$$

where ξ may be any of the symbols $+ - \times /$ and is given by the current ξ_s.

Obviously, the K_ξ are standard three-address instructions always arithmetically combining the two highest elements of H to form the new highest element (after erasing the operands).

The operations executed by the translator are given in Table 7.2.1. Here α means the new symbol of source information, ee means "end expression" which in ALGOL may be indicated by several symbols all extraneous to expressions themselves, "repeat" means that the test is to be repeated with the *present* symbol α and the new ξ_s.

TABLE 7.2.1

ξ_s	α		
ϕ	α	$1 \Rightarrow s;\ \alpha \Rightarrow \xi_s;$	read $\chi;$
$\left.\begin{array}{c}+\\-\\\times\\/\end{array}\right\}$	$\left\{\begin{array}{c}+\\-\\\times\\/\end{array}\right.$ $K_\xi \Rightarrow \sqcap;$		$\alpha \Rightarrow \xi_s;\ h - 1 \Rightarrow h;$ read $\chi;$
$($ $\left.\begin{array}{c}+\\-\\+\\-\\\times\\/\end{array}\right\}$	$\left\{\begin{array}{c}+\\-\\\times\\/\end{array}\right.$ $\left\{\begin{array}{c}\times\\/\end{array}\right.$ $($	$s + 1 \Rightarrow s;\ \alpha \Rightarrow \xi_s;$	read $\chi;$
$($	$)$	$s - 1 \Rightarrow s;$	read $\chi;$
$\left.\begin{array}{c}\times\\/\\+\\-\\\times\\/\end{array}\right\}$	$\left\{\begin{array}{c}+\\-\\)\\ee\end{array}\right.$ $K_\xi \Rightarrow \sqcap;\ s - 1 \Rightarrow s;$		$h - 1 \Rightarrow h;$ repeat;

The list may conveniently be arranged to form a matrix where the possible ξ_s designate rows and α's designate columns. This matrix gives a complete syntactical and operative description of arithmetic expressions. The initial state is $s = 0$, $(\xi_s = \phi)$, $h = 0$ (H empty); an admissible final state (complete expression) is $s = 0$, $(\xi_s = \phi)$, $h = 1$ (the value of an expression is always contained in the first location of H).[†]

A simple example (Table 7.2.2, example) may serve to clarify the process

---

[†] Use of a similar matrix for a restricted language and without information cellars, and evaluation of parentheses-free expressions by comparing subsequent operation symbols, may be found in Böhm's paper.[14]

Table 7.2.2. Example: A: $(a \times b + c \times d)/(a - d) + b \times c$

Z	χ	Action
ϕ	(	
(	a	$a \Rightarrow \eta_1$
(	×	
(×	b	$b \Rightarrow \eta_2$
(×	+	$\eta_1 \times \eta_2 \Rightarrow \eta_1$
(	repeat	
(+	c	$c \Rightarrow \eta_2$
(+	×	
(+×	d	$d \Rightarrow \eta_3$
(+×	)	$\eta_2 \times \eta_3 \Rightarrow \eta_2$
(+	repeat	$\eta_1 + \eta_2 \Rightarrow \eta_1$
(	repeat	
ϕ	/	
/	(	
/(	a	$a \Rightarrow \eta_2$
/(	−	
/(	d	$d \Rightarrow \eta_3$
/(	)	$\eta_2 - \eta_3 \Rightarrow \eta_2$
/(	repeat	
/	+	$\eta_1/\eta_2 \Rightarrow \eta_1$
ϕ	repeat	
+	b	$b \Rightarrow \eta_2$
+	×	
+×	c	$c \Rightarrow \eta_3$
+×	ee	$\eta_2 \times \eta_3 \Rightarrow \eta_2$
+	repeat	$\eta_1 + \eta_2 \Rightarrow \eta_1$
ϕ		

by showing for a given formula A the sequence of contents of symbols cellar Z, current new source symbol χ, and the instruction generated (if any). The state of the counters s (symbols cellar Z) and h (numbers cellar H) is adequately described by the number of symbols in Z, and the subscripts of the η, respectively.

The example shows that sequence of operations in the resulting program is completely determined by the formula program, and no attempt at optimizing the program by using associative laws is made. The reason is that the choice of sequence should be the concern of the programming mathematician, since in computing with floating point, the associative laws are not valid and application may lead to undesirable numerical consequences.

7.2.5. COMPLETE ARITHMETICAL EXPRESSIONS

We have to discuss the variations of the above scheme required by the omission of the initial simplifications. We begin with the values of the operands.

The example given contains a number of unnecessary data transfers of the form $I = \eta_h$, which cannot be tolerated in the resulting program. To eliminate them we split up numbers cellar H into a new numbers cellar, also called H, and a new address cellar ϕ with the same last-in-first-out structure as H. The new H serves only to store intermediate results not explicitly designated by variables whenever, in the case of one-address machines to which we restrict ourselves[†] from now on, the arithmetic unit must be cleared for subsequent operations.

The new address cellar ϕ, on the other hand, assumes the functions of the old numbers cellar where, however, the values of the variables are replaced by the corresponding addresses, and entries and clearings are performed by the translator which, for each variable, enters the corresponding address into the current highest position of ϕ, for generation of operations instructions extract always the addresses in the two highest positions and enters the address of the result in the new highest position. Since results in a one-address machine usually appear in the accumulator, it is convenient to assign an identifiable address to this register. Insertion of storing instructions to secure intermediate results is indicated by an opening parenthesis as source symbol and the accumulator address in the highest location of address cellar ϕ. Such parentheses are also implied by incoming symbols $\times$ or $/$ meeting a $+$ or $-$ as state indicator in Z. In this case the source symbol preceding the symbol $\times$ or $/$ has been an identifier corresponding to an address which has already been entered into ϕ. Therefore the next to highest element of address cellar ϕ must also be considered here. The address assigned to the intermediate result is always that of the currently highest location η_h in the numbers cellar H. This address replaces the accumulator address in the address cellar ϕ. It needs a special tag indicating an η address causing the position counter h of H to go down when this address is deleted from the address cellar by the translator.

The instructions K_ξ to be generated by the translator have now the general form[‡]

$$K_\xi : \langle \varphi_{f-1} \rangle \Rightarrow AC; \qquad AC\xi\langle\varphi_f\rangle \Rightarrow AC$$

[†] Extension of the methods described to three-address systems is obvious.

[‡] $\langle\varphi_f\rangle$ means the number contained in the storage location indicated by the address φ_f.

However, either one of the addresses φ_{f-1}, φ_f may be the address of the accumulator. If this is the case, the instructions are modified during generation. If ξ represents a commutative operation ($+$ or $\times$), only one instruction $AC\xi\langle\varphi_*\rangle \Rightarrow AC$ is generated, where φ_* is the address in the pair φ_{f-1}, φ_f not representing the accumulator.

If $\xi = -$, or $\xi = /$, and φ_{f-1} is the accumulator address, the first instruction of K_ξ is omitted. In the opposite case, φ_f being the accumulator address, the modified K_- and $K_/$ will be

$$K_-: \quad -AC \Rightarrow AC; \qquad AC + \langle\varphi_{f-1}\rangle \Rightarrow AC$$

$$K_/: \quad AC \Rightarrow \eta_h; \qquad \langle\varphi_{f-1}\rangle \Rightarrow AC; \qquad AC/\eta_h \Rightarrow AC$$

These operations represent expressions of the types $a - (b+c)$ or $a/(b+c)$, respectively. Obviously, handling of such expressions would be much easier for computers that are able to "subtract from storage" or "divide into storage."

The unary operations $+a$, $-a$ are easily recognized and may be treated by attaching sign tags to the addresses in the address cellar α.

Boolean expressions obviously may be treated along the same lines as arithmetic expressions.

Admission of functions means first that sequences of the form "I(" (identifier immediately followed by an opening parenthesis) must be recognized. The set of expressions separated by "," following such sequences and terminated by ")" represents the arguments of the function. Each such expression is evaluated in the manner described above, and the terminating "," or ")" causes a storing operation of the value of the respective argument. These values may be considered to be intermediate results to be stored in the current high location of numbers cellar H. The terminating parenthesis shows that all arguments are evaluated, and instructions initiating evaluation of the function itself must be generated; for example, a jump instruction to a closed subroutine. Subscripted variables may be considered to be functions of integer arguments (the subscripts) with values given by listing instead of a computing rule and a rule to compute from subscript values the correct list location, which rule (the storage mapping function) in ALGOL is derived from the **array** declaration associated with the subscripted variable and the general restriction for rectangular arrays. Therefore, subscripted variables may be treated in the same manner as functions. However, this means complete evaluation of the storage-mapping function for each occurrence of a subscripted variable. This is highly inefficient in loops when subscripts of variables depend on the running variable. Here, optimizing by recursive evaluation of the storage mapping function is essential. We return to this question in Section 7.2.8.

7.2.6. STATEMENTS

Evaluation of complete statements proceeds in the same way as evaluation of expressions which constitute the main part of statements, and we have only to extend the set of symbols admissible for entry into the symbols cellar Z.

In arithmetic and Boolean statements, this means the defining symbol ":=" which will always be the first symbol to be introduced into the symbols cellar, and this replaces the state "ϕ." The function of the terminating symbol "ee" is assumed now by the statement separator ";" or the "**end**" terminating compound statements, which in conjunction with ":=" in Z indicates the end of the expression and causes generation of the final storing instruction.

The verbal parentheses **begin** and **end** of compound statements can be treated like arithmetic parentheses. Every **begin** is entered upon appearance into Z, and every **end** causes symbols contained in the symbols cellar to be evaluated (transformed into machine operations) successively until the highest symbol in Z is a **begin**, which then is canceled out against the **end**.

Treatment of the jump **go to** L, which is practically a machine order, is obvious.

In qualifier statements "**if** B" and "**for** v $:= l$" (where l is a list of expressions E or triples $E_i(E_s)E_e$ of expressions) the initial verbal delimiter is introduced into the symbols cellar, and the following sequence B or v $:= 1$ respectively evaluated. The ";" indicates the end of this evaluation. However, in both cases the function of the verbal delimiter is not finished.

In **if** statements a conditional jump must be generated, where the target address for the negative case (condition not met) is still unknown, since it is given by the statement separator ";" or **end** terminating the statement following the **if** statement. For this reason the symbol **if** must be transformed into a new state symbol **if** 1, say, which remains in Z until it is met by the next incoming ";" or **end** marking the end of the qualified statement. This determines the jump address to be entered at the appropriate place (given, e.g., in the address cellar ϕ), whereupon the **if** 1 can be deleted from Z.

Treatment of the **for** statement is more complicated. However, this statement is only an abbreviation of a sequence of ALGOL statements of types already discussed, and we can describe the translation process by giving the expanded counterpart, where we only have to add a new set of identifiers to be generated by the translator and to be distinguishable from all identifiers appearing explicitly in ALGOL, which we will discriminate here by priming.

If now the list l in

$$\textbf{for } v := l \; ; \; \Sigma$$

is of the form $E_1, E_2, \ldots, E_k$, which is indicated by the comma "," as a source symbol meeting the ":=" in Z, we have to transform the list of expressions into a list of statements assigning the values of the expressions to the components of an auxiliary vector

$$v'[1] := E_1; \qquad v'[2] := E_2; \qquad \ldots; \qquad v'[k] := E_k$$

and join the following statements where i' is an auxiliary counting variable:

$$\textbf{for } i' := 1(1)k; \quad \textbf{begin } v := v'[i']; \quad \Sigma \textbf{ end}$$

In this way we have reduced this case to the case of the arithmetic progression. The case of a list of progressions can be reduced in a similar way. It seems simpler, however, to expand this form by treating each progression and the statement following the **for** as a separate qualified statement.

Therefore we can restrict ourselves to treating the single progression

$$\textbf{for } v := E_i(E_s)E_e; \; \Sigma$$

After the **for** has been introduced into Z, we again have to expand the following into a series of assignment statements involving auxiliary variables, where the first terminating symbol is the opening parenthesis between E_i and E_s, and the second one is the closing parenthesis between E_s and E_e.

In the loop to be generated, the condition depends on the sign of the value of E_s. If E_s is a number only, the sign and the correct loop condition can be determined by the translator itself. If, on the other hand, E_s contains variables, determining the correct condition must be delegated to the resulting program by the translator.

Evaluation of the progression description terminated by ";" does not exhaust the functions of the **for** which has to generate the closing of the loop including counting and the decision. Therefore, the pairing of **for** in Z and ";" as source symbol must lead to a new state symbol **for** 1 in Z, which at the end of the statement qualified by the **for** statement (and following it) effects the closing of the loop. In order to take care of empty loops of the type

$$\textbf{for } v := 1(1)0; \quad \Sigma$$

the loop must be entered at the decision point.

As a consequence, the translator has to expand the statement

$$\textbf{for } v := E_i(E_s)E_e;$$

into

$$v := E_i; \ s' := E_s; \ e' := E_e;$$
$$\# := (\geq \textbf{ if } s' < 0, \leq \textbf{ if } s' > 0); \textbf{ go to } L_p; \ L_B : \Sigma;$$
$$v := v + s'; \ L_p : \textbf{if } v \# e'; \textbf{ go to } L_B; \ v := v - s';$$

where in the fourth statement we have abused ALGOL in an easily understood manner. The second, third, and fourth statements may be executed by the translator itself as stated above whenever E_s or E_e, respectively, is a number only.

The **procedure** statement finally is nothing but a library program call with sequential listing of parameters as given in the statement. Since subroutine calls are standard techniques, no elaboration is necessary.

7.2.7. DECLARATIONS

Declarations generally define subroutines which may be open or closed according to taste and capacity of the computer used. **Type** declarations have to be considered in an obvious way during evaluation of arithmetic and Boolean assignment statements. **Function** and **array** declarations lead to static subroutines, **procedure** declarations permit dynamic routines. Whenever closed routines are to be used, linkage must be provided in order to enter parameters into the subroutine. In addition, dynamic routines require an adapter computing, from program parameters and dynamic array declarations, internal storage requirements and addresses relative to this storage. In the case of open subroutines, these functions are taken over by the translator. Since techniques for calling in subroutines are well known and vary considerably between different computers, no detailed discussion is necessary.

7.2.8. RECURSIVE ADDRESS CALCULATION

As mentioned before, subscripted variables fit into the translation technique discussed as long as complete evaluation of the storage mapping
function in closed form is acceptable. This mapping function, for a variable
a [i, k], with supporting array declaration

$$\textbf{array } a \,[1, 1 : n, m]$$

is given by

$$a[i, k] := \langle k \times n + i + \rangle a[0, 0]\langle \;\rangle$$

where $\rangle a \langle$ is an integer variable the value of which is the address of the
storage location assigned to the variable a. $\langle E \rangle$ is the function the value of
which is the number contained in the storage location which has the value
of the expression E as its address.

For variables with running subscript in inner loops, evaluation of the
storage-mapping function in closed form means an intolerable loss of time,
and is commonly replaced by recursive evaluation, often by means of index
registers (b-lines).

What must be done is clear in principle even when more general storage-
mapping functions of the form

$$a[i, k] := \langle \;\rangle a[0, 0]\langle + P(i, k, p_j)\rangle$$

where P is an arbitrary (integer-valued) function of i, k, and further parameters p_j.

Whenever, in a loop with running variable v, the variable a[i, k] appears
in the form $a[f_1(v), f_2(v)]$, where f_1 and f_2 are given functions, e.g., poly-
nomials in v, these must be entered into the storage mapping function with
the result

$$a[f_1(v), f_2(v)] = \langle \;\rangle a[0, 0]\langle + P(f_1(v), f_2(v), p_i)\rangle$$
$$= \langle \;\rangle a[0, 0]\langle + Q(v, p_i)\rangle$$

The function $Q(v, p_i)$ then has to be expressed by a recursion with regard
to v, which permits evaluation of the storage-mapping function without
multiplications. This would mean generating the construction of the entire
difference table for $Q(v, p_i)$.

Incorporation of such features into the translator would pose a formidable
problem. Since, in the case of storage-mapping functions, the general case

is exceedingly rare (a nontrivial example, however, is triangular storing of triangular matrices), ALGOL (and most other similar languages) allow only rectangular arrays, which means storage-mapping functions linear in all subscripts.

Furthermore, all expressions admissible in subscript positions have been hitherto restricted to linear functions of the running variable. ALGOL refrains from such restrictions. Therefore we admit, for closed evaluation, arbitrary subscript expressions which may even themselves be subscripted. For recursive address computation, however, we also restrict ourselves to linear subscript expressions. This means that only subscripted variables of the form

$$a[c_1 \times i + E_1, \quad c_2 \times i + E_2, \ldots, \quad c_k \times i + E_k]$$

are eligible for recursive address computation, where i is the running variable of the respective loop, the c_j are constants, and the E_j are expressions not depending on i. Using the example given above (which means k = 2) and introducing the abbreviations A for

$$\rangle a[c_1 \times i + E_1, c_2 \times i + E_2]\langle$$

and Anull for

$$\rangle a[0, 0]\langle$$

we get

$$A := (c_2 \times E_i + E_2) \times n + c_1 \times E_i + E_1 + Anull$$
$$A := (c_2 \times n + c_1) \times s + A$$

as the recursion for the components of the array a [,] chosen by the progression i := E_i(s)e. The value of n is to be taken from the associated array declaration; the value of Anull is assigned by the compiler in the course of the final storage assignment preceding an actual run of the program.

If the original formula program has the form

$$\textbf{for } i := E_i(s)e; \ldots; a[c_1 \times i + E_1, c_2 \times i + E_2]\ldots;$$

the translator will expand it (we assume s > 0) to

$$i := E_i$$
$$A := (c_2 \times n + c_1) \times i + E_2 \times m + E_1 + Anull$$
$$deltaA := (c_2 \times n + c_1) \times s$$

go to L_p;

$L_B : \ldots \langle A \rangle \ldots$;

$A := A + \text{deltaA}$

$i := i + s$

$L_p : \textbf{if } i \leqq e, \textbf{ go to } L_B$;

$i := i - s$;

Here the symbol $\langle A \rangle$ can be interpreted as an indirect address in the usual sense.

If we include the use of index registers, the expansion of the formulae will be different. We introduce new variables IRK designating the index registers enumerated by K unambiguously (this is assured if the variables are generated by the translator; otherwise we have to introduce a new type declaration). A variable a[IRK] then means that the instruction generated with the address of a[ ] is indexed by index register K.

Using this notation, the example given above is to be expanded by the translator as follows:

$$i := E_i$$
$$A := E_2 \times n + E_1 + \text{Anull}$$
$$\text{deltaA} := c_2 \times n + c_1$$
$$\text{IRK} := \text{deltaA} \times i$$
$$\text{deltaA} := \text{deltaA} \times s$$
$$\textbf{go to } L_p ; L_B : \ldots \langle A \rangle[\text{IRK}] \ldots;$$
$$\text{IRK} := \text{IRK} + \text{deltaA}$$
$$i := i + s$$
$$L_p : \textbf{if } i \leqq e; \textbf{ go to } L_B;$$
$$i := i - s;$$

The general scheme shows clearly that the optimizing process involved in recursive address computation breaks down the last-in-first-out principle of translation, for only the appearance of a subscripted variable within a loop shows that sequences of instructions must be inserted into the part of the program previously generated. Therefore two different parts of the program, the instructions forming the loop itself and the preparatory instructions giving the recursion quantities, must be generated simultaneously and can be joined only after complete translation of the loop.

Besides, the sequence of symbols cannot be evaluated sequentially after being entered into the cellar: Expressions on subscript positions must be split up into different parallel parts, since, for the calculation of the difference deltaA, coefficients of the running variable on all subscript positions must be extracted and multiplied by the corresponding array dimension constants, whereas for the initial value of A the constant terms of the subscript expression are required.

A number of special checks and comparisons are involved in recursive address calculation, which for the translator always means compiling and interrogating special lists. First, as a prerequisite for recursive address evaluation as described, linearity of subscript expressions must be guaranteed. Especially, no variable appearing in a subscript expression explicitly linear in the running variable may be assigned values within the respective loop, since this would make the variable in question a function of the running variable. Therefore, all variables appearing on the left-hand side of an assignment statement within a loop must be listed and checked against variables in subscript expressions not defined by a **for** statement. This check is unavoidable if arbitrary subscript expressions are admitted.

Furthermore, the running variable of any loop in the process of translation must be available. For this purpose, a new loop cellar is introduced where each running variable is entered upon appearance within a **for** statement, and is deleted when translation of the loop is terminated.

In order to keep the generated program as effective as possible, the translator must carry out identity tests. If several subscripted variables appear within one loop, the corresponding differences deltaA, etc., must be tested. As long as no index registers are used, such identities only shorten the preparatory calculations and save auxiliary storage. Considerably more is gained when index registers are used. Since identical differences deltaA imply identical initial index (register) values, all variables with identical differences may be indexed by one single index register.

In most cases the running variable i of a loop appears in subscript expressions only. Furthermore, most computers containing index registers have conditional jump instructions depending on index register contents. To make use of this feature, the translator must check whether the running variable appears in expressions other than subscripts within the loop. If this is not the case, the values of the running variable can be treated as addresses (fixed point numbers) and can be stored in an index register only. As a consequence the final condition must be attached to the index register.

Our example (where we now assume several subscripted variables with identical subscript differences deltaA) now is to be expanded by the translator as follows:

$$\text{deltaA} := c_2 \times n + c_1;$$
$$\text{IRK} := (E_i) \times \text{deltaA};$$
$$e' := e \times \text{deltaA};$$
$$\text{deltaA} := s \times \text{deltaA};$$
$$A := E_2 \times n + E_1 + \text{Anull};$$
$$A_1 := E_{12} \times n_1 + E_{11} + \text{Anull}_1; \ldots$$
$$\textbf{go to } L_p;$$
$$L_B : \ldots \langle A \rangle [\text{IRK}] \ldots \langle A_1 \rangle [\text{IRK}] \ldots;$$
$$\text{IRK} := \text{IRK} + \text{deltaA};$$
$$L_p : \textbf{if } \text{IRK} \leqq e'; \textbf{ go to } L_B;$$

The examples given by no means exhaust possibilities of simplifying loops. The main points, however, are indicated.

As mentioned before, recursive address calculation is of primary importance in innermost loops, and index registers should be used there. But the fact that a loop is innermost is ascertained at the end of the corresponding statement only, and the final decision on the instructions effecting address calculation therefore must wait until this end is reached. This is another serious handicap for sequential single-run translation, which would be greatly relieved by a preparatory run determining flow structure of the program only.

7.2.9. SUMMARY

The preceding description shows that translation of formula programs into machine operations, with the exception of recursive address calculation, can be done sequentially, without storing of the formula program, as a pure input process. Long-range connections are given by addresses only, which may be taken from lists built up during input and translation. Therefore, adapting the translation process described to immediate interpretive execution of the formula program even by electronic circuitry is extremely simple. Recursive address calculation, however, would then pose extreme difficulties.

REFERENCES

1. Goldstine, H., and von Neumann, J., *Planning and Coding for an Electronic Computing Instrument*. Institute for Advanced Study, Princeton, N.J., 1947-1948.

2. International Business Machines Corp., FORTRAN *Manual*.

3. Melahn, W. S., "A Description of a Cooperative Venture in the Production of an Automatic Coding System," *J. Assoc. Comp. Mach.*, vol. 3 (1956), pp. 266–271.

4. Rutishauser, H., "Über automatische Rechenplanfertigung bei programmgesteuerten Rechenanlagen," *Z. Angew. Math. Mech.*, vol. 31 (1951), p. 255.

5. Rutishauser, H., *Automatische Rechenplanfertigung bei programmgesteuerten Rechenmaschinen*. Mitt. Inst. f. Angew. Math. der ETH Zurich, Nr. 3 (1952).

6. Samelson, K., *Probleme der Programmierungstechnik*. Intern. Kolloquium über Probleme der Rechentechnik, Dresden 1955, pp. 61–68.

7. Sheridan, P. B., "The Arithmetic Translator-Compiler of the IBM FORTRAN Automatic Coding System," *Comm. Assoc. Comp. Mach.*, vol. 2, no. 2 (1959), pp. 9–21.

8. Wilkes, M. V., Wheller, D. J., Gill, S., *The Preparation of Programmes for an Electronic Digital Computer* (Cambridge, Mass., 1951).

9. Wilkes, M. V., "The Use of a Floating Address System for Orders in an Automatic Digital Computer," *Proc. Cambridge Philos. Soc.*, vol. 49 (1953), pp. 84–89.

10. Adams, Charles W., and Laning, J. H., Jr.: "The MIT System of Automatic Coding: Comprehensive, Summer Session and Algebraic," in *Symposium on Automatic Programming for Digital Computers*, U.S. Department of Commerce.

11. ACM Committee on Programming Languages and GAMM Committee on Programming, "Report on the Algorithmic Language ALGOL," A. J. Perlis and K. Samelson (eds.), *Num. Math.*, vol. 1 (1959), pp. 41–60.

12. Zemanek, H., "Die algorithmische Formelsprache ALGOL," *Elektronische Rechenanlagen*, vol. 1 (1959), pp. 72–79, 140–143.

13. Bauer, F. L., The Formula Controlled Logical Computer Stanislaus." (To appear in *Math. Tables Aids Comp.*)

14. Böhm.

15. Samelson, K., and Bauer, F. L., "Sequentielle Formelübersetzung," Elektronische Rechenanlagen, vol. 1 (1959), pp. 176–182.

16. Samelson, K., and Bauer, F. L., "The Cellar Principle for Formula Translation," Proc. ICIP, Paris, 1959, UNESCO (1960), pp. 154–155.

17. Bauer, F. L., and Samelson, K., "Verfahren zur automatischen Verarbeitung von kodierten Daten und Rechenmaschinen zur Ausübung des Verfahrens." German Patent Application from Mar. 30, 1957.

7.3. Thunks

by P. Z. Ingerman

7.3.1. INTRODUCTION

This article presents a technique for the implementation of procedure statements, with some comments on the implementation of procedure declarations. It was felt that a solution which had both elegance and mechanizability was more desirable than a brute-force solution. It is to be explicitly understood that this solution is *one* acceptable solution to a problem soluble in many ways.

7.3.2. ORIGIN OF THUNK

The basic problem involved in the compilation of procedure statements and declarations is one of transmission of information. If a procedure declaration is invoked several times by several different procedure statements, the actual parameters which are substituted for the formal parameters may differ. Even if the several invocations are from the same procedure statement, the value of the actual parameters may change from call to call.

EDITOR'S NOTE: This article reproduced by permission of the author and the publisher: *Comm. ACM*, vol. 4, no. 1 (January 1961), pp. 55–58.

There are three basic types of information that need to be transmitted: first, the value of a parameter; second, the place where a value is to be stored; and third, the location to which a transfer is to be made.

In each of the three cases above, the requirements can be met by providing an address: first, the address in which the desired value is located; second, the address into which a value is to be stored; and third, the address to which a transfer is to be made. (This is somewhat simplified; more details are considered below.)

A *thunk* is a piece of coding which provides an address. When executed, it leaves in some standard location (memory, accumulator, or index register, for example) the address of the variable with which it is associated. There is precisely one thunk associated with each actual parameter in each specific procedure statement. (The handling of arrays requires a slightly extended definition—see Section 7.3.4.) If an actual parameter is an expression, the associated thunk (each time it is used) evaluates the expression, stores the value in some temporary location, and delivers the address of the temporary location. If an actual parameter is a subscripted variable, the thunk (each time it is used) delivers the address of the specified element of the array. If an actual parameter is a conditional expression, the thunk selects from the alternatives and delivers the appropriate address.

In the most general case, the address transmitted by the thunk may be desired information, the address of the desired information, or the address where information is stored, enabling the calculation of the desired information. The translator knows what kind of thunk to create by considering the syntax of the formation of the actual parameter and the previously scanned declarations. On the other hand, when a procedure declaration is being compiled, the translator, again by observing syntax, knows what kind of address to expect from a thunk.

7.3.3. THE SIMPLE CASE

The simplest case, for explanatory purposes, involves a procedure whose formal parameters are all either labels or simple (nonsubscripted) variables called by name. To compile such a procedure, one must consider both the procedure statement and the procedure declarations.

The procedure statement or function designator in its ALGOL-60 form looks like:

$$\text{glub}(a, b, \ldots, m, n) \qquad (3.2.1, 4.7.1)^\dagger$$

---

† Article numbers in parentheses refer to P. Naur (ed.), "Revised Report on the Algorithmic Language ALGOL 60," *Comm. ACM*, vol. 6, no. 1 (January 1963), pp. 1–17.

where "glub" is the procedure identifier. For simplicity's sake, the comma has been used exclusively, rather than the optional parameter delimiter ") ⟨letter string⟩ :(", as mentioned in the above-cited paragraphs.

When this procedure statement is compiled, it produces coding of the following description:

return-jump to glub

thunk a

thunk b

.
.

thunk m

thunk n

The procedure declaration heading corresponding to the above procedure statement contains in part:

procedure glub (p, q, ..., y, z)

in which formal parameter p corresponds to actual parameter a, etc.

In the simple case under consideration, there are three types of parameters: those on the right side of a :=, and those on the left side of a :=, and those embedded in **go to** statements. Also, a formal parameter in the procedure body is identifiable because of its appearance in the procedure heading.

When a formal parameter appears on the right side of a :=, the generated coding may be described thus:

(1) Store any necessary registers.
(2) Return-jump to the appropriate thunk.
(3) Remove the desired quantity from the address provided by the thunk.
(4) Restore the status quondam.

When the formal parameter appears on the left side of a :=, what is needed at run time is not a quantity, but merely a location. In this case, step 3 above is replaced by

(3a) Store the calculated quantity at the address provided by the thunk.

When the formal parameter is embedded in a **go to**, step (3) is replaced by

(3b) Transfer control to the address provided by the thunk.

Step 4 is vacuous. Note that in each of the three cases, the thunk provided only an address; the interpretation of that address is a function of point-of-call on the thunk. This means that procedure declarations and procedure statements can be interpreted without cross reference at compile time.

7.3.3.1. *More Detail*

A simple, nonsubscripted variable is a special case of an expression; in addition to expressions, strings, array identifiers, switch identifiers, and procedure identifiers are also valid actual parameters (3.2.1, 4.7.1).[†] In this section, the thunks for expressions in general and for strings will be discussed.

If an actual parameter is a string (2.6.1),[†] the thunk delivers the address of the string. Note that in some machine implementations this might involve delivering the address of the first character of the string, with the expectation that the end of the string is marked by some suitable delimiter.

If an actual parameter is a simple variable (3.1.1),[†] the associated thunk—each time it is used—delivers the address of the quantity named by the simple variable.

If the actual parameter is a label (3.5.1),[†] the associated thunk (each time it is used) delivers the address to which transfer is to be made. This may require some additional mechanisms, as described in the paper on Recursive Procedures and Blocks, Article 7.4.

If an actual parameter is a Boolean or arithmetic expression (3.3.1, 3.4.1),[†] the associated thunk (each time it is used) evaluates the expression, stores the value in some temporary storage location, and delivers the address of the temporary location. For example, if an actual parameter is a subscripted variable, the thunk delivers the address of the specified element in the array.

If an actual parameter is a conditional expression (3.3.1, 3.4.1),[†] the associated thunk (each time it is used) evaluates the conditions and, if necessary, the expression selected by them, and delivers the address as described in the preceding paragraph.

If an actual parameter is a function designator (3.2.1),[†] the associated thunk (each time it is used) delivers the address to which transfer should be made. Note that this may involve several steps if the desired element of the switch declaration is itself a switch designator, etc. (3.5.3).[†]

If the actual parameter is a conditional designational expression (3.5.1),[†] the associated thunk (each time it is used) evaluates the conditions to select the alternative and delivers the address to which transfer is to be made, using one of the two techniques described above.

[†] *Ibid.*

7.3.4. ARRAY IDENTIFIERS

When an actual parameter is an array identifier, its interpretation becomes somewhat more involved. At the time the procedure declaration heading is being scanned, there may be no way of telling that a formal parameter is an array identifier. However, when the body of the declaration is scanned, the sequence

$$\langle \text{formal parameter} \rangle [$$

identifies the parameter as an array identifier. This sequence can occur on either side of a :=. In this case the return-jump to the thunk provides not the specific address, but rather the address of a table in which the necessary information for the subscription operation will be found. (The necessary information is a residue from the corresponding array declaration, which may have been evaluated dynamically when the block was entered.)

When the procedure statement is being compiled and the array declaration is available, it is obvious that the actual parameter is an array identifier, and the thunk which is compiled will provide the address of the table.

7.3.5. SWITCH IDENTIFIERS

A switch declaration may be construed as a vector whose elements are unconditional transfer instructions rather than data. With this interpretation, a switch identifier as a formal parameter may be interpreted in precisely the same manner as the array identifier discussed above. In other words, a switch declaration may be treated in the same manner as a static, non-**own,** one-dimensional array.

7.3.6. PROCEDURE IDENTIFIERS

If one makes the (not severely) restrictive assumption that the address (in the final coding) of the exit line of a procedure declaration can be determined if the address (in the final coding) of the entrance line is known, procedure identifiers cause no difficulty when used as formal parameters. In this case, the thunk provides the address of the entrance line of the procedure. The coding which calls on the thunk calculates the address of the exit line and places the two addresses into a return-jump. (Note again that this is a philosophical description; on, e.g., the IBM 704, the technique is actually simpler.)

However, there are some additional complications when using procedure identifiers as actual parameters. The technique described above works in all cases except when the formal parameter part is empty and the procedure is a function designator. In this case, the associated thunk (each time it is used) return-jumps to the procedure and delivers the address of the location in which the value of the procedure had been placed.

7.3.7. PROCEDURE DECLARATIONS

When the formal parameter part of a procedure heading is scanned by the compiler, a list is made of the formal parameters. This list is used to distinguish those identifiers for which return-jumps to thunks must be generated. With the exception of the two cases to be discussed below, this is the only nonconventional coding generated. (By conventional is here meant the coding that would be turned out if the same statements were to be written outside a procedure declaration.)

7.3.8. CALLS BY VALUE

Normally, the procedure declaration introduces no coding as such. If the heading contains a value part, the corresponding formal parameters are understood to be replaced with generated local identifiers which must have values assigned to them each time the body of the procedure is entered. This is equivalent to inserting a number of ALGOL-60 statements of the form

$$\langle \text{generated local identifier} \rangle := \langle \text{formal parameter} \rangle$$

immediately in front of the coding provided by the programmer, and then interpreting these statements as though they had been there all along. If a formal parameter was an array identifier, and the array was called by value, the generator ALGOL-60 statements must have the effect of (nested) **for** loops to move the array. The generated local identifiers replace the corresponding formal parameters wherever they appear in the body of the procedure declaration.

7.3.8.1. More Details

If a formal parameter is called by value, it must have its value bound before entering the body of the procedure, and must be considered as a local identifier inside the procedure body.

If a formal parameter called by value is not used as an array identifier, coding of the following general description is turned out:

Return jump to appropriate thunk.

Fetch quantity from address provided by the thunk and assign it as the value of the associated generated local parameter.

It is worth noting that if a formal parameter called by value is used as a procedure identifier in the procedure body, the identifier identifies a procedure which has an empty formal parameter part and defines the value of a function designator (4.7.5.4).[†] Thus the same general coding scheme applies to this case.

If a formal parameter called by value is used as an array identifier, the generated coding is of the form:

Return-jump to the appropriate thunk to get the address of the dope vector for the array.

Activate the FUSBUDGET mechanism and move the array to the newly assigned storage.

The FUSBUDGET mechanism is described in a paper by Sattley.[‡]

7.3.9. NESTED PROCEDURES

A formal parameter in a procedure declaration heading might appear only as an actual parameter of a procedure statement contained in the procedure declaration body. This is illustrated:

> **procedure** glub (a, b, ... , m, n)
> :
> :
> george (a, x, y)

The same technique applies here. The procedure statement is replaced by

> return-jump to george
> thunk a
> thunk x
> thunk y

[†] *Ibid.*

[‡] K. Sattley, "Allocation of Storage for Arrays in ALGOL 60," *Comm. ACM*, vol. 4, no. 1 (January 1961), pp. 60–65.

However, at the time the procedure statement for george is being scanned, thunk a has already been noted as a formal parameter in the procedure declaration. Hence, the thunk that is compiled for thunk a under the return-jump to george is in itself a return-jump to the thunk for the formal parameter a which is associated with the return-jump to glub.

Thus, if a *formal parameter called by name* in a procedure declaration appears as an actual parameter of some contained procedure statement, the thunk for that parameter (generated when the procedure statement is read) jumps to the thunk for the formal parameter. The thunk for the formal parameter may again jump (the chain may continue indefinitely) or may store the necessary information in the standard place.

In other words, if a formal parameter in a procedure declaration heading appears only as an actual parameter in some contained procedure statement, the thunk generated by the procedure statement must go up one level, and must pass down unchanged the information there acquired. Hence it will call on the thunk corresponding to the formal parameter involved. The chain so set up can continue to any depth; it is only at the two ends of the chain that anything need be known about the type of address that is being transmitted.

7.3.10. FURTHER COMMENTS

This article, admittedly, gives no attention to the question of the correct matching of arithmetic types within the procedure body when one operand is a formal parameter. Hence, this article assumes that a programmer composing a call on a procedure must observe all the explicit and implicit assumptions of the procedure. (In addition, it assumes a doctrine like, for example, the following: "The value of a formal parameter appearing in an arithmetic expression in the body of the procedure will be assumed to be of type **real,** unless the formal parameter has been *specified* to be of type **integer** in the procedure heading".)

An alternative means of handling this question might be: Have the thunk for the formal parameter return not only the required address, but also a type code for the value of the actual parameter. The correct data matching would then be done dynamically during the execution of the procedure.

ACKNOWLEDGMENTS

The author wishes to acknowledge the valuable contributions made to this paper by K. Sattley and W. Feurzeig of the University of Chicago, Laboratory for Applied Sciences; and E. T. Irons, Princeton University and Institute for Defense Analyses. Others who contributed were R. Floyd, Armour Research Foundation; and Miss M. L. Lind, and H. Kanner, University of Chicago, Institute of Computer Research.

This work was supported by the University of Pennsylvania, Office of Computer Research and Education, and the U.S. Air Force under Contract AF-49(638)-951.

7.4. Comments on the Implementation of Recursive Procedures and Blocks in ALGOL 60

by E. T. Irons and W. Feurzeig

7.4.1. INTRODUCTION

The possibility of recursive procedures in ALGOL 60 is heralded with something less than dramatic fanfare in the second paragraph of Section 5.4.4 in Naur's report[1] the section on values of function designators. It is stated there that "any other [than the value assignment to the procedure identifier] occurrence of the procedure identifier within the procedure body denotes activation of the procedure."

Because of the importance, from the theoretical point of view, of recursive functions and because of the growing extent and direction of application of recursion in programming research and experimental mathematics, it is worth some effort to implement recursion, given that the costs in compilation and execution time and storage requirements in the compiler with a recursion capability are not too great.

The mechanism for treating recursive procedures described here does not put a compiler in jeopardy in these respects. The costs in time and storage to procedures which are not involved in recursion are negligible. The costs in time and storage to procedures involved in recursion are no more than necessary for a completely general recursion mechanism for ALGOL 60.

EDITOR'S NOTE: This article reproduced by permission of the authors and the publisher: *Comm. ACM*, vol. 4, no. 1 (January 1961), pp. 65–69.

466

7.4.2. PROCEDURE AND BLOCK ENTRANCES AND EXISTS, AND GO TO STATEMENTS

The sequence in which statements of an ALGOL 60 program are executed is normally the sequence in which they were written. This sequence may be changed in one of two ways: by a **go to** statement, or by a **procedure** (or function) call. (A function call is considered equivalent to a procedure call in this discussion.) Since a procedure call will, in general, be compiled as a reference to a closed subroutine, there will be certain entrance and exit processes to be executed before and after the execution of the main body of the procedure. Also, since at least **array** declarations must cause the execution of some process at the beginning and end of a block, there will be comparable entrance and exit procedures for blocks. **Go to** statements are connected with any discussion of either type of entrance-exit process because they may implicitly call for block or procedure exits by referencing a label or switch which is outside the scope of the block or procedure in which the **go to** statement appears.

The nature of the entrance and exit processes is influenced by several features of the language, the most important of which is the possible recursion of procedures. Since a procedure may directly or indirectly call itself, it is clear that it may be entered several times before an exit occurs. (The use of the words **entrance** and **exit** will be more or less technical throughout the discussion.)

Entrance to a block will be defined as that time in the execution of a program when control passes into the statements of a block. Entrance to a procedure will be defined as the time when control passes to the procedure by virtue of a call on the procedure. Exit from either will be defined as the time just after the execution of the last statement of the block or procedure, or the time when a **go to** statement leading outside the block or procedure is executed.

Since the body of a procedure may be a block (or a series of nested blocks) inside of which the recursive call appears, a block may, in general, be entered a number of times in succession with no intervening exits. Moreover, the depth of recursion may not be known at compile time, since the parameter determining this depth may be a quantity computed at run time by the program.

If a procedure is involved in recursion, it is clear that at least variables local to the procedure (including parameters called by value) must retain a unique identity for each level of the recursion. In terms of the machine, this means that for each of these variables there must be reserved (or

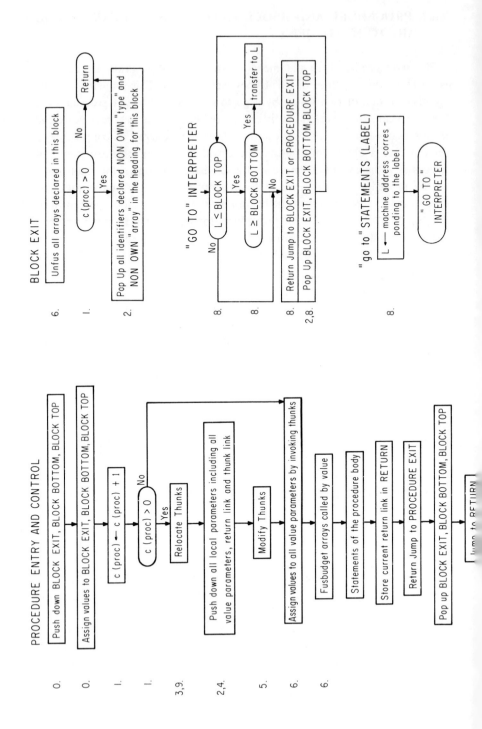

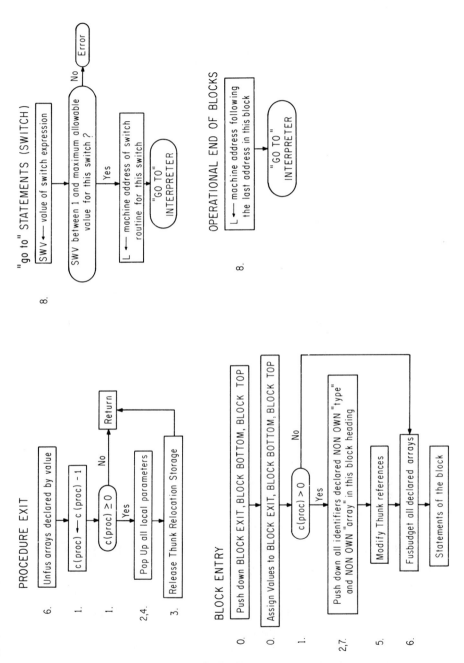

"go to" STATEMENTS (SWITCH)

8.

SWV ←— value of switch expression

SWV between 1 and maximum allowable value for this switch ?

No → Error

Yes

L ←— machine address of switch routine for this switch

"GO TO" INTERPRETER

OPERATIONAL END OF BLOCKS

8.

L ←— machine address following the last address in this block

"GO TO" INTERPRETER

PROCEDURE EXIT

6. Unfus arrays declared by value

1. c(proc) ←— c(proc) - 1

1. c(proc) ≥ 0

No → Return

Yes

2,4. Pop Up all local parameters

3. Release Thunk Relocation Storage

BLOCK ENTRY

0. Push down BLOCK EXIT, BLOCK BOTTOM, BLOCK TOP

0. Assign Values to BLOCK EXIT, BLOCK BOTTOM, BLOCK TOP

1. c(proc) > 0

No

Yes

2,7. Push down all identifiers declared NON OWN "type" and NON OWN "array" in this block heading

5. Modify Thunk references

6. Fusbudget all declared arrays

Statements of the block

FIGURE 7.4.1

created) one memory cell for each recursive call of the procedure. (In the case of array called by value, the entire array must be preserved in some way.) Since the depth of recursion is not usually knowable at compile time, it will be necessary to create dynamically at run time as many cells as are required for variables. However, it is advisable to recognize those procedures and blocks *not* involved in recursion so that their execution will not be slowed or unnecessarily taxed in storage allocation by whatever mechanism is necessary to handle recursion.

7.4.3. FLOW DIAGRAMS OF PROCESSES

The detailed explanation of the processes for handling block and procedure entries and exits, and **go to** statements, is in the form of the following flow diagrams. Each box of the flow diagram gives a short indication of the action to be taken. These are the diagrams for the *run-time* processes to be carried out at the indicated points of execution of a translated ALGOL 60 program. For an explanation of the reasoning and for details relating the action to a more precise discussion, refer to the numbered notes following the flow diagrams in Fig. 7.4.1.

7.4.4. NOTES FOR FLOW DIAGRAMS

7.4.4.1. *Block Exit, Block Bottom, Block Top*

A procedure declaration is effectively treated like a block in that at least the return link and the thunk link (see note 4 and Article 7.3 this volume) are implicitly declared as local parameters to the procedure just as variables are declared local to a block. Thus, though BLOCK ENTRANCE (EXIT) and PROCEDURE ENTRANCE (EXIT) differ somewhat in detail, they are essentially the same processes. In particular, the quantities BLOCK EXIT, BLOCK BOTTOM, BLOCK TOP can characterize the implicit block associated with a procedure declaration. BLOCK EXIT, BLOCK BOTTOM, and BLOCK TOP are three internal parameters of all programs. Their current values at any time during the operation of a program are:

BLOCK EXIT: The address of the exit routine for the smallest block (or procedure) in which the program is executing instructions.

BLOCK BOTTOM and BLOCK TOP: The lowest and highest memory address (respectively) of the smallest block (or procedure) in which the program is executing instructions. It is assumed that all the instructions for any block are contiguous in memory.

Whenever a block or procedure is entered, the current values of these three parameters are pushed down (see note 2) and the appropriate values for the block or procedure being entered are assigned to the parameters. Hence, pushdown storage will contain a dynamic record of the block entrances now in effect. The use of this record of entrances is explained in note 8 on the "**go to**" interpreter.

7.4.4.2. *Procedure Recursion—Depth Counter*

C(proc) is a counter unique to the procedure referencing it, which indicates the current depth of recursion of the procedure at any time during the execution of a program. C(proc) is used also to determine at run time whether the procedure is involved in recursion. It is possible to determine this at compile time (whether recursion exists, *not* the depth of recursion). However, since more than one procedure may be involved jointly through recursive chains of procedures, some of which might be in an ALGOL library, and since the existence of recursion is indicated in some cases only by the matching of actual and formal parameters, it might be exceedingly difficult to detect recursion at compile time. Recursion is easily detectable at run time, and we have chosen to detect it then.

The initial value of C is -1 for each procedure at the beginning of the program. During the operation of the program the value of C for any procedure is (the number of times the procedure has been entered) minus (the number of times it has been exited) minus 1. During the operation of a nonrecursive procedure, then, its counter has the value $C = 0$.

Since a block cannot be entered more than one time without an intervening exit, unless it is contained in a recursive procedure, it suffices to maintain a counter only for each procedure, rather than for all blocks as well.

Whenever a procedure or block is entered (or exited), the counter for the procedure which is entered (exited), or (in the case of blocks) for the procedure containing the block which is entered (exited) is referenced to determine whether the mechanism for handling recursion must be called into play.

Blocks not contained in a procedure reference a counter for the main program whose value is always zero.

7.4.4.3. *Pushdown Storage for Local Parameters*

Whenever it is required that the value of any parameter of a program be saved, that value will be stored in general pushdown storage. Since the entrance-exit processes in ALGOL 60 form a parenthesis-like structure, a simple pushdown list will suffice, provided that when parameters are pushed down in a given entrance process they are recovered in reverse order in the corresponding exit process. Hence, to push down a parameter, the value of the parameter is stored at the top of the general pushdown list; and to recover (pop up) a parameter, the value stored at the top of the list is transferred to the *normal cell* for the parameter (see below).

Parameters are always referenced by referring to the cell in memory bearing the "name" of the parameter. Because of the pushdown, pop-up processes invoked at block and procedure entrances and exits where necessary, the value of *current* interest at any point in a program is always contained in this cell, which is called the normal cell for the parameter.

Since **own** variables specifically must *not* have their values saved during recursion, they will never be pushed down.

The above discussion applies to arrays as well as to simple variables, since an array is referenced by exactly one cell which contains a link address to the dimensional information for the array and to the array itself. In this sense the single value associated with an array identifier is the address which locates the array.

The general pushdown storage is also used to keep a record of the order of procedure and block entrances and exits, and to store relocated thunks in a recursive procedure process. (See Sections 7.4.4.4. and 7.4.4.10.)

7.4.4.4. *Relocate Thunks*

Whenever a procedure is involved in recursion, parameters local to the procedure are pushed down. For all references to parameters called by name, the procedure refers to the thunks (see Article 7.3) following the last call (in the dynamic sense) of the procedure to find the addresses of the actual parameters. Assume that the thunks are executed as written. If the recursion is of the simple type, where the procedure calls itself directly, and if any of the thunks after the recursive call refer to parameters local to the procedure, these thunks will now reference the wrong memory cells for the local parameters. The thunks *should not* reference the values of these parameters which are associated with the current depth of recursion, but should reference the values associated with the last depth of recursion. In other words, they should reference the addresses in the pushdown list where the values associated with the last depth of recursion have just been stored. Hence it is necessary to modify any references to parameters we have pushed down so that they will refer to the pushed-down value rather than to the current value.

In order to allow for this modification, this part of the entrance process for a procedure creates a *new* copy of the thunks, which will be modified during the pushdown processes so that the thunks will refer to the correct values. (See note 9, Fig. 7.4.1.)

7.4.4.5. *Pushdown and Pop-up Value Parameters*

If a parameter of a procedure is called by value, a variable (bearing the name of the formal parameter) is implicitly declared at the procedure entry. That variable is then local to the procedure in question and hence must be pushed down in any recursive activation of the procedure.

The link (denoted *return link*) supplied to the procedure declaration by the return jump of the procedure call and the link to the thunks for this operation of the procedure (denoted *thunk link*) (which may not be the same as the return link if the thunks have been relocated) are also local parameters of the procedure and hence must be pushed down and popped up at the same time as the value parameters and any other local parameters of the procedure.

7.4.4.6. *Modify Thunks*

Although this process is shown as following the pushdown-variables operation, it is executed at the same time as that operation.

Since, in entering values of parameters in the pushdown list and making the normal cells available for new storage in a recursive process, we may move the value to which a thunk for a called-by-value-parameter refers, we must modify any reference to this parameter in the thunk. Hence, when we push down a parameter, it is necessary to look through the relocated

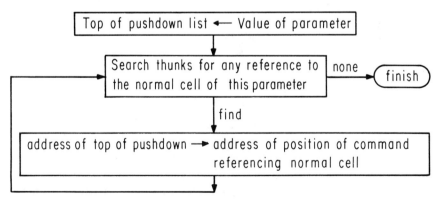

FIGURE 7.4.2 Pushdown one-parameter and modify thunks.

thunks for any reference to the normal cell for this parameter. If we find such a reference, it must be changed to refer to the cell in pushdown storage where we have just stored the value of interest to the thunk.

Because the relocated thunk may be a subthunk [a thunk for a procedure call which is itself in a thunk, e.g., the thunk for B or C in the procedure call FUNC (A, FUNC (B, C))], such references would have been modified previously during the original relocation of the outermost thunk.

The combined pushdown-modify-thunks operation can be flow diagrammed as in Fig. 7.4.2.

7.4.4.7. *Assign Values to Parameters Called by Value:* FUSBUDGET *Arrays Called by Value*

In addition to the specifically mentioned operations, values must also be assigned to the parameters of the procedure which indicate the return link and the thunk link for the procedure. This must be done before the thunks are referenced for assignment of values to value parameters, since these evaluations may trigger additional recursive calls. In this case all such calls are to be executed forthwith. For details on the assignment of values to value parameters and FUSBUDGET, see Article 7.3 and Ref. 2.

7.4.4.8. *Identity of Identifiers*

If any identifier in an ALGOL 60 program appears in two (or more) declarations, there will be assigned two (or more) memory cells at the beginning of a compilation. Hence, if the following two declarations appeared in different blocks of an ALGOL 60 program:

integer A, B, C

real A, D, E

the compiler would consider them as being

integer A, B, C

real A', D, E

for the purposes of storage assignment. The same applies to array identifiers, but the efficiency of storage allocation for arrays is maintained, since the space for an array is allocated dynamically. For the purposes of storage assignment, an array identifier is like any other identifier, except that, at run time, the value associated with the array identifier will be a link to the location of the array; this location has been assigned dynamically by the running program.[2]

7.4.4.9. *"Go to" Interpreter*

Since a **go to** statement may lead out of a block (or procedure) and in fact may lead to a statement several block levels outside the **go to** statement, and since every block entered must be properly exited, it is necessary to examine each **go to** statement to determine which blocks (or procedures) must be exited. Since blocks may be embedded in recursive procedures, it may be necessary to exit from some of these blocks more than one time, as it may be necessary to exit from a recursive procedure more than one time.

The current and pushed-down values of BLOCK EXIT, BLOCK BOTTOM, and BLOCK TOP determine which exits must be invoked in the execution of any **go to** statement, and how many times each must be invoked.

A **go to** statement will cause the machine address of the label (or switch control program) to be stored in a standard cell (L), and will then invoke the **go to** interpreter. Similarly, after the last statement of a block has been executed, the address of the next set of instructions to be executed will be stored in L and the **go to** interpreter will be invoked.

The **go to** interpreter looks at the current values of BLOCK BOTTOM and BLOCK TOP to determine whether the current block (or procedure) is to be exited. If so, the interpreter calls the exit routine for the current block or procedure and then pops up BLOCK BOTTOM, BLOCK TOP, and BLOCK EXIT so that the program will now be in the block which was entered just before the current block (just being exited) was entered. The **go to** interpreter now repeats the interrogation of BLOCK BOTTOM and BLOCK TOP to determine if the program is in the block indicated by L, and so on.

7.4.4.10. *Reduction in Pushdown Storage Requirements for Thunks*

There are particular instances of recursive procedures for which it is not necessary to store all of the modified thunks in relocated pushdown storage. This is true, for example, for simple self-recursive procedures in which the thunks associated with value parameters can be modified and executed from the original skeleton in the procedure body, given the values of the parameters associated with the last depth of recursion from pushdown storage.

The general conditions under which further efficiencies in pushdown storage can be realized are under investigation at the present time.

ACKNOWLEDGMENTS

P. Z. Ingerman of the University of Pennsylvania Office of Computer Research and Education, K. Sattley of the University of Chicago Laboratories for Applied Sciences, and R. Floyd of The Armour Research Foundation contributed conversation and ideas on the problems and techniques of implementing recursion in ALGOL 60.

This work was sponsored in part by the Wright Air Development Division, Air Research and Development Command, U.S. Air Force.

REFERENCES

1. Naur, P., *et al.*, "Report on the Algorithmic Language ALGOL 60," *Comm. ACM*, vol. 3 (May 1960), pp. 299–314.

2. Sattley, K., "Allocation of Storage for Arrays in ALGOL 60," *Comm. ACM*, vol. 4, no. 1 (January 1961), pp. 60–65.

8.

ADDITIONAL TOPICS

8.0. OVERVIEW

This chapter deals with topics relating to compiler construction, all of which lie outside the mainstream of research. The subjects presented are, however, important in specialized areas, and many of the techniques are currently in use within the academic environment.

Meta compilers and compiler-compilers have been in existence since about 1963; pioneering work done by Schorre on meta compilers (see *Proc. ACM* (1964), D1.3) and by Brooker, Morris, and Rohl on compiler-compilers (see, e.g., Annual Review in Automatic Programming, Vol. 3, 1963) are described in the literature. A meta compiler may be described as a compiler that translates a source language into instructions for a meta machine. These (meta) instructions are then interpreted, compiled, or assembled. A meta machine may be thought of as a software implementation of a hardware computer that is simulated by programs rather than by physical models. Meta compilers may translate source languages to object code for several meta machines, all or some of which may be realized on the same physical computer. Most meta compilers are explicitly syntax directed, incorporating syntax and semantics within each statement. Compilers such as META, META-V and Tree-META are most valuable for the quick construction of translators for experimental languages.

477

Compiler-compilers may be contrasted with meta compilers in that they generally translate one source language to another. Compiler-compilers also are invariably syntax directed, but the link between syntax and semantics may not be so explicitly apparent as in the case of meta compilers. The descriptions of meta compilers and compiler-compilers presented here should not be considered as definitive: Some existing meta compilers translate source language to source language, and some compiler-compilers translate source languages directly to physical machine code or to code for some meta machine. Furthermore, there is little uniformity in the field, and one implementer may describe a compiler as a meta compiler while another may term the same translator a compiler-compiler.

When considering the execution of meta machines, the concept of interpreters is important because an interpreter is perhaps the easiest way to implement a meta machine. However, little research has been done on the construction of interpreters, possibly because interpreters are frequently implemented as large finite-state machines. The reader is referred to the papers on LISP (McCarthy *et al.*, MIT Computation Lab. Rept., 1962) and LCC (Mitchel *et al.*) for descriptions of interpreter systems, and to the paper on APL/360 (Breed and Lathwell) for a description of the implementation of interpreters. Both the LCC and APL/360 papers appear in *Symposium on Interactive Systems for Experimental Applied Mathematics*, edited by Klerer and Reinfelds (Academic Press, 1968); it is perhaps the best available book describing these topics.

Another topic that arises when discussing meta compilers and compiler-compilers is bootstrapping. If a compiler is sufficiently general so as to be capable of accepting its own formal description as input, it can produce its own compiler as output. This procedure is called bootstrapping. One current controversy in the field of computer science regards the practicality of self-compiling compilers. One faction holds that unless a compiler is sufficiently powerful to compile itself, it has little merit; the opposing group believes that any such compiler is too general to be truly adaptable to anything else. Regardless, bootstrapping compilers are useful for two purposes: the initial construction of a compiler on a machine and the transferral of an existing compiler from one computer to another.

Macro facilities have been available in assembly languages for a long time, but their use in compilers is a relatively recent development. Macros may be used in a translator to construct a compiler for a completely new language, or they may be used during a precompile phase to extend the capabilities of an existing compiler. The articles in this chapter illustrate both applications of macros.

The subject of incremental compilers has become increasingly important with the advent of time-sharing and terminal-oriented systems. An incremental compiler is one that translates each line of source code as it is entered. The translation may be to physical machine instructions or to instructions for a meta machine which are interpreted during execution. If the compiler has the facility for execution of "direct" or "immediate" statements, then the translated statement is executed (interpreted) immediately rather than being stored in its translated form as part of a program to be executed at a later time. Literature on incremental compilers is scarce. Some descriptions of the BASIC language compiler, originally developed at Dartmouth College, discuss its implementation, but little else is available.

A final topic of current interest is that of extendible and enhansible compilers. Enhansible compilers are those that provide built-in facilities for the addition or modification of operators, data types, and the like. Extendible compilers not only allow those extensions but also provide for the modification and addition of new statement types. On this topic, too, literature seems to be unavailable, for we have been unable to find a paper suitable for inclusion in this book. Perhaps the best documented enhansible languages are LISP and APL, and the reader is again referred to the works of McCarthy *et al.* for the former and to the works of Falkoff and Iverson (Research Report RC 1922, IBM Watson Research Center) for the latter.

The chapter opens with Article 8.1 by Rosen, which discusses the compiler-building system developed by Brooker and Morris for the Ferranti ATLAS computer.

Article 8.2 by McIlroy describes a macro processor that facilitates the extension of programming languages, and Article 8.3 concludes the chapter with a discussion by Katzan of batch, conversational, and incremental compilers.

8.1. A Compiler-Building System Developed by Brooker and Morris

by Saul Rosen

8.1.1. SUMMARY

In a number of articles, R. A. Brooker and D. Morris (joined by J. S. Rohl in their most recent paper) have presented a very interesting programming system that they have developed for the Ferranti ATLAS computer.

The present article describes some of the major features of their system. It expands on some points that the original authors cover briefly, and treats only very lightly some topics to which they devote considerable space.

The purpose of this article is purely expository. Except in some very small details, and in some comments, it does not intentionally depart from or add to the material published in the listed references.

In the opinion of the writer, systems of this kind are well worth implementing and will provide useful research tools in the development of languages and techniques. This opinion is true even when such systems turn out to be of limited usefulness in producing "production" compilers, where compiling speed and object code optimization may be considered more important than language flexibility and elegance or generality of system organization.

EDITOR'S NOTE: This article reproduced by permission of the author and the publisher: *Comm. ACM*, vol. 7, no. 7 (July 1964), pp. 403–414.

8.1.2. INTRODUCTION AND SUMMARY

It is convenient to break the description of a compiler into two parts. One is the description of the source language—the formats in which the programmer may write source statements, and the classes of elements or phrases that may appear in such statements.

Formal descriptions of source languages have been published; the best known is the ALGOL report.[6] It has been noted by a number of writers[1,2,7,8,9] that it is relatively easy to produce standard service routines that will convert the formal definition of the syntax of a language like ALGOL into a set of tables in a computer memory. It is then also relatively easy to write a routine which, when given a source statement, will search the definition tables and determine the format of the source statement, and will provide an analysis of just how the symbols that make up the source statement satisfy the definitions and subdefinitions that define the format.

An analysis routine of this kind can be written so as to be independent of the actual definitions. It depends only on their form. It is therefore independent of the source language, being dependent only on the meta language.

The second part of the description of a compiler is a description of the actual processing routines or generators that take whatever action is indicated when a source language statement is recognized. This action may produce object language directly, or may add to or otherwise modify lists and indicators that guide future compiler action. It is assumed that the object language is implicitly defined in these routines.

The system discussed in this article associates a macro instruction (or generator), called a *format routine*, with each format. A source statement is analyzed and found to be in a particular format. It is interpreted as a call on the format routine associated with that format. The *analysis routine* may be looked upon as a preliminary translator that converts the source statements into generator calls in a standard form.

The system provides a language in which the format routines can be conveniently written. This language is described in the same formal terms as the source language and is converted into tables by the same service routines. The language provides formats for the instructions that make up the format routines. A format routine consists of a list of such instructions which are themselves statements in system formats and are therefore calls on format routines.

The system contains a basic structure consisting of a number of basic instruction formats with built-in format routines, a general-purpose analysis routine and a number of service routines which handle general system sequencing, additions to and deletions from lists.

A compiler is built up on this structure by adding definitions of classes of phrases, definitions of source statement formats, and definitions of statement formats that define the instructions that may be used in the format routines. Corresponding to each format, a format routine is added. The format routine itself is a list of statements in formats that are already in the system.[†] In this way enough source statement formats are added to define a useful language, and at this point the system will act as a compiler, with this language as its source language. Additions to, changes to, and deletions from the language can be made, and completely new languages can be introduced with relative ease.

8.1.3. PHRASES AND CLASSES

There is a set of elementary symbols that is recognized by the system. However, if it is convenient to make use of more symbols than are available in the character set that is recognized by the computer hardware, an input routine can recognize certain combinations of external symbols as the equivalent of single internal elementary symbols.

A *class identifier* is a string of elementary symbols enclosed in square brackets [ ]. The elementary symbols used in a class identifier may not include the symbols /, (,), *, ?, since these symbols are used to terminate or modify class identifiers.

A *phrase* is a string of components which may be either elementary symbols or class identifiers. A phrase class is defined by writing a class identifier followed by the symbol = which is in turn followed by a list of phrases separated by commas. For example,

$$C1 \quad [ES] = 1, 2, \ldots, 9, 0, a, b, \ldots, z, +, -, \ldots, *$$

$$C2 \quad [L] = a, b, c, d, e, \ldots, u, v, w, x, y, z$$

$$C3 \quad [D] = 0, 1, 2, 3, 4, 5, 6, 7, 8, 9$$

The class [ES] is the class of all of the elementary symbols defined in the system. Subclasses of this class are the class [L] of letters and the class [D] of digits.

[†] Their format routines need not be in the system until they are actually used.

The , separates the alternatives or categories of a class. Definition *C2* states that a member of class [L] is an a or b or c, etc. There are 26 categories in the class [L] and the category number of c in this class is 3. The category number of 3 in the class [D] is 4.

Similarly, [D] can be said to be of category 3 in the class [PI] of defined phrase class identifiers.

Classes *C1, C2, C3* are defined in terms of elementary symbols alone. Their class identifiers can be used to define new classes of phrases. The definition

$$C4 \quad [L, D] = [L], [D]$$

defines a class whose members are letters or digits. The class identifier [L] appearing in the definition means "any phrase of the class [L]." Any letter is of category 1 with respect to the class [L, D]. Any number is of category 2 with respect to this class.

The class

$$C5 \quad [LD] = [L][D]$$

defines a class whose members are phrases of the form a9, b7, z4. This is an example of a class that has only one category. Category 1 in this class has the two components [L] and [D].

The special symbol * is used to define a string that may consist of any number of phrases of a class. In the definition

$$C6 \quad [N] = [D*]$$

[D*] is interpreted as meaning a string of one or more [D]'s. [N] is the class of all integers.

The special symbol ? is used to indicate the optional presence of a member of a class, as in the definition of the class [V] of variables,

$$C7 \quad [V] = [L][L, D*?]$$

The ? indicates that a member of class [V] may consist of a member of class [L] alone or it may be a member of class [L] followed by a member of class [L, D*]. This means, of course, that a variable may be a letter or any combination of letters and digits beginning with a letter.

In order to describe arithmetic expressions in an ALGOL-like language, the following definitions are introduced:

$C6A$ $[N] = 1, 2, 3, 4, \ldots, 0$

$C8$ $[K] = [N], [N]., .[N], [N]. [N]$

$C9$ $[P] = [K], [V], ([SAE])$

$C10$ $[\uparrow P] = \uparrow [P]$

$C11$ $[F] = [P][\uparrow P*?]$

$C12$ $[\times/F] = \times [F], /[F]$

$C13$ $[T] = [F][\times/F*?]$

$C14$ $[\pm] = +, -$

$C15$ $[\pm T] = [\pm][T]$

$C16$ $[SAE] = [\pm ?][T][\pm T*?]$

The class [K] is the class of floating-point numbers. It would be more consistent with ALGOL to omit the second alternative [N]. These definitions define the class [P] of primaries, the class [F] of factors, the class [T] of terms, and finally the class [SAE] of simple arithmetic expressions.

The definition of [N] in $C6A$ replaces the definition in $C6$. In most cases it is convenient to treat [N] as a built-in class in which an integer is represented by the actual value of that integer. As pointed out in Ref. 5, the two definitions are not equivalent, since the definition in $C6A$ will not distinguish between the strings 3, 03, 003, and so forth.

8.1.4. ANALYSIS RECORD

To demonstrate that a string S of elementary symbols is a member of a particular class C, it is necessary to show that it satisfies the definition of one of the alternatives or categories of C. In general the categories of C will be defined in terms of class identifiers which may themselves be defined in terms of class identifiers. The question as to whether S is or is not a member of C can be answered only if a trace through a sufficient number of levels of class definitions leads to definitions in terms of elementary symbols against which it is possible to test the elementary symbols of S.

An *analysis record* is a diagram of a successful trace of this kind. The record takes the form of a multilevel branched structure which is a tree. There is a branch of the tree corresponding to each class identifier that appears in the trace. The branch points to a node which contains the selected category number within that class. There is a branch from this node corresponding to every component of the definition of this category which is itself a class identifier. If the definition is in terms of elementary symbols only, the node degenerates into a terminal point.

In constructing an analysis record, an optional class is always treated as a class with two alternatives, as if for each class identifier [CI] there existed a class definition [CI?] = [CI], NIL where NIL is the null class.

Similarly, a starred class is treated as if for each class identifier [CI] there existed a recursive definition [CI∗] = [CI][CI∗], [CI].

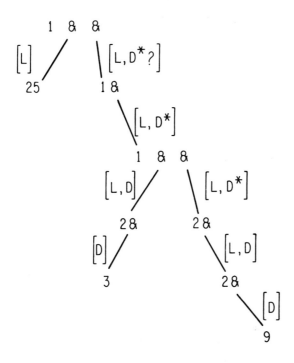

FIGURE 8.1.1   Analysis record of y28 with respect to [V].

Figure 8.1.1 is the analysis record of the phrase y28 with respect to the class [V]. The class [V] has one category which has the two components [L] and [L, D∗?]. Category 25 of class [L] is a y which matches the first symbol in the string y28. The class [L, D∗?] is the optional form of [L, D∗] and has two alternatives: 1 = present and 2 = not present. The alternative 1 leads to the class [L, D∗] which also has two alternatives: 1 = more than 1 present and 2 = only 1 present. The first alternative of [L, D∗] has the two components [L, D] and [L, D∗]. The component [L, D] leads to the terminal category 3 in the class [D] which corresponds to the elementary symbol 2. The class [L, D∗] leads to the elementary symbol 9.

The & symbol at the head of each branch symbolizes an address word when the tree is stored as a linear array in memory. The tree in Fig. 8.1.1 is stored as Fig. 8.1.2. Each category number and each address word (&) occupies a position in memory. An address word contains the address of the category word to which it points.

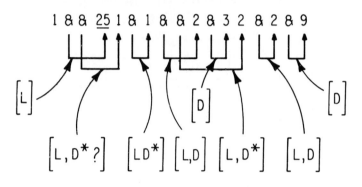

FIGURE 8.1.2

8.1.5. FORMAT CLASSES

A *format class* is like a phrase class in that it is defined in terms of a list of categories which are phrases, i.e., strings of elementary symbols and class identifiers. Each category in a format class is called a format.

The basic distinction between format classes and phrase classes is that there is a *format routine* associated with each format (category) in a format class.

Format classes also differ from phrase classes in that format classes are open-ended. Their categories are submitted to the system individually, and the system itself can grow by the addition of new formats along with their associated format routines.

An example of a format class is the class [SS] of source statements. Examples of source statement formats as they would be defined to the system are:

SS1   FORMAT [SS] = [V] = [SAE]

SS2   FORMAT [SS] = GO TO [V]

The phrase (statement)

$$y2 = a \times u \uparrow 2 + b \times u$$

is a source statement which satisfies the definition of the format [V] = [SAE].

The source statement formats taken together define a source language. The format routines associated with the source statement formats are the generators or macroinstructions which perform translation and other compiling operations that convert a source language program into an output that is a program in an object language.

In addition to the source language the system provides a language in which the format routines themselves are written. This language is defined in terms of two additional format classes: the class [BS] of built-in statements and the class [AS] of auxiliary statements.

The format routines corresponding to built-in statement formats are built-in routines. They are programmed and put into machine code outside the system, and may be considered part of the initial state of the system. The built-in statement formats, which are discussed in detail in Section 8.1.7, define the basic instructions of the system from which all format routines are ultimately constructed.

Auxiliary statement formats are introduced to provide instruction formats that are convenient for use in writing format routines.

The format routines for auxiliary statement formats and for source statement formats are lists of instructions which may be basic statements, auxiliary statements or source statements. Figure 8.1.3 shows such a format routine as it is written by the programmer and as it would be punched on cards or paper tape to be submitted to the computer.

Auxiliary statements are placed in a separate class from source statements in order to save time when the expression recognition routine (see Section 8.1.6) is analyzing a source language program.

It is consistent with the system philosophy to have only a very few basic statement formats, since these form a rigid base for the system and cannot be changed within the system. However, the introduction of additional basic statement formats may have considerable effect on reducing compiling time, since it is usually much faster to execute a built-in routine than to execute an equivalent format routine written out in terms of system instructions.

Brooker and Morris[1] discuss format classes other than [SS], [AS], and [BS] which might be introduced. The other possible format classes will not be treated here.

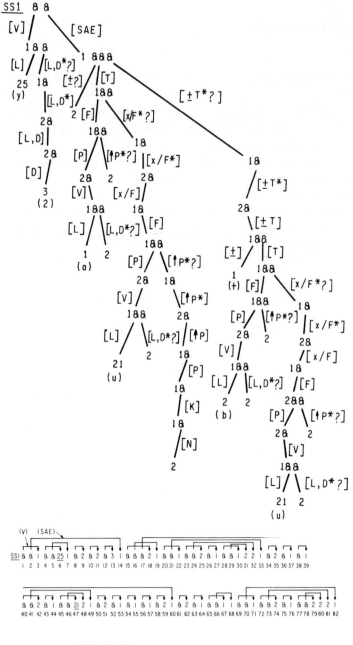

FIGURE 8.1.3   Analysis record of $y2 = a \times u \uparrow 2 + b \times u$.

8.1.6. EXPRESSION RECOGNITION ROUTINE

When a source statement is submitted to the compiler, it is analyzed by a routine which is called the *expression recognition routine*, abbreviated as ERR.

The ERR attempts to match the source statement with one of the formats of the class [SS]. If it is not successful, the source statement is an illegal statement. The class [SS] is considered to be an ordered class, and it is assumed that if the source statement agrees with more than one format in [SS], it is the first one that is to be used.

In the case of a valid source statement the ERR will find a unique format, and thus a unique category number for the source statement in the class [SS]. In the process of determining that the statement actually satisfies the format, the ERR constructs the analysis record of the source statement with respect to the class [SS]. The analysis record is a tree whose trunk or initial node consists of the category number of the format in the class [SS], and address words leading to branches corresponding to each of the class identifiers that appear in the definition of the format.

Figure 8.1.3 shows the analysis record of the statement

$$y2 = a \times u \uparrow 2 + b \times u$$

which corresponds to the format [V] = [SAE]. The figure shows the tree diagram and the equivalent linear array as it would be stored in the computer memory. The significance of the address words and category words in the analysis record has already been discussed in Section 8.1.3.

The expression recognition routine uses a trial-and-error procedure to construct the tree which is the analysis record for a source statement. A node in the tree corresponds to a category in the class whose identifier is determined by the branch leading into the node.

The routine tentatively assumes a category number at the node, starting with number 1. The components of the category are then examined in turn. A component is either an elementary symbol, which can be checked against the next elementary symbol in the source statement, or it is a class identifier. If it is a class identifier, an address word is inserted at the node and a branch leads to a node at the next lower level. The routine tentatively assumes a category number at this node and the process continues.

Whenever a category consists only of elementary symbols, these can be compared with the symbols in the statement being analyzed. If the comparison fails, the routine backs up and tries the next category. If there are no more categories to try, the routine backs up to the next higher level and tries the next category there.

If the comparison is successful, the routine backs up and examines the next component at the next higher level. When all components at that level have led to successful comparisons, the routine backs up to the next component at the next higher level, and the process continues.

A routine of this type can be described very simply in terms of a recursive subroutine that calls itself in order to advance from one level to the next. An exit from the routine at any level represents backing up to the previous level.

A routine of this type can be very time-consuming, even on a very fast computer. An important factor in determining the efficiency of the analysis procedure is the organization of the storage of class definitions in the computer memory.

Stored along with the definition of each class is a set of information words containing a bit corresponding to each of the elementary symbols. A1 at a bit position states that members of that class exist which start with that symbol. A0 states that no such members exist. The ERR can examine these information words to avoid a useless search through all the categories of the class.

The class definitions are organized so that categories that have a number of initial components in common can be recognized as such by the ERR. If the ERR has made successful comparison on $k - 1$ components of one category, and then fails on the kth component, it will be able to proceed immediately to a test of the kth component of the next category, provided that the first $k - 1$ components of the two categories are identical.

The ordering of the source statement formats can affect the analysis time. If the most used formats are put first, the average amount of search time will be improved.

8.1.7. FORMAT ROUTINES

8.1.7.1. *The Basic Language*

In Section 8.1.5 it was pointed out that there is a format routine associated with each format. When a source statement is recognized as definitely belonging to a particular category or format, the format routine associated with that format is executed. This can happen only after the ERR has constructed the complete analysis record of the source statement in the computer memory. The category number of the format is an indirect address that locates the format routine in question. The rest of the analysis record is the data input—the set of parameter values for the format routine.

This section describes the basic language in which format routines are written.

The programming system as a whole contains a set of system registers referred to as B1, B2, B3, ... These B-registers may correspond to hardware index registers on a computer that has enough such index registers. In most cases these registers are conveniently thought of as pointers or address registers. One of them, B_i, will point to the current position in the input string. Another, B_o, will point to the next position to be filled in the output string. B_s will point to the first available location in the main working area, and B_f will point to the beginning of the routine that is currently being executed. Others will be defined as needed.

A format routine has access to the B-registers and to the locations to which they point. The notation (B3) is used to designate the contents of the location in main memory whose address is in B3.

A format routine may require temporary storage for its own internal purposes. It may refer to any number of A-registers, A1, A2, A3, ... The system will allocate temporary storage registers equal in number to the number of A's used whenever the format routine is called.

The basic formats provide for the manipulation of numbers, A-registers, B-registers, and the contents of locations specified by A-registers and B-registers. The following class and format definitions specify a useful set of basic statements. Additional basic statement formats will be introduced later.

$$[A] = A1, A2, A3, \ldots$$

$$[B] = B1, B2, B3, \ldots$$

$$[AB] = [A], [B]$$

$$[ABN] = [A], [B], [N]$$

$$[ADDR] = [AB] + [ABN], [AB] - [ABN], [AB]$$

$$[WORD] = [ADDR], ([ADDR]), - [N], [N], [OW]$$

$$[OW] = *\text{Followed by an octal word}$$

$$[OPERATOR] = +, -, \times, /, \&, V$$

$$[COMPARATOR] = =, \neq, >, <, \geq, \leq$$

$$[IU] = \text{IF, UNLESS}$$

$$[LABEL] = [ABN]$$

BS1   [BS] = [AB] = [WORD]

BS2   [BS] = [AB] = [WORD][OPERATOR][WORD]

BS3   [BS] = ([ADDR]) = [WORD]

BS4   [BS] = ([ADDR]) = [WORD][OPERATOR][WORD]

BS5   [BS] = JUMP [LABEL]

BS6   [BS] = JUMP [LABEL][IU][WORD][COMPARATOR][WORD]

BS7   [BS] = CALL R [ABN]

BS8   [BS] = END

Instructions illustrating the first four of these formats respectively are

$$A4 = 10$$
$$B4 = B4 + B2$$
$$(B4 + 1) = B6$$
$$(B3) = (B2) + B1$$

The first of these will store the number 10, perhaps a tally, in the temporary location A4. The second will add the numbers in B4 and B2 and put the result in B4. The third will put the number in register B6 into the computer memory location whose address is found by adding 1 to the number in B4. The fourth will add the contents of register B1 to the number in memory at the location whose address is in B2, and put the result in memory at the location whose address is in B3.

A *format routine* is a list of instructions that are executed in sequence unless the sequence is broken by a conditional or unconditional transfer of control. To permit such transfers of control, an instruction may be preceded by an integer label followed by a right bracket]. For example,

$$2] (B3) = (B2) + B1$$
$$3] A5 = B2 + 5$$

The jump instruction formats then provide instructions like

$$\text{JUMP } 3$$
$$\text{JUMP } 2 \text{ UNLESS } A4 > 5$$

It is possible to set up and use switches. Thus one might write

JUMP A3

JUMP A3 IF B3 = B4

These instructions must be preceded in the logical flow of the routine by instructions that set the value of A3 equal to an integer which appears as a label in the routine.

Each of the sample basic instructions listed above is a member of the class [BS] of basic statements; i.e., it corresponds to one of the formats (categories) of the class [BS]. The expression recognition routine can therefore form the analysis record of these instructions with respect to the class [BS].

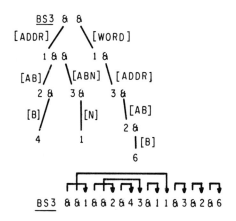

FIGURE 8.1.4

As an example, the instruction (B4 + 1) = B6 corresponds to the format ([ADDR]) = [WORD]. Its analysis record would be as in Fig. 8.1.4. The symbol *BS3* represents the category number of the format ([ADDR]) = [WORD] in the class [BS].

The analysis record with respect to a format class is also referred to as the analysis record with respect to the format within the format class.

8.1.7.2. *Parameters*

A parameter is a class identifier that appears in an instruction in a format routine. An example is the class identifier [AB] in the instruction [AB]

= [AB] + 1. This instruction is a member of the class [BS] corresponding to the format [AB] = [WORD]. An analysis record of [AB] = [AB] + 1 with respect to [BS] cannot be completed until a value is assigned to the class identifier [AB].

Instructions with parameters are stored as incomplete analysis records. A parameter word P_i is used in place of an address to indicate the presence of a parameter in the statement being analyzed. A parameter word contains a parameter number and a tag that identifies it as a parameter word.

Before a typical instruction can be executed, values must be substituted for all of its parameters. A parameter substitution is effected by replacing a P_i word corresponding to the parameter by an address word which is the address of an analysis record with respect to the class identifier which defines the parameter.

As an example, consider a very trivial routine:

ROUTINE [AS] = ADD [WORD] to SIMPLE LIST [AB]

([AB]) = [WORD]

[AB] = [AB] + 1

This routine would correspond to a format

AS1 FORMAT [AS] = ADD [WORD] to SIMPLE LIST [AB]

in the class [AS] of auxiliary statements. The routine has two parameters [WORD] and [AB] which are referred to as P_1 and P_2, respectively. It assumes that a member of class [AB], an A- or a B-register, is pointing to the next location to be filled in a simple list. It stores a [WORD] in that location and increments the pointer.

The instruction ([AB]) = [WORD] corresponds to the format ([ADDR]) = [WORD], and its analysis record with respect to this format is

The analysis record of [AB] = [AB] + 1 which is of the format [AB] = [WORD] is

$$
\begin{array}{l}
\underline{\text{BS1}} \quad P_2 \quad \& \\
\qquad \quad \diagdown [\text{WORD}] \\
\qquad \qquad 1 \;\& \\
\qquad \qquad \Big| [\text{ADDR}] \\
\qquad \qquad \quad 1 \; P_2 \;\& \\
\qquad \qquad \qquad \diagdown [\text{ABN}] \\
\qquad \qquad \qquad \quad 3 \;\& \\
\qquad \qquad \qquad \qquad \diagdown [\text{N}] \\
\qquad \qquad \qquad \qquad \quad 1
\end{array}
$$

The two instruction routine will be stored in the format routine library in the form

$$
\begin{array}{l}
\underline{\text{BS3}} \quad \& \; P_1 \; 3 \; P_2 \\
\underline{\text{BS1}} \quad P_2 \;\& \; 1 \;\& \, 1 \, P_2 \;\& \, 3 \;\& \, 1
\end{array}
$$

An instruction like ADD (B4) to SIMPLE LIST B6 might appear as an instruction in another format routine. This instruction is a particular case of the format ADD [WORD] to SIMPLE LIST [AB] and has the analysis record

$$
\begin{array}{l}
\qquad \qquad \qquad \diagup P_1 \\
\underline{\text{AS1}} \quad \&\;\& \text{---} P_2 \\
[\text{WORD}] \diagup \; \diagdown [\text{AB}] \\
\qquad \quad 1 \;\& \quad 2\,\& \\
[\text{ADDR}] \diagup \qquad \diagdown [\text{B}] \\
\qquad \quad 3 \;\& \qquad 6 \\
[\text{AB}] \diagup \\
\quad 2 \;\& \\
\quad \diagup [\text{B}] \\
\; 4
\end{array}
$$

which would appear in the form

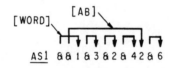

This analysis record of an instruction that satisfies the format ADD [WORD] to SIMPLE LIST [AB] provides values for the input parameters of the corresponding routine. The first address word is the address of an analysis record with respect to [WORD] which can replace P_1. Similarly, the second address word can replace the parameter word P_2.

The class identifier that represents a parameter may be modified by a label or by an index or by both.

A label is a string in the form /[N]. It is used where it is necessary to distinguish between different parameters which may have the same class identifier.

As an example consider a simple list that is specified by two registers, one of which contains the starting address, and the second containing the number of entries already in the list. A format for adding a word to such a list might be

> *AS2* FORMAT [AS]
>
> = ADD [WORD] TO SIMPLE LIST [AB/1][AB/2]

and an associated format routine might be

> ROUTINE [AS] = ADD [WORD] TO SIMPLE LIST [AB/1][AB/2]
>
> ([AB/1] + [AB/2]) = [WORD]
>
> [AB/2] = [AB/2] + 1

An index is a string in the form ([ABN]). It can be used only in connection with a class that appears in a definition with a * which indicates a string consisting of any number of members of that class, and it is used to refer to a particular member in the string. For example, one may refer to [±T(2)] and [±T(4)] to refer to the second and fourth [±T] appearing in a simple arithmetic expression [SAE] which satisfies the definition

$$[SAE] = [±?][T][±T*?]$$

Clearly $[\pm T(2)]$ and $[\pm T(4)]$ refer, respectively, to the third and fifth terms in the definition of the expression that is being analyzed.

It is possible to have a parameter in the form $[P/5(A3)]$. The value of A3 at the time the instruction containing this parameter is transplanted (see Section 8.1.7.3) is the value that is used.

All combinations of class identifiers and labels are treated as distinct parameters. The parameters $[AB/1]$ and $[AB/2]$ in the example given above would have the associated parameter words P_2 and P_3.

Parameters which have the same class identifier and label but different indices are treated as cases of the same parameter. They have the same P-number, but a P_i word referring to an indexed parameter will contain the index as well as the number i. When the P_i word is to be replaced by an address, the routine which does this replacement searches through that part of the tree corresponding to the starred class definition/label and determines the address word corresponding to the occurrence number determined by the index.

8.1.7.3. *Storage of Format Routines*

It is now possible to describe in some detail the processing of a source statement at compile time. A source statement may be a statement that is to be translated into machine code, or it may contain declarations or other information relative to the compiling process. It can always be interpreted as a request that the compiler perform a task—translation in the first case, and making entries or modifications in its internal tables and lists in the second.

The expression recognition routine determines the format of the source language statement, and in the course of determining the format it constructs the analysis record of the statement with respect to the class [SS].

A main working area has been set aside for the processing of source statements. When an analysis record with respect to a format class is constructed in, or moved into, the main working area, it is interpreted as a call on the associated format routine. The first word of the analysis record, the category number of the format in its format class, is the indirect address of the format routine. The address words in the analysis record provide the values that are to be substituted for the parameters in the instructions that make up the format routine.

A format routine is a list of instructions which may be source statements, auxiliary statements or built-in statements. Those instructions which are source statements or auxiliary statements are themselves interpreted as calls on format routines, which are lists of instructions which may themselves call on format routines, etc. The built-in statements cause built-in format routines to be executed, and the process terminates, since all format routines are ultimately defined in terms of built-in statements.

It should perhaps be emphasized that a source statement that appears in a format routine is itself a call on a format routine. Its effect is to cause object language code to be generated, not executed.

The instructions of a format routine are stored as analysis records with respect to their format classes. Instructions that have parameters are stored as incomplete analysis records. An alternative form for storing instructions that contain no parameters is discussed in Section 8.1.7.7.

Within an instruction the address words are relative to the first word in the instruction. The instruction is thus stored in a relocatable form. An instruction is always moved into the next available space in the main working area when it is to be executed. The process by which an instruction in the form of an analysis record is moved into the main working area and modified for execution is called *transplanting*. Parameter substitution takes place during this transplanting operation, as does the replacement of relative addresses by absolute addresses.

8.1.7.4. *Execution of Format Routines*

Assume that the analysis record of the source statement with respect to the class [SS] has been constructed in the main working area. This is a call on the format routine that is associated with the format of the statement, and the following sequence of operations is performed.

1. The pointer B_S points to the next available location in the main working area. Information is now placed in locations B_S to $B_S + 3$ that will serve as a link back to the next step in the calling routine after the execution of the format routine has been completed. B_S is advanced by 4 and the pointers B_E, B_F and B_P are set as follows:

B_E is set to the value B_S and points to the beginning of the area allocated to the execution of the format routine. It also remembers the location of the return link.

B_F points to the beginning of the format routine in the format routine library.

B_P points to the instruction (initially the first) in the format routine that is currently being executed.

2. A number N has been stored with each format routine. N is the number of storage locations needed during execution of the format routine for absolute parameter addresses and for temporary storage. It is the number of different parameters P_i plus the number of different A-registers A_j that occur in the format routine. The number of P_i is the number of different class identifier/label combinations that occur in the format routine. B_S is now increased by $N + 1$ to allocate locations $B_E + 1$ to $B_E + N$ for this purpose. The location B_E itself will be used to store the value of B_S if and when the current routine calls in another format routine. The reason for storing this forward link is explained in Section 8.1.7.6.

A pointer B_A is now set equal to the value of B_S. B_A is the value that B_S must be set back to after each instruction in the format routine has been executed.

3. The structure of an analysis record is such that the first set of address words (up to the first category word) contains the addresses of the sub-analysis records that are the input parameters to the format routine. These addresses are now inserted into locations $B_E + 1$, $B_E + 2$, ...

4. The analysis record which is the first instruction (in the general case, the next instruction) of the format routine is now transplanted into the main working area starting with location B_A. B_S is, of course, increased by an amount equal to the length of the analysis record. Some changes are made in the analysis record as it is moved. The address words which are relative to the beginning of the analysis record when it is stored as an instruction in the format routine in the library are now made into absolute addresses. Parameter addresses in the location $B_E + i$ are substituted for the parameter word P_i. In addition, special parameter words and temporary storage words are modified by the address B_E as described in Section 8.1.7.6.

5. The transplanted analysis record corresponds to a format in one of the format classes and is now interpreted as call on the associated format routine. If the format class is the class [BS], the format routine is a built-in routine which is now executed. If the format class is [SS] or [AS], B_S is stored in (B_E) as a forward link and the values of B_E, B_F, B_P, and B_A are now stored as a return link in B_S to $B_S + 3$ and the entire process described in steps 1–5 is repeated.

Whenever a built-in routine that is not a jump instruction is executed, B_S is set back to the value B_A, thus making available again the space taken up by the instruction (the analysis record) that called in the built-in routine. B_P is advanced to the next instruction in the format routine pointed to by B_F, and the process continues with the transplanting of the next instruction. The execution of jump instructions is discussed in Section 8.1.7.6.

If the next instruction is the instruction END, the execution of the current format routine has been completed. Locations B_E–1 to B_E–4 contain the return link, the values that B_E, B_P, B_F, and B_A had before the current format routine was called. These B values are now restored. The format routine just completed was called by an instruction in the format routine pointed to by the previous value B_F. That format routine now proceeds to its next instruction, and the process continues until it finally reaches the END instruction in the format routine associated with the original source statement. The link at this level is a return to the master-sequencing routine, which now proceeds to the next source statement.

During the execution of a format routine, control may go up and down through many levels of format routines, calling on other format routines which call on still other format routines. It is possible for the same format routine to appear at more than one level, and it is clear that the procedure described above will handle such recursive calls on format routines.

8.1.7.5. *Parameter Operations*

The class identifiers that appear in a format definition are the input parameters of the associated format routine.

One of the most important characteristics of this system is the fact that instructions in format routines may involve parameters that are not explicitly defined as input parameters. Instructions may contain as parameters not only the class identifiers in the format definition, but also any class identifiers that are used in defining the class identifiers that appear in the format definition. The analysis process carried out by the expression recognition routine makes available as a parameter any class identifier that corresponds to a branch in an analysis record with respect to the format.

The substitution of values for input parameters is done automatically when the format routine is called. The substitution of actual values (addresses) for other parameters is handled by a number of basic instructions which are among the instructions referred to as parameter operations.

An example of a nontrivial format routine will help explain how some of these operations are used. Figure 8.1.5 is a format routine associated with FORMAT [SS] = [V] = [SAE]. The routine is presented as it would be written and punched. During the compiler-building phase of system operation, a service routine which makes use of the expression recognition routine converts this input form into the standard form in which it is stored in the format routine library.

Figure 8.1.3 is an analysis record with respect to this format, and therefore represents a call on the format routine in Fig. 8.1.5. Assume that the analysis record of Fig. 8.1.5 is in memory at locations 1000 to 1098. A return link is set up in locations 1099 to 1102 and B_E is set to 1103, indicating the beginning of the memory area to be used by the format routine.

	ROUTINE [SS] = [V] = [SAE]	01
	LET [SAE] = [± ?][T][±T* ?]	02
	Ac = [± ?][T]	03
	JUMP 1 UNLESS [±T* ?] = [±T*]	04
	A1 = NUMBER OF [±T*]	05
	A2 = 1	06
2]	LET [±T*(A2)] = [±][T]	07
	Ac = Ac [±][T]	08
	A2 = A2 + 1	09
	JUMP 2 IF A1 ≥ A2	10
1]	[V] = Ac	11

FIGURE 8.1.5   An example of a format routine.

This format routine has seven parameters,[†] which are labeled P_1 to P_7, and makes use of two A-registers. The value of N for this routine is 9, and the locations 1104 to 1112 are set aside as follows:

$$P_1 = [V] \qquad \sim 1104$$
$$P_2 = [SAE] \quad \sim 1105$$
$$P_3 = [±?] \qquad \sim 1106$$
$$P_4 = [T] \qquad \sim 1107$$
$$P_5 = [±T*?] \sim 1108$$
$$P_6 = [±T*] \sim 1109$$
$$P_7 = [±] \qquad \sim 1110$$
$$A1 \sim 1111$$
$$A2 \sim 1112$$

[†] Brooker and Morris[5] would count the format class identifier [SS] as a parameter and would count eight parameters in this routine.

The input parameters are the first pair of address words in the analysis record in Fig. 8.1.5. These addresses, 1003 and 1014, are now inserted into 1104 and 1105.

Line 02 contains the first instruction of the format routine. It is an instruction, corresponding to the new basic format

BS9   FORMAT [BS] = LET [PI] = [RESOLVED-P]

The members of the class [PI] are all the class identifiers that have been defined. In an instruction in this format, [PI] will be replaced by a particular class identifier, and [RESOLVED-P] will be replaced by a phrase which represents a member of that class. This phrase will contain class identifiers which are parameters in the format routine in which the LET [PI] = [RE-SOLVED-P] instruction is contained. The purpose of the instruction is to substitute actual values for the parameters that appear in [RESOLVED-P]. The actual values are addresses taken from the analysis record that called the format routine. The parameters for which values have been substituted can be used as parameters in subsequent instructions of the format routine.

An instruction in the format

LET [PI] = [RESOLVED-P]

is stored as an analysis record with respect to that format. An analysis record with respect to [RESOLVED-P] is formed as if for every class identifier CI there existed a definition [RESOLVED-CI] = [CI]. The analysis record [1] of instruction 02 is

$$
\begin{array}{l}
\underline{BS9} \quad P_2 \quad \& \\
\qquad \Big| \\
\qquad \Big| [\text{RESOLVED-P}] \\
\qquad \Big| \\
\qquad 1 \quad \& \\
\qquad\qquad \Big\backslash \\
\qquad\qquad \Big\backslash [\text{SAE}] \\
\qquad\qquad \Big\backslash \\
\qquad\qquad 1 \quad P_3' \quad P_4' \quad P_5'
\end{array}
$$

---

[1] Brooker and Morris use an information item (see Section 8.1.7.6) rather than a simple parameter word like P_2 in an analysis record with respect to [PI]. The simple parameter word can be used here because the instruction will be executed by a built-in routine.

The primed P words are specially marked to indicate that the values of these parameters are not known and therefore values cannot be substituted for these P words when this instruction is transplanted for execution. The execution of the instruction will result in the substitution of addresses for the P′ words.

This instruction is transplanted into locations 1113 to 1121. During the transplanting the address 1014, which is the value of P_2, replaces the parameter word P_2.

In a practical implementation of the system it will probably be necessary to mark the end of an instruction, either by a special word or by a tag in the last word. It is assumed here that there is a tag of this kind in order to recognize the end of an instruction.

The format routine for LET [PI] = [RESOLVED-P] is a built-in routine, so that the four-word link is not established. During execution, the analysis record starting from P_2 which now points to 1014 is compared with the analysis record with respect to [RESOLVED-P] starting at the branch corresponding to [SAE]. Unless there is an error of some kind, these will be identical except in those cases where a terminal P′ word in the latter corresponds to an address word in the former. This address word is the value of the parameter and is substituted into the position in the parameter list determined by adding B_E to the parameter number. In this case, it is found that the parameters P_3, P_4, and P_5 have the values 1018, 1019, and 1060, and these values are substituted into locations 1106, 1107, and 1108, respectively.

During the execution of this instruction, B_A was equal to 1113. B_S is now set back to 1113 and instruction 03 can now be executed. Instruction 03 is an auxiliary statement corresponding to the format

$$AS3 \quad FORMAT \ [AS] = Ac = [\pm?][T]$$

The associated format routine will not be given here. The symbol Ac is a special symbol designating an accumulator, and the format routine constructs and places in the output string the coding that puts the value of $[\pm?][T]$ into the accumulator. Instruction 03 is stored as an analysis record with respect to this format in the form: $AS3 \quad P_3P_4$.

Instruction 03 is transplanted into 1113 to 1115 and the parameter values that are now known, 1018 and 1019, are substituted for P_3 and P_4 in locations 1114 and 1115, respectively.

The transplanted instruction 03 is now a call on the format routine associated with *AS3*. The values B_E, B_F, B_P, B_A are placed in locations 1116 to 1119 as a return link, and B_E is set to 1120. The parameters for this format routine will start in location 1121, and the first two will be input parameters whose values come from the first set of address words in the call. These are the values 1018 and 1019 in locations 1114 and 1115. The placing of these values in 1121 and 1122 passes these parameter values down to the format routine for $Ac = [\pm?][T]$, and illustrates the process by which parameter values are transmitted to subroutines.

The format routine for $Ac = [\pm?][T]$ is now executed, instruction by instruction, in the area starting from 1120. It may call other format routines which extend farther into memory, which may in turn call other format routines themselves. Eventually, all the instructions of the $Ac = [\pm?][T]$ routine are executed and the routine exits by resetting the B values stored in the link at 1116 to 1119. The value of B_A is restored to 1113 and B_S is reset to this value.

The substitution of a parameter value may also be done by an instruction in the format

BS10   LET [PI] = [GENERATED-P]

Just as in the case of [RESOLVED-P], the expression recognition routine implicitly assumes that for every class identifier [CI] there exists a class definition of the form [GENERATED-CI] = [CI].

In the case of LET [PI] = [RESOLVED-P], the value of the parameter corresponding to [PI] is known and the execution of the instruction inserts values for the parameters that appear in [RESOLVED-P]. In the case of LET [PI] = [GENERATED-P], values must already have been substituted for the parameters that appear in [GENERATED-P], and the execution of the instruction substitutes a value for the parameter corresponding to [PI].

An example given in Ref. 5 is

LET [WORD/1] = (B8 − [ABN/2])

Assume that [WORD/1] corresponds to P_4 and [ABN/2] corresponds to P_5 in the format routine in which the instruction occurs. P_5 is either an input parameter or it has appeared on the right-hand side of a previous LET [PI] = [RESOLVED-P] instruction. The analysis record for the present instruction is

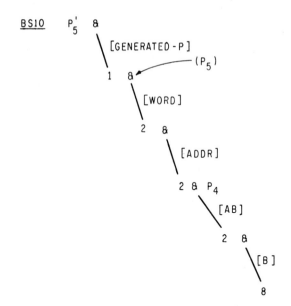

When this analysis record is transplanted, the known value of P_4 in the parameter list will be substituted for P_4. P_5' is a marked parameter word and no substitution takes place. Instead, the routine which executes LET [PI] = [GENERATED-P] will place in the P_5 position in the parameter list the address marked P_5 in the above analysis record. The transplanted analysis record will remain in working storage as an extension of the analysis record that called the format routine. This is accomplished by increasing P_A so that it points beyond the end of the transplanted analysis record.

Instruction 05 in Fig. 8.1.5 corresponds to the format

BS11 FORMAT [BS] = [AB] = NUMBER OF [PI]

The class identifier that replaces [PI] in an instruction of this format must be in the form [CI*]. If the string corresponding to [CI*] contains only one member of [CI], the category number with respect to the first [CI*] will be 2. If there are more than one, the category number will be 1 and the second address word will point to the next [CI*]. The routine that interprets this instruction starts from the beginning of the analysis record with respect to [CI*] and counts the number of appearances of category 1 before category 2 appears. Similarly, the routine that interprets instruction 07 will examine the current value of A2. Then, starting from the beginning of the analysis record with respect to [±T*], it will trace through the analysis record until it finds the analysis record corresponding to the A2-nd member of [±T] in the string [±T*].

Other formats similar to *BS11* are

$$BS12 \quad [AB] = CATEGORY \ OF \ [PI]$$
$$BS13 \quad [AB] = CLASS \ OF \ [PI]$$

BS12 places in [AB] the first category number that appears in the analysis record with respect to [PI]. *BS13* finds the category number of the particular [PI] with respect to class [PI].

8.1.7.6. *Labels and Information Items*

Instructions 04 and 10 in the format routine in Fig. 8.1.5 contain jumps to the labels 1 and 2, respectively. In the most general case, jumps to labels (switches) like A5 and B15 may be included. In order to handle this case, a label directory is stored along with the format routine. This directory has one entry for each labeled statement. The position within the directory corresponds to the label number. The entry in the directory is the address of the labeled statement. It is the value that must be placed in B_P to execute a jump to that label.

Instruction 04 is an instruction in the format

$$BS14 \quad JUMP[LABEL] \ [IU] \ [PI] = [RESOLVED\text{-}P]$$

Its analysis record could be stored as

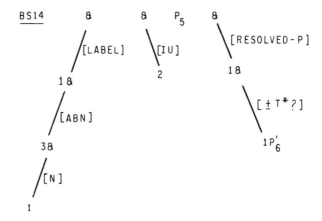

It would not actually be stored this way for a number of reasons.

For the handling of labels it is convenient to introduce a special [ABN] word which contains an indicator to distinguish the three categories [A], [B], or [N]. This special [ABN] word can replace that part of the analysis record corresponding to [ABN]. In the case of a format routine in which there are no switches, as determined by the absence of any jumps to an [AB], even the special [ABN] word need not be used. It can be replaced in the analysis record by the absolute address that would normally be carried in the label directory of the format routine, and in this case the format routine need not contain an explicit label directory.

The analysis record that was constructed for instruction 04 is adequate only because of the fact that instruction 04 is to be executed by a built-in format routine. The class identifiers [LABEL], [PI], [RESOLVED-P] and [A] require special treatment when they occur in formats that are not in the format class [BS]. They will normally not occur in the format class [SS], but they can occur in formats of class [AS].

Consider first the class [LABEL]. A label like 1 or 2 is defined only in the format routine within which it occurs. The label value is a reference to the label directory in that format routine. It cannot be passed down as a parameter value to routines on a lower level without additional information that will permit the lower level routine to locate that particular format routine.

So far, analysis records have consisted of address words, category words, and parameter words. An additional kind of word, the block word, is now introduced to permit the analysis record to carry additional or special information where necessary. In addition to an identifying tag, a block word B_n contains an integer n and indicates that it is followed by an n-word information item.

When the identifiers [LABEL] or [PI] occur in a format, the analysis record of an instruction in that format will contain a corresponding B_n word and a two- or three-word information item. One of the words in the information item is a blank which is filled in with the value of B_E when the instruction is transplanted for execution. The address word pointing to the information item is the value of the parameter that is transmitted from level to level. Regardless of where it occurs, it always permits the recovery of the value that B_E had in the format routine in which the parameter was defined. The word in B_E is a forward link. It points to the location of the link addresses, which are the B_E, B_F, B_P, and B_A for the original format routine. In the case of a jump to a [LABEL], these values permit the jump to be executed in the format routine in which it occurs.

For a label, the second information word is the [ABN] word described above. Corresponding to a [PI], there is a second information word which is an ordinary parameter word and a third information word which is the category number of the particular member of [PI] in the class [PI].

For the same reasons as discussed above, the P_i' words in an analysis record with respect to [RESOLVED-P] are modified when transplanted by the addition of B_E. This makes them absolute memory references, which can be transmitted as much. Similarly references to an A_j are converted into absolute references by adding $B_E + $ (number of parameters) to the value of j.

The right-hand part of instruction 04 is handled just like an instruction in the format LET [PI] = [RESOLVED-P], except that the actual substitution of values for parameters is performed only if the equality condition is satisfied.

8.1.7.7. *Primary Assembly Routines*

During compilation, the system acts as an interpretive system. The format routines are written and submitted to the computer as sequences of instructions in system formats. These instructions are translated into a standard format by the ERR, but they are not translated into machine language. They are stored as encoded calls on format routines which are the subroutines, generators, or macro instructions of the system. The actual calls are made during the compilation, which is run time from the point of view of the format routines.

The reason for this interpretive treatment of instructions in format routines is to permit the very general parameter substitution scheme that was described in Section 8.1.7.4. There is no advantage gained in handling instructions without parameters in this way, and an alternative procedure is provided in this case.

When a format routine is added to the system, each instruction is submitted to the ERR which determines its format and sets up the corresponding analysis record. If the instruction has parameters, the resulting incomplete analysis record is stored as the instruction.

If an instruction has no parameters, a routine (a primary assembly routine) associated with the format will be called in to translate the instruction into a sequence of machine-code instructions which are stored in the format routine in place of the instruction.

It is not necessary to have such a primary assembly routine for every format, since instructions without parameters can be stored as complete analysis records and executed in the standard way. The only reason for the use of primary assembly routines is the saving of time during compilation, a saving that can be quite considerable.

Format routines will therefore be stored in the library as analysis records and machine-code sequences. The execution of a format routine proceeds as described in Section 8.1.7.4 except that whenever the next instruction to be executed is stored as a machine code sequence, that sequence is executed at that time.

8.1.8. SYSTEM ROUTINES

Routines which are considered to be service routines of the system may themselves be written just like format routines, as lists of instructions in system formats. They may be executed by the same mechanism which executes the format routines. The instruction format *BS7* FORMAT [BS] = CALL R [ABN] may be used within such routines and also within format routines to call system routines as subroutines. The routines are numbered, and an instruction like CALL R25 will cause subroutine number 25 to be executed.

The system may be modified and extended by the addition of new system routines written in terms of system instruction formats.

8.1.9. COMMENTS AND CONCLUSIONS

In handling declarations in a language like ALGOL, the format routine which is called in by the declarations that appear in a block head would call on the table-building routines of the system to enter new identifiers into appropriate classes—real, integer, Boolean, array, etc. The format routine called at the end of a block would call routines which make the necessary deletions.

It is probably desirable, in handling ALGOL-like languages, to have a special built-in routine for recognizing variables, and perhaps another for searching tables of variables.

The compiling phase of the system has been described as a one-pass compiler. There seems to be no reason why the same techniques could not be used in more elaborate multipass compiling systems.

The system as described here can be implemented without great difficulty on almost any large computer. The chief problems are those of time and space. It was originally proposed for the FERRANTI ATLAS which has a unique organization of storage that permits the programmer to refer directly to a very large storage area consisting of cores and drums. The executive routine, aided by the hardware design, permits very rapid access to this extended storage. In more conventional systems the time taken for references to intermediate storage may be so great as to make the size of core storage the practical limit on the size of the system. Ingenuity in the packing of information can save core storage. Brooker and Morris[3] propose an elaborate packing scheme for analysis records, but in Ref. 5 they indicate that they will not use it because of the time consumed in packing and unpacking.

The very elegance and generality of the system is bound to make it relatively slow. As pointed out earlier, there are ways in which speed can be improved at the expense of generality. In an extreme case one can go back to a rigid but very fast compiler.

More experience with systems of this type will show just how much time is sacrificed and whether the compensations are adequate. Probably even on the ATLAS, and certainly on other computers, compilers produced by more conventional techniques will exist alongside compilers produced by systems of this type, and it will be possible to make some very interesting comparisons.

REFERENCES

1. Brooker, R. A., and Morris, D., "An Assembly Program for a Phrase Structure Language," *Comput. J.*, vol. 3 (1960), p. 168.
2. ———, "Some Proposals for the Realization of a Certain Assembly Program," *Comput. J.*, vol. 3 (1961), p. 220.
3. ———, "A Description of Mercury Autocode in Terms of a Phrase Structure Language," in *Second Annual Review of Automatic Programming*, Pergamon, New York, 1961.
4. ———, "A General Translation Program for Phrase Structure Languages," *J. ACM*, vol. 9 (January 1962), p. 1.
5. Brooker, R. A., Morris, D., and Rohl, J. S., "Trees and Routines," *Comput. J.*, vol. 5 (1962), p. 33.
6. Naur, P. (ed.), "Report on the Algorithmic Language ALGOL 60," *Comm. ACM*, vol. 3 (May 1960), p. 299.

7. Irons, E. T., "A Syntax Directed Compiler for ALGOL 60," *Comm. ACM*, vol. 4 (January 1961), p. 51.

8. ————, PSYCO, *the Princeton Syntax Compiler* (a manual). Institute for Defense Analyses, Princeton, N.J.

9. Warshall, S., "A Syntax-Directed Generator," *Proc. Eastern Joint Comput. Conf.*, Washington, D.C., December 1961.

8.2. Macro-Instruction Extensions of Compiler Languages

by M. Douglas McIlroy

8.2.1. ABSTRACT

Macro instruction compilers constructed from a small set of functions can be made extremely powerful. In particular, conditional assembly, nested definitions, and parenthetical notation serve to make a compiler capable of accepting very general extensions to its ground language.

8.2.2. INFORMAL DEVELOPMENT

The idea of macro instructions is not new. Many existing compilers permit macros in forms more or less sophisticated. Complex macro operations, however, are often quite laborious to incorporate in a programming system because special-purpose generators must be built to handle each addition. It is our aim to show a limited set of functions readily implemented for a wide variety of programming systems which constitute a powerful tool for extending source languages conveniently and at will. Our development will be for the most part informal, avoiding technical detail. We will illustrate ideas with an informal compiler as we go along,

EDITOR'S NOTE: This article reproduced by permission of the author and the publisher: *Comm. ACM*, vol. 3, no. 4 (April 1960), pp. 214–220.

leaving one formal realization based on ALGOL for the appendix. As a source of examples, we have chosen the familiar field of algebraic translation.

At base, a macro instruction is simply a pattern for an open subroutine. For example, a single-address machine might be converted in appearance to a three-address machine by defining a set of macros such as

$$\text{ADD, A, B, C} \equiv \text{FETCH, A}$$
$$\text{ADD, B} \qquad\qquad (1)$$
$$\text{STORE, C}$$

In (1) the identity sign, $\equiv$, is used to separate the definiendum on the left from the definiens on the right. The first component—ADD—on the left names the macro being defined as a function of the dummy parameters specified by the remaining components, A, B, and C. A compiler designed to accept macro definitions could read (1) and therefore properly assemble any macro call such as

$$\text{ADD, X, Y, Z} \qquad\qquad (2)$$

8.2.2.1. *Pyramided Definitions*

An obvious extension of this simple macro compiler is to allow new definitions in terms of old, as in

$$\text{COMPLEXADD, A, B, C} \equiv \text{ADD, A, B, C}$$
$$\text{ADD, A} + 1, \text{B} + 1, \text{C} + 1$$

which defines three-address addition of complex numbers whose real and imaginary parts are stored sequentially in terms of real three-address addition.

8.2.2.2. *Conditional Macros*

Until recently, macro compilers did not grow beyond this level of sophistication, but such a compiler is weak and inflexible. For example, a programmer using the three-address addition of (1) would be most unhappy if he had to store a result in C that was intended to be used only in the very next instruction. In order to add $P + Q + R$ and store the result in S, he would like to make a call such as

$$\text{ADD, P, Q, ACC}$$
$$\text{ADD, ACC, R, S} \qquad\qquad (3)$$

where ACC is used to refer to the accumulator as a special address. The compiler should recognize this special symbol and construct code appropriately. Such conditional assembly might be specified in the definition

$$\text{ADD, A, B, C} \equiv \begin{cases} \text{if A is not ACC} \\ \text{FETCH, A} \end{cases}$$

$$\text{ADD, B} \qquad\qquad (4)$$

$$\begin{cases} \text{if C is not ACC} \\ \text{STORE, C} \end{cases}$$

Given this definition, the compiler would produce efficient code from the call (3), purged of redundant STORE and FETCH instructions:

FETCH, P

ADD, Q

ADD, R

STORE, S

For an actual machine-language compiler, one would devise a standard shorthand notation for the conditions in (4), but that is inessential to this discussion.

8.2.2.3. *Created Symbols*

The matter of labels on coding lines within a macro definition proves bothersome in cases such as

OVERDRAW, X, Y, ACTION, Z ≡ FETCH, X

SUB, Y

PLUSJUMP, Z

ACTION

Z: empty line of code

Here the label Z must be supplied as a parameter in order to assure that it gets a unique name each time OVERDRAW is called. But, since the label has no significance outside the macro, its naming should not be of concern to the programmer. This problem may be handled by providing a mechanism to create names; for example:

$$\text{OVERDRAW, X, Y, ACTION} \equiv \text{create Z}$$

$$\text{FETCH, X}$$

$$\text{SUB, Y} \qquad\qquad (5)$$

$$\text{PLUSJUMP, Z}$$

$$\text{ACTION}$$

$$\text{Z: empty line of code}$$

Created names will be generated sequentially as needed from some special alphabet that the programmer is forbidden to use.

8.2.2.4. *Grouping by Parentheses*

The example (5) illustrates another difficulty in our simple compiler: Suppose the programmer wishes to put SETZERO, X in place of ACTION. In order to avoid ambiguity in the call, some indication of grouping is required. Parentheses are used to accomplish this:

$$\text{OVERDRAW, X, Y, (SETZERO, X)}$$

Parentheses so used result in standard notation for compounding functions.

A simple algebraic translator can be built from the macro compiler as already described. For example, one might define

$$A \equiv \text{FETCH, A}$$

$$B \equiv \text{FETCH, B}$$

$$\text{etc.}$$

$$\text{SET, X, Y} \equiv Y$$

$$\text{STORE, X}$$

$$\text{SUM, X, Y} \equiv X$$

$$\text{STORE, T} \qquad\qquad (6)$$

$$\text{T: redefine to be } T + 1$$

$$Y$$

$$\text{T: redefine to be } T - 1$$

$$\text{ADD, T}$$

$$\text{COS, X} \equiv X$$

$$\text{SUBJUMP, COS}$$

The machine is assumed to have a "subroutine jump" operation, SUB-JUMP, the compiler is assumed to have a pseudo-operation "redefine" that allows one to modify equivalences of symbols during compilation. A block of storage must have been set aside at location T for temporary storage of intermediate results. Repetitive redefinition of T accomplishes overlapping but noninterfering use of this temporary storage.

With the definitions (6) one may write suggestive calls in functional notation; for example:

$$\text{SET, C, (SUM, A (COS, (SUM, A, B)))} \tag{7}$$

means in ALGOL notation

$$C := A + \cos(A + B)$$

The coding produced from the call (7) by our "algebraic translator" is shown in Fig. 8.2.1. The scope of each macro is indicated to the right of the code. This naive translator produces inefficient code, but one could take advantage of conditional assembly macros to improve it. Thus the macro SUM is more advantageously defined by

$$\text{SUM, X, Y} \equiv \begin{cases} \text{if Y is a symbol} \\ \text{X} \\ \text{ADD, Y} \\[1em] \text{if Y is not a symbol} \\ \text{X} \\ \text{STORE, T} \\ \text{T: redefine T} + 1 \\ \text{Y} \\ \text{T: redefine T} - 1 \\ \text{ADD, T} \end{cases}$$

Such ideas may be elaborated at will.

8.2.2.5. Nested Definitions

Among the definitions (6) was included for each variable a definition such as $A \equiv$ FETCH, A. The programmer must remember to make a definition like this for every variable storage name he assigned. Since the pattern is well fixed, why not let the macro compiler do the work? Assign-

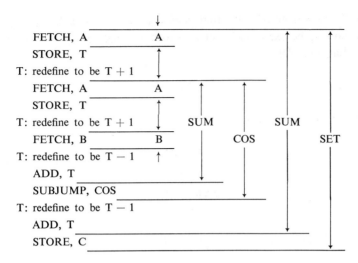

FIGURE 8.2.1 A compilation of SET, C, (SUM, A, (COS, (SUM, A, B))).

ment of variable storage and definition of the associated macro can be done simultaneously by

$$VARIABLE, A \equiv A: \text{reserve } 1$$
$$A \equiv FETCH, A \tag{9}$$

where "reserve n" is a pseudo-operation to set aside n storage locations. Buried within the definition for VARIABLE is a second-definition scheme that produces a new definition as a result of every call for VARIABLE. The programmer is now insulated from the internal mechanism of the translator. However, he is still saddled with repetitive work in writing

$$VARIABLE, X$$
$$VARIABLE, Y$$
$$\text{etc.}$$

He may be relieved of this burden by adding an iterative feature to the compiler, say in the form

$$VARIABLES, X \equiv \text{repeat over } X$$
$$VARIABLE, X \tag{10}$$

where "repeat over X" says that X is expected to be a list and that the macro should be expanded over and over for each entry on the list until it is exhausted. Thus

$$\text{VARIABLES (X, Y, Z)} \qquad (11)$$

is equivalent to the sequence of calls

VARIABLE, X

VARIABLE, Y

VARIABLE, Z

8.2.3. VARYING LANGUAGE STYLES

The new aspect of a source language to which definitions have been added may be termed a *definitional extension* of that language. This term is borrowed from logic.[2] A macro compiler is seen to be nothing more than a machine for performing logical reductions from the extended language to the ground language. Since the rules for reduction are not part of the ground language, a macro compiler might be made to yield as output any one of a large class of ground languages. It appears that most existing machine-input languages might be subsumed under a properly designed macro compiler that could be fairly readily implemented. (As a particular example, the author has produced FORTRAN algebraic compiler language as output from a relatively naive working compiler for the SAP machine-assembly language on the IBM 704.)

The principal problem in implementing a compiler of varying ground languages is making the extensions of the languages appear natural to users of each. This is mostly a question of adopting the compiler's method of scanning to accept input in ground language style. As an added dividend, such a compiler will free the tight style restrictions of any one ground language, allowing great latitude in specifying the appearance of its extensions.

Scanners included in most compilers work in one of two quite simple fashions, usually called fixed and variable field scanning. The former method, gradually losing importance by comparison to variable field scanning, will be neglected in this discussion. Variable field scanning involves extracting linguistic elements as blocks of characters separated by selected break characters. Break characters may serve merely as separators (e.g., commas to indicate parallel structure), as signs denoting a treatment to be performed on the separated blocks (e.g., the operation signs in ALPHA = BETA + GAMMA), or as delimiters (paired parentheses) to impose tree structure on otherwise linear text. Occasionally break "characters" may actually be blocks such as the **begin** and **end** delimiters in ALGOL, but this obvious extension is not hard to handle.

Typical operation of a scanner consists in scanning to the next break character to isolate a linguistic element and then performing some action signified by the break character or by the isolated element. High flexibility of source language style may be accomplished simply by permitting the set of break characters to be modified. Further power accrues from including directions as to the interpretation of break characters. Both improvements may be bought cheaply in a properly designed macro compiler. For example, completely parenthesized algebraic expressions on binary operators might be added to the source language of our informal compiler whose ground language is single-address symbolic machine language as follows:

First specify the break characters to be used in decoding calls for algebraic macros. This might be done by defining ALGEBRAIC, a macro that signals the compiler to modify its set of break characters

$$ \text{ALGEBRAIC} \equiv \text{replace the comma break class by} $$
$$, + - \times / = \tag{12} $$

then, similarly to (6), defining for each symbol a macro like

$$ A = X \equiv \text{ALG}, (X) \tag{13} $$
$$ \text{STORE, A} $$

(Again, the programmer may be relieved of writing the details of such definitions by burying (13) inside another macro.) The macro ALG will write a program for computing the value of expression X. As shown in Fig. 8.2.2, ALG is quite lengthy, but in execution not prohibitively long because large segments are alternatives, so that the whole macro will not be executed for any one particular subexpression. The definition is recursive by virtue of the macro definition $Z \equiv \text{ALG}, (X)$ which will cause the first operand of a binary operation to be evaluated and the macro call $T = (X)$ for the second. We have again used T as the symbolic address of a zone of

ALG, X ≡ if X is not a symbol go to 5
        FETCH, X
        go to 7

5: create Z, C
   repeat over X thru 7
   if C is defined go to 6

Z ≡ ALG, (X)
   if break is not + go to 8

C: redefine to be 1
   go to 7

8: if break is not − go to 9

C: redefine to be 2
   go to 7

9: ···
   [similarly set C = 3 for ×, C = 4 for /]
   ···

6: empty line of code
   T = (X)

T: redefine to be T + 1
   Z

T: redefine to be T − 1
   go to C

1: ADD, T
   go to 7

2: SUB, T
   go to 7

3: MULT, T
   go to 7

4: DIV, T
   go to 7

7: empty line of code

FIGURE 8.2.2 A macro for algebraic translation.

temporary storage common to all algebraic expressions. The **repeat** statement is used to perform a scan of the algebraic expression. The inner definition $Z \equiv ALG, (X)$ is used as a way to save the first operand during the scan of the second. The quantity C, simply a parameter in the ground language, is used to determine which operand is currently being examined and to remember the break character during the scan of the second.

It may be useful to regard algebraic translation as a special case of macro-expansion—translating a formula into machine code is nothing more than recursively placing parameters into certain open subroutine patterns.

For the sake of clarity, we have not invented symbolism for the various special types of statement used in the definition. A uniform grammar conformable to that of the ground language would be easier to mechanize. It is sufficient to note that there are only the following types of statements peculiar to macros:

1. **if** ... **go to** n

   a. **go to** n
   b. **if** X is (not) Y **go to** n
   c. **if** X is (not) of class Y
   d. **if** XRY **go to** n

      where R is $>$, $=$, $<$, $\neq$, etc.

   e. **if** break is (not) X **go to** n

2. **repeat** over X thru n
3. **create** X
4. **replace** the X break class by Y

8.2.4. RECAPITULATION

Having completed the informal outline of a macro compiler, let us summarize its salient features:

1. Definitions may contain macro calls.
2. Parenthetical notation for compounding calls.
3. Conditional assembly.
4. Created symbols.
5. Definitions may contain definition schemata.
6. Repetition over a list.

Items 1 and 5 are examples of a familiar propensity of mathematicians to widen the domain of applicability of any particular concept as far as possible. Applied to macros, the principle becomes: *Allow anything in the body of a definition that is acceptable outside.* Items 2, 3, 4, and 6 transfer the same spirit to a higher level; all are analogs of types of statements found convenient in algebraic translators, but their effect is at compile time rather than object time. Parenthetical notation allows compounding of compiler functions just as it provided compounding of object functions in an algebraic translator. Conditional assembly is analogous to ALGOL **if** statements. Created symbols serve as internal names in much the same way as those generated by algebraic translators. Repetition over a list corresponds to **for** statements. To recapitulate: *Statements effective at object time should have counterparts effective at compile time.* Couched in yet another way: A compiler should include within it an interpreter for its source language or something equivalent.

8.2.5. SIGNIFICANCE OF NESTED DEFINITIONS

Surprising power is achieved as a result of allowing the definiens of a macro instruction to include definition schemata. Trivial examples like that of (8) are easily multiplied; there nested definitions were used only to save the programmer obvious repetitive writing. Far more significant is the use in Fig. 8.2.2 of the hidden macro Z. In effect, the macro definition here serves as a temporary storage for a subexpression while the scanner simulated by "repeat" isolates and translates the next subexpression. In like ways nested macros can be used to accomplish complex symbol manipulating tasks within the compiler. Using this feature the author programmed a Bell Telephone Laboratories compiler (Eastwood) to do symbolic differentiation and to be a universal Turing machine. These demonstrations in themselves are of little value[†]; it is in performing symbol manipulation tasks incidental to new source language styles that generated macro definitions come to the fore. Conditional assembly and repetition over a list were offered in Section 8.2.4 as examples of the principle that operations (in this case, conditional transfer and indexing) effective at object time

---

[†] The Turing machine demonstration does prove that all machine operations have some image in a macro compiler, or in other words, that such a compiler is a general-purpose computer.

should have counterparts effective at compile time. Nested definitions turn out not only to be ways of generating sets of similar definitions, but also to be the counterpart of the fundamental machine operation STORE.

8.2.6. IMPLEMENTATION

We describe the apparatus that must be added to a compiler to convert it to handle macro instructions. Existing scanning mechanisms can be adapted to examine macro definitions, identifying occurrences of dummy parameters, and to analyze the parameter string of a macro call. Only the simplest parenthesis analysis need be available—identifying paired outermost parentheses in macro calls; and perhaps identifying grouping of statements as was indicated by brackets in (4).

A table of definitions must be constructed, probably in a condensed notation[4] with occurrences of dummy parameters replaced by uniform placeholders; say, (1), (2), (3), ... Further, if the scheme of **go to** statements indicated in Fig. 8.2.2 is to be used, the labels to which they refer must be located.[†]

A generator routine must be available to take the parameter list of a macro call and the definition and from these to generate line-by-line coding. The resultant code is turned over to the compiler for further processing, just as if the code had come from normal input channels. The generator must be recursive in that it can leave off expanding a macro and continue on the inner one whenever a macro call is generated, returning to the outer macro upon completing the inner expansion.

In their simplest realization, special statements such as **create** and **if** ... **go to** ... may be added straightforwardly to the normal complement of compiler statements. They would then be generated during macro expansion, just like any other line of code. Since these statements have meaning only to the macro facility, they might instead be identified at definition time and specially flagged in order to speed the generating process.

Using the logic outlined here, it turns out that nothing special need be done in order to allow nested definitions.

[†] It is sufficient to locate the labels alone and not the references. One may look up the location of labels at expansion time.

8.2.7. ORIGINS OF THESE TECHNIQUES

Though most of this article reflects lore current throughout the computing world, priority for a few of the ideas contained here can be assigned to individuals. Earlier programming systems (Remington-Rand UNIVAC) have included extensive use of generative techniques, but typically generators were described in ground language. Macros as outlined here are in effect descriptions of such generators. Their work is done by one generator working interpretively from definition schemata. Conditional macros were devised independently by several persons besides the author within the past year. In particular, Perlis[6] pointed out that algorithms for algebraic translation could be expressed in terms of conditional macros. Some uses of nested definitions were discovered by the author; their first application in symbol manipulation was by J. Bennett, also of Bell Telephone Laboratories. Repetition over lists is due to V. Vyssotsky. Perlis also noted that macro compiling may be done by routines to a large degree independent of ground language. One existing macro compiler, MICA,[5] though working in only one ground language is physically separated from its ground-language compiler. An analyzer of variable-style source languages exists in the SHADOW routine of Barnett,[1] but lacks an associated mechanism for incorporating extensions. Created symbols and parenthetical notation are obvious loans from the well-known art of algebraic translation.

8.2.8. APPENDIX

As a concrete example of a macro-compiler language of the type discussed in this article, we describe such a compiler built around ALGOL. Two new declarations, **macro** and **text**, are added to the already existing ALGOL set. Existing apparatus such as **if**, **for**, **begin**, **end** are taken over with obvious application in macros. The **for** statement has been generalized particularly for convenience in macros. The **copy** statement becomes superfluous as its work may be done by macros.

8.2.8.1. *Macro Declaration*

A **macro** declaration specifies a pattern of code with replaceable identifiers to be called for by a later macro statement. Replaceable (bound) identifiers are of two sorts, ordinary and created parameters:

$$\text{Form:} \quad \Delta \sim \textbf{macro } \text{I}(\text{I, I}, \ldots, \text{I; I, I}, \ldots, \text{I}) := \pi$$

The identifier before the parentheses is the macro name. Identifiers within parentheses are parameters, ordinary before the semicolon, created after.

The following alternative forms are permissible in special cases:

(i)   **macro** I $:= \pi$ means

       macro I(;) $:= \pi$

(ii)   **macro** I(I, I, ... , I) $:= \pi$ means

       macro I(I, I, ... , I;) $:= \pi$

The symbol π stands for a program consisting of one ALGOL statement or a sequence of ALGOL statements delimited by **begin** and **end** or by **begin** and **end** I, where I is the macro name. If **text** does not appear explicitly in π, its presence is assumed. Macro definitions are dynamically replaceable.

8.2.8.2. *Text Declaration*

$$\text{Form:} \quad \Delta \sim \textbf{text } \pi$$

Within a macro, a **text** declaration specifies portions of program that are to replace the macro when it is called. Parts of a definition outside **text** are interpreted as instructions to the compiler.

A **macro** statement is a call for an already defined macro.

$$\text{Form:} \quad \text{I}(\text{X, X}, \ldots, \text{X})$$

The strings, X, of symbols are substituted for appearances of corresponding ordinary parameters through the definition. Outermost parentheses are stripped from each X before substitution. This substituted segment functionally replaces the macro statement in the program.

8.2.8.3. *Generalized* **for** *Statement*

$$\text{Form:} \quad \textstyle\sum \sim \textbf{for } \text{I} := \text{X, X}, \ldots, \text{X, I} = \text{X, X},$$
$$\ldots, \text{I} := \text{X, X}, \ldots, \text{X}\pi$$

Let the number of X's associated with each identifier I be *n*. Then the program π is to be repeated *n* times with the occurrences of each I replaced in turn by successive X's from its associated list. (X may stand for any kind of ALGOL object, provided only that it makes sense to place it for an occurrence of I.)

The following example shows two ways of defining the ALGOL alternative statement using macros. In the first way, "alternative" will be used in a form such as

$$\text{alternative } ((a > 0, a < 0, a = 0)$$
$$(y := a + 2, \ y := a - 2, \ y := 0))$$

meaning assign the values a + 2, a − 2, or 0 to y according as a is positive, negative, or zero. Alternative has two parameters, the first a list of conditions, and the second a list of outcomes associated with the conditions

> **macro** alternative (B, S; X, Y, Z) :=
> **begin**
>   **for** X := B, Y := S
>   **text if** X
>   **begin** Y; **go to** Z **end**
>   **text** Z;
> **end** alternative

The second way of defining alternative makes it a one-parameter macro, that parameter being a list of grouped conditions and outcomes. It would be used after the fashion

$$\text{alternative } ((a > 0, \ \text{yields}, \ y := a + 2)$$
$$(a < 0, \ \text{yields}, \ y := a - 2)$$
$$(a = 0, \ \text{yields}, \ y := 0))$$

The noise word "yields" has been added for the sake of literacy. Had some scanner-modifying apparatus been included in the specifications of ALGOL, nuisances such as the commas around "yields" and the extra pair of parentheses might have been eliminated. This version of alternative is defined by a two-level declaration:

> **macro** alternative (BS; X, Y)
>> **begin**
>>> **for** X := BS
>>>> **text** subaltern (X, Y)
>>>
>>> **text** Y;
>>
>> **end**
>
> **macro** subaltern (B, yields, S, Y)
>> **if** B **begin** S; **go to** Y **end**

A simple variant on the inner macro subaltern provides the possibility of statements like

> alternative ((a > 0, yields, y := a + 2)
>> (a < 0, yields, y := a − 2)
>>
>> (otherwise, y := 0))
>
> **macro** subaltern (B, Z, S, Y)
>> **begin**
>>> **if** B = "otherwise"
>>>> **text** Z
>>>
>>> **if** B ≠ "otherwise"
>>>> **text** S
>>>
>>> **text go to** Y
>>
>> **end** subaltern

REFERENCES

1. Barnett, M., "Macro-Directive Approach to High Speed Computing," Solid State Physics Research Group, MIT, Cambridge, Mass., 1959.

2. Curry, H. B., and Feys, R., *Combinatory Logic*, vol. I. North Holland Publishing Co., Amsterdam, 1958, pp. 62–67.

3. Eastwood, D. E., and McIlroy, M. D., "Macro Compiler Modification of SAP." Bell Telephone Laboratories Computation Center, 1959.

4. Greenwald, I. D., "Handling of Macro Instructions," *Comm. Assoc. Comp. Mach.*, vol. 2, no. 11 (1959), pp. 21–22.

5. Haigh, M., "User's Specification for MICA," SHARE User's Organization for IBM 709 Electronic Data Processing Machine, SHARE Secretary Distribution SSD-61, C-1462 (1959), pp. 16–63.

6. Perlis, A. J., Official Notice on ALGOL Language," *Comm. Assoc. Comp. Mach.*, vol. 1, no. 12 (1958), pp. 8–22.

7. Perlis, A. J., *Quarterly Report of the Computation Center*, Carnegie Institute of Technology, October 1959.

8. Remington-Rand UNIVAC Division, "UNIVAC Generalized Programing," Philadelphia, 1957.

8.3. Batch, Conversational, and Incremental Compilers

by Harry Katzan, Jr.

8.3.1. INTRODUCTION

Compiler-writing techniques have received a great deal of pragmatic and academic attention and are now fairly well defined.[1,2] It was and still is generally felt that the compiler is independent of the operating system in which it resides, if it resides in one at all. The invention of time-sharing systems with conversational capability, however, has required that compiler experts re-evaluate existing concepts to make better use of external facilities. This was done, and conversational and incremental compilers have evolved. A generalized and consolidated discussion of these relatively new concepts is the subject of this article. First, a model of a batch compiler is introduced. The concepts are then modified and extended for a conversational programming environment. Finally, a recent development termed "incremental" compilation, which satisfies the needs of both batch and conversational compiling as well as interactive computing, is presented. First, some introductory material is required.

EDITOR'S NOTE: This article reproduced by permission of the author and the publisher: *Proc. AFIPS*, vol. 34 (1969), SJCC, pp. 47–56.

8.3.1.1. *Basic Concepts*

In the classical data processing environment,[1] the "compile phase" or "source language processing phase" is of prime importance, as are definitions of *source program* and *object program*. The latter are redefined in light of the time-sharing or interactive environment. Extraneous items, such as where the object program is stored or whether or not the compiler should produce assembler language coding, are practically ignored.

The *source program* is the program as written by the programmer. It is coded in symbolic form and punched on cards or typed in at the terminal. The *object program* is the program after being transformed by the compiler into a machine-oriented form which can be read into the computer and executed with very few (if any) modifications. Also of interest is the *information vector*, which gives initial conditions for compilation and denotes the types of output desired. A sample of specifications which might be found in an information vector follow: (1) location of the source program; (2) name of the program; (3) the extent of compiler processing, i.e., syntax check only, optimize, etc.; (4) computer system parameters; (5) compiler output desired; and (6) disposition of the object module. The form of the source program is sometimes required, although in most cases this information is known implicitly. This pertains to different BCD codes and file types which may range from sequential or indexed files on conventional systems to list-structured files in virtual machines.

Similarly for output, the user can request a specialized form of object module or none at all, source or object program listing, and cross-reference listings. The object module is known as a Program Module which contains the machine language text and relocation information. Additionally, it may contain an Internal Symbol Dictionary for use during execution-time debugging. The Internal Symbol Dictionary is especially useful in conversational time-sharing systems where execution can be stopped on a conditional basis and the values of internal variables can be displayed or modified.

8.3.1.2. *Batch Compilation*

Batch compilation methods are required, quite naturally, in a batch-processing environment. The term "batch processing" stems from the days when the programmer submitted his job to the computer center and subsequently received his results later in time. A collection of different jobs was accumulated by operations personnel and the batch was then presented to the computer system on an input tape. The important point is that the programmer has no contact with his job between the time it is submitted to operations and when he receives his output. The concept has been extended to cover Multiprogramming Systems, Remote Job Entry (RJE), and the trivial case where no operating system exists and the programmer runs the compiler to completion.

8.3.2. THE GENERALIZED BATCH ENVIRONMENT

The most significant aspect of the batch-processing environment is that the entire source program is available to the compiler initially and that all compiler output can be postponed until a later phase. The compiler writer, therefore, is provided with a liberal amount of flexibility in designing his language processor. For example, specification (i.e., declarative) statements can be recognized and processed in an initial phase and storage allocated immediately. In the same pass, statement labels are recognized and entabled; then in a later phase, validity decisions for statements that use statement labels can be made immediately rather than making a later analysis on the basis of table entries. If desired, source program error diagnostics can be postponed. Moreover, the designer may specify his compiler so that the source program is passed by the compiler or so that the compiler is passed over the source program, which resides semipermanently in memory.

This inherent flexibility is not exploited in the compiler model which follows. Instead, an attempt has been made to present the material in a conceptually straightforward manner.

8.3.2.1. *A Generalized Batch Compiler*

By itself, a model of a generalized batch compiler is of limited interest. The concept is useful, however, for comparison with those designed to operate in time-shared computer systems. Therefore the presentation is pedagogical in nature as compared to one which might present a step-by-step procedure for building one.

Processing by the compiler is rather naturally divided into several phases which tend to be more logical than physical. Each phase has one or more specific tasks to perform. In so doing, it operates on tables and lists, possibly modifying them and producing new ones. One phase, of course, works on the source program from the system input device or external storage and another produces the required output. The entire compiler is described therefore by listing the tasks each phase is to perform; ordinarily, the description would also denote which tables and lists each phase uses and what tables and lists it creates or modifies. The specific tables and lists which are required, however, tend to be language dependent and are beyond the scope of this treatment.

The compiler is composed of five phases and an executive routine, as follows:

THE COMPILER EXECUTIVE (EXEC).   The various phases run under the control of a compiler executive routine (EXEC) which is the only communication with the outside world. It establishes initial conditions and calls the different phases as required. It can be assumed that EXEC performs all system input/output services, upon demand from the phase modules. More specifically, the EXEC has five major and distinct functions:

1. To interface with the compiler's environment
2. To prepare the source statements for processing by phase one
3. To control and order the operation of the phases
4. To prepare edited lines for output
5. To provide compiler diagnostic information

Phase 1.   Phase 1 performs the source program syntactic analysis, error analysis, and translation of the program into a tabular representation. Each variable or constant is given an entry in the symbol table, with formal arguments being flagged as such. Initial values and array dimensions are stored in a table of preset data.

Lastly, information from specification statements is stored in the specification table. The most significant processing, however, occurs with respect to the *Program Reference File* and the *Expression Reference File.*

Each executable statement and statement label is placed in the Program Reference File in skeletal form. In addition to standard Program Reference File entries, the Program Reference File contains pointers to the Expression Reference File for statements involving arithmetic or logical expressions.

The Expression Reference File stores expressions in an internal notation, using pointers to the symbol table when necessary. As with the Expression Reference File, the Program Reference File also contains pointers to the symbol table.

Phase 2. In general, phase 2 performs analyses that cannot be performed in phase 1. It makes storage assignments in the Program Module for all variables that are not formal parameters. It detects illegal flow in loops and recognizes early exits therefrom. It also determines blocks of a program with no path of control to them; and lastly, it detects statement labels which are referenced but not defined.

Phase 3. The object of phase 3 is to perform the global optimizations used during object code generation, which is accomplished in phase 4.

The first major function of phase 3 is the recognition and processing of *common subexpressions.* Phase 3 determines which arithmetic expressions need be computed only once and then saved for later use. In addition, it determines the range of statements over which expressions are not redefined by the definition of one or more of their constituents. If the occurrence of an expression in that range is contained in one or more DO[†] loops which are also entirely contained in that range, Phase 3 determines the outermost such loop outside which such an expression may be computed, and physically moves the expression to the front of that DO loop. Only the evaluation process is removed from the loop; any statement label or replacement operation is retained in its original position. The moved expression is linked to a place reserved for that purpose in the program reference file entries corresponding to the beginning of the respective DO loops.

The second major function of phase 3 is the recognition and processing of *removable statements.* A "removable statement" is one whose individual operands do not have "definition points" inside the loop; obviously, the execution of this statement for each iteration would be unnecessary. A definition point is a statement in which the variable has, or may have, a new variable stored in it (e.g., appears on the left-hand side of an equal sign). In removing statements, they are usually placed before the DO statement.

Phase 3 also processes formal parameters and develops the prologue to the program; it optimizes the use of registers; and it merges the Program Reference File and the Expression Reference File to form a Complete Program File in preparation for phase 4.

[†] Although the DO keyword is a constituent part of several programming languages, it should be interpreted as representing the class of statements from different languages which effectively enable the programmer to write program loops in a straightforward manner.

Phase 4. Phase 4 performs the code-generation function. Its input consists of the symbol table and the Complete Program File, and its output is the Code File, which represents completed machine instructions and control information.

Phase 5. Phase 5 is the output phase and generates the *Program Module*, the source and object listings, and the cross-reference listing. Upon request, an *Internal Symbol Dictionary* is also included in the Program Module.

Any compiler model of this type is clearly an abstraction; moreover, there is almost as much variation between different compilers for the same programming language as there is between compilers for different languages. The model does serve a useful purpose, which is to present a conceptual foundation from which conversational and incremental compilers can be introduced.

8.3.3. CONVERSATIONAL COMPILATION

Compared with the "batch" environment in which the user has no contact with his job once it is submitted, the conversational environment provides the exact opposite. A general-purpose time-sharing system of one kind or another is assumed,[†] with users having access to the computer system via terminal devices.

In the batch environment, the user was required to make successive runs on the system to eliminate syntax and setup errors with the intervening time ranging from minutes to days. Excluding execution-time "bugs," it often took weeks to get a program running. In the conversational mode, syntactical and setup errors can be eliminated in one terminal session. Similarly, execution-time debugging is also possible in a time-sharing system, on a dynamic basis.

Conversational programming places a heavy load on a compiler and an operating system; the magnitude of the load is reflected in the basic additions necessary to support the conversational environment.

8.3.3.1. *The Time-Sharing Environment*

The time-sharing environment is characterized by versatility. Tasks can exist in the "batch" or "conversational" mode. Furthermore, source

---

[†] Two typical general-purpose time-sharing systems are TSS-360[3,4] and MULTICS.[5]

program input can reside on the system input device or be prestored. The time-sharing operating system is able to distinguish between batch and conversational tasks; therefore, batch tasks are recognized as such and processed as in any operating system. The ensuing discussion will concern conversational tasks. It is assumed, also, that the user resides at a terminal and is able to respond to requests by the system.

During the compile phase, the source program may be entered on a statement-by-statement basis or be prestored. In either case, the compiler responds immediately to the terminal with local syntactic errors. The user, therefore, is able to make changes to the source program immediately. Changes to the source program other than in response to immediate diagnostics cause a restart of the compilation process. Obviously, the system must keep a fresh copy of the source program for the restart case. To satisfy this need, a copy of the current up-to-date source program is maintained on external storage; if the source was prestored, the original version is updated with change requests; if the source program is not prestored, the compiler saves all source (and changes) as they are entered, line by line. With the user at a terminal, the compiler is also able to stop midway during compilation (usually after the global statement analysis and before optimization) to inquire whether or not the user wants to continue. Under error conditions, the user may abort the compilation or make changes and restart the compilation process. Moreover, the user can utilize this pause to have only his program syntax checked.

During the execution phase, dynamic debugging is often desirable. This facility is usually a part of the command structure of the operating system. In preparation for execution-time debugging, the user would probably request an Internal Symbol Dictionary during compilation so that internal variables could be addressed symbolically. Since execution-time debugging is a relatively new concept, it is discussed briefly.

Debugging commands usually fall into three categories: (1) program control; (2) program modification; and (3) debugging output. Debugging commands may be embedded in the program itself or the program can be stopped (either asynchronously or with an AT command) and the actions performed immediately. Examples of typical *program control* commands are

> AT   symbolic-location ... STOP
>
> RUN
>
> RUN   symbolic-location

Examples of *program modification* commands are

$$SET \ A = 1.0$$
$$IF \ A \langle 0, \ SET \ A = 0$$

Examples of *debugging output* commands are

$$DISPLAY \ MAIN.I:MAIN.A$$
$$DUMP \ ARRAY$$

Furthermore, they can be used in combination as follows:

$$AT \ PTWO.100 \qquad IF \ A = 0, \qquad STOP$$
$$AT \ T34.360 \ DUMP \ T34.A \ SET \ CNT = CNT + 1$$

As was mentioned earlier, a considerable amount of the compiler's effort is devoted to producing an efficient object program. As a result, the instructions to perform certain computations are sometimes not located where one would expect to find them. In fact, this is a direct consequence of *common subexpressions* and *removable statements*, which were discussed previously. Although these processes contribute to efficiency, they have a side effect which hinders the debugging effort. Therefore, when expecting to use dynamic debugging, the user should request an Internal Symbol Dictionary and select the option which does not produce optimized code.

The conversational compiler and the time-sharing operating system must support several aspects of the conversational environment. These are summarized as follows: (1) the ability to change or forget the effects of the preceding statement; (2) restart logic; (3) maintenance of the entire source program, in up-to-date form, on external storage; (4) the ability to scan statements and produce diagnostics on an individual statement basis; and (5) the option to produce optimized or unoptimized code.

8.3.3.2. *The Conversational Compiler*

Basically, the conversational compiler is a conventional batch processor containing special features making it suitable for conversational, terminal-oriented operation.

Structurally, the major addition over a batch compiler is Compiler Control Program (CCP), which in effect controls compilation. CCP is cognizant of whether the mode of operation is batch or conversational, and is able to fetch source records and dispose of output print lines, accordingly. Ccp is the facility which maintains the source program on external storage and is able to tell if a new source record is indeed new, a change to last one entered, or a change to a previous one. When processing a request to fetch a source record for the compiler, CCP can use this information to simply return the record, return it with the "forget" flag on, or call the compiler at its initial entry for the restart case. The function to fetch a source record is termed GETLINE and is summarized in Table 8.3.1. Accordingly, an overview of the CCP is given in Fig. 8.3.1.

Table 8.3.1   GETLINE Function of the Compiler Control Program (CCP)

	Conversational		Batch	
	Prestored	Not Prestored	Prestored	Not Prestored
GETLINE:	A	B	A	C

A.   Fetches the next source record from external storage and returns it to compiler EXEC.

B.   Fetches another source record from the terminal input device and updates the source file on external storage. If it is the next source record, the line is returned to the compiler with the "forget" flag off. If the given source record is to replace the previous one, the "forget" flag is turned on and the line is again returned. Otherwise, a previous line has been modified and the compiler is entered at the "initial" entry point for the restart case.

C.   Fetches the next source record from the system input device and updates the source file on external storage; the line is returned to EXEC with the "forget" flag off.

The overall logic of the conversational compiler is shown in Fig. 8.3.2. Clearly, it differs very little from the batch version. The differences in the compiler itself are found in phase 1 and at the end of phase 2. In phase 1, as shown in Fig. 8.3.3, the compiler uses CCP as its external interface. Moreover, the compiler always compiles a statement conditionally; later it uses the "forget flag" to freeze or delete the compiled information.

After phase 2, as shown in Figs. 8.3.1 and 8.3.2, the conversational compiler again exits to CCP. In the batch mode, of course, CCP simply

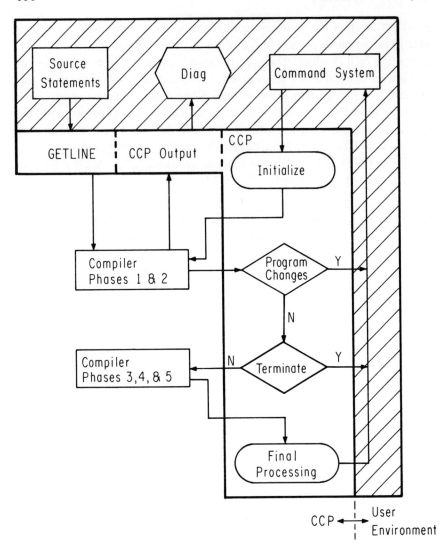

FIGURE 8.3.1.

returns to the compiler. In the conversational mode, as shown in Fig. 8.8.3, the user is asked for changes and whether he wants to continue. At the user's request, CCP can change the source program, still residing on external storage, and restart the compiler at the "initial" entry. If the user desires to continue, the compiler is entered at the "continue" entry. Otherwise, CCP exits to the command system and the remainder of the compilation is aborted.

Conversational compilation offers significant advantages over standard batch processing, most of which deal with the interactive mode of operation.

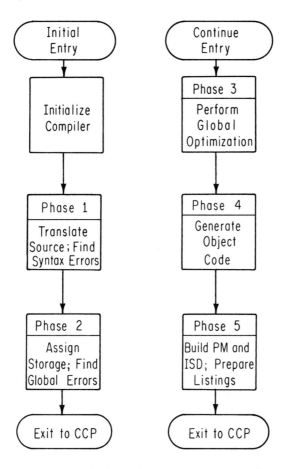

FIGURE 8.3.2 Logic of the conversational compiler.

The major disadvantage is that the entire source program must be available before execution can be attempted. In other words, one would like the versatility and flexibility of a language interpreter with the performance of a conversational or batch processor. Moreover, the performance must be reflected in the execution time as well as the compile time.

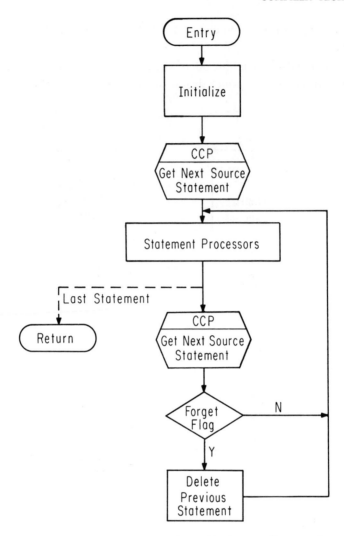

FIGURE 8.3.3   Compiler phase I interface with the compiler-control program.

8.3.4. INCREMENTAL COMPILATION

One of the most promising ideas in this era of on-line computing is a concept termed Incremental Compilation. In an interactive programming environment, one would like to achieve both the speed factors inherent in compiled programs and the flexibility available with interpretive systems. Incremental compilers are an attempt to achieve these goals. Much of the pioneering work in this area is reported in two papers: the first by Lock[7] entitled "Structuring Programs for Multiprogram Time-Sharing On-Line Applications" and the second by Ryan[8] and others entitled "A Conversational System for Incremental Compilation and Execution in a Time-Sharing Environment." In order that the above goals can be realized, the following capabilities are required:

1. The ability to execute a statement immediately
2. The ability to modify a prior statement without forcing a recompilation
3. The ability to execute a source program as it is being input
4. The ability to execute selected portions of programs
5. A language processor that can also operate in the batch mode

Clearly, all of the above requirements, except speed, are met with an appropriate interpretive program. In a large time-sharing environment, however, this resource is of prime importance, especially when 50 or more terminals are being serviced.

8.3.4.1. *The Environment for Incremental Compilation*

Basically, the environment for incremental compilation is the same as for its conversational counterpart. By assuming a sophisticated operating system such as TSS/360[3,4] or MULTICS,[5] many of the problems described in the cited papers by Lock[7] and by Ryan,[8] such as memory protection among users, an effective command system, and memory organization and management, are obviated. Dynamic loading facilities for utilizing hand-coded subroutines and a memory relocation feature,[9] for mapping virtual addresses to real addresses simplify problems involving the execution of code compiled incrementally and are also assumed. The programming language is naturally of importance and of great interest to most systems programmers. A language more powerful than standard FORTRAN or assembler language is expected, although the techniques would work satisfactorily therewith. A rich language which would enable a significant amount of computation per interaction is most desirable. Languages such as PL/I[10] and Iverson's language[11] are well suited to incremental compiling and executing.

8.3.4.2. *The Incremental Compiler*

This method of compilation permits two modes of operation: batch and incremental. In the *batch mode*, the user may compile a prestored source program but may not modify or execute the program during compilation.

In the *incremental mode*, normally used only conversationally, special facilities are available to permit the modification, execution, and check out of the program during compilation. These operations are performed through a combination of control and source language statements.

Incremental compilation consists of accepting a source program on a statement-by-statement basis. Each statement is compiled as it is received and the code generated for it is immediately made available for execution. Associative links between the source program and object code are maintained, thus permitting the user, during compilation, to modify his source program and have the modification immediately reflected in the object code. The ability to compile, execute, and modify a program on a statement-by-statement basis gives the user a degree of flexibility over his program usually available only with an interpreter, yet reduces the principal objection to interpreters—that of requiring an excessive amount of execution time. While in an interpreter each statement must be processed each time it is executed, in an incremental compiler it needs to be processed only when it is entered initially or when the user makes a source program modification. The Incremental Compiler has the added advantage of ensuring that the object code the user tests incrementally is virtually the same as the code produced for an object module, since the same code generators are used in both modes.

When an Incremental Compiler is used in the batch mode, all of the usual facilities are available to the user. When used in the incremental mode, all of the batch facilities are available in addition to those provided to control the execution and debugging of the generated code. During both modes of compilation, the following options are permitted:

1. Analyze the program only for syntactic errors; do not perform a global analysis or generate code.

2. Analyze the program for syntactic and global errors; do not generate code.

3. Analyze the program for syntactic and global errors and generate object code as well.

The object program may be executed in either the batch or incremental mode only if the third option is selected. In most compilers of this type, the user may select one of several modes of executing the incremental code concurrently with compilation; as errors are uncovered, he may make modifications to the source language without, in most cases, requiring a recompilation of the existing code or affecting previous execution.

In order to provide the user with the degree of control desired, two categories of *control statements* are necessary—transient statements and commands. A *transient statement* is a statement in the source language being compiled which is executed and discarded immediately. It allows the user to intervene during the execution of his program and print results or change values. *Commands* are control statements which allow the user to make modifications outside the scope of the source language. A good example would be to change the control point of the program.

Source program compilation and execution in the incremental mode is under direct control of a Language Controller (LC). Each interaction by LC with the user is divided into a processing cycle and/or an execution cycle, depending upon the input parameters. The compiler is called by LC to process source language and transient statements, and if execution is

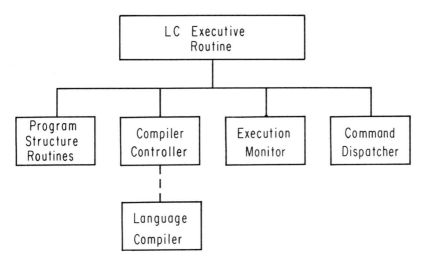

FIGURE 8.3.4 Structure of the language controller for incremental compilation and execution.

requested, it is initiated and monitored accordingly. After execution, transient statements are discarded, whereas source language statements are retained. The command system of the operating system is called by the Language Controller to process commands. Clearly, there is a need to tie the various elements of a program together, for operational reasons, and this requirement is satisfied by the Program Structure Table, described below. Since the Language Controller controls a major portion of the processing when in the incremental modes, it is structured accordingly. As pictured in Fig. 8.3.4, it contains program elements for maintaining the source program and the Program Structure Table, for controlling the compiler, for monitoring the execution of incremental code, and for interpreting and then dispatching or processing control statements. These functions are summarized in the following descriptions of the modules which comprise the Language Controller.

PROGRAM STRUCTURE ROUTINES.   The program structure routines maintain the source program on external storage and manage the Program Structure Table, which contains an entry for each source language statement in the program being compiled. The relationship of statements is also established for subsequent use by the Execution Monitor.

COMPILER CONTROLLER.   The compiler controller provides the interface between the user and the compiler. It passes the identity and location of source statements to the compiler EXEC and receives the location of the compiled code in return. In so doing, it handles diagnostics and updates the Program Structure Table.

EXECUTION MONITOR.   The Execution Monitor controls program execution as determined by the established mode of operation. It passes control between statements or halts execution after specific statements, as required. It utilizes the dynamic loader of the operating system and invokes other program modules when requested to do so.

COMMAND INTERPRETER AND DISPATCHER.   The Command Interpreter analyzes control statements and calls either the Compiler Controller or the command system of the operating system, depending upon whether a transient statement or a command is being processed.

   The Program Structure Table is obviously of great importance, since it indicates the relationship of statements and the static properties of the program. Elements in the table are generated dynamically as source language statements are entered and are composed from the following quantities[†]:

   1. A *type indicator* specifying the type of statement
   2. A list of *structure pointers* linking this statement to preceding and

---

[†] The article by Lock[7] contains a comprehensive description of internal program structure in a programming environment such as this.

succeeding statements and to any function module[†] in which it might be contained

3. A pointer to the *compiled machine code* for the statement

4. A locator, such as data set name or physical location, of the *source program* on external storage

5. A statement identification, such as a *line number*, used for referencing the statement and for making insertions, deletions, and changes to the program.

Due to the nature of the incremental compilation process and the Program Structure Table, it is not necessary that the incremental code for a given program reside in contiguous memory locations. In fact, only rarely will this be the case. Although this is conceptually different from the established practice of generating object code, it poses no serious problem in the incremental mode of operation.

In general, the incremental compiler is composed of the same basic components as the batch and conversational versions. Some differences, which tend to be related to the interrelationship of statements, do exist but are relatively minor. The "global" analysis of statements, for example, is severly crippled by the fact that all statements in a source module may not be available for analysis. The "global" optimization of statements is in the same category but must be eliminated entirely. It is very feasible, however, to include it as a special phase in the batch mode or provide a mechanism to convert from incremental to object code, including global optimization, in the conversational mode.

The basic compiler-processing cycle begins when it is called at its source input entry. (Another entry could conceivably exist which might be to convert incremental code to object code.) The compiler EXEC obtains the source text to be processed from the Language Controller and builds a Program Table consisting of the text to be processed during the cycle; information on additions, insertions, and deletions; location of the existing symbol table; and parameter data relating to mode of compilation, listing options, BCD codes, etc. The EXEC then invokes phase 1 of the compiler, which performs a statement classification and syntax analysis and builds the Program Reference File and Expression Reference File from all of the

---

[†] The term "function module" is used to represent either a *block* or internal *procedure* as found in ALGOL or PL/I.

statements specified in the Program Table. Pointers to the encoded statements are then returned to the EXEC, where the encoded statements are linked back to the Program Table. Phase 2 is then invoked to perform a global analysis, when possible, and to assign storage for the statements indicated in the Program Table. This phase updates the symbol table and merges the Program Reference File and Expression Reference File to form the Complete Program File maintaining the links to the Program Table, as required. Phase 4[†] is now called to translate the encoded statements into object code forming the Code File. Phase 5, which must generate either object code or incremental code, is considered below.

Operation of the compiler for each of the two basic modes, batch and incremental, can now be described. In a *batch compilation*, the source text available at entry consists of the complete program. The Program Table passed to each component points to every statement in the source program, so that in a single cycle, the complete compilation is produced. Other than the Executive (EXEC), the only phase which must be aware of the batch parameter is phase 5, which must build an object module instead of generating incremental code. Again, the object module consists of a program module (i.e., text and relocation data) and, optionally, an Internal Symbol Dictionary. The text portion consists of the object code produced and is entirely self-contained, with the code generated for a statement linking directly to the code for the next statement. The source text available at entry to an *incremental compilation* may represent anything from a single statement to a complete program. Normally, however, the source text available represents only a portion of a program. The Program Table, therefore, contains a group of statements to be added or deleted in the current program. The Program Table is in the same form as for a batch compilation and does not require different handling by phases 1, 2, and 4. In this mode, phase 5 generates incremental code. Incremental code differs from an object module in that the Program Module (i.e., the relocation information) must be dynamically generated, requiring some special processing by the Language Controller and the system's dynamic loader. The text is organized on a statement-by-statement basis with interstatement linkage provided to allow the intervention by the Language Controller[‡] at statement boundaries.

As a result of the incremental process, four modes of execution are

---

[†] Recognizing that no phase 3 exists.

[‡] That is, the Execution Monitor.

possible: automatic, controlled, block step, and step. In the *automatic mode*, statements are executed by the Language Controller immediately after they are processed by the compiler. In the *controlled mode*, statements are executed only when explicitly requested by a RUN command, which may designate a range of statements. In the block step-and-step modes, an entire program (i.e., an external procedure) is available for execution. For the *block step* case, the Language Controller pauses for user intervention after each block (or possible subroutine) in the program. When the *step* mode is specified, the Language Controller suspends object program execution after each statement.

8.3.4.3. *Early Efforts and Special Problem Areas*

The two specific references to incremental compilation, i.e., by Lock[7] and by Ryan,[8] are in a sense complementary. Lock tends to emphasize the structural aspects whereas Ryan emphasizes the systems aspects, even though different computers are involved.

The effort by Lock, and probably others, at the California Institute of Technology is part of an experimental time-sharing project for the IBM 7040 computer. The programming languages supported are ALGOL, FORTRAN, and LISP, with much of the article being devoted to the internal organization of programs in an on-line programming environment. The Conversational Compiler System, reported by Ryan and others, is an outgrowth of Lock's work and runs under an SDS 940 time-sharing system. ALGOL and FORTRAN are also supported here, with the article emphasizing the command language, memory organization, and compiling techniques.

These projects have uncovered some interesting problems, of which the most significant, perhaps, is considered here. It involves changing a data declaration when executable code exists which uses the variables declared therein. In fact, the code may have been executed previously. Lock solved the problem by designing his pseudomachine code so that all references to identifiers are indirectly addressed through nonrelocatable entries in the user's symbol table. This certainly solves the problem, but it partially nullifies one of the basic objectives of incremental compilation; that is, to gain the speed factor inherent in compiled code. A hardware mapping of identifiers to physical locations is feasible if relocation hardware and possibly a small associative memory are available, although it remains to be seen whether dynamic address translation can be used in this particular manner. Finally, one might ask the following philosophical question: "Is it unreasonable to require a recompilation following a change to a data declaration?" Clearly, the answer must be evaluated in light of the other benefits to be gained through incremental compilation.

8.3.5. CONCLUSIONS

The world of time-sharing and its potential for interactive computing at a general level has raised some interesting topics.

First, it should be recognized that although batch techniques are currently very efficient and well defined, they were developed of necessity. When these techniques gained their acceptance, the batch mode was the only operational procedure available for using the computer. The programming community should also recognize that program development in a batch environment may not be the most natural or the optimum method.

Second, it should be recognized further that conversational techniques do not offer a complete solution in that execution of parts of a program is usually not permitted. Clearly, language syntax errors can be detected as they are being input, and this is certainly a step in the right direction. But if a programmer has to develop his algorithm completely before any of it can be executed, he might as well compile in the batch mode and rely on execution-time debugging.

Some form of incremental compiling, therefore, seems to be the only answer in sight to questions regarding the development of algorithms in an interactive computing environment. The ability to execute a program as it is being compiled is certainly a natural way and very well may be optimum from a development point of view. It remains to be seen if the gains can justify the complexity of an incremental compiler.

REFERENCES

1. Lee, J. A. N., *The Anatomy of a Compiler*. Reinhold Book Co., New York, 1967.
2. Randell, B., and Russel, L. J., *Algol 60 Implementation*. Academic Press, New York, 1964.
3. Comfort, W. T., "A Computing System Design for User Service," Proc. FJCC, 1965.
4. Gibson, C. T., "Time-Sharing in the IBM/360: Model 67," Proc. SJCC, 1966.
5. Corbató, F. J., and Vyssotsky, V. A., "Introduction and Overview of the MULTICS System," Proc. FJCC, 1965.
6. "IBM System/360 Time-Sharing System," in FORTRAN IV *Program Logic Manual*. IBM Corp., Y28-2019, Yorktown Heights, N.Y., 1967.

7. Lock, K., "Structuring Programs for Multiprogram Time-Sharing On-line Applications," Proc. FJCC, 1965.

8. Ryan, J. L., Crandall, R. L., and Medwedeff, M. C., "A Conversational System for Incremental Compilation and Execution in a Time-Sharing Environment," Proc. FJCC, 1966.

9. Randall, B., and Kuchner, C. J., "Dynamic Storage Allocation Systems," CACM, vol. 11, no. 5 (May 1968).

10. Radin, G., and Rogoway, H. P., "Highlights of a New Programming Language," CACM, vol. 8, no. 1 (January 1965).

11. Iverson, K. E., *A Programming Language*. John Wiley & Sons, Inc., New York, 1964.

INDEX

551